2학기 전과정
적중 100 plus

영어 기출문제집

중 3

능률 | 김성곤

*Best Collection*

# 구성과 특징

교과서의 주요 학습 내용을 중심으로 학습 영역별 특성에 맞춰 단계별로 다양한 학습 기회를 제공하여
단원별 학습능력 평가는 물론 중간 및 기말고사 시험 등에 완벽하게 대비할 수 있도록 내용을 구성

## Words & Expressions

| | |
|---|---|
| Step1 | Key Words 단원별 핵심 단어 설명 및 풀이 |
| | Key Expression 단원별 핵심 숙어 및 관용어 설명 |
| | Word Power 반대 또는 비슷한 뜻 단어 배우기 |
| | English Dictionary 영어로 배우는 영어 단어 |
| Step2 | 실력평가 단원별 수시평가 대비 주관식, 객관식 문제풀이 |
| Step3 | 서술형 대비 학업성취도 및 수행능력평가 대비 서술형 문제풀이 |

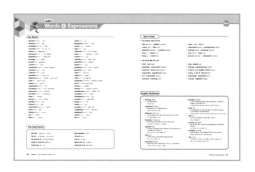

## Conversation

| | |
|---|---|
| Step1 | 핵심 의사소통 소통에 필요한 주요 표현 방법 요약 |
| | 핵심 Check 기본적인 표현 방법 및 활용능력 확인 |
| Step2 | 대화문 익히기 교과서 대화문 심층 분석 및 확인 |
| Step3 | 교과서 확인학습 빈칸 채우기를 통한 문장 완성 능력 확인 |
| Step4 | 기본평가 시험대비 기초 학습 능력 평가 |
| Step5 | 실력평가 단원별 수시평가 대비 주관식, 객관식 문제풀이 |
| Step6 | 서술형 대비 학업성취도 및 수행능력평가 대비 서술형 문제풀이 |

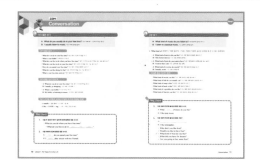

## Grammar

| | |
|---|---|
| Step1 | 주요 문법 단원별 주요 문법 사항과 예문을 알기 쉽게 설명 |
| | 핵심 Check 기본 문법사항에 대한 이해 여부 확인 |
| Step2 | 기본평가 시험대비 기초 학습 능력 평가 |
| Step3 | 실력평가 단원별 수시평가 대비 주관식, 객관식 문제풀이 |
| Step4 | 서술형 대비 학업성취도 및 수행능력평가 대비 서술형 문제풀이 |

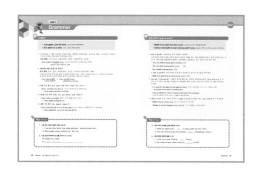

## Reading

| | |
|---|---|
| Step1 | 구문 분석 단원별로 제시된 문장에 대한 구문별 분석과 내용 설명 |
| | 확인문제 문장에 대한 기본적인 이해와 인지능력 확인 |
| Step2 | 확인학습A 빈칸 채우기를 통한 문장 완성 능력 확인 |
| Step3 | 확인학습B 제시된 우리말을 영어로 완성하여 작문 능력 키우기 |
| Step4 | 실력평가 단원별 수시평가 대비 주관식, 객관식 문제풀이 |
| Step5 | 서술형 대비 학업성취도 및 수행능력평가 대비 서술형 문제풀이 |
| | 교과서 구석구석 교과서에 나오는 기타 문장까지 완벽 학습 |

# Composition

**|영역별 핵심문제|**

단어 및 어휘, 대화문, 문법, 독해 등 각 영역별 기출문제의 출제 유형을 분석하여 실전에 대비하고 연습할 수 있도록 문제를 배열

**|단원별 예상문제|**

기출문제를 분석한 후 새로운 시험 출제 경향을 더하여 새롭게 출제될 수 있는 문제를 포함하여 시험에 완벽하게 대비할 수 있도록 준비

**|서술형 실전 및 창의사고력 문제|**

학교 시험에서 점차 늘어나는 서술형 시험에 집중 대비하고 고득점을 취득하는데 만전을 기하기 위한 학습 코너

**|단원별 모의고사|**

영역별, 단계별 학습을 모두 마친 후 실전 연습을 위한 모의고사

on the textbook

**교과서 파헤치기**

• **단어Test1~3** 영어 단어 우리말 쓰기, 우리말을 영어 단어로 쓰기, 영영풀이에 해당하는 단어와 우리말 쓰기

• **대화문Test1~2** 대화문 빈칸 완성 및 전체 대화문 쓰기

• **본문Test1~5** 빈칸 완성, 우리말 쓰기, 문장 배열연습, 영어 작문하기 복습 등 단계별 반복 학습을 통해 교과서 지문에 대한 완벽한 습득

• **구석구석지문Test1~2** 지문 빈칸 완성 및 전문 영어로 쓰기

# Lesson 5

# Environmental Innovations

## 🎤 의사소통 기능

- 의견 표현하기
  In my opinion, taking care of the environment starts with the little things.

- 희망 · 기대 표현하기
  I can't wait to see it!

## 🔧 언어 형식

- to부정사의 의미상 주어
  It is important **for us** to find ways to protect the environment.

- 관계부사
  Cancun is a city **where** 4.8 million tourists travel every year.

# Words & Expressions

## Key Words

- **additional** [ədíʃənl] 형 추가적인
- **architect** [á:rkətèkt] 명 건축가
- **architecture** [á:rkitèktʃər] 명 건축(술)
- **artwork** [ártwərk] 명 (예술적) 작품
- **attract** [ətrǽkt] 동 끌다, 매혹시키다
- **awareness** [əwɛ́ərnis] 명 인식, 의식
- **bright** [brait] 형 영리한, 똑똑한
- **chemical** [kémikəl] 명 화학물질
- **climate** [kláimit] 명 기후
- **company** [kámpəni] 명 회사
- **contain** [kəntéin] 동 포함하다
- **creative** [kriéitiv] 형 창의적인
- **damage** [dǽmidʒ] 동 손상시키다
- **design** [dizáin] 동 설계하다
- **direct** [dirékt] 형 직접적인, 직행의
- **disappear** [dìsəpíər] 동 사라지다
- **eco-friendly** [ékoufréndli] 형 친환경적인
- **encourage** [inkə́:ridʒ] 동 격려하다, 장려하다
- **environment** [inváiərənmənt] 명 환경
- **explanation** [èksplənéiʃən] 명 설명
- **flow** [flou] 명 흐름
- **goal** [goul] 명 목표, 목적
- **grain** [grein] 명 곡물, 알곡
- **greenery** [grí:nəri] 명 푸른 잎, 푸른 나무
- **hopefully** [hóupfəli] 부 바라건대
- **incredible** [inkrédəbl] 형 믿기 힘든, 굉장한
- **innovation** [ìnəvéiʃən] 명 혁신
- **instead** [instéd] 부 대신에
- **material** [mətíəriəl] 명 자료, 소재, 재료
- **natural** [nǽtʃərəl] 형 자연적인

- **opinion** [əpínjən] 명 의견
- **place** [pleis] 동 두다
- **plastic bag** 비닐봉지
- **pollution** [pəlú:ʃən] 명 오염
- **prevent** [privént] 동 예방하다, 막다, 방지하다
- **properly** [prápərli] 부 적절하게
- **protect** [prətékt] 동 보호하다, 지키다
- **provide** [prəváid] 동 제공하다
- **quality** [kwáləti] 명 품질, 질
- **realize** [rí:əlàiz] 동 깨닫다
- **reduce** [ridjú:s] 동 줄이다
- **remind** [rimáind] 동 상기시키다
- **resource** [rí:sɔːrs] 명 자원
- **reusable** [riúzəbəl] 형 재사용할 수 있는
- **ride** [raid] 명 탑승, 타기
- **separate** [sépərèit] 동 분리하다
- **seriously** [síəriəsli] 부 심각하게, 진지하게
- **shade** [ʃeid] 명 그늘
- **statue** [stǽtʃu:] 명 조각, 조각상
- **structure** [strʌ́ktʃər] 명 구조(물)
- **suggestion** [səgdʒéstʃən] 명 제안
- **support** [səpɔ́:rt] 동 지지[지원]하다, (필요한 것을 제공하여) 존재하게[살게] 하다
- **surface** [sə́:rfis] 명 표면
- **theme** [θi:m] 명 주제
- **throughout** [θru:áut] 전 내내, 줄곧, 가로질러
- **underwater** [ʌndərwɔ́tər] 명 수중, 해저 형 물속의, 수중의
- **unique** [ju:ní:k] 형 유일무이한, 독특한
- **unwanted** [ʌnwántid] 형 원치 않는, 불필요한
- **waste** [weist] 명 낭비 동 낭비하다

## Key Expressions

- **a variety of** 다양한
- **be bored with** ~에 지루해하다
- **be made of** ~로 만들어지다
- **break down** 무너지다, 고장 나다, (썩어서) ~이 되다
- **come up with** ~을 생각해 내다
- **contribute to** ~에 기여하다, (~의) 원인이 되다
- **get better** 회복하다, 좋아지다
- **have a point** 일리가 있다
- **hold a contest** 대회를 개최하다
- **in harmony with** ~와 조화하여
- **in addition to** ~ 이외에도

- **in my opinion** 내 생각에는
- **make a suggestion about** ~에 대하여 제안하다
- **raise awareness** 인식을 높이다
- **take care of** ~을 돌보다
- **take the stairs** 계단을 이용하다
- **That's why ~.** 그것이 바로 ~한 이유이다.
- **throw ~ away** ~을 버리다
- **Why don't you/we ~ ?** ~하는 것이 어떠니?
- **would like to** ~하고 싶다
- **You have a point.** 네 말이 일리가 있다.

## Word Power

※ 서로 비슷한 뜻을 가진 어휘

- **awareness** 인식, 의식 : **perception** 지각
- **creative** 창의적인 : **original** 독창적인
- **goal** 목표, 목적 : **target** 목표
- **opinion** 의견 : **idea** 생각
- **provide** 제공하다 : **supply** 공급하다

- **company** 회사 : **corporation** 회사
- **damage** 손상시키다 : **harm** 해를 끼치다
- **incredible** 믿기 힘든 : **unbelievable** 믿을 수 없는
- **properly** 적절하게 : **suitably** 적절하게
- **reduce** 줄이다 : **cut down** 줄이다

※ 서로 반대의 뜻을 가진 어휘

- **bright** 영리한 ↔ **dull** 우둔한
- **disappear** 사라지다 ↔ **appear** 나타나다
- **incredible** 믿기 힘든 ↔ **credible** 믿을 만한

- **direct** 직접적인 ↔ **indirect** 간접적인
- **encourage** 격려하다 ↔ **discourage** 의욕을 꺾다
- **natural** 자연적인 ↔ **artificial** 인공적인

※ 명사 – 형용사

- **addition** 추가 – **additional** 추가적인
- **environment** 환경 – **environmental** 환경적인
- **nature** 자연 – **natural** 자연적인

- **creation** 창조 – **creative** 창의적인
- **innovation** 혁신 – **innovative** 혁신적인
- **reuse** 재사용 – **reusable** 재사용할 수 있는

※ 동사 – 명사

- **add** 더하다 – **addition** 추가
- **encourage** 격려하다 – **encouragement** 격려
- **innovate** 혁신하다 – **innovation** 혁신
- **protect** 보호하다 – **protection** 보호
- **separate** 분리하다 – **separation** 분리

- **attract** 끌다 – **attraction** 매력
- **explain** 설명하다 – **explanation** 설명
- **prevent** 예방하다 – **prevention** 예방
- **reduce** 줄이다 – **reduction** 감소
- **suggest** 제안하다 – **suggestion** 제안

## English Dictionary

- **architect** 건축가
  → a person who designs buildings 건물을 설계하는 사람
- **artwork** (예술적) 작품
  → something created to be beautiful by a painter, sculptor, etc. 화가, 조각가 등에 의해서 아름답도록 만들어진 것
- **climate** 기후
  → the general weather of a region
  어느 지역의 전체적인 날씨
- **damage** 손상시키다
  → to harm something 어떤 것에 해를 끼치다
- **disappear** 사라지다
  → to no longer be seen 더 이상 보이지 않다
- **explanation** 설명
  → information to help people understand something

사람들이 어떤 것을 이해하도록 돕기 위한 정보

- **greenery** 푸른 잎, 푸른 나무
  → plants or vegetation 식물 또는 초목
- **opinion** 의견
  → one's beliefs, ideas, thoughts, and assumptions about a matter 어떤 문제에 관한 믿음, 아이디어, 생각 및 추정
- **reusable** 재사용할 수 있는
  → capable of being used more than once
  한 번 이상 사용될 수 있는
- **surface** 표면
  → the top layer of something 사물의 꼭대기 층
- **underwater** 수중에, 해저에
  → below the water 수면 아래

**01** 다음 짝지어진 단어의 관계가 같도록 빈칸에 알맞은 말을 쓰시오.

> direct : indirect = appear : _____

**02** 다음 영영풀이가 가리키는 것을 고르시오.

> a person who designs buildings

① architect     ② artist
③ greenery     ④ artwork
⑤ protector

**03** 다음 중 밑줄 친 부분의 뜻풀이가 바르지 <u>않은</u> 것은?

① Using <u>reusable</u> cloth bags is a great way to protect our environment. (재사용할 수 있는)
② Did you have any <u>suggestion</u> to improve your school? (자원)
③ What method is used to <u>separate</u> oil from water? (분리하다)
④ The campaign <u>encourages</u> people to save water. (격려하다)
⑤ The songs <u>remind</u> me of my grandmother. (상기시키다)

**서답형**

**04** 다음 문장의 빈칸에 들어갈 말을 〈보기〉에서 골라 쓰시오.

> ┌ 보기 ┐
> support / materials / additional / unique / artwork

(1) Can we use other _____ instead of plastics?

(2) Artists should be able to _____ themselves without any help.
(3) If you require _____ information, please let me know.
(4) The _____ was originally created by a British artist.
(5) This tower has a _____ view of Seoul.

**05** 다음 주어진 문장의 밑줄 친 bright와 같은 의미로 쓰인 것은?

> Sujin is one of the <u>bright</u> students in her class.

① I really like your <u>bright</u> yellow dress.
② My brother is watching a <u>bright</u> star shining in the sky.
③ The boy gave me a <u>bright</u> smile.
④ I noticed that his eyes were <u>bright</u> with excitement.
⑤ I chose her as the leader because she is <u>bright</u>, kind, and humorous.

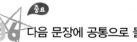

**06** 다음 문장에 공통으로 들어갈 말을 고르시오.

> • They are living together _____ harmony by helping each other.
> • _____ addition to teaching English, my teacher aims to motivate them.
> • _____ my view, this book would be helpful to study English grammar.

① in[In]     ② to[To]     ③ of[Of]
④ for[For]     ⑤ by[By]

**01** 다음 짝지어진 단어의 관계가 같도록 빈칸에 알맞은 말을 쓰시오.

> encourage : discourage = credible : _____

**02** 다음 문장의 빈칸에 들어갈 말을 〈보기〉에서 골라 쓰시오.

> ┤ 보기 ├─
>
> surface / statue / explanation / damage / prevent

(1) Despite her careful _____, we are still confused.

(2) The dust can _____ your eyes.

(3) There are ways to _____ plastic from getting to the ocean.

(4) You can see a small black dot on the sun's _____.

(5) The _____ of Mr. Ban welcomes visitors at the entrance.

**03** 다음 우리말에 맞게 빈칸에 알맞은 말을 쓰시오. (철자가 주어진 것은 그 철자로 시작할 것.)

(1) 우리는 처음으로 요리 대회를 개최할 것입니다.
➡ We'll _____ _____ _____ _____ for the first time.

(2) 나는 이 캠페인이 어린이 교육의 중요성에 대한 인식을 높일 수 있기를 희망한다.
➡ I hope this campaign will r_____ a_____ of the importance of children's education.

(3) 나는 사진 대회에 대해 제안을 하고 싶습니다.
➡ I would like to _____ _____ _____ about the photo contest.

(4) 만약 이 책을 읽는 것이 지루해지면, 내게 알려 주세요.
➡ If you get b_____ _____ reading this book, let me know please.

**04** 다음 우리말과 일치하도록 주어진 단어를 모두 배열하여 완성하시오.

(1) 한옥은 나무로 만들어진 한국의 전통적인 구조물이다.
(a / of / made / Korean / *hanok* / structure / wood / is / traditional)
➡ _____

(2) 우리는 어떻게 물의 흐름의 방향이 바뀌었는지 배울 것이다.
(to / going / changed / learn / how / the / direction / has / we / of / water / are / flow)
➡ _____

(3) 창의성과 혁신은 성공의 열쇠이다.
(creativity / keys / success / innovation / to / and / are)
➡ _____

(4) 거리에 쓰레기를 버리지 마세요.
(throw / trash / away / don't / the / the / street / on)
➡ _____

# Conversation

## ① 의견 표현하기

> • In my opinion, taking care of the environment starts with the little things.
> 내 생각에는, 환경을 보호하는 것은 작은 것들부터 시작한다고 생각해.

■ 자신의 생각이나 의견을 말하고자 할 때 많이 사용하는 표현으로 'In my opinion'이 있다. 우리말로는 '내 (개인적인) 생각은'이라는 뜻으로 문장의 맨 앞에 사용하고 이 표현 뒤에는 콤마(,)를 찍는다. 'In my opinion, ~'과 유사 표현으로는 'In my view, ~', 'I think ~', 'I believe ~', 'I feel ~' 등이 있고 'It seems to me ~'를 쓸 수도 있다.

■ 동사 seem을 사용하여 'It seems (to me) that ~'이라고 하는 것은 '내 생각은 ~이다'라는 뜻으로 자신의 의견을 완곡하게 이야기할 때 사용하는 표현이다. 또한 'It seems to ~' 혹은 'It seems like ~' 등의 형태로 사용하여 '~인 것처럼 보인다, ~하는 것처럼 보인다'라는 의미로 자신의 의견을 나타낸다.

■ '내가 알기로는 ~'이라는 뜻으로 'as far as I know', 'as far as I'm concerned' 등에 이어서 원하는 내용을 덧붙여 자신의 의견을 표현하거나 'I'm convinced that ~ (나는 ~라고 확신한다.)'를 통해서도 자신의 의견을 표현하는 것이 가능하다.

### 의견 제시하기

- In my opinion/view, ~ 내 견해/의견으로는
- It seems to me that ~ 나에게는 ~인 것 같다
- As far as I know, 내가 알기로는
- I think/feel/believe ~ 내 생각은/느낌에는/내가 믿기로는
- I'm sure ~ 분명 ~이다
- I'm convinced that ~ 나는 ~라고 확신한다

### 의견을 물을 때 쓰는 여러 표현

- What do you think (of/about) ~? ~에 대해서 어떻게 생각해?
- How do you feel about ~ ? ~에 대한 너의 느낌은 어떠니?
- What is your view/opinion? 너의 견해/의견은 무엇이니?

### 핵심 Check

1. 다음 대화의 밑줄 친 우리말을 주어진 단어를 사용하여 영작하시오.

   B: I think we're using too many plastic bags.

   G: I agree. It's not good for the environment.
   How can we reduce our use of plastic bags?

   B: <u>내 생각에는 물건을 사러 갈 때 재사용할 수 있는 가방을 가져가야 해.</u>

   (opinion, reusable, bring, go)

   ➡ _____

## ② 희망 · 기대 표현하기

> • **I can't wait to see it!** 나도 어서 그것을 보고 싶다!

■ 'I can't wait to ~!(너무 기대된다!, 빨리 ~하고 싶어!)'는 원하던 일이 다가오고 있을 때, 빨리 하고 싶은 기대감을 나타내는 표현이며, 직역의 의미는 '~하는 것을 기다릴 수 없다'이고, 보통 '당장 ~하고 싶다, 빨리 ~했으면 좋겠다.'로 해석한다. 'I can't wait'는 뒤에 to부정사가 올 수 있고, 명사가 올 때는 전치사 for와 함께 써서 'I can't wait to+동사원형' 또는 'I can't wait for+명사/동명사'의 구조가 된다.

■ 말하는 사람의 기대 · 희망을 표현할 때는 '기대하다'라는 의미의 'expect'를 써서 'I'm expecting to+동사원형 ~'이라고 하거나 '열망하다'는 의미의 동사 'long'을 사용하여 'I'm longing to+동사원형, I'm longing for+명사'라고 하고, 형용사 'eager(열망하는)'를 써서 'I'm eager to+동사원형, I'm eager for+명사'의 형태로 나타내기도 한다

■ 앞으로 일어날 일이나 하고 싶은 일에 대하여 희망 · 기대를 표현할 때 'I am looking forward to ~.'나 'I look forward to ~.'같은 표현을 사용하기도 한다. 'look forward to'는 '기대하다'의 의미이다. 희망을 나타낼 때는 'I hope to ~', 'I want to ~', 'I wish to ~'라고 할 수 있다.

■ 'look forward to'에서 to는 전치사이기 때문에 뒤에 명사나 동명사가 와서 'look forward to+명사[동명사]'가 되어야 한다. hope, want, expect는 모두 to부정사를 목적어로 가지기 때문에 'want/hope/expect to+동사원형'이 되어야 한다.

### 희망 · 기대 표현하기

| | |
|---|---|
| • I can't wait to+동사원형/for+명사 ~. | 빨리 ~하고 싶다. |
| • I'm looking forward to+동명사/명사(구) ~. | ~하기를 기대한다. |
| • I am expecting to+동사원형 ~. | ~하기를 기대한다. |
| • I am eager for+명사/to+동사원형 ~. | ~하기를 기대한다. |

### 핵심 Check

**2.** 다음 밑줄 친 (A)의 우리말을 영어로 가장 적절하게 표현한 것은?

G: I want to buy a new bag. I'm bored with my old bags.

B: Then how about using old clothes to make a new bag? You can find out how to do it online.

G: Oh, that sounds interesting! (A)어서 나만의 가방을 만들고 싶어!

① I'm looking forward to make my own bag!　② I hope making my own bag!

③ I can't wait to make my own bag!　④ I'm longing make my own bag!

⑤ I'm eager to making my own bag!

**Listen & Talk 1 B**

G: Jiho, hurry up! The elevator is going up soon.

B: The science room is just on the third floor. ❶Why don't we take the stairs?

G: I don't want to walk all the way up there.

B: Come on. Elevators use lots of energy. We need to save energy to ❷protect the environment.

G: But one elevator ❸ride doesn't use ❹that much energy.

B: That's true, but the energy from all the elevator rides ❺adds up over time. ❻In my opinion, taking care of the environment starts with the little things.

G: ❼You have a point. Let's take the stairs.

여: 지호야, 서둘러! 엘리베이터가 곧 올라간다.

남: 과학실은 겨우 3층에 있잖아. 우리 계단을 오르는 건 어때?

여: 그 모든 계단을 올라서 가고 싶진 않아.

남: 잘 생각해 봐. 엘리베이터는 전기를 많이 쓰잖아. 우리는 환경을 보호하려면 에너지를 아껴야 해.

여: 하지만 엘리베이터를 한 번 탄다고 그렇게 많은 에너지를 사용하진 않잖아.

남: 그렇지. 하지만 엘리베이터를 타면서 사용하는 에너지는 시간이 흐르면서 누적될 거야. 내 생각에는, 환경을 보호하는 것은 작은 것부터 시작한다고 생각해.

여: 네 말이 일리가 있네. 계단을 이용하자.

❶ Why don't we ~? = How about ~? = What about ~? = ~하는 게 어때?   ❷ protect: 보호하다   ❸ ride: 탑승
❹ that은 부사로 '그렇게, 그 정도로'를 뜻한다.   ❺ add up: 합산하다   ❻ In my opinion: 내 생각은 = In my view
❼ You have a point.: 네 말이 일리가 있다.

**Check(√) True or False**

(1) The girl and the boy are going up to the 3rd floor.　　T ☐　F ☐

(2) The boy didn't want to take the elevator because one elevator ride uses a lot of energy.　T ☐　F ☐

**Listen & Talk 2 B**

G: I read a cool article today.

B: What was ❶it about?

G: It was about a new bag. ❷It just looks like a ❸plastic bag, but ❹ it's made mostly of corn.

B: That sounds really amazing.

G: Yes, but there's more. The bag ❺breaks down in soil in only three months and disappears in about three minutes in warm water!

B: Wow! That will help us reduce plastic waste ❻by a lot!

G: I know! The company will start selling the bag sometime this year. ❼I can't wait to use it!

여: 오늘 굉장한 기사를 읽었어.

남: 무엇에 대한 기사였니?

여: 새로운 봉지에 관한 기사였어. 그것은 비닐봉지처럼 생겼지만, 대부분 옥수수로 만든 거야.

남: 그것 참 놀랍구나.

여: 응, 하지만 놀라운 게 더 있어. 그 봉지는 흙 속에서 3달 만에 분해되고 따뜻한 물속에서는 3분 만에 사라져!

남: 와! 그건 우리가 플라스틱 쓰레기를 줄이는 데 많이 도움이 되겠구나!

여: 내 말이 그 말이야! 그 회사는 올해 중으로 그 봉지를 팔기 시작할 거야. 어서 사용하고 싶어!

❶ it은 a cool article을 가리킨다.   ❷ It은 a new bag을 가리킨다.   ❸ plastic bag: 비닐봉지
❹ be made of: ~로 만들어지다   ❺ break down: 분해되다   ❻ by a lot: 많이
❼ I can't wait to ~: '너무 기대된다, 빨리 ~하고 싶어'라는 의미로 원하던 일이 다가오고 있을 때, 빨리하고 싶은 기대감을 나타내는 표현이다.

**Check(√) True or False**

(3) The article the girl read is about the new bag made mostly of corns.　　T ☐　F ☐

(4) The new bags break down in only three months in warm water.　　T ☐　F ☐

**Listen & Talk 1 A**

B: I think we're using too many ❶plastic bags.

G: ❷I agree. It's not good for the environment. How can we reduce our use of plastic bags?

B: ❸In my opinion, we should bring ❹reusable bags when we go shopping.

❶ plastic bag: 비닐봉지
❷ 상대방의 의견에 동의하는 표현으로 'I can't agree with you more.' 등으로 바꾸어 쓸 수 있다.
❸ 자신의 의견을 나타내는 표현으로 'I think ～' 또는 'In my view, ～.' 등으로 바꾸어 표현할 수 있다.
❹ reusable: 재사용할 수 있는

 **Listen & Talk 1 C**

B: Today, ❶I'd like to ❷make a suggestion about the trash problem at our school. I've found that many students just ❸throw things away instead of recycling them. As you know, however, recycling is very important because ❹it saves resources and helps protect the environment. So, in my opinion, we need to reduce the number of ❺trash cans at school to encourage recycling. Why don't we ❻place four different colored recycling bins on every floor instead? This will remind students to ❼ separate the paper, glass, plastic, and cans properly.

❶ I'd like to ～: ～하고 싶다　　❷ make a suggestion: 제안하다
❸ throw ～ away: ～을 버리다　　❹ it은 recycling을 가리킨다.
❺ trash can: 쓰레기통　　❻ place: 놓다, 두다
❼ separate: 분리하다

 **Listen & Talk 2 A**

B: Our club is ❶holding a photo contest next week.

G: What kinds of photos will be in ❷it?

B: The ❸theme is pollution around the world. We are holding this contest to ❹ raise students' awareness of environmental problems.

G: That sounds nice. I can't wait to see it!

❶ hold a contest: 대회를 열다
❷ it은 a photo contest를 가리킨다.
❸ theme: 주제
❹ raise awareness: 인식을 높이다

 **Listen & Talk 2 C**

B: What are we going to do this weekend, Mihee?

G: ❶Why don't we go to the sheep park near my house?

B: A sheep park? How interesting! Are there really sheep in the park?

G: Yes. They are there to protect the environment.

B: How can they help the environment?

G: You know, people usually use ❷chemicals to kill ❸unwanted plants. The sheep in the park eat those plants, so the chemicals ❹are not needed.

B: ❺What a bright idea! I can't wait to visit the park!

❶ Why don't we ～?: '～하는 게 어때?'라고 제안하는 표현으로 'Let's ～'로 바꾸어 표현할 수 있다.
❷ chemical: 화학물질
❸ unwanted plants: 잡초
❹ be+p.p. 형태로 수동태이다.
❺ 감탄문으로 'What+a(n)+형용사+명사(+주어+동사)!' 순서로 이어진다.

 **Do It Yourself**

G: I want to buy a new bag.

B: You already have too many bags. In my opinion, you don't need any more.

G: But ❶I'm bored with my old bags.

B: Then how about using old clothes to make a new bag? You can find out ❷how to do it online.

G: Oh, that sounds interesting! I can't wait to make my own bag.

❶ be bored with: ～에 지루해하다
❷ how to ～ : ～하는 방법

● 다음 우리말과 일치하도록 빈칸에 알맞은 말을 쓰시오.

### Listen & Talk 1 A

B: I think we're using too many _____ _____.

G: I agree. It's not good for the _____. How can we reduce our use of _____ _____?

B: _____ _____ _____, we should bring _____ _____ when we go shopping.

### Listen & Talk 1 B

G: Jiho, hurry _____! The elevator is _____ _____ soon.

B: The science room is just on the third floor. Why don't we _____ _____ _____?

G: I don't want to walk _____ _____ _____ up there.

B: Come on. Elevators use lots of energy. We need to _____ energy to _____ _____ _____.

G: But _____ _____ _____ doesn't use that much energy.

B: That's true, but the energy from all the elevator rides _____ _____ over time. _____ _____ _____, _____ _____ _____ the environment starts with the little things.

G: You _____ _____ _____. Let's take the stairs.

### Listen & Talk 1 C

B: Today, I'd like to _____ _____ _____ about the trash problem at our school. I've found that many students just _____ things _____ instead of _____ them. As you know, however, recycling is very important because it saves _____ and helps _____ the environment. So, _____ _____ _____, we need to reduce the number of _____ at school to encourage recycling. Why don't we _____ four different _____ _____ on every floor instead? This will _____ students to _____ the paper, glass, plastic, and cans properly.

남: 내 생각엔 우리는 비닐봉지를 너무 많이 쓰는 것 같아.
여: 내 생각도 그래. 그건 환경에 좋지 않아. 우리 비닐봉지 사용을 어떻게 줄일 수 있을까?
남: 내 생각에는 물건을 사러 갈 때 재사용할 수 있는 가방을 가져 가야 해.

여: 지호야, 서둘러! 엘리베이터가 곧 올라간다.
남: 과학실은 겨우 3층에 있잖아. 우리 계단을 오르는 건 어때?
여: 그 모든 계단을 올라서 가고 싶진 않아.
남: 잘 생각해 봐. 엘리베이터는 전기를 많이 쓰잖아. 우리는 환경을 보호하려면 에너지를 아껴야 해.
여: 하지만 엘리베이터를 한 번 탄다고 그렇게 많은 에너지를 사용하진 않잖아.
남: 그렇지, 하지만 엘리베이터를 타면서 사용하는 에너지는 시간이 흐르면서 누적될 거야. 내 생각에는, 환경을 보호하는 것은 작은 것부터 시작한다고 생각해.
여: 네 말이 일리가 있네. 계단을 이용하자.

남: 오늘 저는 우리 학교의 쓰레기 문제에 대해 제안을 하나 하고자 합니다. 저는 많은 학생들이 쓰레기를 재활용하는 대신에 그냥 버리는 것을 발견했습니다. 하지만, 여러분도 알다시피, 재활용은 자원을 아낄 수 있고 환경을 보호하는 것을 돕기 때문에 재활용하는 것은 정말 중요합니다. 그래서 제 생각에는 재활용을 권장하기 위해 학교에 있는 쓰레기통의 수를 줄이는 것이 필요하다고 생각합니다. 대신에 모든 층에 각기 색이 다른 4개의 재활용 통을 두는 것이 어떨까요? 이는 학생들이 종이, 유리, 플라스틱, 캔을 적절하게 구분할 수 있도록 상기시킬 것입니다.

### Listen & Talk 2 A

**B:** Our club is _____ a photo contest next week.

**G:** _____ _____ _____ photos will be in it?

**B:** The _____ is pollution around the world. We are holding this contest to _____ _____ _____ of environmental problems.

**G:** That sounds nice. I can't _____ _____ _____ _____!

### Listen & Talk 2 B

**G:** I read a cool _____ today.

**B:** What was it about?

**G:** It was about a new bag. It just looks like a _____ _____, but it's _____ mostly _____ corn.

**B:** That sounds really _____.

**G:** Yes, but there's more. The bag _____ _____ in _____ in only three months and _____ in about three minutes in warm water!

**B:** Wow! That will help us _____ _____ _____ by a lot!

**G:** I know! The _____ will start selling the bag sometime this year. I can't _____ _____ _____ it!

### Listen & Talk 2 C

**B:** What are we going to do this weekend, Mihee?

**G:** Why don't we go to the _____ _____ near my house?

**B:** A sheep park? How _____! Are there really sheep in the park?

**G:** Yes. They are there to _____ _____ _____.

**B:** _____ _____ they help the environment?

**G:** You know, people usually use _____ to kill _____ _____. The sheep in the park eat those plants, so the _____ are not needed.

**B:** What a _____ idea! I can't _____ _____ visit the park!

### Do It Yourself

**G:** I want to buy a new bag.

**B:** You already have too many bags. _____ _____ _____, you don't need _____ _____.

**G:** But I'm _____ _____ my old bags.

**B:** Then how about _____ old clothes to make a new bag? You can find out _____ _____ _____ _____ _____ online.

**G:** Oh, that sounds _____! I can't wait _____ _____ my own bag.

해석

남: 다음 주에 우리 동아리에서 사진 대회를 개최할 거야.

여: 어떤 종류의 사진들이 출품되니?

남: 주제는 세계의 환경오염이야. 우리는 학생들이 환경 문제에 대해 인식을 높일 수 있도록 이 대회를 개최하는 거야.

여: 그거 참 멋지네. 나도 어서 대회를 보고 싶다!

여: 오늘 굉장한 기사를 읽었어.

남: 무엇에 대한 기사였니?

여: 새로운 봉지에 관한 기사였어. 그것은 비닐봉지처럼 생겼지만, 대부분 옥수수로 만든 거야.

남: 그것 참 놀랍구나.

여: 응, 하지만 놀라운 게 더 있어. 그 봉지는 흙 속에서 3달 만에 분해되고 따뜻한 물속에서는 3분 만에 사라져!

남: 와! 그건 우리가 플라스틱 쓰레기를 줄이는 데 많이 도움이 되겠구나!

여: 내 말이 그 말이야! 그 회사는 올해 중으로 그 봉지를 팔기 시작할 거야. 어서 사용하고 싶어!

남: 이번 주말에 무엇을 할 계획이니, 미희야?

여: 우리 집 근처에 있는 양 공원에 가는 것은 어때?

남: 양 공원? 그것 참 흥미로운데! 공원에 정말로 양이 있는 거야?

여: 응. 양들은 환경을 보호하기 위해 거기에 있어.

남: 그들이 어떻게 환경에 도움을 줄 수 있지?

여: 있지, 사람들은 잡초를 없애기 위해 화학 물질을 사용하잖아. 그 공원에 있는 양들이 그런 잡초들을 먹어서, 화학물질이 필요하지 않게 돼.

남: 그것 참 놀라운 생각이구나! 어서 그 공원에 가보고 싶다!

여: 나 새로운 가방을 사고 싶어.

남: 넌 이미 너무 많은 가방을 가지고 있어. 내 생각에 넌 가방이 더 필요하지 않아.

여: 하지만 난 나의 오래된 가방들에 질렸는걸.

남: 그럼 새로운 가방을 만들기 위해 오래된 옷들을 사용하는 것은 어때? 만드는 방법은 온라인상에서 찾아볼 수 있어.

여: 오, 그것 참 흥미로운데! 어서 나만의 가방을 만들고 싶어!

[01~02] 다음 대화를 읽고 물음에 답하시오.

Minsu: Our club is holding a photo contest next week.

Sora: What kinds of photos will be in it?

Minsu: The theme is pollution around the world. We are holding this contest to raise students' awareness of environmental problems.

Sora: That sounds nice. (A)I can't wait to see it!

**01** 위 대화의 밑줄 친 (A)와 바꾸어 쓸 수 있는 말로 적절하지 <u>않은</u> 것은?

① I'm looking forward to seeing it!
② I hope to see it!
③ I'm expecting to see it!
④ I'm eager to see it!
⑤ I'm tired of seeing it!

**02** 위 대화의 내용과 일치하지 <u>않는</u> 것은?

① 다음 주 동아리에서 사진 대회를 개최할 것이다.
② 동아리 사진 대회의 주제는 세계의 환경오염이다.
③ 학생들이 환경 문제에 대해 인식을 높이기 위해 대회를 개최한다.
④ 소라는 대회를 보는 것에 기대를 나타냈다.
⑤ 소라는 대회를 기다리다 지쳤다.

[03~04] 다음 대화를 읽고 물음에 답하시오.

Tom: I think we're using too many plastic bags.

Jane: _____(A)_____ It's not good for the environment. How can we reduce our use of plastic bags?

Tom: In my opinion, we should bring reusable bags when we go shopping.

**03** 위 대화의 빈칸 (A)에 들어갈 말로 나머지와 의도가 <u>다른</u> 것은?

① I agree.
② I can't agree with you more.
③ I disagree with you.
④ That's what I thought.
⑤ I think so, too.

서답형
**04** 위 대화에서 다음 영영풀이가 나타내는 말을 찾아 쓰시오.

capable of being used more than once

➡ _____

**01** 다음 대화가 자연스럽게 이어지도록 순서대로 배열하시오.

> (A) That sounds nice. I can't wait to see it!
> (B) What kinds of photos will be in it?
> (C) Our club is holding a photo contest next week.
> (D) The theme is pollution around the world. We are holding this contest to raise students' awareness of environmental problems.

➡ _____

[02~04] 다음 대화를 읽고 물음에 답하시오.

Sujin: Jiho, hurry up! The elevator is going up soon.

Jiho: The science room is just on the third floor. Why don't we take the stairs?

Sujin: I don't want to walk all the way up there.

Jiho: Come on. Elevators use lots of energy. We need to save energy (A)[protect / to protect] the environment.

Sujin: But one elevator ride doesn't use that much energy.

Jiho: That's true, but the energy from all the elevator rides (B)[add / adds] up over time. In my opinion, (C)[take / taking] care of the environment starts with the little things.

Sujin: (a)You have a point. Let's take the stairs.

**02** 위 대화의 (A)~(C)에 들어갈 말이 바르게 짝지어진 것은?

① protect　　－ add　　－ take
② protect　　－ adds　　－ taking
③ to protect　－ adds　　－ take
④ to protect　－ adds　　－ taking
⑤ to protect　－ add　　－ take

**03** 위 대화의 밑줄 친 (a)의 의미를 우리말로 쓰시오.

➡ _____

**04** 위 대화의 내용과 일치하지 않는 것은?

① 과학실은 3층에 있다.
② 지호는 수진에게 엘리베이터를 타고 올라갈 것을 제안했다.
③ 지호는 환경을 보호하려면 에너지를 아껴야 한다고 생각한다.
④ 수진은 엘리베이터를 한 번 탄다고 그렇게 많은 에너지를 사용하지는 않는다고 생각한다.
⑤ 지호는 엘리베이터를 타면서 사용하는 에너지가 시간이 흐르면서 누적될 것이라고 생각한다.

[05~06] 다음 글을 읽고 물음에 답하시오.

B: Today, I'd like to make a suggestion about the trash problem at our school. I've found that many students just throw things away instead of recycling them. As you know, ___(A)___, recycling is very important because it saves resources and helps protect the environment. So, in my opinion, we need to reduce the number of trash cans at school to encourage recycling. Why don't we place four different colored recycling bins on every floor instead? This will remind students to separate the paper, glass, plastic, and cans properly.

**05** 위 글의 빈칸 (A)에 들어갈 말로 적절한 것은?

① however　　　② moreover
③ in addition　　④ furthermore
⑤ therefore

**06** 위 글을 읽고 대답할 수 <u>없는</u> 것은?

① What problem is the boy talking about?

② Why is recycling important?

③ What does the boy suggest?

④ How many different colors of recycling bins does the boy need?

⑤ What color recycling bin should the students throw away the paper in?

[07~09] 다음 대화를 읽고 물음에 답하시오.

> Emily: I read a cool article today.
>
> Brian: What was it about?
>
> Emily: ⓐIt was about a new bag. It just looks like a plastic bag, but ⓑit's made mostly of corn.
>
> Brian: That sounds really (A)[amazing / amazed].
>
> Emily: Yes, but there's more. The bag breaks down in soil in only three months and (B)[disappear / disappears] in about three minutes in warm water!
>
> Brian: Wow! That will help us (C)[reduce / reducing] plastic waste by a lot!
>
> Emily: I know! The company will start selling the bag sometime this year. I can't wait to use it!

**서답형**

**07** 위 대화의 밑줄 친 ⓐ와 ⓑ가 가리키는 것을 찾아 쓰시오.

➡ ⓐ ＿＿＿＿＿＿＿ ⓑ ＿＿＿＿＿＿＿

**08** 위 대화의 괄호 (A)~(C)에 알맞은 말이 바르게 짝지어진 것은?

① amazing — disappear — reduce

② amazing — disappears — reducing

③ amazing — disappears — reduce

④ amazed — disappears — reducing

⑤ amazed — disappear — reduce

**09** 위 대화의 내용과 일치하지 <u>않는</u> 것은?

① Emily는 새로운 봉지에 관한 기사를 읽었다.

② 새로운 봉지는 비닐봉지처럼 생겼지만, 대부분 옥수수로 만들어졌다.

③ 새로운 봉지는 흙 속에서 3달 만에 분해되고 따뜻한 물속에서는 3시간 만에 사라진다.

④ 새로운 봉지는 플라스틱 쓰레기를 줄이는 데 도움이 될 것이다.

⑤ 회사는 올해 중으로 새로운 봉지를 팔기 시작할 것이다.

[10~11] 다음 대화를 읽고 물음에 답하시오.

> Minsu: Our club is holding a photo contest next week.
>
> Sora: What kinds of photos will be in it?
>
> Minsu: The theme is (A)[pollute / pollution] around the world. We are holding this contest to (B)[rise / raise] students' awareness of environmental problems.
>
> Sora: That sounds nice. I (C)[can / can't] wait to see it!

**10** 위 대화의 (A)~(C)에 들어갈 말이 바르게 짝지어진 것은?

① pollute — rise — can

② pollute — raise — can't

③ pollution — raise — can

④ pollution — raise — can't

⑤ pollution — rise — can

**11** 위 대화를 읽고 알 수 <u>없는</u> 것은?

① 사진 대회 개최 시기

② 사진 대회의 주제

③ 사진 대회의 개최 목적

④ 사진 대회의 주관 동아리

⑤ 사진 대회 개최 장소

**01** 다음 대화의 내용과 일치하도록 빈칸을 완성하시오.

> Minsu: Our club is holding a photo contest next week.
>
> Sora: What kinds of photos will be in it?
>
> Minsu: The theme is pollution around the world. We are holding this contest to raise students' awareness of environmental problems.
>
> Sora: That sounds nice. I can't wait to see it!

> Sora is looking forward to (A)_____ _____. It will be held by (B)_____ next week. The theme is pollution around the world. It is planned to (C)_____ _____ .

[02~05] 다음 대화를 읽고 물음에 답하시오.

> Emily: I read a cool article today.
>
> Brian: What was it about?
>
> Emily: It was about a new bag. It just looks like a plastic bag, but it's made mostly of corn.
>
> Brian: That sounds really amazing.
>
> Emily: Yes, but there's more. The bag breaks down in soil in only three months and disappears in about three minutes in warm water!
>
> Brian: Wow! That will help us reduce plastic waste by a lot!
>
> Emily: I know! The company will start selling the bag sometime this year. I can't wait to use it!

**02** What is the new bag mostly made of?

➡ _____

**03** How long does it take for the new bag to break down in soil?

➡ _____

**04** How does the new bag help protect the environment?

➡ _____

_____

**05** 위 대화의 내용과 일치하지 않는 것을 찾아 바르게 고치시오.

Get the Incredible Bag!

a. It's made mostly of corn.

b. It breaks down in soil in three months.

c. It disappears in about three minutes in cold water.

➡ _____

**06** 다음 대화가 자연스럽게 이어지도록 순서대로 배열하시오.

> Sujin: Jiho, hurry up! The elevator is going up soon.
>
> Jiho: The science room is just on the third floor. Why don't we take the stairs?
>
> (A) But one elevator ride doesn't use that much energy.
>
> (B) I don't want to walk all the way up there.
>
> (C) Come on. Elevators use lots of energy. We need to save energy to protect the environment.
>
> (D) You have a point. Let's take the stairs.
>
> (E) That's true, but the energy from all the elevator rides adds up over time. In my opinion, taking care of the environment starts with the little things.

➡ _____

# Grammar

### 1. to부정사의 의미상 주어

> • It is important **for us** to find ways to protect the environment.
> 우리가 환경을 보호할 수 있는 방법을 찾는 것은 중요하다.
>
> • It was very smart **of him** not to miss the chance.
> 그는 아주 약빠르게도 그 기회를 놓치지 않았다

■ **쓰임과 형태**

- 쓰임: to부정사가 행하는 동작 또는 상태의 주체를 나타낼 때 쓴다.
- 형태: 'for+목적격+to부정사'

■ **to부정사의 의미상의 주어**

to부정사의 동작을 실제로 하는 주체를 to부정사의 의미상의 주어라고 하며 그 행위의 주체가 문장의 주어나 목적어와 다를 때 to부정사 바로 앞에 'for+목적격'으로 나타낸다.

- I want **him** to go there. 나는 그가 그곳에 가기를 바란다. (그가 to go there의 의미상의 주어임)
- It is important **for him** to attend the meeting every day. 그가 매일 회의에 참석하는 것이 중요하다.
  (그가 to attend의 의미상의 주어임)

■ 이때 사람의 성격이나 성품을 나타내는 형용사(kind, nice, polite, rude, smart, stupid, wise 등)가 보어로 쓰일 때는 'of+목적격'의 형태로 나타낸다.

- It is nice **of you** to show me the way. 길을 가르쳐 주셔서 감사합니다.
- It was so rude **of you** to send her away empty. 그녀를 빈손으로 돌려보내다니 넌 무례했다.

■ to부정사의 의미상의 주어가 일반적인 사람일 경우는 보통 생략한다. 또한 to부정사의 부정은 to부정사 앞에 not이나 never를 써서 'not[never]+to부정사'로 나타낸다.

- Air is necessary **(for us)** to live. 공기는 (우리가) 살아가는 데 필수적이다.

### 핵심 Check

**1.** 빈칸에 알맞은 말을 어법에 맞게 쓰시오.

(1) It was necessary _____ help the young children.

(2) It'll take time _____ her to recover from the illness.

(3) It was wise _____ you to keep out of debt.

## ② 관계부사

• Cancun is a city **where** 4.8 million tourists travel every year.
칸쿤은 매년 480만 명의 관광객이 여행하는 도시이다.

• There was a time **when** computers were very rare. 컴퓨터가 아주 희귀한 시대가 있었다.

■ 관계부사는 두 문장을 연결하는 접속사의 역할과 부사구의 역할을 동시에 한다. 관계부사 앞에 오는 수식을 받는 명사를 선행사라 하고, 그 선행사에 따라 관계부사 when(시간), where(장소), why(이유), how(방법)를 쓴다.

  • There was a time **when** things were very different. 상황이 아주 달랐던 때가 있었지.
  • I know a place **where** the food is first-class. 음식이 최고인 곳을 한 군데 알아.

■ 선행사에 따른 관계부사

| | 선행사 | 관계부사 | 전치사+관계대명사 |
|---|---|---|---|
| 때 | the day, the time 등 | when | in/on/at which |
| 장소 | the place, the country 등 | where | in/on/at which |
| 이유 | the reason | why | for which |
| 방법 | the way | how | in which |

■ 관계부사 how는 선행사 the way와 함께 쓰지 않고 반드시 둘 중의 하나만 써야 하며 the way that이나 the way in which를 쓸 수 있다. 다른 관계부사의 경우 선행사가 'the time', 'the place', 'the reason'처럼 일반적인 뜻을 나타낼 때, 선행사나 관계부사 중 하나를 생략할 수 있다.

  • The way how he acts really makes me mad.　　　( × ) 그의 행동 방식은 나를 화나게 만든다.
  • **The way**[또는 **How**] he acts really makes me mad. (○)

■ 관계부사는 '전치사+관계대명사(which)'로 바꿔 쓸 수 있으며, which를 쓸 때는 전치사를 which 바로 앞에 쓰거나 관계사절의 끝에 쓴다.

  • We visited the house **where** Shakespeare was born. 우리는 셰익스피어의 생가를 방문했다.
  = We visited the house **in which** Shakespeare was born.
  = We visited the house **which** Shakespeare was born **in**.

■ 주의: 관계대명사는 관계사절에서 주어나 목적어의 역할을 하므로 주어나 목적어가 빠진 불완전한 절이 나오지만 관계부사는 부사 역할을 하므로 완전한 절이 나온다.

### 핵심 Check

**2.** 다음 괄호 안에서 알맞은 말을 고르시오.

(1) He cares for the children on the days (when / where) he's not working.

(2) The house (when / where) I live was built at the turn of the century.

(3) I'd like to know the reason (why / how) you're so late.

**01** 다음 빈칸에 알맞은 것을 고르시오.

It is not easy _____.

① him to find out the answer    ② he finds out the answer
③ he to find out the answer    ④ for him to find out the answer
⑤ of him to find out the answer

**02** 다음 중 어법상 <u>어색한</u> 문장은?

① I remember the day when we went to the beach.
② Is this the place where the accident happened?
③ I don't like the way how he talks.
④ Give me one good reason why I should help you.
⑤ Galileo's ideas were well in advance of the age in which he lived.

**03** 다음 ①~⑤ 중 생략할 수 있는 것은?

①A good educational background can make ②it easier ③for people ④to develop ⑤good social contacts.

①          ②          ③          ④          ⑤

**04** 다음 괄호 안에서 알맞은 말을 고르시오.

(1) It took three hours for me (write / to write) the report.
(2) It is possible for (she / her) to memorize the poem in ten minutes.
(3) It is necessary (for / of) us to prepare for the winter.
(4) Do you know the reason (how / why) Lisa called me?
(5) George grew up in a village (when / where) there was no electricity.
(6) I remember the day (when / where) I met you.

**01** 다음 중 어법상 올바른 것은?

① It was very kind for you to meet me.
② It is easy catches a disease in winter.
③ It's good for children do things on their own sometimes.
④ It's time for them to wake up.
⑤ That was great for Kevin to rest for a week.

**02** 다음 중 어법상 <u>어색한</u> 것은?

① I vividly remember the day when we first met.
② This is the reason how I'm here.
③ People gathered around the hotel where he was staying.
④ Explain how you solved the question.
⑤ The age at which a person can begin driving varies from state to state.

**03** 다음 빈칸에 알맞은 말이 바르게 짝지어진 것은?

- 2010 was the year _____ he published his first novel.
- It is difficult _____ Jackson to work out early in the morning.

① how – of
② how – for
③ when – for
④ when – of
⑤ that – of

**서답형**

**04** 다음 괄호 안에서 알맞은 말을 고르시오.

(1) It was not easy (wake / to wake) him up this morning.
(2) It is impossible (of / for) us to emphasize safety training too much.
(3) It is considerate (of / for) you to advise me.
(4) I don't know the reason (when / why) I didn't remember anything during the exam.
(5) Thursday is traditionally the day (which / when) the British go to vote.
(6) This is the house (which / where) Yun Bonggil was born in.
(7) He showed me (the way how / how) he packed his suitcase.

**서답형**

**05** 다음 두 문장을 한 문장으로 바꿔 쓸 때 빈칸에 들어갈 알맞은 말을 쓰시오.

- The author has moved his family to a small town.
- He now writes his awesome novels in the town.
→ The author has moved his family to a small town _____ he now writes his awesome novels.

**06** 다음 중 어법상 어색한 것은?

① It is very important of me to make the fans happy.
② It's dangerous for kids to walk home alone.
③ It's impossible to hold a conversation with all this noise.
④ It was silly of me to want to marry Ann.
⑤ It is difficult for him to get around without a cane.

**07** 밑줄 친 부분의 쓰임이 주어진 문장과 같은 것은?

> Sep. 23 is the day when I got married to Jake.

① When did she promise to meet him?
② It was a magic moment when the two sisters were reunited after 30 years.
③ Since when did you get interested in collecting stamps?
④ He told me the when and the where of the event.
⑤ When he goes out, he takes his dog with him.

**08** 다음 우리말을 바르게 영작한 것을 고르시오.

> 이곳은 내가 예전에 살았던 집이다.

① This is the house when I used to live.
② This is the house why I used to live.
③ This is the house which I used to live.
④ This is the house where I used to live in.
⑤ This is the house where I used to live.

**09** 주어진 어휘를 이용하여 다음 우리말을 영작하시오.

> 그들에게 김치를 만드는 것은 어려웠다.
> (Gimchi, them, make, hard, it, to)

➡ _____

**10** 다음 두 문장을 한 문장으로 바르게 연결한 것은?

> • My family will go to the beach.
> • My parents first met at the beach.

① My family will go to the beach how my parents first met.
② My family will go to the beach why my parents first met.
③ My family will go to the beach when my parents first met.
④ My family will go to the beach where my parents first met.
⑤ My family will go to the beach which my parents first met.

**11** 다음 우리말과 일치하도록 빈칸에 알맞은 단어로 묶은 것은?

> 우리가 환경을 보호할 수 있는 방법을 찾는 것은 중요하다.
> = _____ is important _____ us to find ways to protect the environment.

① That – for
② That – of
③ It – for
④ It – of
⑤ This – with

**12** 다음 빈칸에 들어갈 말로 알맞은 말은?

> It was brave _____ to speak on behalf of the people.

① for him
② for his
③ of his
④ of he
⑤ of him

**서답형**

**13** 다음 문장에서 생략할 수 있는 것을 찾아 쓰시오.

(1) Now is the time when we have to make a decision.

➡ _____

(2) What is the reason why you removed him from his post?

➡ _____

**서답형**

**14** 다음 문장에서 어법상 어색한 것을 바르게 고쳐 다시 쓰시오.

(1) Of him to live without her even for a single day was really hard.

➡ _____
_____

(2) I suppose it was rude for me to listen to a private conversation.

➡ _____
_____

(3) It is very important for him making a decision soon.

➡ _____
_____

(4) We should find a place which we can be safe!

➡ _____
_____

(5) Do you know the reason which John left so early?

➡ _____
_____

(6) I have to say I like the way how he solved the situation.

➡ _____
_____

**중요**

**15** 다음 중 어법상 어색한 것을 고르시오. (2개)

① It was very nice of her showing me the way.

② The movie was too difficult for me to understand.

③ It is not easy for Leo to get up early in the morning.

④ We are going to visit the city which my grandparents were born.

⑤ My room is a place where I can relax.

**16** 다음 각 문장의 밑줄 친 it[It]이 어떤 용법으로 쓰였는지 쓰시오.

(1) 가주어 ~ 진주어 구문
(2) It ~ that 강조 구문

ⓐ It was the architect that drew up plans for the new office.

ⓑ It is boring for Junho to watch baseball games.

ⓒ It was impossible for me to understand the system.

ⓓ It is the air that we breathe.

ⓔ How long does it take for the plastic bag to break down in soil?

ⓕ What was it that he wanted you to do?

➡ (1) _____ (2) _____

**중요**

**17** 다음 중 빈칸에 들어갈 말로 알맞은 것을 고르시오.

> That is the reason _____ I don't like living in the city.

① which     ② where     ③ how
④ when      ⑤ why

**01** 다음 두 문장의 뜻이 비슷하도록 빈칸에 들어갈 알맞은 말을 쓰시오.

(1) She is rarely seen in public nowadays.

= It is hard for _____ see her in public nowadays.

(2) They nicely invited us.

= It was nice _____ invite us.

**02** 다음 우리말에 맞게 주어진 어구를 바르게 배열하시오.

(1) 나는 우리가 어제 차를 마셨던 그 카페를 좋아한다. (I, we, the café, tea, like, had, where, yesterday)

➡ _____

_____

(2) 서울을 떠나기로 결정한 이유를 물어봐도 될까요? (I, you, you, the reason, Seoul, decided, ask, may, why, leave, to)

➡ _____

_____

(3) 그 가방들은 우리가 들고 가기에 너무 무거웠다. (the bags, us, carry, were, too, heavy, for, to)

➡ _____

_____

(4) 인부들이 길을 보수하는 데는 몇 주가 걸렸다. (the workers, the street, weeks, a, it, took, repair, few, for, to)

➡ _____

_____

(5) 그녀가 혼자서 외국에 간 것은 용감했다. (her, it, go, was, abroad, brave, alone, to, of)

➡ _____

_____

**03** 그림을 보고, 주어진 어휘를 이용하여 빈칸을 알맞게 채우시오.

(1)

She didn't know _____ the problems. (the way, solve, could)

(2)

The Eiffel Tower is the place _____. (I, want, go)

**04** 괄호 안에 주어진 말을 이용하여 어법에 맞게 문장을 완성하시오.

(1) It was not easy _____ up early this morning. (me, wake)

(2) It is really thoughtful _____ my birthday. (you, remember)

**05** 주어진 두 문장을 관계부사를 이용하여 하나의 문장으로 쓰시오.

(1) • They made an underwater museum away from the places.
  • Sea life was dying at the places.

➡ _____

(2) • I can't forget the day.
  • I won the class election on the day.

➡ _____

(3) • They talked about the way.
  • He scored the goal in the final match in the way.

➡ _____

(4) • That is the reason.
  • I like documentaries for the reason.

➡ _____

**06** 다음 문장에서 어법상 어색한 것을 바르게 고치시오.

(1) The cake was big enough of us to share.
  _____ ➡ _____

(2) It is very foolish for you to waste your precious time on it!
  _____ ➡ _____

(3) It was heartless for him to say such a thing to the sick man.
  _____ ➡ _____

(4) It was easy for her to not miss a word.
  _____ ➡ _____

**07** 어법상 어색한 것을 바르게 고치시오.

(1) I still remember the day where my class got first place on Sports Day.

➡ _____

(2) The reason which he did it is not clear to me.

➡ _____

(3) I can recognize him by the way how he walks.

➡ _____

(4) I miss the summers when we used to go to the beach in.

➡ _____

**08** 다음 우리말을 괄호 안의 지시대로 영작하시오.

(1) 나는 내가 파티를 일찍 떠난 이유를 설명했다.
  ➡ _____
  (관계부사를 써서)
  ➡ _____
  (관계대명사를 써서)

(2) 그는 그가 인생을 살았던 방식을 후회한다.
  ➡ _____
  (관계부사를 생략해서)
  ➡ _____
  (선행사를 생략해서)
  ➡ _____
  (that을 써서)

## Join Hands, Save the Earth

It is important for us to find ways to protect the environment. Some people have found creative ways to save the earth. One example is an underwater museum in Cancun, Mexico. Let's meet Dr. Rosa Allison, an art professor, and listen to her explanation about the special museum.

**Rosa:** Cancun is a city where 4.8 million tourists travel every year. One of the most popular activities to do there is looking at the area's beautiful sea life underwater. However, tourist activities are seriously damaging parts of the sea near Cancun. To prevent this, artists did something interesting. They thought if they attracted tourists to a different part of the sea, the dying areas could have time to get better. They made an underwater museum away from the places where sea life was dying. It's about 14 meters below the surface and contains 500 statues. The statues are made from materials that support sea life. They provide additional places for plants and animals to live on. Over time, many types of sea life will grow on the statues, which will make the artwork unique. The artists want people to see a variety of sea life on the statues.

environment: 환경

creative: 창의적인

underwater: 물속의, 수중의

explanation: 설명

damage: 손상시키다

prevent: 막다, 예방하다

surface: 표면

statue: 조각상

material: 재료, 자료

support: 지원하다

additional: 추가적인

---

📎 **확인문제**

● 다음 문장이 본문의 내용과 일치하면 T, 일치하지 않으면 F를 쓰시오.

1  Dr. Rosa Allison doesn't know about art well. ☐

2  The sea near Cancun was protected by tourist activities. ☐

3  Sea life in the sea near Cancun was dying. ☐

4  It will be hard to see various sea creatures at the underwater museum. ☐

If people realize how rich sea life is, they will understand how important it is to save the sea.

> 간접의문문(의문사+주어+동사): realize의 목적어
> 간접의문문의 가주어 / 진주어

In Singapore, people are using architecture to protect the environment on land. Let's hear what Rajesh Khan, an architect, says about eco-friendly buildings.

> to부정사의 부사적 용법 중 목적(~하기 위해서)
> 관계대명사

**Rajesh:** Singapore is hot throughout the year. Most buildings need air conditioning, which uses a lot of energy and contributes to climate change. That's why architects in Singapore have begun to design eco-friendly buildings that use less air conditioning but are still cool inside. For example, many buildings in Singapore are designed to have an open structure. This structure makes it possible for outside air to move throughout a building. This natural air flow is how these buildings stay cool. In addition to making open structures, architects add large gardens. This greenery provides shade and protects parts of the building from direct sunlight, which keeps the building cooler.

> air conditioning에 수의 일치 / uses와 병렬 연결
> That's why+결과 / 현재완료
> eco-friendly buildings에 수의 일치 / use와 병렬 연결
> 가목적어 it / 의미상 주어
> 진목적어
> 전치사구(목적어로 동명사구가 나옴)
> protect A from B: B로부터 A를 보호하다
> 앞 문장 전체를 선행사로 취하는 관계대명사

Eco-friendly buildings like these not only help protect the environment, but also provide people with a good quality of life. Those are the goals of this new style of architecture. Hopefully, architects will keep coming up with new eco-friendly ideas.

> not only A but also B: A 뿐만 아니라 B도(=B as well as A)
> provide A with B: A에게 B를 제공하다
> keep Ving: 계속해서 V하다

Every field has different ways of protecting the environment. With more innovation, humans and nature will be able to live together in harmony far into the future.

> every+단수명사: 단수 취급
> 동격의 전치사
> will can(×)

---

architecture: 건축(술)

architect: 건축가

contribute to: ~에 기여하다,
(~의) 원인이 되다

climate: 기후

structure: 구조(물)

flow: 흐름

greenery: 푸른 잎, 푸른 나무

shade: 그늘

in harmony: 조화를 이루어

---

📎 **확인문제**

● 다음 문장이 본문의 내용과 일치하면 T, 일치하지 않으면 F를 쓰시오.

1 People in Singapore protect the environment by means of architecture. ☐

2 Using air conditioning can be a factor resulting in climate change. ☐

3 The open structure protects the building from direct sunlight. ☐

4 Eco-friendly buildings are helpful not for humans but for the environment. ☐

● 우리말을 참고하여 빈칸에 알맞은 말을 쓰시오.

Join Hands, Save the Earth

**1** It is important _____ _____ _____ _____ to protect the environment.

**2** Some people have found _____ ways _____ _____ the earth.

**3** One example is an _____ _____ in Cancun, Mexico.

**4** Let's _____ Dr. Rosa Allison, an art _____, and _____ _____ her explanation about the special museum.

**5** Rosa: Cancun is a city _____ 4.8 million _____ _____ every year.

**6** One of _____ _____ _____ activities _____ _____ there _____ looking _____ the area's beautiful sea life underwater.

**7** _____, tourist activities _____ seriously _____ _____ of the sea _____ Cancun.

**8** _____ _____ _____, artists did _____ _____.

**9** They thought _____ they _____ tourists _____ a different part of the sea, the _____ _____ could have time _____ _____ _____.

**10** They _____ an _____ museum _____ _____ the places _____ sea life was _____.

**11** It's _____ 14 _____ _____ the surface and _____ 500 _____.

**12** The statues _____ _____ _____ materials _____ _____ sea life.

**13** They _____ additional places _____ plants and animals _____ _____ _____.

**14** Over time, many types of sea life _____ _____ _____ the statues, _____ _____ the artwork _____.

**15** The artists _____ _____ _____ _____ a variety of sea life _____ the statues.

함께 손잡고, 지구를 구합시다

**1** 우리가 환경을 보호할 수 있는 방법을 찾는 것은 중요하다.

**2** 몇몇 사람들은 지구를 구하기 위한 창의적인 방법을 찾았다.

**3** 한 예로 멕시코 칸쿤에 있는 수중 박물관이 있다.

**4** 미술학 교수인 Rosa Allison 박사를 만나서 이 특별한 박물관에 대한 설명을 들어보자.

**5** Rosa: 칸쿤은 매년 480만 명의 관광객이 여행하는 도시이다.

**6** 그곳에서 할 수 있는 가장 인기 있는 활동 중 하나는 그 지역의 바닷속의 아름다운 해양 생물을 관찰하는 것이다.

**7** 하지만, 관광 활동들이 칸쿤 근처의 바다 일부를 심각하게 훼손시키고 있다.

**8** 이러한 일을 방지하기 위해서, 예술가들이 흥미로운 생각을 해냈다.

**9** 그들은 만약 관광객들을 바다의 다른 쪽으로 유인한다면, 그 죽어가는 지역이 호전될 시간을 가질 수 있을 것이라 생각했다.

**10** 그들은 해양 생물이 죽어가는 지역으로부터 떨어진 해저에 수중 박물관을 만들었다.

**11** 그 박물관은 해수면에서 14미터 아래에 있으며 500개의 조각상이 있다.

**12** 그 조각상들은 해양 생물에게 도움이 되는 재료들로 만들어졌다.

**13** 그것들은 식물과 동물들이 살 수 있는 추가적인 장소를 제공한다.

**14** 시간이 흐르면, 많은 형태의 바다 생명체들이 그 조각상에서 자라게 될 것이며, 이것이 그 예술 작품을 독특하게 만들 것이다.

**15** 예술가들은 사람들이 그 조각상들에서 (살고 있는) 다양한 해양 생명체들을 보길 원한다.

**16** If people realize _____ _____ _____ _____ _____ _____,
they will understand _____ _____ _____ _____ to
save the sea.

**17** In Singapore, people are _____ architecture _____ _____
the environment _____ _____.

**18** Let's hear _____ Rajesh Khan, an architect, _____ _____
eco-friendly buildings.

**19** Rajesh: Singapore is hot _____ _____ _____.

**20** Most buildings _____ air conditioning, _____ _____ a lot
of energy and _____ _____ climate change.

**21** _____ _____ architects in Singapore _____ _____
_____ design eco-friendly buildings _____ _____
_____ air conditioning but _____ _____ cool inside.

**22** _____ _____, many buildings in Singapore _____
_____ _____ _____ an open structure.

**23** This structure makes _____ possible _____ _____
_____ _____ _____ throughout a building.

**24** This _____ air flow is _____ _____ _____
_____.

**25** _____ _____ _____ _____ _____ open structures, architects
add large gardens.

**26** This greenery _____ shade and _____ parts of the building
_____ _____ _____, which _____ the building cooler.

**27** Eco-friendly buildings like these _____ _____ _____
protect the environment, _____ _____ _____ people
_____ a good quality of life.

**28** Those are the _____ of this _____ _____ of _____.

**29** Hopefully, architects _____ _____ _____
_____ new eco-friendly ideas.

**30** _____ _____ _____ different ways of _____ the
environment.

**31** _____ more innovation, humans and nature _____ _____
_____ _____ in harmony _____
_____ the future.

**16** 만약 사람들이 해양 생물이 얼마나 풍부한지 깨닫는다면, 그들은 바다를 지키는 것이 얼마나 중요한지 이해할 것이다.

**17** 싱가포르에서는 사람들이 육지의 환경을 보호하기 위해 건축을 이용하고 있다.

**18** 건축가인 Rajesh Khan이 친환경 건물에 대해 말하는 것을 들어보자.

**19** Rajesh: 싱가포르는 연중 더운 곳이다.

**20** 대부분의 건물들은 에어컨 가동이 필요한데, 이로 인해 많은 에너지가 사용되고 있으며 기후 변화의 원인이 되고 있다.

**21** 그것이 싱가포르의 건축가들이 에어컨을 덜 쓰면서도 실내에서 여전히 시원한 느낌이 들 수 있는 친환경적인 건물들을 디자인하기 시작한 이유이다.

**22** 가령, 싱가포르의 많은 건물들은 개방형 구조를 포함하게 디자인되었다.

**23** 이러한 구조는 외부 공기가 건물을 관통하는 것을 가능케 한다.

**24** 이러한 자연적인 공기의 흐름이 이 건물을 시원하게 유지해 주는 방법이다.

**25** 건축가들은 개방형 구조를 만드는 것 외에도 큰 정원을 더한다.

**26** 이러한 녹지 공간은 그늘을 제공하고 직사광선으로부터 건물의 부분들을 지켜주어 건물을 시원하게 유지한다.

**27** 이와 같은 친환경적인 건물들은 환경을 보호하는 것을 도울 뿐만 아니라 사람들에게 양질의 삶을 제공한다.

**28** 그것들이 바로 이러한 새로운 건축 방식의 목표이다.

**29** 바라건대, 건축가들은 새로운 친환경 아이디어를 계속해서 생각해 낼 것이다.

**30** 모든 분야에서 환경을 보호하는 다른 방식이 있다.

**31** 더 나은 혁신으로 인해 먼 미래에 인간과 자연은 함께 조화를 이루며 살아갈 수 있을 것이다.

● 우리말을 참고하여 본문을 영작하시오.

**1** 우리가 환경을 보호할 수 있는 방법을 찾는 것은 중요하다.

➡ _____

**2** 몇몇 사람들은 지구를 구하기 위한 창의적인 방법을 찾았다.

➡ _____

**3** 한 예로 멕시코 칸쿤에 있는 수중 박물관이 있다.

➡ _____

**4** 미술학 교수인 Rosa Allison 박사를 만나서 이 특별한 박물관에 대한 설명을 들어보자.

➡ _____

**5** Rosa: 칸쿤은 매년 480만 명의 관광객이 여행하는 도시이다.

➡ _____

**6** 그곳에서 할 수 있는 가장 인기 있는 활동 중 하나는 그 지역의 바닷속의 아름다운 해양 생물을 관찰하는 것이다.

➡ _____

**7** 하지만, 관광 활동들이 칸쿤 근처의 바다 일부를 심각하게 훼손시키고 있다.

➡ _____

**8** 이러한 일을 방지하기 위해서, 예술가들이 흥미로운 생각을 해냈다.

➡ _____

**9** 그들은 만약 관광객들을 바다의 다른 쪽으로 유인한다면, 그 죽어가는 지역이 호전될 시간을 가질 수 있을 것이라 생각했다.

➡ _____

**10** 그들은 해양 생물이 죽어가는 지역으로부터 떨어진 해저에 수중 박물관을 만들었다.

➡ _____

**11** 그 박물관은 해수면에서 14미터 아래에 있으며 500개의 조각상이 있다.

➡ _____

**12** 그 조각상들은 해양 생물에게 도움이 되는 재료들로 만들어졌다.

➡ _____

**13** 그것들은 식물과 동물들이 살 수 있는 추가적인 장소를 제공한다.

➡ _____

**14** 시간이 흐르면, 많은 형태의 바다 생명체들이 그 조각상에서 자라게 될 것이며, 이것이 그 예술 작품을 독특하게 만들 것이다.

➡ _____

**15** 예술가들은 사람들이 그 조각상들에서 (살고 있는) 다양한 해양 생명체들을 보길 원한다.

➡ _____

**16** 만약 사람들이 해양 생물이 얼마나 풍부한지 깨닫는다면, 그들은 바다를 지키는 것이 얼마나 중요한지 이해할 것이다.

➡ _____

**17** 싱가포르에서는 사람들이 육지의 환경을 보호하기 위해 건축을 이용하고 있다.

➡ _____

**18** 건축가인 Rajesh Khan이 친환경 건물에 대해 말하는 것을 들어보자.

➡ _____

**19** Rajesh: 싱가포르는 연중 더운 곳이다.

➡ _____

**20** 대부분의 건물들은 에어컨 가동이 필요한데, 이로 인해 많은 에너지가 사용되고 있으며 기후 변화의 원인이 되고 있다.

➡ _____

**21** 그것이 싱가포르의 건축가들이 에어컨을 덜 쓰면서도 실내에서 여전히 시원한 느낌이 들 수 있는 친환경적인 건물들을 디자인하기 시작한 이유이다.

➡ _____

**22** 가령, 싱가포르의 많은 건물들은 개방형 구조를 포함하게 디자인되었다.

➡ _____

**23** 이러한 구조는 외부 공기가 건물을 관통하는 것을 가능케 한다.

➡ _____

**24** 이러한 자연적인 공기의 흐름이 이 건물을 시원하게 유지해 주는 방법이다.

➡ _____

**25** 건축가들은 개방형 구조를 만드는 것 외에도 큰 정원을 더한다.

➡ _____

**26** 이러한 녹지 공간은 그늘을 제공하고 직사광선으로부터 건물의 부분들을 지켜주어 건물을 시원하게 유지한다.

➡ _____

**27** 이와 같은 친환경적인 건물들은 환경을 보호하는 것을 도울 뿐만 아니라 사람들에게 양질의 삶을 제공한다.

➡ _____

**28** 그것들이 바로 이러한 새로운 건축 방식의 목표이다.

➡ _____

**29** 바라건대, 건축가들은 새로운 친환경 아이디어를 계속해서 생각해 낼 것이다.

➡ _____

**30** 모든 분야에서 환경을 보호하는 다른 방식이 있다.

➡ _____

**31** 더 나은 혁신으로 인해 먼 미래에 인간과 자연은 함께 조화를 이루며 살아갈 수 있을 것이다.

➡ _____

[01~02] 다음 글을 읽고 물음에 답하시오.

It is important for us to find ways to protect the environment. Some people have found creative ways to save the earth. One example is an underwater museum in Cancun, Mexico. Let's meet Dr. Rosa Allison, an art professor, and listen to her explanation about (A)the special museum.

**01** 밑줄 친 (A)에 대한 설명으로 적절한 것은?

① It was built to make Mexico famous.
② Rosa Allison built it.
③ It is under the sea.
④ It is harmful for the environment.
⑤ It was found by Rosa Allison.

서답형
**02** 다음과 같이 풀이되는 말을 위 글에서 찾아 쓰시오.

a building where a large number of interesting and valuable objects, such as works of art or historical items, are kept, studied, and displayed to the public

➡ _____

[03~05] 다음 글을 읽고 물음에 답하시오.

**Rosa:** Cancun is a city where 4.8 million tourists travel every year. One of the most popular activities to do there is looking at the area's beautiful sea life underwater. _____(A)_____, tourist activities are seriously damaging parts of the sea near Cancun. To prevent this, artists did something interesting. They thought if they attracted tourists to a different part of

the sea, the dying areas could have time to get better. They made an underwater museum away from the places where sea life was dying. It's about 14 meters below the surface and contains 500 statues.

**03** 빈칸 (A)에 들어갈 말로 가장 적절한 것은?

① For example　　② Therefore
③ Nevertheless　　④ On the other hand
⑤ However

서답형
**04** How many tourists visit Cancun every year? Answer in English.

➡ _____

중요
**05** 위 글을 읽고 답할 수 있는 것은?

① How can people get to Cancun?
② Why do people travel to Cancun?
③ Where did they make an underwater museum?
④ What was another tourist attraction of Cancun?
⑤ How many artists took part in making the museum?

[06~07] 다음 글을 읽고 물음에 답하시오.

The statues are made from materials ① that support sea life. They provide additional places for plants and animals ②to live on. Over time, many types of sea life will grow ③ on the statues, which will make the artwork ④uniquely. The artists want people to see a variety of sea life on the statues. If people realize ⑤how rich sea life is, they will understand how important it is to save the sea.

**06** 밑줄 친 ①~⑤ 중 어법상 바르지 <u>않은</u> 것은?

**서답형** ①　　　②　　　③　　　④　　　⑤

**07** According to the passage, what do the artists want people to see? Answer in English.

➡ _____

_____

**[08~10]** 다음 글을 읽고 물음에 답하시오.

In Singapore, people are using architecture to protect the environment on land. Let's hear what Rajesh Khan, an architect, says about eco-friendly buildings.

**Rajesh:** Singapore is hot throughout the year. ① Most buildings need air conditioning, which uses a lot of energy and contributes to climate change. ② That's why architects in Singapore have begun to design eco-friendly buildings that use less air conditioning but are still cool inside. ③ For example, many buildings in Singapore are designed to have an open structure. ④ This natural air flow is how these buildings stay cool. ⑤

**08** ①~⑤ 중 주어진 문장이 들어가기에 가장 적절한 곳은?

This structure makes it possible for outside air to move throughout a building.

①　　　②　　　③　　　④　　　⑤

**09** 위 글의 내용과 일치하는 것은?

① Rajesh Khan built many buildings.
② Singapore is hot all year round.
③ Eco-friendly buildings use lots of energy.
④ The environment in Singapore is not damaged.
⑤ Air conditioning is rarely used in Singapore.

**10** What do most buildings in Singapore need? Answer in English with seven words.

➡ _____

**[11~13]** 다음 글을 읽고 물음에 답하시오.

In addition to making open structures, architects add large ___(A)___ . This greenery provides shade and protects parts of the building from direct sunlight, which keeps the building cooler.

Eco-friendly buildings like these not only help protect the environment, but also provide people with a good quality of life. Those are the goals of this new style of architecture. Hopefully, architects will keep coming up with new eco-friendly ideas. (B)모든 분야에서 환경을 보호하는 다른 방식이 있다. With more innovation, humans and nature will be able to live together in harmony far into the future.

**11** 빈칸 (A)에 들어갈 말로 가장 적절한 것은?

① fans　　② gardens　　③ mirrors
④ roofs　　⑤ refrigerators

**12** 다음 중 위 글 앞에 나올 내용으로 가장 적절한 것은?

① how to grow plants in buildings
② well known traditional architecture
③ other eco-friendly buildings
④ the ways to protect wild life
**서답형** ⑤ hitting on innovative ideas

**13** 주어진 단어를 활용하여 밑줄 친 우리말 (B)를 영어로 쓰시오. (어형 변화 가능.)

(every / ways / of / protect / field)

➡ _____

_____

[14~15] 다음 글을 읽고 물음에 답하시오.

It is important for us ___(A)___ ways to protect the environment. Some people have found creative ways to save the earth. One example is an underwater museum in Cancun, Mexico. Let's meet Dr. Rosa Allison, an art professor, and listen to her explanation about the special museum.

**14** 빈칸 (A)에 들어갈 동사 find의 형태와 <u>다른</u> 것은?

① I was glad _____ the key.
② She went out _____ something to read.
③ He woke up _____ himself alone.
④ I enjoy _____ various insects.
⑤ We were advised _____ another route.

**15** 다음 중 위 글을 읽고 알 수 있는 것은?

① Rosa Allison lives in Mexico.
② People find ways to use the earth.
③ Rosa Allison is an environmentalist.
④ People aren't interested in saving the earth.
⑤ The underwater museum was made to protect the environment.

[16~19] 다음 글을 읽고 물음에 답하시오.

Cancun is a city where 4.8 million tourists travel every year. One of the most popular activities to do there is looking at the area's beautiful sea life underwater. However, tourist activities are seriously damaging parts of the sea near Cancun.

To prevent this, artists did something interesting. They thought if they attracted tourists to a different part of the sea, the dying areas could have time to get better. They made an underwater museum away from the places where sea life was dying. It's about 14 meters below the surface and contains 500 statues.

The statues are made from materials that support sea life. They provide additional places for plants and animals to live on. Over time, many types of sea life will grow on the statues, which will make the artwork unique.

The artists want people to see a variety of sea life on the statues. If people realize how rich sea life is, they will understand how important it is to save the sea.

서답형
**16** What will grow on the statues over time? Answer in English.

➡ _____

_____

**17** According to the passage, what made the sea near Cancun damaged?

① too many artistic activities of artists
② tourist activities
③ various kinds of sea life
④ the limited use of the sea
⑤ the garbage that people threw away

서답형
**18** What are the statues in the underwater museum made from? Answer in English.

➡ _____

_____

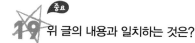

**19** 위 글의 내용과 일치하는 것은?

① Cancun is not a well known tourist attraction.

② The underwater museum has nothing to see.

③ There is only a little sea life at the sea of Cancun.

④ The underwater museum is close to the places where sea life was dying.

⑤ The underwater museum was built to distract people from the place which was seriously damaged.

**[20~23]** 다음 글을 읽고 물음에 답하시오.

In Singapore, people are using architecture to protect the environment ①on land. Let's hear what Rajesh Khan, an architect, says about eco-friendly buildings.

Singapore is ②hot throughout the year. Most buildings need air conditioning, which uses a lot of energy and contributes to climate change. That's why architects in Singapore have begun to design eco-friendly buildings that use ③less air conditioning but are still cool inside. For example, many buildings in Singapore are designed to have an open structure. This structure makes it possible for outside air to move throughout a building. This natural air flow is how these buildings stay cool.     (A)     making open structures, architects add large gardens. This greenery provides shade and protects parts of the building from ④direct sunlight, which keeps the building cooler. Eco-friendly buildings like these not only help protect the environment, but also provide people with a good quality of life. Those are the goals of

(B)this new style of architecture. Hopefully, architects will keep coming up with new eco-friendly ideas.

Every field has different ways of protecting the environment. With more innovation, humans and nature will be able to live together in ⑤isolation far into the future.

**20** 빈칸 (A)에 들어갈 말로 가장 적절한 것은?

① Instead of          ② In addition to

③ According to        ④ Due to

⑤ Regardless of

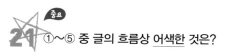

**21** ①~⑤ 중 글의 흐름상 어색한 것은?

①          ②          ③          ④          ⑤

**22** 밑줄 친 (B)에 대한 설명으로 가장 적절한 것은?

① architecture which is good for animals

② the building structures nobody can imitate

③ architecture good for both nature and human beings

④ the building method helpful for the poor

⑤ the buildings that make people comfortable to live their lives

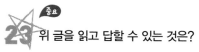

**23** 위 글을 읽고 답할 수 있는 것은?

① How many buildings has Rajesh built?

② Why is Singapore hot all year round?

③ When was an eco-friendly building first invented?

④ What makes people innovative in their field?

⑤ What provides people with a good quality of life?

**[01~02] 다음 글을 읽고 물음에 답하시오.**

(A)우리가 환경을 보호할 수 있는 방법을 찾는 것은 중요하다. Some people have found creative ways to save the earth. One example is an underwater museum in Cancun, Mexico. Let's meet Dr. Rosa Allison, an art professor, and listen to her explanation about the special museum.

**01** 주어진 어구를 활용하여 밑줄 친 우리말 (A)를 영어로 쓰시오.

(it / to / the environment / ways / protect)

➡ _____

_____

**02** Where is Cancun located? Answer in English.

➡ _____

**[03~08] 다음 글을 읽고 물음에 답하시오.**

Cancun is a city where 4.8 million tourists travel every year. One of the most popular activities to do there is looking at the area's beautiful sea life underwater. However, tourist activities are seriously damaging parts of the sea near Cancun. To prevent (A)this, artists did something interesting. They thought if they attracted tourists to a different part of the sea, the dying areas could have time to get better. They made an underwater museum away from the places where sea life was dying. It's about 14 meters below the surface and contains 500 statues. The statues are made from materials that support sea life. They provide additional places for plants and animals to live on. Over

time, many types of sea life will grow on the statues, which will make the artwork unique. The artists want people to see a variety of sea life on the statues. If people realize how rich sea life is, they will understand how important it is to save the sea.

**03** What is one of the most popular activities to do in Cancun? Answer in English with ten words.

➡ _____

_____

**04** 밑줄 친 (A)가 의미하는 것을 우리말로 쓰시오.

➡ _____

_____

**05** What was the purpose of making an underwater museum? Answer in English and use the word 'give.'

➡ _____

**06** 위 글의 내용에 맞게 빈칸에 알맞은 말을 쓰시오.

In addition to being made from _____
_____, the statues provide
_____ on which _____
_____.

**07** How many statues does the museum contain? Answer in English.

➡ _____

**08** According to the passage, what will make the statues unique? Answer in English. (10 words)

➡ _____

_____

**[09~14]** 다음 글을 읽고 물음에 답하시오.

In Singapore, people are using architecture to protect the environment on land. Let's hear what Rajesh Khan, an architect, says about ___(A)___ buildings.

Rajesh: Singapore is hot throughout the year. Most buildings need air conditioning, which uses a lot of energy and contributes to climate change. That's why architects in Singapore have begun to design eco-friendly buildings that use less air conditioning but are still cool inside. For example, many buildings in Singapore are designed to have an open structure. This structure makes it possible for outside air to move throughout a building. This natural air flow is how these buildings stay cool.

In addition to making open structures, architects add large gardens. This greenery provides shade and protects parts of the building from direct sunlight, which keeps the building cooler.

Eco-friendly buildings like (B)these not only help protect the environment, but also provide people with a good quality of life. Those are the goals of this new style of architecture. (C)바라건대, 건축가들은 새로운 친환경 아이디어를 계속해서 생각해 낼 것입니다.

Every field has different ways of protecting the environment. With more innovation, humans and nature will be able to live together in harmony far into the future.

**09** 빈칸 (A)에 들어갈 말을 위 글에서 찾아 쓰시오.

➡ _____

**10** What is the problem of using air conditioning? Answer in English.

➡ _____

_____

**11** 위 글의 내용에 맞게 빈칸에 알맞은 말을 쓰시오.

An open structure of a building enables
_____ to _____.

**12** 밑줄 친 (B)가 가리키는 것을 우리말로 쓰시오.

➡ _____

**13** 주어진 단어를 바르게 나열하여 밑줄 친 우리말 (C)를 영어로 쓰시오. (필요하다면 어형을 바꾸시오.)

(will / hopefully / architects / eco-friendly / come / with / keep / up / new / ideas)

➡ _____

_____

**14** 다음 질문에 대한 답을 위 글의 표현을 활용하여 쓰시오.

Q: What roles do the large gardens of the buildings play?

➡ _____

_____

해석

### Listen & Talk 2 D Talk Together

**A:** Have you heard of edible spoons? They're amazing!
have+p.p.: 현재 완료 시제로 ~해 본 적이 있는지 경험을 묻는다.

**B:** No, I haven't. Tell me about them.
= edible spoons

**A:** They are made of grain. They will save resources.
~로 만들어지다

**B:** That sounds awesome. I can't wait to use them.
= I'm looking forward to using them.

구문해설 · **edible:** 먹을 수 있는 · **grain:** 곡물, 낟알 · **resource:** 자원 · **awesome:** 멋진, 훌륭한

A: 먹을 수 있는 수저에 대해 들어봤니? 정말 놀라워!

B: 아니, 들어 본 적이 없어. 그것에 대해 이야기해 봐.

A: 수저는 곡물로 만들어져. 그것들은 자원을 절약할 거야.

B: 정말 멋지다. 나는 그것들을 사용하는 게 정말 기다려져.

### Presentation Time

How can we make our school eco-friendly? In my opinion, we need a green
5형식 동사+목적어+목적격보어)

wall. The front wall of our school is a great place for it. A green wall helps to
a green wall

keep the building cool by blocking sunlight. This could reduce the amount of
5형식 동사(목적어+목적격보어)    by+Ving: V함으로써    햇빛을 차단하여 건물을 시원하게 유지하는 것

energy used for air conditioning.

구문해설 · **eco-friendly:** 친환경적인 · **opinion:** 의견 · **front:** 앞 · **block:** 막다

우리는 어떻게 우리 학교를 친환경적으로 만들 수 있을까요? 제 의견으로는, 우리는 식물로 덮인 벽이 필요합니다. 우리 학교의 앞 벽은 그것을 위한 훌륭한 공간입니다. 식물로 덮인 벽은 햇빛을 차단함으로써 건물을 시원하게 유지하는 것을 돕습니다. 이것은 에어컨을 위해 사용되는 에너지의 양을 줄일 수 있습니다.

### Think & Write Step 3

**Eat Your Cup and Save the Earth!**

Here's an innovative, environmentally friendly item! It is a cookie cup. It's a

cookie that is made in the shape of a cup. After you use the cup, you can just
주격 관계대명사(= which)              시간을 나타내는 접속사

eat it. By doing this, you can save paper or plastic.
by ~ing: ~함으로써    앞 문장의 내용

The cookie cup can change the world.

Be a part of the change!

구문해설 · **innovative:** 혁신적인 · **save:** 절약하다

**컵을 먹고 지구를 구하세요!**

여기 혁신적이며 친환경적인 상품이 있습니다! 이것은 과자컵입니다. 이것은 컵 모양으로 만들어진 과자입니다. 컵을 사용한 후에 그냥 그것을 먹을 수 있습니다. 이렇게 함으로써 종이나 플라스틱을 절약할 수 있습니다.

과자컵은 세상을 바꿀 수 있습니다.

변화의 일부가 되십시오!

## Words & Expressions

**01** 다음 짝지어진 단어의 관계가 같도록 빈칸에 알맞은 말을 쓰시오.

> addition : additional
> = environment : _____

**02** 다음 영영풀이가 가리키는 것을 고르시오.

> the general weather of a region

① climate  ② state  ③ theme
④ flow  ⑤ quality

**03** 다음 중 밑줄 친 부분의 뜻풀이가 바르지 <u>않은</u> 것은?

① The study shows a growing <u>awareness</u> of animal rights. (인식)
② He found out something <u>incredible</u> about his wife. (믿을 수 있는)
③ By using fewer plastic bottles, we can <u>protect</u> lots of sea animals. (보호하다, 지키다)
④ These <u>chemicals</u> are mostly used in cleaning products. (화학물질)
⑤ There were many <u>unwanted</u> guests at the ceremony. (원치 않는)

**04** 다음 우리말에 맞게 빈칸에 알맞은 말을 쓰시오.

(1) 안토니 가우디는 스페인의 유명한 건축가였다.
➡ Antoni Gaudi was a famous _____ from Spain.
(2) 사람들이 프라하에서 즐길 수 있는 것 중 하나는 그곳의 건축이다.
➡ One thing that people can enjoy in Prague is its _____.

(3) 과학 과정은 추가적인 수학 강의와 과학 강의를 포함한다.
➡ The science track includes _____ math and science courses.
(4) 비닐봉지가 물에 떠 있다.
➡ The _____ _____ is floating in the water.

**05** 다음 주어진 문장의 밑줄 친 <u>company</u>와 다른 의미로 쓰인 것은?

> <u>Company</u> profits were 5% lower than last year.

① Mike is working at the largest computer <u>company</u> in the world.
② This deal will be advantageous to your <u>company</u>.
③ We are planning to make a new <u>company</u>.
④ A man is known by the <u>company</u> he keeps.
⑤ The <u>company</u> is investing $9 million to renovate its factories.

**06** 다음 문장의 빈칸에 공통으로 들어갈 말을 고르시오.

> • It's a ten-minute bus _____ from here to town.
> • Steve gave me a _____ on his motorbike.
> • When I was young, I learned to _____ a bike.

① provide  ② realize  ③ ride
④ remind  ⑤ separate

**07** 다음 우리말에 맞게 주어진 단어를 사용하여 영작하시오.

(1) 당신 말이 일리가 있네요. (point)

➡ _____

(2) 무엇이 당신의 좋은 건강에 영향을 끼쳤다고 생각하십니까? (contributed, have)

➡ _____

_____

(3) 우리는 다른 사람들과 조화를 이루며 살아야 한다. (harmony, should)

➡ _____

**Conversation**

**[08~09]** 다음 대화를 읽고 물음에 답하시오.

July: (A) I want to buy a new bag.

David: (B) You already have too many bags. In my opinion, you don't need any more.

July: (C) But I'm bored with my old bags.

David: (D) You can find out how to do it online.

July: (E) Oh, that sounds interesting! I can't wait to make my own bag.

**08** 위 대화의 (A)~(E) 중 주어진 문장이 들어가기에 적절한 곳은?

Then how about using old clothes to make a new bag?

① (A)　② (B)　③ (C)　④ (D)　⑤ (E)

**09** 위 대화의 내용과 일치하지 않는 것은?

① July는 새 가방을 사고 싶어 한다.
② July는 이미 많은 가방을 갖고 있다.
③ July는 오래된 가방에 질렸다.
④ David는 새 가방을 만들기 위해 오래된 옷들을 사용해 볼 것을 조언했다.
⑤ David는 오래된 옷을 사용해 새 가방을 만드는 법을 알고 있다.

**[10~11]** 다음 대화를 읽고 물음에 답하시오.

Jack: What are we going to do this weekend, Mihee?

Mihee: Why don't we go to the sheep park near my house?

Jack: A sheep park? How @interesting! Are there really sheep in the park?

Mihee: Yes. They are there ⓑto protect the environment.

Jack: How can they help the environment?

Mihee: You know, people usually use chemicals to kill ⓒunwanted plants. The sheep in the park eat those plants, so the chemicals are not ⓓneeding.

Jack: What a bright idea! I can't wait ⓔto visit the park!

**10** 위 대화의 밑줄 친 @~ⓔ 중 어법상 어색한 것을 찾아 바르게 고치시오.

➡ _____

**11** 위 대화의 내용과 일치하도록 Jack의 일기를 완성하시오.

Saturday, August 26
I went to (A)_____ near Mihee's house. It was fun to see the animals. What's more, they eat (B)_____. This can help reduce the use of (C)_____ to kill those plants.

**[12~14]** 다음 대화를 읽고 물음에 답하시오.

Minsu: Our club is holding a photo contest next week.

Sora: What kinds of photos will be in it?

Minsu: The theme is pollution around the world. We are holding this contest to raise students' awareness of environmental problems.

Sora: That sounds nice. (A)나는 어서 그것을 보고 싶어!

**12** 위 대화의 밑줄 친 (A)를 주어진 단어를 사용하여 6 단어로 영작하시오. (wait)

➡ _____

**13** What is the subject of the photo contest?

➡ _____

**14** Why is Minsu's club holding the photo contest?

➡ _____

_____

[15~16] 다음 대화를 읽고 물음에 답하시오.

> Sujin: Jiho, hurry up! The elevator is going up soon.
>
> Jiho: The science room is just on the third floor. Why don't we take the stairs?
>
> Sujin: I don't want to walk all the way up there.
>
> Jiho: Come on. Elevators use lots of energy. We need to save energy to protect the environment.
>
> Sujin: But one elevator ride doesn't use that much energy.
>
> Jiho: That's true, but the energy from all the elevator rides adds up over time. In my opinion, taking care of the environment starts with the little things.
>
> Sujin: You have a point. Let's take the stairs.

**15** Why does Jiho suggest that Sujin take the stairs?

➡ _____

_____

**16** Where are Sujin and Jiho going to?

➡ _____

### Grammar

**17** 다음 문장의 빈칸에 알맞은 말은?

> He knew it was silly _____ to feel so disappointed.

① for he　　　② for him
③ for his　　　④ of him
⑤ of his

**18** 다음 그림을 보고, 주어진 어휘를 이용하여 빈칸을 알맞게 채우시오.

> He explained to her _____ to carry out the experiment. (way, follow, has to)

**19** 다음 빈칸에 들어갈 말이 나머지와 다른 하나는?

① It is difficult _____ Juho to study math.
② It's foolish _____ you to think so.
③ It's important _____ you to avoid danger!
④ It was difficult _____ us to visit those historic sites.
⑤ It is boring _____ Yuna to ride a roller coaster.

**20** 다음 빈칸에 알맞지 <u>않은</u> 것은?

> It's _____ for me to jump that high.

① possible     ② easy     ③ natural

④ brave        ⑤ difficult

**21** 주어진 두 문장을 관계부사를 이용하여 하나의 문장으로 쓰시오.

(1) • I want to go to a place.
     • I can breathe fresh air there.

➡ _____

       _____

(2) • Lunch break at school is the time.
     • Junho can play soccer with his friends at the time.

➡ _____

       _____

(3) • I know the reason.
     • The manhole covers are round for the reason.

➡ _____

       _____

(4) • My mom doesn't like the way.
     • My sister drives in the way.

➡ _____

       _____

**Reading**

**[22~25]** 다음 글을 읽고 물음에 답하시오.

Cancun is a city where 4.8 million tourists travel every year. One of the most popular activities to do there is looking at the area's beautiful sea life underwater. ① However, tourist activities are seriously damaging parts of the sea near Cancun. ② To prevent this, artists did something interesting. They thought if they attracted tourists to a different part of the sea, the dying areas could have time (A) <u>to get</u> better. ③ It's about 14 meters below the surface and contains 500 statues. ④ The statues are made from materials that support sea life. They provide additional places for plants and animals to live on. ⑤ Over time, many types of sea life will grow on the statues, which will make the artwork unique. The artists want people to see a variety of sea life on the statues. If people realize _____ⓐ_____, they will understand how important it is to save the sea.

**22** 주어진 단어를 바르게 나열하여 빈칸 ⓐ에 들어갈 말을 완성하시오.

> (is / life / rich / sea / how)

➡ _____

**23** ①~⑤ 중 주어진 문장이 들어가기에 가장 적절한 곳은?

> They made an underwater museum away from the places where sea life was dying.

①      ②      ③      ④      ⑤

**24** 밑줄 친 (A)와 쓰임이 같은 것은?

① I called you <u>to say</u> that I love you.

② Jane woke up early <u>to catch</u> the bus.

③ Is there any chance <u>to talk</u> with you?

④ It is necessary <u>to listen</u> carefully.

⑤ My goal is <u>to win</u> the game.

**25** 다음 중 위 글의 내용과 일치하는 것은?

① Over five million tourists visit Cancun every year.

② The underwater museum is about 14 meters above the sea level.

③ Cancun is famous for its beautiful landscape on countryside.

④ The underwater museum will make various sea life unable to live in the sea.

⑤ The artists want people to realize the importance of saving the sea.

[26~28] 다음 글을 읽고 물음에 답하시오.

In Singapore, people are using architecture to protect the environment on land. Let's hear what Rajesh Khan, an architect, says about eco-friendly buildings.

Rajesh: Singapore is hot throughout the year. Most buildings need air conditioning, which uses ①a lot of energy and contributes to climate change. ②That's because architects in Singapore have begun to design eco-friendly buildings that use less air conditioning but are still ③cool inside. For example, many buildings in Singapore are designed to have an open structure. This structure makes it possible for outside air to move throughout a building. This natural air flow is how these buildings stay cool. In addition to making open structures, architects add large gardens. ④This greenery provides shade and protects parts of the building from direct sunlight, which keeps the building cooler.

Eco-friendly buildings like these not only help protect the environment, but also provide people ___(A)___ ⑤a good quality of life. Those are the goals of this new style of architecture.

Hopefully, architects will keep coming up ___(B)___ new eco-friendly ideas.

**26** ①~⑤ 중 글의 흐름상 어색한 것을 바르게 고쳐 쓰시오.

_____ ➡ _____

**27** 빈칸 (A)와 (B)에 공통으로 들어갈 말을 쓰시오.

➡ _____

**28** 위 글을 읽고 답할 수 있는 것은?

① How large are the gardens?

② How does inside air flow naturally?

③ What does an open structure make possible?

④ Why didn't some buildings have an open structure?

⑤ What is another cause of climate change?

[29~30] 다음 글을 읽고 물음에 답하시오.

**(A)**

Here's an innovative, environmentally friendly item! It is a cookie cup. It's a cookie that is made in the shape of a cup. After you use the cup, you can just eat it. By (B)doing this, you can save paper or plastic.

The cookie cup can change the world.

Be a part of the change!

**29** 주어진 단어를 바르게 나열하여 빈칸 (A)에 들어갈 위 글의 제목을 완성하시오.

(the Earth / and / Eat / Save / Cup / Your)!

➡ _____

**30** 밑줄 친 (B)가 의미하는 것을 우리말로 쓰시오.

➡ _____

출제율 95%

**01** 다음 대화가 자연스럽게 이어지도록 순서대로 배열하시오.

> (A) In my opinion, we should bring reusable bags when we go shopping.
> (B) I think we're using too many plastic bags.
> (C) I agree. It's not good for the environment. How can we reduce our use of plastic bags?

➡ _____

출제율 100%

**02** 다음 중 짝지어진 대화가 어색한 것은?

① A: What causes the environmental problem?
B: In my opinion, producing too much waste is one of the causes.

② A: What do you think about the new novel?
B: In my view, it is so interesting.

③ A: How can we reduce our use of plastic bags?
B: In my opinion, we should bring reusable bags when we go shopping.

④ A: Have you heard about edible spoons? That's amazing!
B: That sounds awesome. I can't wait to use them.

⑤ A: How can we make our school eco-friendly?
B: That'll be helpful. I can't wait to use it.

[03~04] 다음 대화를 읽고 물음에 답하시오.

Sujin: Jiho, hurry up! The elevator is going up soon.
Jiho: (A) The science room is just on the third floor. Why don't we take the stairs?

Sujin: (B) I don't want to walk all the way up there.
Jiho: (C) Come on. Elevators use lots of energy. We need to save energy to protect the environment.
Sujin: (D) But one elevator ride doesn't use that much energy.
Jiho: (E) In my opinion, taking care of the environment starts with the little things.
Sujin: You have a point. Let's take the stairs.

출제율 90%

**03** 위 대화의 (A)~(E) 중 주어진 문장이 들어가기에 적절한 곳은?

> That's true, but the energy from all the elevator rides adds up over time.

① (A)  ② (B)  ③ (C)  ④ (D)  ⑤ (E)

출제율 100%

**04** 위 대화를 읽고 대답할 수 없는 것은?

① Where is the science room?
② What do elevators use a lot?
③ What does Jiho suggest to protect the environment?
④ What does taking care of the environment start with?
⑤ How much energy does one elevator ride use?

[05~07] 다음 글을 읽고 물음에 답하시오.

B: Today, I'd like to make a suggestion about the trash problem at our school. I've found that many students just throw things away (A)[instead / instead of] recycling them. As you know, however, (B)[recycle / recycling] is very important because it saves resources and helps protect the environment. So, in my opinion, we need to reduce the number of trash cans at school to encourage recycling. Why don't we place four different colored recycling bins on every floor instead? This will remind students to separate the paper, glass, plastic, and cans (C)[proper / properly].

출제율 90%

**05** 위 글의 (A)~(C)에 들어갈 말이 바르게 짝지어진 것은?

|     | (A) | (B) | (C) |
| --- | --- | --- | --- |
| ① | instead | recycle | proper |
| ② | instead | recycling | properly |
| ③ | instead of | recycling | proper |
| ④ | instead of | recycling | properly |
| ⑤ | instead of | recycle | proper |

출제율 100%

**06** 위 글의 내용과 일치하지 <u>않는</u> 것은?

① 소년은 학교의 쓰레기 문제에 대해 제안을 하고자 한다.

② 학교 학생들이 쓰레기를 재활용하는 대신에 그냥 버리고 있다.

③ 소년은 재활용이 정말 중요하다고 주장한다.

④ 소년은 재활용을 권장하기 위해 학교에 있는 쓰레기통의 개수를 늘리는 것이 필요하다고 생각한다.

⑤ 소년은 학교의 모든 층에 각기 색이 다른 4개의 재활용통을 둘 것을 제안하였다.

출제율 95%

**07** 위 글에서 다음 영영풀이가 나타내는 말을 찾아 쓰시오.

> to divide things into different parts or groups

➡ _____

---

**[08~09]** 다음 대화를 읽고 물음에 답하시오.

Jack: What are we going to do this weekend, Mihee?

Mihee: Why don't we go to the sheep park near my house?

Jack: A sheep park? How interesting! Are there really sheep in the park?

Mihee: Yes. They are there to protect the environment.

Jack: How can they help the environment?

Mihee: You know, people usually use chemicals to kill unwanted plants. The sheep in the park eat those plants, so the chemicals are not needed.

Jack: What a bright idea! (A)I can't wait to visit the park! (looking)

출제율 90%

**08** 위 대화의 밑줄 친 (A)와 의미가 같도록 주어진 단어를 사용하여 다시 쓰시오.

➡ _____

출제율 95%

**09** 위 대화의 내용과 일치하지 <u>않는</u> 것은?

① 미희는 Jack에게 주말에 그녀의 집 근처에 있는 양 공원에 갈 것을 제안했다.

② 양들은 환경을 보호하기 위해 공원에 있다.

③ 공원에 있는 양들은 잡초를 먹어 환경을 보호한다.

④ 양 공원에는 잡초를 없애기 위해 많은 화학 물질이 필요하다.

⑤ Jack은 양 공원에 가 보고 싶어 한다.

출제율 90%

**10** 다음 두 문장이 같도록 할 때 빈칸에 알맞은 말을 쓰시오.

> Ann will never forget the day. Her dog joined her family on the day.
> = Ann will never forget the day _____ her dog joined her family.

**11** 다음 중 어법상 적절한 문장은?

① It is easy of children to learn foreign languages.
② This structure makes possible for outside air to move throughout a building.
③ It was boring of her to ride a bike.
④ It was careless of her to open the door for the stranger.
⑤ They don't have enough food to eating.

**12** 다음 빈칸에 알맞은 말이 순서대로 짝지어진 것은?

> • We should find the reason _____ our goods didn't sell well at the flea market.
> • It was difficult _____ him to pass the test.

① why – of
② when – of
③ why – for
④ when – for
⑤ which – for

**13** 다음 ⓐ~ⓖ 중 어법상 옳은 것을 모두 고르시오.

> ⓐ I want to stop by the café which Felix bought this cupcake.
> ⓑ Autumn is the time where leaves fall.
> ⓒ I will show my classmates how I made peanut sauce.
> ⓓ It is bad of the health to smoke like a chimney.
> ⓔ They had enough food for us to eat.
> ⓕ It is hard for Janet getting along with Tommy.
> ⓖ It is impossible for him to finish the homework by tomorrow.

➡ _____

**14** 다음 우리말을 주어진 어휘를 이용하여 영작하시오.

(1) 그는 폭력이 거의 없는 도시에서 성장했다. (a city, violence, grow up, rare)

➡ _____

(2) 내가 그 보고서를 작성하는 데는 세 시간이 걸렸다. (the report, take, write, for, to)

➡ _____

**[15~16]** 다음 글을 읽고 물음에 답하시오.

It is important for us to find ways to protect the environment. Some people have found creative ways to save the earth. One example is an underwater museum in Cancun, Mexico. Let's meet Dr. Rosa Allison, an art professor, and listen to her explanation about the special museum.

**15** What creative way to protect the environment is used in Cancun? Answer in English.

➡ _____

**16** 위 글에 이어질 내용으로 가장 적절한 것은?

① the records of Rosa Allison's life
② the explanation about an underwater museum
③ how to construct a museum on land
④ the explanation about how to travel Cancun
⑤ the reason why Rosa Allison became an art professor

**[17~18]** 다음 글을 읽고 물음에 답하시오.

Cancun is a city where 4.8 million tourists travel every year. One of the most popular activities to do there is looking at the area's beautiful sea life underwater. However, tourist activities are seriously damaging parts of the sea near Cancun. To prevent this, artists did something interesting. ⓐThey thought if ⓑthey attracted tourists to a different part of the sea, the dying areas could have time to get better. ⓒThey made (A)an underwater museum away from the places where sea life was dying. It's about 14 meters below the surface and contains 500 statues. The statues are made from materials that support sea life. ⓓThey provide additional places for plants and animals to live on. Over time, many types of sea life will grow on the statues, which will make the artwork unique.

출제율 95%

**17** ⓐ~ⓓ에서 같은 것을 지칭하는 것끼리 바르게 묶은 것은?

① ⓐ - ⓑ, ⓒ, ⓓ
② ⓐ, ⓑ - ⓒ, ⓓ
③ ⓑ, ⓒ - ⓐ, ⓓ
④ ⓐ, ⓑ, ⓒ - ⓓ
⑤ ⓒ - ⓐ, ⓑ, ⓓ

출제율 95%

**18** 밑줄 친 (A)에 관한 설명으로 바르지 않은 것은?

① 해수면에서 약 14미터 아래에 지어졌다.
② 해양 생물에게 도움이 되는 재료들로 만들어진 조각상이 있다.
③ 칸쿤 근처 바다를 보호하기 위하여 만들어졌다.
④ 많은 형태의 바다 생명체들이 조각상에서 자라게 될 것이다.
⑤ 현재 많은 관광객들로 인해 훼손되었다.

**[19~21]** 다음 글을 읽고 물음에 답하시오.

Singapore is hot throughout the year. Most buildings need air conditioning, which uses a lot of energy and ①contributes to climate change. That's why architects in Singapore have begun to design eco-friendly buildings that use less air conditioning but are still cool ②inside.          (A)          , many buildings in Singapore are designed to have an open structure. This structure makes it possible for ③outside air to move throughout a building. This natural air flow is how these buildings stay cool. In addition to making open structures, architects add large gardens. This greenery provides shade and ④protects parts of the building from direct sunlight, which keeps the building ⑤warmer.

Eco-friendly buildings like these not only help protect the environment, but also provide people with a good quality of life. Those are the goals of this new style of architecture. Hopefully, architects will keep coming up with new eco-friendly ideas.

출제율 95%

**19** 빈칸 (A)에 들어갈 말로 가장 적절한 것은?

① In addition
② For example
③ However
④ Still
⑤ In other words

출제율 100%

**20** ①~⑤ 중 글의 흐름상 어색한 것은?

① ② ③ ④ ⑤

출제율 90%

**21** Besides making open structures, what do architects add? Answer in English.

➡ _____

[01~03] 다음 글을 읽고 물음에 답하시오.

B: Today, I'd like to make a suggestion about the trash problem at our school. I've found that many students just throw things away instead of recycling them. As you know, however, recycling is very important because it saves resources and helps protect the environment. So, in my opinion, we need to reduce the number of trash cans at school to encourage recycling. Why don't we place four different colored recycling bins on every floor instead? This will remind students to separate the paper, glass, plastic, and cans properly.

**01** According to the boy, what's the matter with many students at school?

➡ _____

_____

**02** What does the boy suggest to encourage recycling?

➡ _____

_____

**03** What does the boy want to place on every floor?

➡ _____

_____

**04** 관계부사를 사용하여 주어진 두 문장을 한 문장으로 바꾸어 쓰시오.

(1) • He was born in the year.
 • The war ended then.

➡ _____

_____

(2) • Jane didn't come here yet.
 • I know the reason for that.

➡ _____

_____

(3) • This is the city.
 • I lived there 10 years ago.

➡ _____

_____

(4) • This is the way.
 • He caught the big fish in the way.

➡ _____

_____

**05** 괄호 안에 주어진 단어를 활용하여 빈칸을 채우시오.

(1) It is very dangerous _____ in the country which has corona virus all over. (they, live)

(2) It was a great honor _____ Korea. (I, visit)

(3) Was it smart _____ it a secret? (she, keep)

**06** 다음 두 문장의 의미가 같도록 문장의 빈칸을 완성하시오.

(1) It is natural that a baby should cry.
 = It is natural _____.

(2) Jane was considerate to let us know it.
 = It was _____ us know it.

(3) He kindly showed me the way to the station.
 = It was kind _____ me the way to the station.

[07~08] 다음 글을 읽고 물음에 답하시오.

### Eat Your Cup and Save the Earth!

Here's an innovative, environmentally friendly item! It is a cookie cup. It's a cookie that is made in the shape of a cup. After you use the cup, you can just eat it. By doing this, you can save paper or plastic.

The cookie cup can change the world.

Be a part of the change!

**07** What can you save by using the cup? Answer in English.

➡ _____

**08** What does the cookie cup look like? Answer in English.

➡ _____

[09~11] 다음 글을 읽고 물음에 답하시오.

Singapore is hot throughout the year. Most buildings need air conditioning, which uses a lot of energy and contributes to climate change. That's why architects in Singapore have begun to design eco-friendly buildings that use less air conditioning but are still cool inside. For example, many buildings in Singapore are designed to have an open structure. This structure makes it possible for outside air to move throughout a building. This natural air flow is how these buildings stay cool. In addition to making open structures, architects add large gardens. This greenery provides shade and protects parts of the building from direct sunlight, which keeps the building cooler.

Eco-friendly buildings like these not only help protect the environment, but also provide people with a good quality of life. Those are the goals of this new style of architecture. Hopefully, architects will keep coming up with new eco-friendly ideas.

**09** Write the reason why most buildings in Singapore need air conditioning. Use the phrase 'It's because.'

➡ _____
_____

**10** What is the goal of eco-friendly buildings? Answer in English and use the phrase 'as well as.'

➡ _____
_____

**11** 위 글의 내용과 일치하도록 빈칸에 알맞은 말을 쓰시오.

| *Environmental problem* |
| --- |
| In Singapore, most buildings need (1)_____, which uses (2)_____ and contributes to (3)_____. |

| *Ideas to solve the problem* |
| --- |
| Thanks to (4)_____, outside air moves throughout a building, so the building can be kept (5)_____. Large (6)_____ provide shade and protect parts of the building (7)_____, which keeps the building cooler. |

**01** 다음 대화의 내용과 일치하도록 수진이의 일기를 완성하시오.

> Sujin: Jiho, hurry up! The elevator is going up soon.
>
> Jiho: The science room is just on the third floor. Why don't we take the stairs?
>
> Sujin: I don't want to walk all the way up there.
>
> Jiho: Come on. Elevators use lots of energy. We need to save energy to protect the environment.
>
> Sujin: But one elevator ride doesn't use that much energy.
>
> Jiho: That's true, but the energy from all the elevator rides adds up over time. In my opinion, taking care of the environment starts with the little things.
>
> Sujin: You have a point. Let's take the stairs.

> I reflected on myself today. I used to ride an elevator when I went up to the science room on (A)_____. When I tried to go up there, Jiho suggested (B)_____. Actually, I didn't want to (C)_____. But, Jiho persuaded me to take the stairs. I thought that one elevator ride didn't use (D)_____, but Jiho reminded me of the importance of starting with little things to (E)_____. To protect the environment, I decided to save the energy with the little things.

**02** A와 B에 주어진 것 중 각각 하나씩과 가주어를 이용하여 어법에 맞게 3 문장 이상 쓰시오.

| **A** | she/dangerous | she/difficult | he/necessary | he/rude |
|---|---|---|---|---|
| **B** | talk loudly like that | learn German | take care of the children | ride a bike |

(1) _____

(2) _____

(3) _____

(4) _____

# 단원별 모의고사

**01** 다음 영영풀이가 가리키는 것을 고르시오.

> a new or better idea, method, or device

① company     ② chemical
③ resource     ④ shade
⑤ innovation

**02** 다음 우리말에 맞게 빈칸을 완성하시오.

(1) 그늘에서부터 열매까지, 나무는 우리에게 많은 좋은 것들을 줍니다!

➡ From _____ to fruits, trees give us many good things!

(2) 기후 변화 때문에 전 세계적으로 온도가 상승하고 있다.

➡ Because of _____ change, _____ are rising around the world.

**03** 다음 문장의 빈칸에 들어갈 말을 〈보기〉에서 골라 알맞은 형태로 쓰시오.

> ┤ 보기 ├
>
> contribute to / a variety of / break down / take the stairs / would like to

(1) This furniture was made of _____ different wood.
(2) When did this elevator _____?
(3) Online classes _____ a better education.
(4) I _____ take the picture with my cousin.

(5) It is good for your health to _____ instead of using the elevator.

**[04~05]** 다음 대화를 읽고 물음에 답하시오.

> Emily: I read a ⓐcool article today.
> Brian: What was it about?
> Emily: It was about a new bag. It just looks like a plastic bag, but it's made mostly of corn.
> Brian: That sounds really ⓑamazing.
> Emily: Yes, but there's more. The bag ⓒbreaks down in soil in only three months and disappears in about three minutes in warm water!
> Brian: Wow! That will help us ⓓincrease plastic waste by a lot!
> Emily: I know! The company will start selling the bag sometime this year. I ⓔcan't wait to use it!

**04** 위 대화의 ⓐ~ⓔ 중 흐름상 어색한 것을 고르시오.

① ⓐ cool     ② ⓑ amazing
③ ⓒ breaks down     ④ ⓓ increase
⑤ ⓔ can't

**05** 위 대화를 읽고 대답할 수 없는 것은?

① What is the article Emily read about?
② What is the new bag made of?
③ How long does the new bag take to break down in soil?
④ When is the company going to sell the new bag?
⑤ What is Brian looking forward to?

[06~07] 다음 글을 읽고 물음에 답하시오.

B: Today, I'd like to make a suggestion about the trash problem at our school. (A) I've found that many students just throw things away instead of recycling them. (B) As you know, however, recycling is very important because it saves resources and helps protect the environment. (C) So, in my opinion, we need to reduce the number of trash cans at school to encourage recycling. (D) This will remind students to separate the paper, glass, plastic, and cans properly. (E)

**06** 위 글의 (A)~(E) 중 주어진 문장이 들어가기에 적절한 곳은?

> Why don't we place four different colored recycling bins on every floor instead?

① (A)  ② (B)  ③ (C)  ④ (D)  ⑤ (E)

**07** 위 글의 내용과 일치하도록 빈칸을 완성하시오.

> <A New Recycling System in Our School>
> a. Reduce (A)_____.
> b. Place four different colored recycling bins on (B)_____.
> c. (C)_____ items into different bins to recycle.

**08** 다음 대화가 자연스럽게 이어지도록 순서대로 배열하시오.

> (A) But I'm bored with my old bags.
> (B) Oh, that sounds interesting! I can't wait to make my own bag.
> (C) I want to buy a new bag.

> (D) You already have too many bags. In my opinion, you don't need any more.
> (E) Then how about using old clothes to make a new bag? You can find out how to do it online.

➡ _____

**09** 다음 대화의 내용과 일치하도록 빈칸을 완성하시오.

> Tom: I think we're using too many plastic bags.
> Jane: I agree. It's not good for the environment. How can we reduce our use of plastic bags?
> Tom: In my opinion, we should bring reusable bags when we go shopping.

> To protect the environment, we need to _____. For example, it can be one of the ways to _____ when we go shopping.

**10** 다음 우리말을 주어진 단어를 이용하여 영작하시오.

(1) 우리는 미래 세대를 위해 환경을 보호해야 한다. (generations, should)
➡ _____
_____

(2) 창의적인 사람은 새로운 아이디어들을 떠올리는 것을 잘한다. (good, up)
➡ _____
_____

(3) 중국의 수중 도시는 전 세계의 잠수부들을 매료시킨다. (attract, over)
➡ _____
_____

**11** 다음 중 어법상 어색한 것을 고르시오.

① It is not easy for him to find out the answer.
② Wasn't it clever for him to solve the puzzle?
③ It is difficult for me to take care of the baby.
④ It was impossible for me to cross the river by swimming.
⑤ It is easy for Jeongmin to study math.

**12** 다음 중 어법상 어색한 것은?

① I've left my wallet in the restaurant where we had lunch.
② Describe the way how you did it.
③ This is the house where I used to live.
④ I still remember the day when I went to Paris.
⑤ I want to know the reason why Eden hasn't come home yet.

**13** 다음 빈칸에 들어갈 말을 순서대로 묶은 것은?

> • It is fun _____ Jihun to ride a roller coaster.
> • This natural air flow is _____ these buildings stay cool.

① of – how　　② of – when
③ for – how　　④ for – when
⑤ with – why

**14** 다음 문장에서 어법상 어색한 것을 바르게 고치시오.

(1) He regrets the way how he lived his life.

➡ _____

(2) Do you remember that restaurant which we met for the first time?

➡ _____

(3) It is exciting of Jia to ride a roller coaster.

➡ _____

(4) It is kind for you to invite me.

➡ _____

**15** 〈보기〉와 같이 문장을 바꿔 쓰시오.

> ┤ 보기 ├
> You should choose good friends.
> → It is important for you to choose good friends.

(1) She should study English diligently every day.

➡ It is important _____
_____.

(2) She kindly explained the process of making a newspaper.

➡ It was nice _____
_____.

**16** 다음 중 밑줄 친 부분의 쓰임이 〈보기〉와 같은 것은?

> ┤ 보기 ├
> Sunday is the day when I can relax.

① It was a time when fountain pens were rare.
② Until when can you stay here?
③ I loved history when I was at school.
④ When did you see him last?
⑤ He works when he might rest.

**17** 다음 우리말을 주어진 어휘를 이용하여 영작하시오.

(1) 그녀는 때때로 자기가 건강했던 때를 생각한다.
(about, healthy)

&#10142; _____

_____

(2) 우리가 지난주에 피자를 먹었던 식당의 이름이 무엇인가요? (what, the name, had)

&#10142; _____

_____

(3) 어떤 사람들은 스마트폰 없이 사는 것이 불가능해 보인다. (seems, some people, their smartphones)

&#10142; _____

_____

(4) 우리는 내일 그 경기에서 이기기가 쉽지 않을 것이다. (won't, the game, win)

&#10142; _____

_____

[18~21] 다음 글을 읽고 물음에 답하시오.

Cancun is a city where 4.8 million tourists travel every year. One of the most popular activities to do there is looking at the area's beautiful sea life underwater. ① However, tourist activities are seriously damaging parts of the sea near Cancun. ② To prevent this, artists did something interesting. They thought if they attracted tourists to a different part of the sea, the dying areas could have time to get better. ③ They made an underwater museum away from the places where sea life was dying. ④ The statues are made from materials that support sea life. They provide additional places for plants and animals to live on.

⑤ Over time, many types of sea life will grow on the statues, which will make the artwork unique. The artists want people to see a variety of sea life on the statues. If people realize how rich sea life is, they will understand (A)바다를 지키는 것이 얼마나 중요한지.

**18** ①~⑤ 중 주어진 문장이 들어가기에 가장 적절한 곳은?

It's about 14 meters below the surface and contains 500 statues.

①      ②      ③      ④      ⑤

**19** 주어진 단어를 활용하여 밑줄 친 우리말 (A)를 영어로 쓰시오.

(important / it / save)

&#10142; _____

**20** What did artists do in order for the dying areas to have time to get better? Answer in English.

&#10142; _____

_____

**21** 위 글의 제목으로 가장 적절한 것은?

① Cancun: the Most Famous Tourist Attraction in Mexico
② A Creative Way to Save the Earth: An Underwater Museum in Cancun
③ What Makes People Attracted to Cancun: Various Activities on Land

④ Various Ways to Protect the Environment All Around the World

⑤ Warning of Animals: Signals Toward Protecting the Environment

**[22~25]** 다음 글을 읽고 물음에 답하시오.

Singapore is hot throughout the year. Most buildings need air conditioning, which ① uses a lot of energy and contributes to climate change.

(A) This natural air flow is how these buildings stay cool. In addition to ②making open structures, architects add large gardens. This greenery provides shade and protects parts of the building from direct sunlight, ③that keeps the building cooler.

(B) For example, many buildings in Singapore are designed to have an open structure. This structure makes it possible ④for outside air to move throughout a building.

(C) That's why architects in Singapore have begun to design eco-friendly buildings that use less air conditioning but are still cool inside.

Eco-friendly buildings like these not only help protect the environment, but also provide people with a good quality of life. Those are the goals of this new style of architecture. Hopefully, architects will keep coming up with new eco-friendly ideas.

Every field ⑤has different ways of protecting the environment. With more innovation, humans and nature will be able to live together in harmony far into the future.

**22** 자연스러운 글이 되도록 (A)~(C)를 바르게 나열하시오.

➡ _____

**23** ①~⑤ 중 어법상 바르지 않은 것은?

①     ②     ③     ④     ⑤

**24** 다음 중 위 글에 나오는 단어의 풀이가 아닌 것은?

① a new thing or a new method of doing something

② less harmful to the environment than other similar products or services

③ the general atmosphere or situation somewhere

④ a person who designs buildings

⑤ a person visiting a place for pleasure and interest, especially when they are on holiday

**25** 다음은 싱가포르 건물의 특징을 소개하는 Tim의 말이다. 틀린 부분을 한 군데 찾아 바르게 고쳐 쓰시오.

Many buildings in Singapore have an open structure. It keeps the people moving throughout a building.

_____ ➡ _____

# MEMO

# Take Part in the Economy

## 🎙 의사소통 기능

- 선호에 대해 묻고 답하기

  A: Which do you prefer?

  B: I prefer the white shoes to the black ones.

- 상기시키기

  Don't forget to talk about their bad points too.

## 🎙 언어 형식

- The+비교급 ~, the+비교급 …

  **The fewer** products we buy, **the more** resources we save.

- 분사구문

  **Seeing** a lot of positive reviews, I decided to borrow a bike helmet.

# Words & Expressions

## Key Words

- **app** [æp] 뗑 애플리케이션, 응용 프로그램
- **allow** [əláu] 똥 허가하다, 허용하다
- **allowance** [əláuəns] 뗑 용돈
- **balanced** [bǽlənst] 뒁 균형 잡힌
- **borrow** [bárou] 똥 빌리다
- **broken** [bróukən] 뒁 망가진, 고장 난
- **camping** [kǽmpiŋ] 뗑 캠핑
- **choose** [tʃuːz] 똥 선택하다, 고르다
- **communicate** [kəmjúːnəkèit] 똥 의사소통하다
- **concern** [kənsə́ːrn] 뗑 우려, 근심
- **condition** [kəndíʃən] 뗑 상태, 조건
- **discount** [dískaunt] 뗑 할인
- **download** [dáunlòud] 똥 다운로드하다
- **economy** [ikánəmi] 뗑 경제
- **exact** [igzǽkt] 뒁 정확한, 정밀한
- **experience** [ikspíəriəns] 똥 경험하다
- **fee** [fiː] 뗑 요금, 수수료
- **fix** [fiks] 똥 고치다
- **freely** [fríːli] 뷘 자유롭게
- **improve** [imprúːv] 똥 향상하다, 개선하다
- **issue** [íʃuː] 뗑 문제(점), 쟁점
- **lender** [léndər] 뗑 빌려주는 사람

- **negative** [négətiv] 뒁 부정적인, 나쁜
- **owner** [óunər] 뗑 주인, 소유주
- **personal** [pə́rsənl] 뒁 개인의, 개인적인
- **policy** [páləsi] 뗑 정책
- **positive** [pázətiv] 뒁 긍정적인
- **prefer** [prifə́ːr] 똥 ~을 더 좋아하다, 선호하다
- **product** [prádʌkt] 뗑 상품
- **provide** [prəváid] 똥 제공하다
- **purpose** [pə́ːrpəs] 뗑 목적
- **reasonable** [ríːzənəbl] 뒁 타당한, 합리적인, (값이) 적당한
- **refund** [rifʌ́nd] 뗑 환불
- **regularly** [régjulərli] 뷘 정기적으로
- **reliable** [riláiəbl] 뒁 믿을 수 있는
- **resource** [ríːsɔːrs] 뗑 자원
- **return** [ritə́ːrn] 똥 돌려주다, 반납하다
- **share** [ʃɛər] 똥 함께 쓰다, 공유하다
- **spend** [spend] 똥 (돈을) 쓰다
- **upload** [ʌ́plòud] 똥 업로드하다, 전송하다
- **upset** [ʌ́pset] 뒁 화난, 속상한
- **user** [júːzər] 뗑 사용자
- **weakness** [wíːknis] 뗑 약점
- **wherever** [hwɛərévər] 뷘 어디든지

## Key Expressions

- **ask for** ~을 요청하다, 필요로 하다
- **be aware of** ~을 알고 있다
- **by -ing** ~함으로써
- **environmentally friendly** 친환경적인
- **focus on** ~에 초점을 맞추다
- **for free** 무료로
- **help+목적어+동사원형** (목적어)가 ~하는 것을 도와주다
- **less than** ~보다 적은, ~ 미만의
- **look after** ~을 돌보다
- **look for** ~을 찾다

- **on sale** 할인 중인
- **out of town** 도시를 떠나, 다른 곳으로 떠나
- **pick up** ~을 찾아오다
- **prefer A to B** A를 B보다 더 좋아하다
- **search for** ~을 찾다
- **send messages to** ~에게 메시지를 보내다
- **take care of** ~을 돌보다
- **What if ~?** ~하면 어쩌지?, ~라면 어떻게 될까?
- **without -ing** ~하지 않고

## Word Power

※ 서로 비슷한 뜻을 가진 어휘

☐ **broken** 망가진, 고장 난 : **out of order** 고장 난

☐ **concern** 우려, 근심 : **worry** 걱정, 근심

☐ **fix** 고치다 : **repair** 고치다, 수선하다

☐ **provide** 제공하다 : **furnish** 제공하다

☐ **reliable** 믿을 수 있는 : **trustworthy** 신뢰할 수 있는, 믿을 수 있는

☐ **upset** 화난, 속상한 : **troubled** 걱정스러운, 곤란한

☐ **choose** 선택하다, 고르다 : **select** 고르다, 선택하다

☐ **exact** 정확한, 정밀한 : **accurate** 정확한, 한 치의 오차 없는

☐ **improve** 향상하다, 개선하다 : **enhance** 향상시키다

☐ **purpose** 목적 : **goal** 목적, 목표

☐ **take care of** ~을 돌보다 : **look after** ~을 돌보다

☐ **weakness** 약점 : **fault** 결점, 단점

※ 서로 반대의 뜻을 가진 어휘

☐ **be aware of** ~을 알다 ↔ **be unaware of** ~을 모르다

☐ **less than** ~보다 적은, ~ 미만의 ↔ **more than** ~보다 많이, ~ 이상의

☐ **positive** 긍정적인 ↔ **negative** 부정적인

☐ **reasonable** 타당한, 합리적인, (값이) 적당한 ↔ **unreasonable** 불합리한, 부당한

☐ **regularly** 정기적으로 ↔ **irregularly** 불규칙적으로

☐ **upload** 업로드하다, 전송하다 ↔ **download** 다운로드하다

☐ **lender** 빌려주는 사람 ↔ **borrower** 빌리는 사람

☐ **reliable** 믿을 수 있는 ↔ **unreliable** 믿을 수 없는

☐ **weakness** 약점 ↔ **strength** 장점

## English Dictionary

☐ **choose** 선택하다, 고르다
→ to decide which person or thing you want to have
원하는 사람이나 사물을 결정하다

☐ **concern** 우려, 근심
→ a fact or situation that worries you
걱정시키는 사실이나 상황

☐ **economy** 경제
→ the system according to which the money, industry and trade of a country or region are organized
한 나라나 지역의 화폐, 산업 및 무역이 구조화되는 체제

☐ **freely** 자유롭게
→ many times or in large quantities
많은 횟수로 혹은 많은 양으로

☐ **improve** 향상하다, 개선하다
→ to achieve or produce something of a better standard or quality than before
이전보다 더 나은 기준이나 품질로 어떤 것을 생산하거나 성취하다

☐ **negative** 부정적인, 나쁜
→ unpleasant, depressing, or harmful
불쾌한, 암울한, 혹은 해를 입히는

☐ **provide** 제공하다
→ to give something that someone needs or wants to them, or make it available
누군가가 필요로 하거나 원하는 무언가를 주거나 이용할 수 있게 하다

☐ **reliable** 믿을 수 있는
→ able to be trusted, or consistently good in quality or performance
신뢰할 수 있는, 혹은 품질이나 성과가 지속적으로 좋은

☐ **reasonable** 타당한, 합리적인, (값이) 적당한
→ based on or using good judgment and therefore fair, practical and sensible
좋은 판단에 기반하거나 좋은 판단을 사용하여서 공정하며, 실질적이고, 분별 있는

☐ **weakness** 약점
→ the state or condition of lacking strength
장점이 부족한 상태나 조건

**서답형**

**01** 다음 짝지어진 단어의 관계가 같도록 빈칸에 알맞은 말을 쓰시오.

> reasonable : unreasonable
> = reliable : _____

**02** 다음 영영풀이가 가리키는 것을 고르시오.

> the state or condition of lacking strength

① weakness
② purpose
③ concern
④ resource
⑤ owner

**03** 다음 중 밑줄 친 부분의 뜻풀이가 바르지 않은 것은?

① This hotel is quite good, and the price is reasonable. (이유 있는)
② She is positive about her future. (긍정적인)
③ We need to discuss this issue right now. (문제, 쟁점)
④ There are many skin treatment programs offered by this clinic. (치료)
⑤ The doctor was worried about the patient's condition. (상태)

**서답형**

**04** 다음 우리말에 맞게 빈칸에 알맞은 말을 쓰시오.

(1) 정부는 새로운 교육 정책을 주의 깊게 고려해야 한다.
➡ The government should consider the new educational _____ carefully.

(2) 그 회사는 내년에 새로운 상품을 출시할 것이다.
➡ The company will release a new _____ next year.

(3) 그녀의 부모님은 그녀에게 적은 용돈을 주신다.
➡ Her parents give her a small _____.

**서답형**

**05** 다음 문장의 빈칸에 들어갈 말을 〈보기〉에서 골라 쓰시오.

> ┤ 보기 ├
> environmentally friendly / looked for / looked after / less than / asked for

(1) I _____ my cat carefully.
(2) Before my mom went out, she _____ the key on her desk.
(3) This product is _____.
(4) Preparing our project, I _____ help to my English teacher.
(5) The whole show is performed in _____ one hour.

**06** 다음 주어진 문장의 밑줄 친 fix와 같은 의미로 쓰인 것은?

> They are sending an engineer to fix the car.

① We need to fix a date for the next meeting.
② Would you fix a post to the wall?
③ Do you know how to fix a mosquito net?
④ I need to fix this machine to make it work again.
⑤ My kid tried to fix a feather in his hat.

**01** 다음 짝지어진 단어의 관계가 같도록 빈칸에 알맞은 말을 쓰시오.

> wide : narrow = positive : _____

 **02** 다음 우리말에 맞게 빈칸에 알맞은 말을 쓰시오.

(1) 5세 이하의 어린이들은 무료로 버스를 탈 수 있다.

➡ Kids under five years old can ride the bus _____ _____.

(2) 회의는 환경적 주제들에 초점이 맞추어졌다.

➡ The meeting was _____ _____ environmental issues.

(3) 지수는 속보를 알고 있었다.

➡ Jisu was _____ _____ the breaking news.

**03** 다음 문장의 빈칸에 들어갈 말을 〈보기〉에서 골라 쓰시오.

> ┌── 보기 ──
> weaknesses / spend / improve / discount / fee

(1) Your first monthly bill includes an installation _____.

(2) Our soccer team didn't win because of a few different _____.

(3) I'm going to _____ my English and go to the US.

(4) How much money do you _____ on food?

(5) Children get a _____ of two dollars on tickets.

**04** 다음 우리말과 일치하도록 주어진 어구를 배열하여 완성하시오.

(1) 그는 가능한 한 빨리 그의 아들의 출생을 등록해야 한다.

(as / register / he / the birth / possible / soon / as / should / of / his son)

➡ _____

_____

(2) 그녀는 아무에게도 그녀의 약점에 대해 터놓고 싶어 하지 않는다.

(to / weakness / doesn't / she / her / anyone / about / open up / want / to)

➡ _____

_____

(3) 현명한 소비자들은 항상 돈을 절약하려고 노력한다.

(to / money / wise / always / save / try / consumers)

➡ _____

_____

 **05** 다음 우리말과 일치하도록 주어진 단어를 이용하여 완성하시오.

(1) 내 여동생은 팝 음악(pop music)보다 록 음악(rock music)을 더 좋아한다. (prefer)

➡ _____

(2) 그 계산대 직원(cashier)은 그 학생에게 할인을 해 주었다. (give)

➡ _____

(3) 그 판매원은 나에게 환불해 주지 않았다. (salesperson)

➡ _____

# Conversation

## ① 선호에 대해 묻고 답하기

> **A** Which sandwich do you prefer, the special one or the classic one?
> 스페셜 샌드위치와 클래식 샌드위치 중 어떤 샌드위치가 더 좋으니?
>
> **B** Well, I prefer the special sandwich to the classic one. It's the healthier choice. 음. 나는 클래식 샌드위치보다 스페셜 샌드위치가 더 좋아. 그게 더 건강한 선택이야.

- A와 B 두 가지 중에서 어떤 것을 선호하는지 물을 때 'Which (one) do you prefer, A or B?'로 표현한다. 같은 표현으로 'Which (one) do you like better, A or B?', 'Which (one) do you like more, A or B?', 'Which (one) do you want to ~ more?' 등을 쓸 수 있다.

- 대답할 때는 'I prefer ~.' 또는 'I like 목적어 better.', 'I like 목적어 more.'라고 말한다. 'B보다 A를 더 선호한다'라고 대답할 때는 'I prefer A to B.', 'I like A better than B.' 또는 'I like A more than B.'라고 말한다.

### 선호 묻고 대답하기

- Which (one) do you prefer, A or B?
- Which (one) do you like better, A or B?
- Which (one) do you like more, A or B?
- Which (one) do you want to ~ more?
- I prefer ~. / I prefer A to B.
- I like 목적어 better. / I like A better than B.
- I like 목적어 more. / I like A more than B.
- I want/would like 목적어 better.
- I want/would like 목적어 more.

### 핵심 Check

**1.** 다음 대화에서 빈칸에 들어갈 말로 적절하지 <u>않은</u> 것은?

A: These two pairs of shoes are on sale! _____
B: Well, I prefer the white shoes to the black ones.
A: Why is that? The black ones are cheaper.
B: Yes, but I like the design of the white ones better.

① Which do you prefer?　　② Which do you like more?
③ Which do you like better?　　④ Which do you want to give?
⑤ Which do you want more?

## 2 상기시키기

**A** Don't forget to feed your puppy before you leave for work.
출근하기 전에 강아지에게 밥 주는 것을 잊지 마.

**B** Right. Thanks for reminding me. 맞아. 상기시켜 줘서 고마워.

■ 상대방에게 어떤 일에 대해 상기시키는 표현으로 'Don't forget to부정사 ~.'라는 말을 쓸 수 있다. 이때, forget 뒤에는 to부정사가 쓰이므로 to 뒤에는 동사원형을 써야 한다. 이에 대한 대답으로 'Thanks for reminding me.'라고 말할 수 있다.

• Don't forget to lock up at night. 밤에 문단속하는 것을 잊지 마.

■ 같은 표현으로 'remember to부정사'나 'Be sure to부정사'를 쓸 수 있다.

• Remember to call me when you arrive! 도착하면 잊지 말고 전화해!

= Be sure to call me when you arrive!

■ 'forget to부정사'와 'forget -ing'

'forget+to부정사'는 '(미래에) ~할/하는 것을 잊다'라는 의미이다. 반면에 'forget+동명사'는 '(과거에) ~한 것을 잊다'라는 의미이다. 따라서 대화 상대에게 무엇을 상기시킬 때는 미래의 의미를 내포한 to부정사를 쓰는 것이 맞다. 이외에도 to부정사와 동명사에 따라 의미가 변하는 동사로는 remember, stop, try, regret 등이 있다.

• Don't forget to take out the garbage tomorrow. 내일 쓰레기를 내놓는 것을 잊지 마라.

• I forgot taking out the garbage last night. 난 어젯밤에 쓰레기를 내놓았다는 사실을 잊었다.

### 핵심 Check

**2.** 다음 대화에서 밑줄 친 우리말을 영작하시오.

A: I'm going to get a refund for these clothes this evening. I found I have similar ones.

B: Okay, <u>영수증 갖고 가는 것을 잊지 마렴</u>. Last time you couldn't get a refund because you didn't bring it.

A: Okay, Mom. I won't forget this time.

➡ _____

**Listen & Talk 1 B**

G: ❶Which do you prefer, the Special Sandwich or the Classic Sandwich?

B: Well, the Special Sandwich is the healthier choice. ❷It's made with lots of fresh vegetables and other healthy ❸ingredients.

G: But it's much more expensive than the Classic Sandwich.

B: I know, but I prefer the Special Sandwich to the Classic Sandwich. ❹Eating healthy is important to me.

G: I prefer the cheaper one. I'll spend my money on books instead.

B: I guess our spending habits are different.

여: 스페셜 샌드위치와 클래식 샌드위치 중 어떤 것이 더 좋으니?

남: 음, 스페셜 샌드위치가 더 건강한 선택이야. 그것은 신선한 야채들과 다른 건강한 재료들로 만들어졌어.

여: 하지만 그건 클래식 샌드위치보다 훨씬 더 비싸잖아.

남: 맞아, 하지만 나는 클래식 샌드위치보다 스페셜 샌드위치가 더 좋아. 나에게는 건강하게 먹는 것이 중요하거든.

여: 나는 더 저렴한 것이 더 좋아. 대신 나는 내 돈을 책 사는 데 쓸래.

남: 우리는 소비 습관이 다른 것 같구나.

❶ A와 B 두 가지 중 어떤 것을 선호하는지 묻는 표현이다.　❷ It은 Special Sandwich를 가리킨다.
❸ ingredient: 재료　❹ 동명사가 주어로 동사로는 단수 동사(is)가 이어진다.

**Check(√) True or False**

(1) The girl likes the Classic Sandwich more than the Special Sandwich.　T ☐ F ☐

(2) The boy has the same spending habit as the girl.　T ☐ F ☐

**Listen & Talk 2 B**

G: What should we sell at the ❶flea market next month?

B: Before we choose anything ❷to sell, I think we need to do some market research.

G: Market research? Why do we need ❸that?

B: Because it helps us ❹find out what items are popular these days.

G: I see. Then we can decide what to sell at the market.

B: That's right. It will also help us set ❺reasonable prices for our items.

G: Cool. Is there anything else we should do?

B: Oh, ❻don't forget to register our names by this Friday.

G: Right. Thanks for reminding me.

여: 우리 다음 달에 벼룩시장에서 무엇을 판매해야 할까?

남: 우리가 판매할 물건을 선택하기 전에 시장 조사부터 좀 해야 할 것 같아.

여: 시장 조사? 우리가 그게 왜 필요한데?

남: 왜냐하면 우리가 시장 조사를 통해 요즘 어떤 물건이 인기 있는지 알아내는 데 도움이 되기 때문이지.

여: 그렇구나. 그럼 벼룩시장에서 무엇을 판매할지 정할 수 있겠다.

남: 맞아. 그리고 시장 조사를 통해 우리는 판매할 물건에 합리적인 가격을 정하는 데 도움이 될 거야.

여: 좋아. 그 외에 우리가 해야 할 다른 게 있을까?

남: 오, 우리 이름을 이번 주 금요일까지 등록하는 것을 잊지 마.

여: 맞아. 알려 줘서 고마워.

❶ flea market: 벼룩시장　❷ anything을 꾸며주는 to부정사의 형용사적 용법이다.
❸ that은 market research를 가리킨다.　❹ help의 목적격보어로 원형부정사 find out이 이어진다.
❺ resonable: 합리적인　❻ 상대방에게 어떤 일에 대해 상기시키는 표현으로 'remember to ~'로 바꾸어 표현할 수 있다.

**Check(√) True or False**

(3) They are preparing something for the flea market.　T ☐ F ☐

(4) The girl forgot registering their names last Friday.　T ☐ F ☐

**Listen & Talk 1 A**

G: These two pairs of shoes are ❶on sale! Which do you prefer?

B: Well, I ❷prefer the white shoes to the black ones.

G: ❸Why is that? The black ones are cheaper.

B: Yes, but I like the design of the white ones better.

❶ on sale: 할인 중인
❷ prefer A to B: B보다 A를 더 선호하다
❸ 선호하는 이유를 묻는 질문으로 'Why do you think so?' 등으로 바꾸어 표현할 수 있다.

 **Listen & Talk 1 C**

G1: I think my hair is too ❶curly. I want to ❷straighten my hair. Can you ❸recommend a good place?

G2: Sure. I know two places, Styles Studio and Hair Castle.

G1: Is there any difference between the two?

G2: Well, Styles Studio provides free treatment to keep your hair healthy.

G1: That's great. What about Hair Castle?

G2: Hair Castle doesn't provide treatment ❹for free, but they give student ❺discounts.

G1: Okay. Which do you prefer?

G2: I prefer Styles Studio to Hair Castle. It's important for me to get hair treatment regularly.

❶ curly: 곱슬거리는      ❷ straighten: 곧게 펴다
❸ recommend: 추천하다      ❹ for free: 무료로
❺ discount: 할인

 **Listen & Talk 2 A**

B: I'm going to ❶get a refund for these clothes this evening. I found I have similar ones.

W: Okay. Don't forget to bring your ❷receipt. Last time you couldn't get a refund because you didn't bring ❸it.

B: Okay, Mom. I won't forget ❸it this time.

❶ get a refund: 환불받다
❷ receipt: 영수증
❸ it은 receipt를 가리킨다.

 **Listen & Talk 2 C**

G: I tried Spring Chips recently, and now I want to review ❶them.

B: That sounds fun. How will you do your review?

G: I'll make a video. I want to ❷focus on their delicious taste!

B: Okay, but don't forget to talk about their bad points too.

G: I won't. I want to give a ❸balanced review.

B: Good. Your video will make it easier for people to choose better products.

G: That's exactly ❹what I want. ❺I'd like to give people more useful information about the product.

❶ them은 Spring Chips를 가리킨다.
❷ focus on: ~에 초점을 맞추다
❸ balanced: 균형 잡힌
❹ 선행사를 포함하는 관계대명사로 '~하는 것'으로 해석한다.
❺ would you like to: ~하고 싶다

 **Do It Yourself**

G: Jinho, look! These two speakers look pretty cool.

B: Yeah, ❶they do. Which do you prefer, the red one or the black one?

G: I prefer the red one to the black one. ❷It's only 20 dollars, and ❷it comes with a discount coupon for music downloads.

B: Although the black one is 40 dollars, I think ❸it's the right one for me. I heard ❸it has better ❹sound quality.

❶ they는 two speakers를 가리킨다.
❷ it은 모두 'the red one'을 가리킨다.
❸ it은 모두 'the black one'을 가리킨다.
❹ sound quality: 음질

● 다음 우리말과 일치하도록 빈칸에 알맞은 말을 쓰시오.

## Listen & Talk 1 A

G: These two _____ of shoes are on sale! _____ _____ _____ _____?

B: Well, I _____ the white shoes _____ the black ones.

G: Why is that? The black ones are _____.

B: Yes, but I like the _____ of the white ones _____.

## Listen & Talk 1 B

G: Which do you _____, the Special Sandwich or the Classic Sandwich?

B: Well, the Special Sandwich is the _____ _____. It's made with lots of fresh vegetables and _____ healthy _____.

G: But it's _____ more _____ than the Classic Sandwich.

B: I know, but I prefer the Special Sandwich to the Classic Sandwich. _____ _____ is important _____ me.

G: I prefer the _____ one. I'll spend my money _____ books _____.

B: I guess _____ _____ _____ are different

## Listen & Talk 1 C

G1: I think my hair is too _____. I want to _____ my hair. Can you _____ a good place?

G2: Sure. I know two places, Styles Studio and Hair Castle.

G1: Is there any _____ between the _____?

G2: Well, Styles Studio provides _____ _____ to keep your hair _____.

G1: That's great. What about Hair Castle?

G2: Hair Castle doesn't provide treatment for _____, but they give _____ _____.

G1: Okay. Which do you _____?

G2: I prefer Styles Studio to Hair Castle. It's important _____ me _____ get hair treatment _____.

해석

여: 이 두 켤레의 신발이 세일 중이네! 어떤 것이 더 좋으니?
남: 음, 나는 검은색 신발보다 흰색 신발이 더 좋아.
여: 왜? 검은색 신발이 더 저렴하잖아.
남: 맞아, 하지만 나는 흰색 신발의 디자인이 더 좋아.

여: 스페셜 샌드위치와 클래식 샌드위치 중 어떤 것이 더 좋으니?
남: 음, 스페셜 샌드위치가 더 건강한 선택이야. 그것은 신선한 야채들과 다른 건강한 재료들로 만들어졌어.
여: 하지만 그건 클래식 샌드위치보다 훨씬 더 비싸잖아.
남: 맞아, 하지만 나는 클래식 샌드위치보다 스페셜 샌드위치가 더 좋아. 나에게는 건강하게 먹는 것이 중요하거든.
여: 나는 더 저렴한 것이 더 좋아. 대신 나는 내 돈을 책 사는 데 쓸래.
남: 우리는 소비 습관이 다른 것 같구나.

여1: 내 머리가 너무 곱슬곱슬한 것 같아. 머리카락을 곧게 펴고 싶어. 좋은 곳을 추천해 줄 수 있니?
여2: 물론이지. 난 스타일 스튜디오와 헤어 캐슬, 두 군데를 알고 있어.
여1: 두 군데의 차이점이 있니?
여2: 음, 스타일 스튜디오는 머리카락을 건강하게 유지해 주는 트리트먼트를 무료로 제공해 줘.
여1: 그것 좋으네. 헤어 캐슬은 어때?
여2: 헤어 캐슬은 트리트먼트를 무료로 제공해 주지는 않지만, 학생 할인을 해줘.
여1: 그렇구나. 넌 어느 곳을 선호하니?
여2: 나는 헤어 캐슬보다 스타일 스튜디오를 선호해. 나한텐 헤어 트리트먼트를 규칙적으로 받는 것이 중요해.

### Listen & Talk 2 A

**B:** I'm going to _____ _____ _____ for these clothes this evening. I found I have _____ ones.

**W:** Okay. _____ _____ to bring your _____. Last time you couldn't _____ _____ _____ because you didn't bring it.

**B:** Okay, Mom. I _____ _____ it this time.

### Listen & Talk 2 B

**G:** What should we sell at the _____ _____ next month?

**B:** Before we choose anything to sell, I think we need to do some _____ _____.

**G:** _____ _____? Why do we need _____?

**B:** Because it helps us _____ out _____ _____ _____ these days.

**G:** I see. Then we can _____ _____ _____ _____ at the market.

**B:** That's right. It will also help us _____ _____ prices for our items.

**G:** Cool. Is there _____ _____ we should do?

**B:** Oh, don't forget to _____ our names _____ this Friday.

**G:** Right. Thanks for _____ me.

### Listen & Talk 2 C

**G:** I tried Spring Chips recently, and now I want to _____ them.

**B:** That sounds fun. _____ will you do your _____?

**G:** I'll make a video. I want to _____ _____ their delicious taste!

**B:** Okay, but don't forget _____ _____ about their _____ _____ too.

**G:** I won't. I want to give a _____ _____.

**B:** Good. Your video will make _____ _____ _____ people _____ _____ _____ _____.

**G:** That's exactly what I want. I'd like to give people more _____ _____ about the product.

### Do It Yourself

**G:** Jinho, look! These two _____ look pretty cool.

**B:** Yeah, they do. _____ _____ _____ _____ _____, the red one or the black one?

**G:** I prefer the red one _____ the black one. It's only 20 dollars, and it comes with a _____ _____ for music downloads.

**B:** Although the black one is 40 dollars, I think it's the right one for me. I heard it has _____ _____ _____.

해석

남: 저 오늘 저녁에 이 옷들을 환불하려고 해요. 제가 비슷한 옷들을 갖고 있다는 것을 발견했거든요.

여: 그래. 영수증 갖고 가는 것 잊지 마렴. 저번에 네가 영수증을 가지고 가지 않는 바람에 환불을 못 받았잖니.

남: 알겠어요, 엄마. 이번에는 잊지 않을게요.

여: 우리 다음 달에 벼룩시장에서 무엇을 판매해야 할까?

남: 우리가 판매할 물건을 선택하기 전에 시장 조사부터 좀 해야 할 것 같아.

여: 시장 조사? 우리가 그게 왜 필요한데?

남: 왜냐하면 우리가 시장 조사를 통해 요즘 어떤 물건이 인기 있는지 알아내는 데 도움이 되기 때문이지.

여: 그렇구나. 그럼 벼룩시장에서 무엇을 판매할지 정할 수 있겠다.

남: 맞아. 그리고 시장 조사를 통해 우리는 판매할 물건에 합리적인 가격을 정하는 데 도움이 될 거야.

여: 좋아. 그 외에 우리가 해야 할 다른 게 있을까?

남: 오, 우리 이름을 이번 주 금요일까지 등록하는 것을 잊지 마.

여: 맞아. 알려 줘서 고마워.

여: 내가 요새 스프링 칩스를 먹어봤는데, 이제 그것을 비평해 보고 싶어.

남: 그거 재밌겠다. 어떻게 비평할 거니?

여: 나는 동영상을 만들려고 해. 스프링 칩스의 맛있는 맛에 초점을 맞추고 싶어!

남: 그래, 하지만 그것의 단점에 대해서도 이야기하는 것을 잊지 마.

여: 잊지 않을 거야. 나는 균형 잡힌 비평을 보여주고 싶어.

남: 좋아. 네 동영상 덕분에 사람들이 더 나은 제품을 선택하는 것이 쉬워지겠구나.

여: 그것이 바로 내가 원하는 거야. 나는 사람들에게 제품에 대한 더 유용한 정보를 주고 싶어.

여: 진호, 이것 봐! 이 스피커 두 개 꽤 멋져 보이는데.

남: 응, 정말 그러네. 빨간색 스피커와 검은색 스피커 중에서 어떤 것이 더 좋니?

여: 나는 검은색 스피커보다 빨간색 스피커가 더 좋아. 그것은 20달러밖에 안 하고, 음악 다운로드를 할인해 주는 쿠폰도 같이 있잖아.

남: 검은색 스피커가 40달러이지만, 그것이 나한테 맞는 것 같아. 그게 더 나은 음질을 갖고 있다고 들었거든.

[01~02] 다음 대화를 읽고 물음에 답하시오.

> **Suji:** Which do you prefer, the Special Sandwich or the Classic Sandwich?
>
> **Brian:** (A) It's made with lots of fresh vegetables and other healthy ingredients.
>
> **Suji:** (B) But it's much more expensive than the Classic Sandwich.
>
> **Brian:** (C) I know, but I prefer the Special Sandwich ___ⓐ___ the Classic Sandwich. Eating healthy is important ___ⓑ___ me.
>
> **Suji:** (D) I prefer the cheaper one. I'll spend my money on books instead.
>
> **Brian:** (E) I guess our spending habits are different.

**01** 위 대화의 (A)~(E) 중 다음 문장이 들어가기에 적절한 곳은?

> Well, the Special Sandwich is the healthier choice.

① (A)     ② (B)     ③ (C)     ④ (D)     ⑤ (E)

**02** 위 대화의 빈칸 ⓐ와 ⓑ에 공통으로 들어갈 전치사를 쓰시오.

➡ _____

[03~04] 다음 대화를 읽고 물음에 답하시오.

> **Jack:** I'm going to get a refund for these clothes this evening. I found I have similar (A)[it / ones / that].
>
> **Mom:** Okay. Don't forget (B)[bring / bringing / to bring] your receipt. Last time you couldn't get a refund because you didn't bring ⓐit.
>
> **Jack:** Okay, Mom. I won't forget ⓑit this time.

**03** 위 대화의 밑줄 친 ⓐ와 ⓑ가 공통으로 가리키는 것을 영어로 쓰시오.

➡ _____

**04** 위 대화의 괄호 (A)와 (B)에 알맞은 말이 바르게 짝지어진 것은?

① it – bringing     ② it – to bring
③ ones – to bring     ④ that – to bring
⑤ ones – bringing

**01** 다음 대화가 자연스럽게 이어지도록 순서대로 배열하시오.

> A: I think my hair is too curly. I want to straighten my hair. Can you recommend a good place?
>
> (A) That's great. What about Hair Castle?
>
> (B) Is there any difference between the two?
>
> (C) Sure. I know two places, Styles Studio and Hair Castle.
>
> (D) Well, Styles Studio provides free treatment to keep your hair healthy.
>
> (E) Hair Castle doesn't provide treatment for free, but they give student discounts.

➡ _____

[02~04] 다음 대화를 읽고 물음에 답하시오.

> Sujin: What should we sell at the flea market next month?
>
> Tom: Before we choose anything ⓐto sell, I think we need to do some market research.
>
> Sujin: Market research? Why do we need ⓑthat?
>
> Tom: Because it helps us find out ⓒwhat items are popular these days.
>
> Sujin: I see. Then we can decide what ⓓto sell at the market.
>
> Tom: That's right. It will also help us set reasonable prices for our items.
>
> Sujin: Cool. Is there anything else we should do?
>
> Tom: Oh, don't forget ⓔregistering our names by this Friday.
>
> Sujin: Right. Thanks for reminding me.

서답형

**02** 위 대화의 밑줄 친 ⓐ~ⓔ 중 어색한 것을 찾아 바르게 고치시오.

➡ _____

**03** 위 대화를 읽고 대답할 수 없는 것은?

① What are they going to prepare for?
② Why do they need the market research?
③ What should Sujin remember to do?
④ What items are popular these days?
⑤ Until when should Sujin finish registering their names?

**04** 위 대화의 내용과 일치하지 않는 것은?

① Tom은 벼룩시장에서 판매할 물건을 선택하기 전에 시장 조사부터 해야 한다고 생각한다.
② 시장 조사를 통해 요즘 어떤 물건이 인기 있는지 알 수 있기 때문에 Tom은 시장 조사를 할 것을 원한다.
③ Tom은 시장 조사를 통해 판매할 물건의 합리적인 가격을 정할 수 있을 것이라고 생각한다.
④ Sujin은 Tom과 그녀의 이름을 이번 주 금요일까지 등록해야 한다.
⑤ Sujin은 시장 조사하기 전에 벼룩시장에서 무엇을 판매할지 정할 수 있다고 생각한다.

**05** 다음 대화의 (A)~(C)에 알맞은 말이 바르게 짝지어진 것은?

> Jane: I tried Spring Chips recently, and now I want to review them.
>
> Chris: That sounds fun. How will you do your review?
>
> Jane: I'll make a video. I want to focus on their delicious taste!
>
> Chris: Okay, but don't forget to talk about their bad points too.
>
> Jane: I (A)[will / won't]. I want to give a (B)[balanced / balancing] review.

Chris: Good. Your video will make it easier for people to choose better products.

Jane: That's exactly (C)[that / what] I want. I'd like to give people more useful information about the product.

|   | (A) | (B) | (C) |
|---|-----|-----|-----|
| ① | will | balanced | that |
| ② | will | balancing | what |
| ③ | won't | balanced | what |
| ④ | won't | balancing | that |
| ⑤ | won't | balanced | that |

[06~08] 다음 대화를 읽고 물음에 답하시오.

Jack: I'm going to get a refund for these clothes this evening. I found I have similar ones.

Mom: Okay. Don't forget to bring your receipt. Last time you couldn't get a refund because you didn't bring it.

Jack: Okay, Mom. I won't forget it this time.

**서답형**

**06** What is Mom asking Jack to remember?

➡ _____

**서답형**

**07** Why does Jack want to get a refund for the clothes?

➡ _____

**서답형**

**08** Why couldn't Jack get a refund last time?

➡ _____

[09~10] 다음 대화를 읽고 물음에 답하시오.

Judy: I think my hair is too curly. I want to (A)[straight / straighten] my hair. Can you recommend a good place?

Gina: Sure. I know two places, Styles Studio and Hair Castle.

Judy: Is there any difference between the two?

Gina: Well, Styles Studio provides free treatment to keep your hair (B)[health / healthy].

Judy: That's great. What about Hair Castle?

Gina: Hair Castle doesn't provide treatment (C)[for / in] free, but they give student discounts.

Judy: Okay. Which do you prefer?

Gina: I prefer Styles Studio to Hair Castle. It's important for me to get hair treatment regularly.

**서답형**

**09** 위 대화의 괄호 (A)~(C)에서 알맞은 단어를 골라 쓰시오.

➡ (A) _____ (B) _____ (C) _____

**10** 위 대화의 내용과 일치하지 <u>않는</u> 것은?

① Judy는 머리가 곱슬곱슬해서 곧게 펴고 싶어 한다.

② 스타일 스튜디오는 머리카락을 건강하게 유지해 주는 트리트먼트를 무료로 제공해 준다.

③ 헤어 캐슬은 트리트먼트를 무료로 제공해 주지는 않는다.

④ 헤어 캐슬은 학생 할인을 해 준다.

⑤ Gina는 헤어 트리트먼트를 정기적으로 받는 게 중요해서 헤어 캐슬을 선호한다.

**01** 다음 대화가 자연스럽게 이어지도록 순서대로 배열하시오.

> (A) Why is that? The black ones are cheaper.
> (B) Yes, but I like the design of the white ones better.
> (C) Well, I prefer the white shoes to the black ones.
> (D) These two pairs of shoes are on sale! Which do you prefer?

➡ _____

[02~04] 다음 대화를 읽고 물음에 답하시오.

Suji: Which do you prefer, the Special Sandwich or the Classic Sandwich?

Brian: Well, the Special Sandwich is the healthier choice. It's made with lots of fresh vegetables and other healthy ingredients.

Suji: But it's much more expensive than the Classic Sandwich.

Brian: I know, but I prefer the Special Sandwich to the Classic Sandwich. Eating healthy is important to me.

Suji: I prefer the cheaper one. I'll spend my money on books instead.

Brian: I guess our spending habits are different.

**02** What is the Special Sandwich made with?

➡ _____
_____

**03** Why does Brian prefer the Special Sandwich to the Classic Sandwich?

➡ _____

**04** Why does Suji like the cheaper sandwich more?

➡ _____
_____

[05~06] 다음 대화를 읽고 물음에 답하시오.

Sujin: What should we sell at the flea market next month?

Tom: Before we choose anything to sell, I think we need to do some market research.

Sujin: Market research? Why do we need that?

Tom: Because it helps us find out what items are popular these days.

Sujin: I see. Then we can decide what to sell at the market.

Tom: That's right. It will also help us set reasonable prices for our items.

Sujin: Cool. Is there anything else we should do?

Tom: Oh, don't forget to register our names by this Friday.

Sujin: Right. Thanks for reminding me.

**05** 위 대화에서 다음 영영풀이가 나타내는 말을 찾아 쓰시오.

> to record your/somebody's/something's name on an official list

➡ _____

**06** 위 대화의 내용과 일치하도록 빈칸을 완성하시오.

> Through the market research, Tom and Sujin can find out (A)_____ these days. In addition, they are able to (B)_____ for their items.

# Grammar

**①** The+비교급 ~, the+비교급 … 구문

- **The fewer** products we buy, **the more** resources we save.
  우리가 제품들을 더 적게 구매할수록, 우리는 더 많은 자원들을 절약한다.

- **The more** you smile, **the happier** you feel.
  당신이 더 많이 웃을수록, 당신은 더 행복하게 느낀다.

■ 'The+비교급+주어+동사 ~, the+비교급+주어+동사 …'는 '~하면 할수록 더 …하다'의 의미로, 상응하는 두 절의 형용사나 부사, 형용사를 포함한 명사절의 비교급 형태를 'the'와 함께 주어 앞으로 이동하여 만든다.

(1) 형용사, 부사

- You are **familiar** with doing something. + You have to do it **sincerely**.
  → **The more familiar** you are with doing something, **the more sincerely** you have to do it.
  당신이 어떤 일에 더 익숙해질수록, 그것을 더욱 진지하게 해야 한다.

- We get up **early**. + We will get there **soon**.
  → **The earlier** we get up, **the sooner** we will get there. 우리가 더 일찍 일어날수록, 그곳에 더 빨리 도착할 것이다.

(2) 형용사를 포함한 명사

- They read good books. + They can enjoy a rich life.
  → **The better books** they read, **the richer life** they can enjoy. 그들이 더 좋은 책들을 읽을수록, 더욱 풍성한 삶을 즐길 수 있다.

(3) 의미가 통할 경우에 '동사' 또는 '주어+동사'의 생략이 가능하다.

- **The more** the money, **the bigger** the car. 돈이 더 많을수록, 차가 더 커진다.
- **The more, the better.** 많으면 많을수록 더 좋다.

■ 'The+비교급 ~, the+비교급 …' 구문은 접속사 If 또는 As를 사용해서 전환할 수 있다.

- **The harder** you study in college, **the better job** you will get.
  = If you study harder in college, you will get a better job.
  = As you study harder in college, you will get a better job.

**핵심 Check**

**1.** 다음 우리말에 맞게 괄호 안의 어구를 바르게 배열하시오.

당신이 더 많이 줄수록, 더 적게 잃게 될 것이다. (the more, the less, give, lose, will, you, you)

➡ _____

## ② 분사구문

- **Seeing** a lot of positive reviews, I decided to borrow a bike helmet.
  많은 긍정적인 후기들을 보고 나서, 나는 자전거 헬멧을 빌리기로 결심했다.
- **Feeling** cold, I put on thick clothes. 추위를 느껴서, 나는 두꺼운 옷을 입었다.

■ 종속접속사가 이끄는 부사절을 분사를 이용하여 간략한 부사구로 바꾼 것이다.

  - **While I was playing** basketball, I hurt my leg.
    = **Playing** basketball, I hurt my leg. 농구를 하다가, 나는 다리를 다쳤다.

■ 부사구와 주절의 관계에 따라 양보, 동시동작, 이유, 시간, 조건 등의 의미로 쓰인다.

  (1) 양보: **Though I live** next door, I seldom see him.
      = **Living** next door, I seldom see him. 비록 나는 이웃에 살지만, 그를 별로 보지 못한다.
  (2) 동시동작(부대상황): **While she ate** ice cream, Amy listened to music.
      = **Eating** ice cream, Amy listened to music. 아이스크림을 먹으며, Amy는 음악을 들었다.
  (3) 이유: **As I had** no money, I gave up buying it.
      = **Having** no money, I gave up buying it. 돈이 없어서 나는 그것을 사는 것을 포기했다.
  (4) 시간: **When she leaves** home, she always smiles.
      = **Leaving** home, she always smiles. 집을 나설 때, 그녀는 항상 미소를 짓는다.
  (5) 조건: **If he turns** right, he'll see the shopping mall.
      = **Turning** right, he'll see the shopping mall. 우회전하면, 그는 쇼핑몰을 보게 될 것이다.

■ 주절과 종속절의 주어가 다를 경우, 분사구문의 주어를 남겨 두는 것을 독립분사구문이라고 하며, 일반인이 주어일 경우에는 생략 가능하다. (비인칭 독립분사구문)

  (1) 독립분사구문: **As it was** stormy, the ships couldn't go out to sea.
      = **It being** stormy, the ships couldn't go out to sea. 폭풍우가 불어닥쳐서, 배들이 바다로 나갈 수 없었다.
  (2) 비인칭 독립분사구문: **frankly speaking**(솔직히 말해서), **considering** ~ (~를 고려하면)
  (3) with+목적어+분사: Daddy fell asleep **with the light turned on**. (불이 켜진 채로)

### 핵심 Check

2. 다음 괄호 안에서 알맞은 것을 고르시오.
   (1) Mary opened the wine, (poured / pouring) it into my glass.
   (2) (Leaving / Left) alone, the baby started to cry.

**01** 다음 빈칸에 들어갈 말로 알맞은 것은?

> The longer the rabbit ran, the _____ it felt.

① tiring      ② most tired      ③ less tiring
④ more tired    ⑤ more tireder

**02** 다음 부사절을 분사구문으로 바꿔 쓸 때, 빈칸에 들어갈 말로 가장 적절한 것은?

> As she saw a lot of negative reviews, she decided not to buy the dress.
> → _____ a lot of negative reviews, she decided not to buy the dress.

① She seeing    ② As she seeing    ③ Seeing
④ Having been seen    ⑤ Being seen

**03** 다음 〈보기〉에서 필요한 단어를 골라, 어법에 알맞은 형태로 빈칸에 써 넣으시오.

> ┌─ 보기
> focus, familiar, wise, loud, high, old, big, much

(1) _____ the size is, the _____ the price will get.

(2) The _____ your surroundings are, the harder it is _____ on work.

(3) The _____ the girl got, the _____ she became.

(4) The _____ time we spend together, the _____ we will become.

**04** 다음 분사구문을 접속사가 이끄는 부사절로 만들 때, 빈칸에 알맞은 말을 써 넣으시오.

(1) Taking a shower, Smith sang a song.
  ⇒ While _____ _____ _____ _____, Smith sang a song.

(2) Being hungry, she dropped by the restaurant.
  ⇒ As _____ _____ _____, she dropped by the restaurant.

(3) Feeling scared, the little boy took a step forward.
  ⇒ _____ _____ _____, the little boy took a step forward.

다음 두 문장의 의미가 같도록 할 때 빈칸에 들어갈 말로 가장 적절한 것은?

> As she felt cold, Sally put on more clothes.
> → _____ cold, Sally put on more clothes.

① She felt
② Having feeling cold
③ To feel
④ Feeling
⑤ Being felt

[02~03] 다음 빈칸에 들어갈 말이 알맞게 짝지어진 것을 고르시오.

**02**

> The _____ you work, the _____ the results will be.

① hard – well
② more hard – more well
③ more – most
④ harder – better
⑤ hardest – best

**03**

> _____ her illness gets, _____ pain she will feel.

① So bad – as much painful
② The more bad – worse
③ The worse – the more
④ Worse – the more worse
⑤ The worse – the most

[04~05] 다음 우리말을 어법상 알맞게 영작한 것을 고르시오.

**04**

> 피아노를 연주하다가, 그녀는 숙제를 해야 할 것을 잊었다.

① While played the piano, she forgot to do her homework.

② As she was played the piano, she forgot to do her homework.
③ Playing the piano, she forgot to do her homework.
④ Having been played the piano, she forgot to do her homework.
⑤ While being played the piano, she forgot to do her homework.

**05**

> 공유 경제 앱을 이용해서, Sean은 돈을 아낄 수 있었다.

① Sean using the sharing economy apps, he could save some money.
② Using the sharing economy apps, Sean being able to save some money.
③ Being used the sharing economy apps, Sean could save some money.
④ Using the sharing economy apps, Sean could save some money.
⑤ Though using the sharing economy apps, Sean could save some money.

[06~07] 다음 주어진 문장의 의미가 자연스럽게 되도록 빈칸에 들어갈 말로 가장 적절한 것은?

**06**

> The less we buy various kinds of products, _____.

① the more money we can spend
② the worse the environment gets
③ the better the sellers will be
④ the more resources we can save
⑤ the more likely we are to ruin the nature

**07**

The more products you borrow instead of buying, _____ .

① the more active the sharing economy will become
② the more actively the sharing economy will become
③ the more active the sharing economy will do
④ the more active the sharing economy will work
⑤ the better active the sharing economy will become

[08~10] 다음 중 밑줄 친 분사구문의 용법이 〈보기〉와 같은 것은?

**08**

┤ 보기 ├
Seeing a lot of good reviews by the users, Cassy decided to borrow the bike.

① Being sick all night, she went to school as if nothing happened.
② Feeling tired from the endless documents, he never lost his smile.
③ Meeting the handsome guy today, Jasmine will fall in love with him.
④ Surrounded by a lot of birds, the woman was feeding them.
⑤ Surprised by his daughter's cry, Roberto rushed in immediately.

**09** 중요

┤ 보기 ├
Using Pet Sitter Find App, you could experience the joy of walking a dog.

① Arriving at the station, I learned that the train had already left for Busan.

② Being tired from the work, Alice can't help falling asleep.
③ Producing fresh air, plant-covered buildings are good for your health.
④ Listening to the song she composed, they will say they will sing it.
⑤ Running along the street, I saw a traffic accident between the buses.

**10**

┤ 보기 ├
Born in Seoul, William isn't good at speaking Korean.

① Turning right at the second corner, you won't miss the cafe.
② Not knowing how much she missed me, I was embarrassed with her tears.
③ Having nothing to do this afternoon, Jasmine was going to sleep in her room.
④ Living in Paris for over 20 years, I still can't understand the conversation between French women.
⑤ Finishing his assignment, Albert went outside to play basketball with friends.

**11** 중요
다음 밑줄 친 부분 중 어법상 어색한 것을 고르시오.

① It being rainy, all the players in the ground couldn't play.
② Wanting to stop him from using her car, Ms. Lee told her son to wait.
③ Being sensitive to the negative reviews, the staff were carefully checking the state of their products.
④ Being no seats available in the bus, the pregnant woman decided to get off.
⑤ Written in the ancient language, the letters on the stone has not been completely interpreted.

**12** 다음 주어진 문장을 분사구문으로 만들 때 가장 적절한 것은?

> Animals aren't allowed in my apartment, so I don't have any pets.

① Not being allowed in my apartment, I don't have any pets.

② Animals not being allowed in my apartment, I don't have any pets.

③ Animals not allowing in my apartment, I don't have any pets.

④ Not animals being allowed in my apartment, I don't have any pets.

⑤ No animals allowed being in my apartment, I don't have any pets.

**13** 다음 〈보기〉의 문장과 가장 가까운 뜻을 가진 문장을 고르시오.

> 보기
>
> As more people use the sharing economy services, they will improve more.

① Even if more people use the sharing economy services, the more will they improve.

② The people use the sharing economy services more, they will improve the more.

③ The more people use the sharing economy services, the more they will improve.

④ When more people use the sharing economy services, the better they will improve.

⑤ Most people use the sharing economy services, the more they will improve.

**[14~15]** 우리말과 일치하도록 괄호 안에 주어진 단어들을 바르게 배열하시오.

**14**

> 당신이 공유 경제 서비스를 더 자주 이용할수록, 지구의 자원은 더 적게 사용된다.
>
> → (the less, use, the sharing economy services, often, resources, the more, you) are used on Earth.

➡ _____

_____

**15**

> 어떤 제품들은 가격이 올라갈수록 더 많은 사람들이 사려고 한다.
>
> → (some products, buy, people, the more, the higher, gets, them, to, the price, want, of).

➡ _____

_____

**16** 다음 밑줄 친 분사구문을 같은 의미의 부사절로 바꿔 쓸 때 적절하지 <u>않은</u> 것은?

① <u>Using various services</u>, we have increased the sharing economy.

　→ As we use various services,

② <u>Waving their hands</u>, the players walked out of the ground.

　→ While they were waving their hands,

③ <u>Eating some baked potatoes</u>, Marco waited for his mom to come home.

　→ As he was eating some baked potatoes,

④ The sharing economy expands rapidly, <u>making a lot of resources saved</u>.

　→ though it makes a lot of resources saved.

⑤ <u>Walking along the street</u>, he saw a man walking six puppies.

　→ When he walked along the street,

**01** 다음 우리말과 일치하도록 괄호 안에 주어진 어구들을 바르게 배열하여 문장을 완성하시오.

(1) 그녀가 더 큰 돈을 벌수록, 그녀의 가족들은 더 많이 원한다. (the more, she, want, makes, money, her family, the bigger)

➡ _____

_____

_____

(2) 그 서비스를 더 자주 이용할수록, 우리는 공유 경제를 더 빨리 촉진하게 될 것이다. (we, we, the sharing economy, the service, often, the more, the faster, use, promote, will)

➡ _____

_____

_____

(3) 그녀가 열심히 일할수록, 그녀의 미래는 더욱 밝아질 것이다. (her future, works, the brighter, she, be, the harder, will)

➡ _____

_____

_____

(4) 그 시스템을 더 자세하게 알수록, 공유 경제에 대한 우리의 신뢰는 더 강해진다. (the system, the stronger, in, closely, we, know, the sharing economy, the more, our trust, becomes)

➡ _____

_____

_____

(5) 그 앱이 더 자주 사용될수록, 개인정보에 대한 우려는 더 커진다. (the greater, the app, is, the personal information, frequently, the concern, about, used, gets, the more)

➡ _____

_____

_____

**02** 다음 〈보기〉에 있는 접속사를 한 번씩만 사용하여, 각 문장의 밑줄 친 분사구문을 부사절로 바꾸시오. (단, 진행형 불가, 주어는 가능한 대명사로 표현할 것.)

┌─ 보기 ─┐
though / and / while / because / when / if
└─────────┘

(1) Looking through the window of the restaurant, Mike suddenly found the woman who had lied to him passing by.

➡ _____

_____

(2) The sharing economy improves the world, making resources less used.

➡ _____

_____

(3) Having trouble that you cannot talk to your loved ones, try sharing it with one that you have never met before.

➡ _____

(4) Not wanting to disturb his daughter, Mr. Brown was quietly waiting for her to finish her practice.

➡ _____

_____

(5) Using various kinds of apps, we can borrow the things that we don't have to buy at a small fee or for free.

➡ _____

_____

(6) There being some weaknesses with the services, you can see a lot of positive reviews on their websites.

➡ _____

_____

**03** 다음 그림을 보고, 우리말에 맞게 괄호 안의 단어를 활용하여 빈칸을 채우시오.

쓰레기를 덜 버릴수록, 교실이 더 깨끗해진다.
→ _____, _____
the classroom becomes. (the, trash, we, little, clean, throw away) 어법상 알맞게 어형 변화할 것, 8 단어)

**04** 다음 우리말과 일치하도록 괄호 안에 주어진 단어들을 바르게 배열하시오.

(1)

자주 필요하지 않은 물건들을 빌려 쓰기 때문에, Jasmine은 돈을 많이 저축해 왔다.
→ (that, doesn't often, borrowing, she, need, things), Jasmine has saved a lot of money.

➡ _____

(2)

불과 2년 전에 건설되었음에도 불구하고, 그 아파트는 비가 올 때마다 물이 샌다.
→ (built, ago, having, only, though, been, two years), the apartment leaks whenever it rains.

➡ _____

(3)

텐트가 없었기 때문에, 우리는 애플리케이션을 이용하여 하나를 빌렸다.
→ (we, having, not, any, one, borrowed, tents) using the application.

➡ _____

(4)

주변에 이용 가능한 공유 경제 서비스 앱들이 있음에도 불구하고, 사람들은 새 제품을 구매하는 경향이 있다.
→ (being, available, service apps, though, sharing economy, there) around them, people tend to buy new products.

➡ _____
_____

**05** 다음 괄호 안에 주어진 단어를 이용하여 어법에 맞게 빈칸을 완성하시오.

(1) _____ _____(many) books the students read, _____ _____ (wise) they will become.

(2) _____ _____(far) the old lady walks every day, _____ _____ (healthy) she will become.

(3) _____ _____(old) the girl grew, _____ _____(much) she looked like her grandmother.

(4) _____ _____(loud) the boy practices speaking, _____ _____(confident) he feels.

# Reading

## Life in the Sharing Economy

**Son:** What should we do this weekend, Dad?

**Dad:** Why don't we go camping?

**Son:** But we don't have a tent. Should we buy one? Also, who will
take care of our dog?
<u>one</u>
= a tent

**Dad:** Don't worry. I know some apps that can help us.
주격 관계대명사

### Borrow from your neighbors!

Ask Your Neighbors helps people easily find items that they can
목적격 관계대명사
borrow from others. First, users download the app and search for
= other people
another user that has the item they need. Then they pick up the item
주격 관계대명사     the item과 they need 사이에 목적격 관계대명사 that[which] 생략
and return it later.
the item

Jasmine: December 12, 2019

I asked for a board game and got one in less than 30 minutes. I love
= a board game
saving money by borrowing things that I don't often need. Also, I think
목적격 관계대명사
it's environmentally friendly. The fewer products we buy, the more
the+비교급 …, the+비교급 ~: …하면 할수록, 더 ~하다
resources we save.

---

share 함께 쓰다, 공유하다

economy 경제

take care of ~을 돌보다

app 애플리케이션(= application), 응
용 프로그램

neighbor 이웃

search for ~을 찾다

resource 자원, 재료

---

📎 **확인문제**

● 다음 문장이 본문의 내용과 일치하면 T, 일치하지 <u>않으면</u> F를 쓰시오.

1 Ask Your Neighbors helps people easily find items that they can borrow from
others. ☐

2 First, lenders download the app and search for another user that has the item they
need. ☐

3 Users of Ask Your Neighbors pick up the item and return it later. ☐

4 Jasmine asked for a board game and got one in more than 30 minutes. ☐

5 Jasmine loves saving money by borrowing things that she doesn't often need. ☐

6 Jasmine thinks that buying things is environmentally friendly. ☐

Cassandra: March 7, 2020

Seeing a lot of positive reviews, I decided to borrow a bike helmet.
분사구문(때). = After I saw a lot of positive reviews.
When I got it, however, it was broken. I was so upset!

Ask Your Neighbors: March 9, 2020

We're sorry that you had such a negative experience. To fix this issue,
such+a+형용사+명사
we are asking lenders to update the pictures of their items regularly.
ask+목적어+to부정사
This will let other users know the exact condition of the product.
let+목적어+원형부정사

**I can look after your pet!**

Pet Sitter Finder is the perfect app for pet lovers and pet owners. It

helps pet owners find reliable people to look after their pets. When a
help+목적어+원형부정사[to부정사]
pet owner is looking for pet sitters, he or she uploads a post. Pet sitters

or dog walkers can then send messages to the owner. The owner checks
V1
their reviews and chooses the best person.
V2

George: November 12, 2019

I use this app whenever I'm going out of town. I have some concerns
복합관계부사: ~할 때는 언제나
about my personal information though. What if people use my phone
하지만(부사)    ~라면 어쩌지?
number for other purposes?

| | |
|---|---|
| positive 긍정적인 | |
| negative 부정적인 | |
| issue 쟁점, 사안 | |
| exact 정확한, 정밀한 | |
| condition 상태, 조건 | |
| look after ~을 살피다[돌보다] | |
| owner 주인, 소유주 | |
| reliable 믿을 수 있는 | |
| pet sitter 반려동물 돌보는 사람 | |
| upload 올리다, 업로드하다 | |
| concern 우려, 근심 | |
| personal 개인의, 개인적인 | |
| what if ~라면 어쩌지? | |

📎 **확인문제**

● 다음 문장이 본문의 내용과 일치하면 T, 일치하지 <u>않으면</u> F를 쓰시오.

1  After she saw a lot of positive reviews, Cassandra decided to borrow a bike
   helmet. ☐

2  When Cassandra got a bike helmet, it was in good condition. ☐

3  Ask Your Neighbors is sorry that Cassandra had such a negative experience. ☐

4  Ask Your Neighbors is the perfect app for pet lovers and pet owners. ☐

5  George doesn't have any concerns in using this app. ☐

Pet Sitter Finder: November 14, 2019

We're aware of this issue. We're now developing a system that
주격 관계대명사
allows users to communicate freely without showing their personal
allow+목적어+to-V(목적격보어)                                   동명사
information.

Samantha: February 22, 2020

Animals aren't allowed in my apartment, so I don't have any pets.
수동태(be+p.p.): 행위자가 불분명하거나 중요하지 않을 때 'by+행위자' 생략 가능
However, by using Pet Sitter Finder, I can experience the joy of

walking a dog.
동명사(전치사 of의 목적어)

**Son:** What great apps! We can borrow a tent and find someone to take
What+(a)+형용사+명사!
care of our dog.

**Dad:** That's right. These kinds of services are part of the "sharing
economy." People can share their items with others and provide
share A with B: A를 B와 공유하다
services to them at a small fee or for free.
무료로
**Son:** But these services do have some weaknesses. Some people left
강조의 조동사
negative reviews about the services.

**Dad:** Well, I think the more people use the services, the more they will
the+비교급 …, the+비교급 ~: …하면 할수록 더 ~하다
improve.

---

📎 **확인문제**

● 다음 문장이 본문의 내용과 일치하면 T, 일치하지 <u>않으면</u> F를 쓰시오.

1  Pet Sitter Finder is aware of the personal information issue. ☐

2  Pet Sitter Finder is now developing a system that allows users to communicate

   freely after showing their personal information. ☐

3  Animals aren't allowed in Samantha's apartment. ☐

4  Samantha doesn't have any pets, so she can't experience the joy of walking a

   dog. ☐

5  The son says that they can borrow a tent and find someone to take care of their

   dog. ☐

---

be aware of ~을 인지하다[알다]

develop 발달시키다, 개발하다

kind 종류, 유형; 친절한

provide 제공하다

fee 요금, 수수료

weakness 약점

improve 개선하다

● 우리말을 참고하여 빈칸에 알맞은 말을 쓰시오.

**1** Life in the _____ _____

**2** Son: _____ _____ _____ _____ this weekend, Dad?

**3** Dad: _____ _____ _____ go camping?

**4** Son: But we _____ _____ a tent.

**5** Should we buy _____?

**6** Also, who will _____ _____ _____ our dog?

**7** Dad: _____ _____. I know some apps that can help us.

**8** _____ **from your neighbors!**

**9** Ask Your Neighbors _____ _____ _____ _____ items that they can borrow from others.

**10** First, users download the app and search for another user that has _____ _____ _____.

**11** Then they pick up the item and _____ _____ later.

**12** Jasmine: _____ _____, 2019

**13** I _____ _____ a board game and got _____ in less than 30 minutes.

**14** I love saving money _____ _____ things that I don't often need.

**15** Also, I think it's _____ _____.

**16** _____ _____ _____ we buy, _____ _____ _____ we save.

---

**17** Cassandra: _____ 7, 2020

**18** _____ a lot of positive reviews, I decided _____ _____ a bike helmet.

**19** When I got it, however, it _____ _____.

**20** I was _____ _____!

**21** Ask Your Neighbors: _____ _____, 2020

**22** We're sorry that you had _____ _____ _____ _____.

**23** _____ _____ this issue, we are asking lenders _____ _____ _____ _____ of their items regularly.

**24** This will _____ other users _____ the exact condition of the product.

**25** **I can _____ _____ your pet!**

**26** Pet Sitter Finder is _____ _____ _____ for pet lovers and pet owners.

**27** It helps pet owners find _____ _____ to look after their pets.

**28** When a pet owner is looking for pet sitters, he or she uploads _____ _____.

**29** Pet sitters or dog walkers can then _____ _____ _____ the owner.

**30** The owner _____ their reviews and _____ the best person.

**31** George: _____ 12, 2019

**32** I use this app _____ I'm going out of town.

17 Cassandra / 2020년 3월 7일

18 많은 긍정적인 후기들을 보고 나서, 저는 자전거 헬멧을 빌리기로 결심했어요.

19 그러나 제가 그것을 얻었을 때, 그것은 망가져 있었어요.

20 저는 몹시 기분이 상했어요!

21 Ask Your Neighbors / 2020년 3월 9일

22 고객님이 그런 부정적인 경험을 겪게 해 드려 죄송합니다.

23 이 문제를 바로잡기 위해서, 저희는 빌려주는 사람들에게 그들의 물건 사진을 정기적으로 업데이트해 줄 것을 요구하고 있습니다.

24 이것이 다른 사용자들에게 그 제품의 정확한 상태를 알 수 있도록 해 줄 것입니다.

25 제가 당신의 반려동물을 돌볼 수 있어요!

26 Pet Sitter Finder는 반려동물을 좋아하는 사람들과 반려동물 주인들을 위한 완벽한 앱이다.

27 그것은 반려동물 주인들이 그들의 반려동물을 돌보는 데 신뢰할 만한 사람들을 찾도록 돕는다.

28 반려동물 주인이 반려동물을 돌보는 사람들을 찾을 때, 그 또는 그녀는 게시물을 올린다.

29 그러고 나서 반려동물을 돌보는 사람들이나 개를 산책시키는 사람들이 주인에게 메시지를 보낼 수 있다.

30 주인은 그들의 후기들을 확인하고 최고의 사람을 선택한다.

31 George / 2019년 11월 12일

32 저는 교외로 나갈 때마다 이 앱을 사용해요.

**33** I have some concerns about my _____ _____ though.

**34** What if people use my phone number _____ _____ _____?

**35** Pet Sitter Finder: _____ _____, _____

**36** We're _____ _____ this issue.

**37** We're now developing a system that _____ users to communicate freely _____ _____ their personal information.

**38** Samantha: _____ 22, 2020

**39** Animals _____ _____ in my apartment, so I don't have any pets.

**40** However, _____ _____ Pet Sitter Finder, I can experience the joy of _____ a dog.

**41** Son: _____ great apps!

**42** We can borrow a tent and find someone _____ _____ _____ _____ our dog.

**43** Dad: That's _____.

**44** These kinds of services are part of the "_____ _____."

**45** People can _____ their items _____ others and provide services to them _____ _____ _____ _____ or _____ _____.

**46** Son: But these services _____ have some _____.

**47** Some people _____ _____ _____ _____ about the services.

**48** Dad: Well, I think _____ people use _____ _____, the more they will improve.

**33** 하지만 저의 개인 정보에 대한 몇 가지 걱정이 있어요.

**34** 만약 다른 사람들이 제 전화번호를 다른 목적으로 사용하면 어쩌죠?

**35** Pet Sitter Finder / 2019년 11월 14일

**36** 저희는 이 문제를 알고 있습니다.

**37** 저희는 현재 사용자들이 자신의 개인 정보를 보여주지 않으면서 자유롭게 소통할 수 있는 시스템을 개발하는 중입니다.

**38** Samantha / 2020년 2월 22일

**39** 동물들이 제 아파트에서는 허락되지 않아서, 저는 반려동물을 키울 수 없어요.

**40** 그런데 Pet Sitter Finder를 이용하면서, 저는 개를 산책시키는 즐거움을 경험할 수 있어요.

**41** 아들: 정말 좋은 앱들이네요!

**42** 우리는 텐트를 빌리고 우리 개를 돌볼 누군가를 찾을 수 있어요.

**43** 아빠: 그렇지.

**44** 이런 종류의 서비스가 '공유 경제'의 일부란다.

**45** 사람들은 자신의 물건을 다른 사람들과 공유할 수 있고 적은 비용이나 무료로 그들에게 서비스를 제공할 수 있어.

**46** 아들: 하지만 사실 이런 서비스들은 몇 가지 약점들을 가지고 있어요.

**47** 몇몇 사람들이 서비스에 대해 부정적인 후기들을 남겼잖아요.

**48** 아빠: 글쎄, 나는 사람들이 그 서비스들을 더 많이 사용할수록, 그것들이 더 개선될 것이라고 생각해.

● 우리말을 참고하여 본문을 영작하시오.

**1** ▶ 공유 경제 속 삶

➡ _____

**2** ▶ 아들: 아빠, 우리 이번 주말에 뭐 할 거예요?

➡ _____

**3** ▶ 아빠: 캠핑 가는 건 어떠니?

➡ _____

**4** ▶ 아들: 그런데 우리 텐트가 없잖아요.

➡ _____

**5** ▶ 하나 사야 할까요?

➡ _____

**6** ▶ 게다가 우리 개는 누가 돌봐요?

➡ _____

**7** ▶ 아빠: 걱정하지 마. 내가 우리를 도와줄 수 있는 몇 개의 앱들을 알고 있지.

➡ _____

**8** ▶ 당신의 이웃들로부터 빌려라!

➡ _____

**9** ▶ Ask Your Neighbors는 사람들이 다른 사람들로부터 빌릴 수 있는 물건을 쉽게 찾도록 돕는다.

➡ _____

**10** ▶ 우선, 사용자들은 그 앱을 내려받고 그들이 필요한 물건을 가지고 있는 또 다른 사용자를 찾는다.

➡ _____

**11** ▶ 그러고 나서 그들은 그 물건을 받아서 나중에 반납한다.

➡ _____

**12** ▶ Jasmine / 2019년 12월 12일

➡ _____

**13** ▶ 저는 보드게임을 요청했고 30분도 안 되어 하나를 구했어요.

➡ _____

**14** ▶ 저는 제가 자주 필요하지 않은 것들을 빌림으로써 돈을 아낄 수 있다는 것이 마음에 들어요.

➡ _____

**15** ▶ 게다가 이것이 환경친화적이라고 생각해요.

➡ _____

**16** ▶ 우리가 제품들을 더 적게 구매할수록, 우리는 더 많은 자원들을 아끼는 거예요.

➡ _____

**17** Cassandra / 2020년 3월 7일

➡ _____

**18** 많은 긍정적인 후기들을 보고 나서, 저는 자전거 헬멧을 빌리기로 결심했어요.

➡ _____

**19** 그러나 제가 그것을 얻었을 때, 그것은 망가져 있었어요.

➡ _____

**20** 저는 몹시 기분이 상했어요!

➡ _____

**21** Ask Your Neighbors / 2020년 3월 9일

➡ _____

**22** 고객님이 그런 부정적인 경험을 겪게 해 드려 죄송합니다.

➡ _____

**23** 이 문제를 바로잡기 위해서, 저희는 빌려주는 사람들에게 그들의 물건 사진을 정기적으로 업데이트해 줄 것을 요구하고 있습니다.

➡ _____

**24** 이것이 다른 사용자들에게 그 제품의 정확한 상태를 알 수 있도록 해 줄 것입니다.

➡ _____

**25** 제가 당신의 반려동물을 돌볼 수 있어요!

➡ _____

**26** Pet Sitter Finder는 반려동물을 좋아하는 사람들과 반려동물 주인들을 위한 완벽한 앱이다.

➡ _____

**27** 그것은 반려동물 주인들이 그들의 반려동물을 돌보는 데 신뢰할 만한 사람들을 찾도록 돕는다.

➡ _____

**28** 반려동물 주인이 반려동물을 돌보는 사람들을 찾을 때, 그 또는 그녀는 게시물을 올린다.

➡ _____

**29** 그리고 나서 반려동물을 돌보는 사람들이나 개를 산책시키는 사람들이 주인에게 메시지를 보낼 수 있다.

➡ _____

**30** 주인은 그들의 후기들을 확인하고 최고의 사람을 선택한다.

➡ _____

**31** George / 2019년 11월 12일

➡ _____

**32** 저는 교외로 나갈 때마다 이 앱을 사용해요.

➡ _____

**33** 하지만 저의 개인 정보에 대한 몇 가지 걱정이 있어요.

➡ _____

**34** 만약 다른 사람들이 제 전화번호를 다른 목적으로 사용하면 어쩌죠?

➡ _____

**35** Pet Sitter Finder / 2019년 11월 14일

➡ _____

**36** 저희는 이 문제를 알고 있습니다.

➡ _____

**37** 저희는 현재 사용자들이 자신의 개인 정보를 보여주지 않으면서 자유롭게 소통할 수 있는 시스템을 개발하는 중입니다.

➡ _____

_____

**38** Samantha / 2020년 2월 22일

➡ _____

**39** 동물들이 제 아파트에서는 허락되지 않아서, 저는 반려동물을 키울 수 없어요.

➡ _____

**40** 그런데 Pet Sitter Finder를 이용하면서, 저는 개를 산책시키는 즐거움을 경험할 수 있어요.

➡ _____

**41** 아들: 정말 좋은 앱들이네요!

➡ _____

**42** 우리는 텐트를 빌리고 우리 개를 돌볼 누군가를 찾을 수 있어요.

➡ _____

**43** 아빠: 그렇지.

➡ _____

**44** 이런 종류의 서비스가 '공유 경제'의 일부란다.

➡ _____

**45** 사람들은 자신의 물건을 다른 사람들과 공유할 수 있고 적은 비용이나 무료로 그들에게 서비스를 제공할 수 있어."

➡ _____

**46** 아들: 하지만 사실 이런 서비스들은 몇 가지 약점들을 가지고 있어요.

➡ _____

**47** 몇몇 사람들이 서비스에 대해 부정적인 후기들을 남겼잖아요.

➡ _____

**48** 아빠: 글쎄, 나는 사람들이 그 서비스들을 더 많이 사용할수록, 그것들이 더 개선될 것이라고 생각해.

➡ _____

[01~03] 다음 글을 읽고 물음에 답하시오.

Son: What should we do this weekend, Dad?
Dad: ⓐWhy don't we go camping?
Son: But we don't have a tent. Should we buy ⓑone? Also, who will take care of our dog?
Dad: Don't worry. I know some apps that can help us.

**01** 위 글의 밑줄 친 ⓐ와 바꿔 쓸 수 없는 말을 고르시오.

① How about going camping?
② What about going camping?
③ Go camping, will you?
④ Let's go camping, shall we?
⑤ Shall we go camping?

**서답형**

**02** 위 글의 밑줄 친 ⓑone이 가리키는 것을 본문에서 찾아 쓰시오.

➡ _____

**중요**

**03** 위 글의 뒤에 올 내용으로 가장 알맞은 것을 고르시오.

① what to do during the weekend
② the best place to go camping
③ the price of the tent for camping
④ the introduction to some apps to solve the son's worry
⑤ the clinics to take care of pets during their owners' vacation

[04~06] 다음 글을 읽고 물음에 답하시오.

Cassandra: March 7, 2020
  Seeing a lot of positive reviews, I decided to borrow a bike helmet. When I got it, however, it was broken. I was so ___ⓐ___ !

Ask Your Neighbors: March 9, 2020
  We're sorry that you had such a negative experience. To fix ⓑthis issue, we are asking lenders to update the pictures of their items regularly. This will let other users know the exact condition of the product.

**04** 위 글의 빈칸 ⓐ에 들어갈 알맞은 말을 고르시오.

① excited          ② upset
③ nervous          ④ pleased
⑤ ashamed

**서답형**

**05** 다음 빈칸 (A)와 (B)에 알맞은 단어를 넣어, 위 글의 밑줄 친 ⓑthis issue가 가리키는 내용을 완성하시오.

When the users get the things they decided to borrow after they saw a lot of (A)_____ _____, they come to find the (B)_____ of the things is not good.

**서답형**

**06** 다음 문장에서 위 글의 내용과 다른 부분을 찾아서 고치시오.

Ask Your Neighbors is asking lenders to download the pictures of their items regularly.

➡ _____ ➡ _____

[07~09] 다음 글을 읽고 물음에 답하시오.

_____ⓐ_____

Ask Your Neighbors helps people easily find items that they can borrow from others. (①) First, users download the app and search for another user that has the item they need. (②)

Jasmine: December 12, 2019

I asked for a board game and got ⓑone in less than 30 minutes. (③) I love saving money by borrowing things that I don't often need. (④) Also, I think it's environmentally friendly. (⑤) The fewer products we buy, the more resources we save.

**07** 위 글의 빈칸 ⓐ에 들어갈 제목으로 알맞은 것을 고르시오.

① Various Apps That Make Our Lives More Convenient
② Borrow from Your Neighbors!
③ What Is Effective to Search for the Users?
④ Which Is Nicer, Buying an Item or Borrowing It?
⑤ Let's Live Environmentally Friendly Lives

**08** 위 글의 흐름으로 보아, 주어진 문장이 들어가기에 가장 적절한 곳은?

Then they pick up the item and return it later.

①　　②　　③　　④　　⑤

서답형

**09** 위 글의 밑줄 친 ⓑone이 가리키는 것을 본문에서 찾아 쓰시오.

➡ _____

[10~12] 다음 글을 읽고 물음에 답하시오.

**I can look after your pet!**

Pet Sitter Finder is the perfect app for pet lovers and pet owners. It helps pet owners find reliable people to (A)look after their pets. When a pet owner is looking for pet sitters, he or she uploads a post. Pet sitters or dog walkers can then send messages to the owner. The owner checks their reviews and ___ⓐ___ the best person.

서답형

**10** 위 글의 빈칸 ⓐ에 choose를 알맞은 형태로 쓰시오.

➡ _____

**11** 위 글의 밑줄 친 (A)look after와 바꿔 쓸 수 있는 말을 모두 고르시오.

① take notice of　　② care for
③ make use of　　④ take after
⑤ take care of

서답형

**12** 다음 빈칸 (A)와 (B)에 알맞은 단어를 넣어, Pet Sitter Finder를 이용하여 반려동물 주인이 반려동물을 돌보는 사람들을 찾는 방법을 완성하시오.

First a pet owner uploads a post and checks the (A)_____ about the pet sitters or dog walkers who (B)_____ _____ to him or her. Then, the owner can choose the best person among them.

[13~14] 다음 글을 읽고 물음에 답하시오.

Samantha: February 22, 2020

Animals aren't allowed in my apartment, so I don't have any pets. However, by (A)using Pet Sitter Finder, I can experience the joy of _____ⓐ_____.

**13** 위 글의 빈칸 ⓐ에 들어갈 알맞은 말을 고르시오.

① developing apps

② walking a dog

③ finding reliable people

④ uploading a post

⑤ becoming a baby sitter

**14** 위 글의 밑줄 친 (A)using과 문법적 쓰임이 <u>다른</u> 것을 <u>모두</u> 고르시오.

① I'm <u>planning</u> to visit his house.

② She is worried about <u>taking</u> an exam.

③ Did you practice <u>playing</u> the cello?

④ I saw him <u>entering</u> the room.

⑤ <u>Playing</u> soccer is fun

[15~17] 다음 글을 읽고 물음에 답하시오.

**Borrow from your neighbors!**

Ask Your Neighbors helps people easily find items that they can borrow from others. First, users download the app and search ____ⓐ____ another user that has the item they need. Then they pick up the item and return it later.

Jasmine: December 12, 2019

I asked for a board game and got one ____ⓑ____ less than 30 minutes. I love saving money by ⓒ<u>borrowing</u> things that I don't often need. Also, I think it's environmentally friendly. The fewer products we buy, the more resources we save.

**15** 위 글의 빈칸 ⓐ와 ⓑ에 들어갈 전치사가 바르게 짝지어진 것은?

|  | ⓐ | ⓑ |  | ⓐ | ⓑ |
|---|---|---|---|---|---|
| ① | for | at | ② | on | for |
| ③ | to | for | ④ | for | in |
| ⑤ | on | in |  |  |  |

**16** 위 글의 밑줄 친 ⓒborrowing과 문법적 쓰임이 같은 것을 <u>모두</u> 고르시오.

① My hobby is <u>playing</u> soccer.

② Look at the <u>sleeping</u> baby.

③ Do you mind <u>turning</u> down the volume?

④ He is good at <u>playing</u> the violin.

⑤ She is <u>watching</u> TV now.

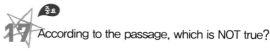

**17** According to the passage, which is NOT true?

① People can easily find items that they can borrow from others through the app, Ask Your Neighbors.

② First, users need to download the app and search for another user who will borrow their item.

③ Jasmine asked for a board game and got one in less than 30 minutes.

④ Jasmine loves to save money by borrowing things that she doesn't often need.

⑤ Jasmine thinks borrowing things is environmentally friendly.

[18~19] 다음 글을 읽고 물음에 답하시오.

Pet Sitter Finder: November 14, 2019

We're aware of this issue. We're now developing a system that allows users to communicate freely without showing their personal information.

Samantha: February 22, 2020

Animals aren't allowed in my apartment, so I don't have any pets. ____ⓐ____, by using Pet Sitter Finder, I can experience the joy of walking a dog.

**18** 위 글의 빈칸 ⓐ에 들어갈 알맞은 말을 고르시오.

① In other words   ② Moreover

③ However   ④ Likewise

⑤ As a result

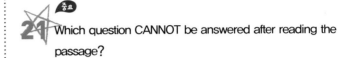

**19** 위 글의 앞에 올 내용으로 가장 알맞은 것을 고르시오.

① the difficulty of developing a system

② a system that allows users to communicate freely

③ the apartment in which animals aren't allowed

④ the way to keep pets

⑤ the issue of showing the personal information

[20~21] 다음 글을 읽고 물음에 답하시오.

### I can look after your pet!

Pet Sitter Finder is the perfect app for pet lovers and pet owners. It helps pet owners find reliable people to look after their pets. When a pet owner is looking for pet sitters, he or she uploads a post. Pet sitters or dog walkers can then send messages to the owner. The owner checks their reviews and chooses the best person.

George: November 12, 2019

I use this app whenever I'm going out of town. I have some concerns about my personal information ⓐthough. What if people use my phone number for other purposes?

**20** 위 글의 밑줄 친 ⓐthough와 같은 의미로 쓰인 것을 고르시오.

① Though he was young, he supported his family.

② Our team lost. It was a good game though.

③ Though he tried very hard, he failed the course.

④ Young though he was, he was very wise.

⑤ The wind was still blowing though it stopped raining.

**21** Which question CANNOT be answered after reading the passage?

① What is Pet Sitter Finder?

② How do pet sitters or dog walkers contact a pet owner?

③ How long does it take for a pet owner to find a reliable person to look after the pet?

④ When does George use the app, Pet Sitter Finder?

⑤ What is George worried about?

[22~23] 다음 글을 읽고 물음에 답하시오.

Son: What great apps! We can borrow a tent and find someone to take care of our dog.

Dad: That's right. These kinds of services are part of the " ⓐ economy." People can share their items with others and provide services to them at a small fee or for free.

Son: But these services do have some weaknesses. Some people left negative reviews about the services.

Dad: Well, I think the more people use the services, the more they will improve.

**서답형**

**22** 본문의 한 단어를 변형하여 위 글의 빈칸 ⓐ에 들어갈 알맞은 단어를 쓰시오.

➡ _____


**중요**

**23** 위 글의 주제로 알맞은 것을 고르시오.

① the great apps that make our lives comfortable

② the way to borrow an item

③ the benefits and weaknesses of "sharing economy"

④ how to provide services to people

⑤ the way to improve the weaknesses of "sharing economy"


**24** 주어진 문장 다음에 이어질 글의 순서로 가장 적절한 것은?

Pet Sitter Finder is the perfect app for pet lovers and pet owners.

(A) When a pet owner is looking for pet sitters, he or she uploads a post. Pet sitters or dog walkers can then send messages to the owner.

(B) The owner checks their reviews and chooses the best person.

(C) It helps pet owners find reliable people to look after their pets.

① (A) – (C) – (B)　　② (B) – (A) – (C)

③ (B) – (C) – (A)　　④ (C) – (A) – (B)

⑤ (C) – (B) – (A)


**[25~27]** 다음 글을 읽고 물음에 답하시오.

Cassandra: March 7, 2020

Seeing a lot of positive reviews, I decided to borrow a bike helmet. When I got it, however, it was broken. I was so upset!

Ask Your Neighbors: March 9, 2020

We're sorry that you had ⓐ그런 부정적인 경험. To ⓑfix this issue, we are asking lenders to update the pictures of their items regularly. This will let other users know the exact condition of the product.


**중요**

**25** 위 글에서 알 수 있는 Cassandra의 심경 변화로 가장 알맞은 것을 고르시오.

① hopeful　　→　bored

② puzzled　　→　upset

③ bored　　→　amazed

④ expectant　　→　disappointed

⑤ nervous　　→　satisfied


**서답형**

**26** 위 글의 밑줄 친 ⓐ의 우리말에 맞게 such를 사용하여 4 단어로 영작하시오.

➡ _____


**27** 위 글의 밑줄 친 ⓑfix와 같은 의미로 쓰인 것을 고르시오.

① The car won't start. Can you fix it?

② He tried to fix a shelf to the wall.

③ I want to fix the rent at forty dollars a month.

④ She likes to fix a feather in her hat.

⑤ Why did he fix his eyes on the ground?

**[01~02]** 다음 글을 읽고 물음에 답하시오.

Son: What should we do this weekend, Dad?

Dad: Why don't we go ___ⓐ___ ?

Son: But we don't have a tent. Should we buy one? Also, who will take care of our dog?

Dad: Don't worry. I know some apps that can help us.

**01** 위 글의 빈칸 ⓐ에 camp를 알맞은 형태로 쓰시오.

➡ _____

**02** 캠핑 가자는 아빠의 제안을 듣고 아들이 걱정하는 내용 두 가지를 우리말로 쓰시오.

➡ (1) _____
   (2) _____

**[03~04]** 다음 글을 읽고 물음에 답하시오.

Son: What great apps! We can borrow a tent and find someone to take care of our dog.

Dad: That's right. These kinds of services are part of the "sharing economy." People can share their items with others and provide services to them at a small fee or ⓐfor free.

Son: But these services do have some weaknesses. Some people left negative reviews about the services.

Dad: Well, I think ⓑ사람들이 그 서비스들을 더 많이 사용할수록, 그것들이 더 개선될 것이라고.

**03** 위 글의 밑줄 친 ⓐfor free와 바꿔 쓸 수 있는 말을 쓰시오.

➡ _____ 또는 _____ 또는 _____

**04** 위 글의 밑줄 친 ⓑ의 우리말에 맞게 주어진 어휘를 알맞게 배열하시오.

| will / use / they / the more / the services / people / improve / the more / , / |

➡ _____
_____

**[05~07]** 다음 글을 읽고 물음에 답하시오.

Cassandra: March 7, 2020

Seeing a lot of (A)[positive / negative] reviews, I decided to borrow a bike helmet. When I got it, however, it was broken. I was so upset!

Ask Your Neighbors: March 9, 2020

We're sorry that you had such a negative experience. To fix this issue, we are asking (B)[lenders / users] to update the pictures of their items regularly. ⓐThis will let other (C)[lenders / users] know the exact condition of the product.

**05** 위 글의 괄호 (A)~(C)에서 문맥상 알맞은 낱말을 골라 쓰시오.

➡ (A) _____ (B) _____ (C) _____

**06** 위 글의 밑줄 친 ⓐThis가 가리키는 것을 우리말로 쓰시오.

➡ _____
_____

**07** 본문의 내용과 일치하도록 다음 빈칸 (A)와 (B)에 알맞은 단어를 쓰시오.

> Ask Your Neighbors apologizes to (A)_____ for having given her a very (B)_____ experience.

**[08~09]** 다음 글을 읽고 물음에 답하시오.

Cassandra: March 7, 2020
ⓐSeeing a lot of positive reviews, I decided to borrow a bike helmet. When I got it, however, it was broken. I was so upset!

Ask Your Neighbors: March 9, 2020
We're sorry that you had such a negative experience. To fix this issue, we are asking lenders to update the pictures of their items regularly. This will let other users know the exact condition of the product.

**08** 위 글의 밑줄 친 ⓐ를 부사절로 고칠 때, 빈칸에 들어갈 알맞은 두 단어를 쓰시오.

➡ After _____ a lot of positive reviews

**09** How can other users know the exact condition of the product that they want to borrow? Fill in the blanks (A) and (B) with suitable words.

> If (A)_____ _____ of the items are updated regularly by (B)_____, other users will be able to know the exact condition of the product.

**[10~12]** 다음 글을 읽고 물음에 답하시오.

George: November 12, 2019
I use this app whenever I'm going out of town. I have some concerns about my personal information though. What if people use my phone number for other purposes?

Pet Sitter Finder: November 14, 2019
We're aware of ⓐthis issue. ⓑWe're now developing a system that allows users to communicate freely without showing their personal information.

Samantha: February 22, 2020
Animals aren't allowed in my apartment, so I don't have any pets. However, by using Pet Sitter Finder, I can experience the joy of walking a dog.

**10** 위 글의 밑줄 친 ⓐthis issue가 가리키는 것을 우리말로 쓰시오.

➡ _____ 또는
_____

**11** 위 글의 밑줄 친 ⓑ를 다음과 같이 바꿔 쓸 때 빈칸에 들어갈 알맞은 단어를 쓰시오.

> We're now developing a system which lets users _____ freely without showing their personal information.

**12** 본문의 내용과 일치하도록 다음 빈칸 (A)와 (B)에 알맞은 단어를 쓰시오.

> Though Samantha has no (A)_____, she can experience the joy of walking a dog (B)_____ _____ _____ _____.

## Do It Yourself

Last Sunday, my family went to see a baseball game. Cheering for our team,

분사구문(= While[As] we cheered for our team. ~)

we had a really nice time together. Happily, our team won the game. Feeling

분사구문(= As[Since/Because] we felt

happy about the win, we decided to celebrate. Eating fried chicken together,

happy about the win. ~)　　　　to부정사의 명사적 용법　　　분사구문(= While[As] we ate

fried chicken together. ~)

we talked about the game.

구문해설　• cheer: 응원하다　• win: 승리하다; 승리　• celebrate: 축하하다

지난 일요일, 우리 가족은 야구 경기를 보러 갔다. 우리 팀을 응원하면서, 우리는 함께 정말 좋은 시간을 가졌다. 행복하게도 우리 팀이 그 경기에서 이겼다. 승리에 대해 기쁨을 느껴서, 우리는 축하하기로 결정했다. 함께 프라이드치킨을 먹으면서, 우리는 그 경기에 대해 얘기했다.

## After You Read C Get the BIG Picture

### Sharing Economy

where people can share their items with or provide services to others

share A with B: A를 B와 공유하다　　　provide A to B: B에게 A를 제공하다

### Ask Your Neighbors

⊕ helps people find items to borrow from others

help+목적어+원형부정사(to부정사)

⊕ helps people save money and resources

help+목적어+원형부정사(to부정사)

⊖ needs regular updates on each item's condition

each + 단수명사

<⊕ benefit, ⊖ weakness>

구문해설　• share: 공유하다　• neighbor: 이웃　• provide: 제공하다　• condition: 상태, 조건
　　　　　• benefit: 혜택　• weakness: 약점

**공유 경제**

사람들이 자신의 물건을 다른 사람들과 공유하거나 그들에게 서비스를 제공할 수 있는 곳

**Ask Your Neighbors**

⊕ 사람들이 다른 사람들로부터 빌릴 수 있는 물건을 찾도록 돕는다

⊕ 사람들이 돈과 자원들을 아끼도록 돕는다

⊖ 각 제품의 상태에 관해 정기적인 업데이트가 필요하다

〈⊕ 이점, ⊖ 약점〉

## Culture Link

### Sharing Economies Around the World

I sometimes give other people a ride on my way to work. They can get to their

give A B : A에게 B를 주다(4형식)　　　　　　　　　　　　　　　= reach. arrive at

destinations for a small fee, and I can make some money. Ride sharing also

fee는 small/large. low/high 등과 함께 쓴다　　　　　　　　동명사(단수 취급)

reduces the number of cars on the road, which is environmentally friendly.

~의 수 a number of (×)　　　계속적 용법의 관계대명사 (앞 문장 전체가 선행사)

구문해설　• destination: 목적지　• fee: 요금　• environmentally: 환경적으로

**세계의 공유 경제**

나는 때때로 출근길에 다른 사람들을 태워준다. 그들은 적은 요금을 내고 목적지에 도착할 수 있고, 나는 약간의 돈을 벌 수 있다. 출근 공유는 또한 도로 위의 차들의 수를 줄여 주는데, 그것은 환경친화적이다.

**01** 다음 짝지어진 단어의 관계가 같도록 빈칸에 알맞은 말을 쓰시오.

> borrow : lend = download : _____

**02** 다음 영영풀이가 가리키는 것을 고르시오.

> to give something that someone needs or wants to them, or make it available

① allow   ② borrow   ③ fix
④ improve   ⑤ provide

**03** 다음 중 밑줄 친 부분의 뜻풀이가 바르지 않은 것은?

① Wherever you visit, you should follow the safety rules. (언제든지)
② My father takes part in the volunteer activity regularly. (규칙적으로)
③ If you don't mind, would you fix this machine for me? (고치다)
④ You can express your ideas freely during the meeting. (자유롭게)
⑤ My sister looked disappointed because of her broken toys. (망가진)

**04** 다음 문장의 빈칸 (A)~(C)에 들어갈 말이 바르게 짝지어진 것은?

> • The shoes are ___(A)___ sale.
> • My father is going to be ___(B)___ of town for two weeks.
> • Birds search ___(C)___ a good place to raise their young in summer.

① to – for – on
② for – in – out
③ for – on – in
④ on – for – out
⑤ on – out – for

**05** 다음 대화가 자연스럽게 이어지도록 순서대로 배열하시오.

> (A) Okay, Mom. I won't forget it this time.
> (B) I'm going to get a refund for these clothes this evening. I found I have similar ones.
> (C) Okay. Don't forget to bring your receipt. Last time you couldn't get a refund because you didn't bring it.

➡ _____

**[06~08]** 다음 대화를 읽고 물음에 답하시오.

Judy: I think my hair is too curly. I want to straighten my hair. Can you recommend a good place?

Gina: Sure. I know two places, Styles Studio and Hair Castle.

Judy: Is there any difference between the two?

Gina: Well, Styles Studio provides free treatment to keep your hair healthy.

Judy: That's great. What about Hair Castle?

Gina: Hair Castle doesn't provide treatment for free, but they give student discounts.

Judy: Okay. Which do you prefer?

Gina: I prefer Styles Studio to Hair Castle. It's important for me to get hair treatment regularly.

**06** What benefit does Styles Studio provide to the customers?

➡ _____

_____

**07** Who can get discounts from Hair Castle?

➡ _____

**08** Why does Gina like Styles Studio more?

➡ _____

_____

**[09~10]** 다음 대화를 읽고 물음에 답하시오.

> Jane: I tried Spring Chips recently, and now I want to review them.
>
> Chris: That sounds fun. How will you do your review?
>
> Jane: I'll make a video. I want to focus on their delicious taste!
>
> Chris: Okay, but _____(A)_____.
>
> Jane: I won't. I want to give a balanced review.
>
> Chris: Good. Your video will make it easier for people to choose better products.
>
> Jane: That's exactly what I want. I'd like to give people more useful information about the product.

**09** 위 대화의 빈칸 (A)에 들어갈 말을 <보기>에 주어진 어구들을 모두 배열하여 완성하시오.

┌─── 보기 ───┐

talk / too / their / to / forget / bad points / don't / about

➡ _____

**10** 위 대화의 내용과 일치하지 <u>않는</u> 것은?

① Jane은 최근에 스프링 칩스를 먹어 보았다.

② Jane은 스프링 칩스의 맛있는 맛을 논평하고 싶어 한다.

③ Chris는 Jane에게 스프링 칩스의 단점도 언급할 것을 상기시켰다.

④ Jane은 균형 잡힌 비평을 내고 싶어 한다.

⑤ Jane은 더 맛있는 음식을 만들어 사람들의 선택을 받고자 한다.

**11** 다음 대화가 자연스럽게 이어지도록 순서대로 배열하시오.

> Which do you prefer, the Special Sandwich or the Classic Sandwich?
>
> (A) I guess our spending habits are different.
>
> (B) But it's much more expensive than the Classic Sandwich.
>
> (C) I prefer the cheaper one. I'll spend my money on books instead.
>
> (D) Well, the Special Sandwich is the healthier choice. It's made with lots of fresh vegetables and other healthy ingredients.
>
> (E) I know, but I prefer the Special Sandwich to the Classic Sandwich. Eating healthy is important to me.

➡ _____

**Grammar**

**[12~13]** 다음 문장의 밑줄 친 분사구문을 부사절로 바르게 바꾼 것은?

**12**

> <u>Seeing a lot of negative reviews online</u>, the researcher decided not to buy the products.

① Though she saw a lot of negative reviews online,

② Once she saw a lot of negative reviews online,

③ If she saw a lot of negative reviews online,

④ As she saw a lot of negative reviews online,

⑤ Should she see a lot of negative reviews online,

**13**

There being a Pet Sitter Finder app made by her friends, she didn't use the service.

① As an app existed there where she could find a pet sitter by her friends,
② If there was a Pet Sitter Finder app made by her friends,
③ Unless there was a Pet Sitter Finder app made by her friends,
④ Even though there was a Pet Sitter Finder app made by her friends,
⑤ Because there was a Pet Sitter Finder app made by her friends,

**14** 다음 중 어법상 어색한 문장을 고르시오.

① The more they earn, the more they have to save for their future.
② The cooler the cold noodle is, the better it tastes.
③ The more promises you make, the harder it becomes to keep them.
④ The less we have, the more we want to receive.
⑤ The higher you go up, the more it is difficult for you to breathe.

**15** 다음 문장의 밑줄 친 부사절을 분사구문으로 알맞게 바꾼 것을 고르시오.

As he wasn't aware of the personal information issues, George often forgot to secure his details.

① As he being not aware of the personal information issues,

② There being not aware of the personal information issues,
③ Being not aware of that the personal information issues,
④ As he not being aware of the personal information issues,
⑤ Not being aware of the personal information issues,

[16~17] 다음 밑줄 친 부분 중 어법상 옳은 것을 고르시오.

**16** ① The sooner they start to work, <u>the more faster they will achieve the goal.</u>
② <u>More the men eat, more</u> weight they will gain.
③ The shorter the break time is, <u>the less relaxed the employees do.</u>
④ The heavier the tables are, <u>the more expensive they become.</u>
⑤ The more they think, <u>the more they will be careful.</u>

**17** ① <u>Caught a severe cold,</u> Catherine was absent from school yesterday.
② <u>Turned to the right,</u> you'll find the shopping mall on your right.
③ <u>Having been raised on a farm,</u> William knows well how to feed pigs and cows.
④ <u>Interesting in the Korean history,</u> Chris reserved the related books at the library.
⑤ <u>Educating in New Zealand,</u> she speaks and writes English well.

**18** 다음 중 주어진 문장과 의미가 가장 가까운 문장을 고르시오.

> Everytime he spends some time with Anne, he feels better than before.

① The more he knows Anne, the happier she will be.

② The more Anne spends time with him, the happier she feels.

③ The more things he does with Anne, the happier they look.

④ The more time he spends with Anne, the happier he is.

⑤ The more time he spends with Anne, the happier he does.

**Reading**

[19~21] 다음 글을 읽고 물음에 답하시오.

Borrow from your neighbors!

Ask Your Neighbors helps people easily find items that they can ____ⓐ____ from others. First, users download the app and search for ⓑ그들이 필요한 물건을 가지고 있는 또 다른 사용자. Then they pick up the item and return it later.

Jasmine: December 12, 2019

I asked for a board game and got one in less than 30 minutes. I love saving money by borrowing things that I don't often need. Also, I think it's environmentally friendly. ⓒThe fewer products we buy, the more resources we save.

**19** 위 글의 빈칸 ⓐ에 들어갈 알맞은 말을 고르시오.

① lend    ② use    ③ buy
④ borrow    ⑤ provide

**20** 위 글의 밑줄 친 ⓑ의 우리말에 맞게 주어진 어휘를 이용하여 8 단어로 영작하시오.

> another, that, the item

➡ _____

**21** 위 글의 밑줄 친 ⓒ를 접속사 As를 사용하여 고칠 때, 빈칸에 들어갈 알맞은 말을 쓰시오.

➡ As we buy _____ _____, we save _____ _____.

[22~24] 다음 글을 읽고 물음에 답하시오.

Cassandra: March 7, 2020

Seeing a lot of positive reviews, I decided to borrow a bike helmet. (①) When I got it, however, it was broken. (②) I was so upset! (③)

Ask Your Neighbors: March 9, 2020

We're sorry that you had such a negative experience. (④) ⓐThis will let other users to know the exact condition of the product. (⑤)

**22** 위 글의 흐름으로 보아, 주어진 문장이 들어가기에 가장 적절한 곳은?

> To fix this issue, we are asking lenders to update the pictures of their items regularly.

①    ②    ③    ④    ⑤

## 23 위 글의 밑줄 친 ⓐ에서 어법상 틀린 부분을 찾아 고치시오.

_____ ➡ _____ 또는

_____ ➡ _____

## 24 위 글의 주제로 알맞은 것을 고르시오.

① the other side of a lot of positive reviews
② the problem and its solution when borrowing things using an app
③ the unreliable "sharing services"
④ how to change the negative experience of the users
⑤ the way to update the pictures of the items regularly

**[25~26] 다음 글을 읽고 물음에 답하시오.**

Son: What great apps! We can borrow a tent and find someone to take care of our dog.
Dad: That's right. These kinds of services are part of the "sharing economy." People can share their items with others and provide services to them at a small fee or for free.
Son: But these services ⓐdo have some weaknesses. Some people left negative reviews about the services.
Dad: Well, I think the more people use the services, the more they will improve.

## 25 위 글의 밑줄 친 ⓐdo와 문법적 쓰임이 같은 것을 고르시오.

① Do you like it?
② We will do what we can to help.
③ You do look tired.
④ They do not want to go there.
⑤ She works harder than you do.

## 26 According to the passage, which is NOT true?

① The son says that the apps are very great.
② Dad says these kinds of services are part of the "sharing economy."
③ People can share their items with others and provide services to them at a small fee or for free.
④ These kinds of services don't have any weaknesses.
⑤ Dad thinks the more people use the services, the more they will improve.

**[27~28] 다음 글을 읽고 물음에 답하시오.**

I Can Share My Jump Rope with You!
  Here is a jump rope that I can share. It's not new, but it's in good condition. You can borrow it for up to two days.

There are two rules:
❶ You can borrow it once a week.
❷ You must pay for the item if you lose or break it.

  If you are willing to follow the rules above, feel free to contact me! I will happily share it with you.

## 27 위 글의 종류로 알맞은 것을 고르시오.

① essay      ② article      ③ manual
④ review      ⑤ notice

## 28 다음 문장에서 위 글의 내용과 다른 부분을 찾아서 고치시오.

> The users can borrow the jump rope for a week.

_____ ➡ _____

**출제율 90%**

**01** 다음 영영풀이가 가리키는 것을 고르시오.

> the system according to which the money, industry and trade of a country or region are organized

① refund      ② economy      ③ issue
④ fee           ⑤ camping

**출제율 95%**

**02** 다음 주어진 문장의 밑줄 친 condition(s)과 같은 의미로 쓰인 것은?

> She is in no <u>condition</u> to walk alone.

① You should check your <u>conditions</u> of employment.
② My grandfather's <u>condition</u> is getting better now.
③ What is a necessary <u>condition</u> for economic growth?
④ A good training programme is one of the <u>conditions</u> for successful industry.
⑤ Does she not like the <u>conditions</u>?

**출제율 100%**

**03** 다음 우리말을 주어진 단어를 이용하여 영작하시오.

(1) 지난주에 그 코트는 할인 중이었다. (sale, coat)

➡ _____

(2) 그녀는 방학 동안 친구의 애완동물을 돌보았다. (take, during)

➡ _____

(3) 이 팬케이크들은 유기농 계란으로 만들어졌다. (with, pancakes, organic)

➡ _____

**[04~05]** 다음 대화를 읽고 물음에 답하시오.

Sue: Jinho, look! These two speakers look pretty cool. (A)

Jinho: (B) Yeah, they do. Which do you prefer, the red one or the black one?

Sue: (C) It's only 20 dollars, and it comes with a discount coupon for music downloads.

Jinho: (D) Although the black one is 40 dollars, I think it's the right one for me. I heard it has better sound quality. (E)

**출제율 90%**

**04** 위 대화의 (A)~(E) 중에서 주어진 문장이 들어가기에 적절한 곳은?

> I prefer the red one to the black one.

① (A)    ② (B)    ③ (C)    ④ (D)    ⑤ (E)

**출제율 100%**

**05** 위 대화의 내용과 일치하지 <u>않는</u> 것은?

① Sue와 진호는 두 개의 스피커를 보고 있다.
② 빨간색 스피커는 20달러이다.
③ 빨간색 스피커는 음악 다운로드 할인 쿠폰도 같이 준다.
④ 진호는 빨간색 스피커가 자신에게 맞는 것 같다.
⑤ 진호는 검은색 스피커가 더 나은 음질을 갖고 있다고 들었다.

**[06~07]** 다음 대화를 읽고 물음에 답하시오.

Judy: I think my hair is too curly. I want to straighten my hair. Can you recommend a good place?

Gina: Sure. I know two places, Styles Studio and Hair Castle.

Judy: Is there any difference between the two?

Gina: Well, Styles Studio provides free treatment to keep your hair healthy.

Judy: That's great. What about Hair Castle?

Gina: Hair Castle doesn't provide treatment for free, but they give student discounts.

Judy: Okay. (A)<u>Which do you prefer?</u>

Gina: I prefer Styles Studio to Hair Castle. It's important for me to get hair treatment regularly.

---

**06** 위 대화의 밑줄 친 (A)와 바꾸어 쓸 수 있는 것을 <u>모두</u> 고르시오.

① What are you planning to do?
② Which do you like more?
③ Which do you like better?
④ Which one do you want to visit?
⑤ What do you want to have?

---

**07** 위 대화의 내용과 일치하도록 빈칸을 완성하시오.

> Gina: Which hair shop do you want to visit to straighten your hair?
>
> Judy: I need to save my money because my father's birthday is coming. I need to buy a present for him. I'll choose (A)_____ because I can get (B)_____.

---

**[08~10]** 다음 대화를 읽고 물음에 답하시오.

G: These two pairs of shoes are ⓐ<u>on sale</u>! ⓑ<u>Which</u> do you prefer?

B: Well, I prefer the white shoes ⓒ<u>than</u> the black ones.

G: Why is that? The black ones ⓓ<u>are</u> cheaper.

B: Yes, but I like the design ⓔ<u>of</u> the white ones better.

---

**08** 위 대화의 내용과 일치하도록 빈칸을 완성하시오.

> Even though the black shoes are (A)_____, the boy prefers the white shoes because of their (B)_____.

---

**09** 위 대화의 밑줄 친 ⓐ~ⓔ에서 어법상 어색한 것을 골라 바르게 고치시오.

_____ ➡ _____

---

**10** 위 대화의 내용과 일치하지 <u>않는</u> 것은?

① 두 켤레의 신발이 할인 중이다.
② 소년은 검은색 신발보다 흰색 신발을 더 좋아한다.
③ 검은색 신발이 더 저렴하다.
④ 소년은 흰색 신발의 디자인을 더 좋아한다.
⑤ 소녀는 검은색 신발을 구매할 것이다.

---

**[11~12]** 다음 주어진 문장의 부사절을 분사구문으로 적절히 전환한 것을 고르시오.

**11**

> As they had not been invited to the party, the couple left the city for a quiet temple.

① Having not invited to the party, the couple left the city for a quiet temple.
② As they not having been invited to the party, the couple left the city for a quiet temple.
③ As they being not invited to the party, the couple left the city for a quiet temple.
④ Not having been invited to the party, the couple left the city for a quiet temple.
⑤ Not having invited to the party, the couple left the city for a quiet temple.

**12** 출제율 90%

As we expand the sharing economy around the world, we can decrease the amount of resources in making a lot of products.

① Expanding the sharing economy around the world, we can decrease the amount of resources in making a lot of products.

② When the sharing economy expanding around the world, we can decrease the amount of resources in making a lot of products.

③ As the sharing economy being expanded around the world, we can decrease the amount of resources in making a lot of products.

④ As the sharing economy expanding around the world, we can decrease the amount of resources in making a lot of products.

⑤ Expanded the sharing economy around the world, we can decrease the amount of resources in making a lot of products.

[13~14] 다음 주어진 우리말을 바르게 영작한 것을 고르면?

**13** 출제율 90%

당신이 더 많은 물건들을 공유한다면, 지구의 자원은 더 적게 사용될 수 있다.

① As the more you share the things, the more resources on earth are less likely to be used.

② When you share the more things, you are likely to use the global resources as little as you imagine.

③ The more you share things with others, the more less resources on earth can be used.

④ The more things you share with other people, the amount of resources used on earth will decrease.

⑤ The more things you share, the less resources on earth can be used.

**14** 출제율 95%

날씨가 더워질수록, 우리는 더 많은 전기 에너지가 필요하다.

① The more hotter the weather, so much more electrical energy we need.

② The hotter the weather is, the more electrical energy we need.

③ The hotter the weather will be, the more electrical energy we are needed.

④ The more hot the weather, we need the more electrical energy.

⑤ The hotter the weather is, the better electrical energy we will need.

**15** 출제율 100%

다음 우리말에 맞도록 괄호 안에 주어진 어휘를 알맞게 배열하여 빈칸을 채우시오.

(1) 우리가 살아가는 환경을 보호하고 싶기 때문에, 나는 공유 경제 서비스 앱을 개발하기로 결심했다. (protect, wanting, in, to, we, the environment, live)

➡ _____

_____, I decided to develop a sharing economy service app.

(2) 비록 나는 학생들이 무엇을 원하는지 알지 못했지만, 그들이 요청한 대로 하려고 최선을 다해 노력했다. (what, not, wanted, though, the students, knowing)

➡ _____

_____, I tried my best to do what they asked.

[16~18] 다음 글을 읽고 물음에 답하시오.

**Borrow from your neighbors!**

Ask Your Neighbors helps people easily find items that they can borrow from others. First, users download the app and search for another user that has the item they need. Then they pick up the item and return ⓐit later.

Jasmine: December 12, 2019

I asked for a board game and got one in less than 30 minutes. I love saving money by borrowing things that I don't often need. Also, I think it's environmentally friendly. ⓑThe less products we buy, the less resources we save.

**16** 위 글의 밑줄 친 ⓐit이 가리키는 것을 본문에서 찾아 쓰시오.

➡ _____

**17** 위 글의 밑줄 친 ⓑ에서 어법이나 흐름상 어색한 부분을 찾아 고치시오. (두 군데)

_____ ➡ _____

_____ ➡ _____

**18** Ask Your Neighbors를 사용하는 방법을 우리말로 설명하시오.

➡ (1) _____

_____

(2) _____

_____

[19~21] 다음 글을 읽고 물음에 답하시오.

ⓐ

Pet Sitter Finder is the perfect app for pet lovers and pet owners. It helps pet owners find reliable people to look after their pets. When a pet owner is looking for pet sitters, he or she uploads a post. Pet sitters or dog walkers can then send messages to the owner. The owner checks their reviews and chooses the best person.

George: November 12, 2019

I use this app ⓑwhenever I'm going out of town. I have some concerns about my personal information though. What if people use my phone number for other purposes?

**19** 위 글의 빈칸 ⓐ에 들어갈 제목으로 알맞은 것을 고르시오.

① How about Using an App If Possible?
② How to Find Reliable People
③ I Can Look After Your Pet!
④ The Best Time to Use Pet Sitter Finder
⑤ How to Check the Reviews about Pet Sitters

**20** 위 글의 밑줄 친 ⓑwhenever와 바꿔 쓸 수 있는 말을 고르시오.

① while        ② every time
③ before long  ④ the moment
⑤ as soon as

**21** According to the passage, which is NOT true?

① Pet Sitter Finder is the perfect app for pet lovers and pet owners.
② Pet Sitter Finder helps pet owners find reliable people to look after their pets.
③ The pet owner tests the pet sitters or dog walkers and chooses the best person.
④ George uses this app whenever he's going out of town.
⑤ George has some concerns about his personal information.

[01~03] 다음 대화를 읽고 물음에 답하시오.

Sujin: What should we sell at the flea market next month?

Tom: Before we choose anything to sell, I think we need to do some market research.

Sujin: Market research? Why do we need that?

Tom: Because it helps us find out what items are popular these days.

Sujin: I see. Then we can decide what to sell at the market.

Tom: That's right. It will also help us set reasonable prices for our items.

Sujin: Cool. Is there anything else we should do?

Tom: Oh, don't forget to register our names by this Friday.

Sujin: Right. Thanks for reminding me.

**01** What does Tom want to do to find out popular items these days?

➡ _____

**02** What should Sujin remember to do?

➡ _____

_____

**03** When is the flea market going to be held?

➡ _____

**04** 다음 〈보기〉에 주어진 단어의 조합들을 한 번씩만 사용해서 글의 흐름에 알맞게 빈칸을 채워 넣으시오. (필요시 변형할 것)

┤ 보기 ├

soon–good, hard–good, small–short, old–wise, few–happy

(1) The _____ the young man grew, the _____ he became.

(2) The _____ the size of the video is, the _____ it will take to post it.

(3) The _____ she finishes the final report, the _____ position she can hold in the negotiation.

(4) The _____ you study, the _____ grade you will get.

(5) The _____ classes there are right after mid term exam, the _____ the students feel.

**05** 다음 밑줄 친 부분에서 어법상 어색한 것을 고쳐 다시 쓰시오.

(1) Having not a car, Ms. Ivy couldn't take her grandson to the hospital.

➡ _____

(2) We frankly speaking, the prime minister of Japan doesn't look good.

➡ _____

(3) Having snowed the day before, the road was icy.

➡ _____

(4) A little being tired, Susie came down the stairs and took some rest.

➡ _____

(5) Found the purse Jenny had lost, he called her to come back quickly.

➡ _____

**I can look after your pet!**

Pet Sitter Finder is the perfect app for pet lovers and pet owners. It helps pet owners find reliable people to look after their pets. When a pet owner is looking for pet sitters, he or she uploads a post. Pet sitters or dog walkers can then send messages to the owner. The owner checks ⓐtheir reviews and chooses the best person.

George: November 12, 2019

I use this app whenever I'm going out of town. I have some concerns about my personal information though. ⓑ만약 다른 사람들이 제 전화번호를 다른 목적으로 사용하면 어쩌죠?

**06** 위 글의 밑줄 친 ⓐtheir가 가리키는 것을 본문에서 찾아 쓰시오.

➡ _____

**07** 위 글의 밑줄 친 ⓑ의 우리말에 맞게 한 단어를 보충하여, 주어진 어휘를 알맞게 배열하시오.

> other / use / what / phone number / purposes / people / for / my

➡ _____
_____

**08** (1) What's the advantage of 'Pet Sitter Finder'? (2) What's the disadvantage of 'Pet Sitter Finder'? Fill in the blanks (A) and (B) with suitable words.

> The advantage of 'Pet Sitter Finder' is that it helps pet owners find reliable people to (A)_____ _____ _____ _____ and the disadvantage of 'Pet Sitter Finder' is that there can be some concerns about the (B)_____ _____.

**Borrow from your neighbors!**

Ask Your Neighbors helps people easily (A)[find / finding] items that they can borrow from others. First, users (B)[download / upload] the app and search for another user that has the item they need. Then they pick up the item and return it later.

Jasmine: December 12, 2019

I asked for a board game and got one in less than 30 minutes. I love saving money by borrowing things that I don't often need. Also, I think it's environmentally friendly. The fewer products we buy, the more resources we (C)[save / waste].

**09** 위 글의 괄호 (A)~(C)에서 문맥이나 어법상 알맞은 낱말을 골라 쓰시오.

➡ (A) _____ (B) _____ (C) _____

**10** 본문의 내용과 일치하도록 다음 빈칸 (A)와 (B)에 알맞은 단어를 쓰시오.

> People can easily find what they can (A)_____ from others thanks to the (B)_____, Ask Your Neighbors.

## 창의사고력 서술형 문제

**01** 다음 대화를 읽고 대화의 내용과 일치하도록 빈칸을 완성하시오.

> Suji: Which do you prefer, the Special Sandwich or the Classic Sandwich?
>
> Brian: Well, the Special Sandwich is the healthier choice. It's made with lots of fresh vegetables and other healthy ingredients.
>
> Suji: But it's much more expensive than the Classic Sandwich.
>
> Brian: I know, but I prefer the Special Sandwich to the Classic Sandwich. Eating healthy is important to me.
>
> Suji: I prefer the cheaper one. I'll spend my money on books instead.
>
> Brian: I guess our spending habits are different.

> Brian and Suji talked about their preferred sandwiches. Brian liked (A)_____ more than (B)_____, because (C)_____ is important to him. On the other hand, Suji chose the (D)_____ one, the Classic Sandwich. She wanted to spend her money on (E)_____ instead. Thus, they found that they had different (F)_____ habits.

**02** 다음 표의 동사, 형용사/부사, 명사 등에 나온 단어들을 각각 1개 이상 조합하여, 〈보기〉와 같이 'The+비교급 ～, the+비교급 …'을 이용한 문장을 3개 이상 만드시오. (비교급 어형 변화 가능)

| Verb | Adjective/Adverb | Noun |
|---|---|---|
| • get | • many / much | • people / they / we |
| • smile | • good / bad / well / ill | • I / you / she / he / it |
| • study | • happy / angry | • student / teacher |
| • go | • often / frequent | • baby / boy / girl |
| • have | • fast / slow | • car / train / boat |
| • save | • few / little | • money / body |
| • see | • cold / hot | • radio / TV / movie |
| • walk | • old / young / new | |
| • become | • rich / healthy | |

보기

> The fewer people want, the happier they will get.
> The faster the girl walks, the harder it is for her to breathe.

(1) _____

(2) _____

(3) _____

## 단원별 모의고사

**01** 다음 우리말에 맞게 빈칸에 알맞은 말을 쓰시오.

(1) 이 앱을 다운로드하는 방법을 아세요?
➡ Do you know how to _____ this app?

(2) 물은 우리의 가장 중요한 천연자원 중 하나이다.
➡ Water is one of our most important _____ _____.

(3) 나는 그 책에 대한 부정적인 서평을 읽었다.
➡ I read some _____ _____ of that book.

(4) 너는 그 단어의 정확한 의미를 알아야 한다.
➡ You need to know the _____ _____ of the word.

**02** 다음 문장의 빈칸에 들어갈 말을 〈보기〉에서 골라 쓰시오.

┌─── 보기 ───┐
personal / provide / owner / reliable / concerns
└────────────┘

(1) We think she is the _____ of that car.
(2) Billy's car repair shop is _____.
(3) You seem to have some _____.
(4) I try not to give out my _____ information.
(5) The company will _____ some snacks at the meeting.

**03** 다음 주어진 우리말과 일치하도록 주어진 어구를 모두 배열하여 영작하시오.

(1) 내일 비가 오면 어쩌지? (tomorrow / if / it / rains / what)
➡ _____

(2) 내가 인터넷에서 요리법을 찾아볼게. (search / I'll / the Internet / the recipe / on / for)
➡ _____

(3) 어떻게 다른 아이들에게 메시지를 보낼 수 있나요? (we / how / can / to / children / other / send / messages)
➡ _____

**[04~05]** 다음 대화를 읽고 물음에 답하시오.

Judy: I think my hair is too curly. I want to straighten my hair. (A)

Gina: Sure. I know two places, Styles Studio and Hair Castle. (B)

Judy: Is there any difference between the two? (C)

Gina: Well, Styles Studio provides free treatment to keep your hair healthy. (D)

Judy: That's great. What about Hair Castle?

Gina: Hair Castle doesn't provide treatment for free, but they give student discounts. (E)

Judy: Okay. Which do you prefer?

Gina: I prefer Styles Studio to Hair Castle. It's important for me to get hair treatment regularly.

**04** 위 대화의 (A)~(E) 중에서 주어진 문장이 들어가기에 적절한 곳은?

┌────────────────────────────┐
│ Can you recommend a good place? │
└────────────────────────────┘

① (A)   ② (B)   ③ (C)   ④ (D)   ⑤ (E)

**05** 위 대화를 읽고 대답할 수 없는 것은?

① Why does Judy want to straighten her hair?
② Where does Gina recommend to Judy?
③ Which place does Judy prefer, Styles Studio or Hair Castle?
④ Where can Judy get student discounts?
⑤ Where does Gina can get treatment for free?

[06~07] 다음 대화를 읽고 물음에 답하시오.

Jack: I'm going to get a refund for these clothes this evening. I found I have similar ones.

Mom: Okay. (A)Don't forget to bring your receipt. Last time you couldn't get a refund because you didn't bring it.

Jack: Okay, Mom. I won't forget it this time.

**06** 위 대화의 밑줄 친 (A)와 바꾸어 쓸 수 있는 것을 모두 고르시오.

① Be sure to bring your receipt.
② Be careful not to bring your receipt.
③ Remember to bring your receipt.
④ You don't have to bring your receipt.
⑤ I'm not sure if you bring your receipt.

**07** 위 대화의 내용과 일치하지 않는 것은?

① Jack은 오늘 저녁에 옷을 환불하려고 한다.
② Jack은 환불하려는 옷들과 비슷한 옷들을 갖고 있다.
③ 엄마는 영수증 갖고 갈 것을 Jack에게 상기시키고 있다.
④ 지난번에 Jack은 영수증을 가지고 가지 않아 환불을 못 받았다.
⑤ Jack은 환불하는 것을 잊지 않을 것이다.

[08~10] 다음 대화를 읽고 물음에 답하시오.

Suji: Which do you prefer, the Special Sandwich or the Classic Sandwich?

Brian: Well, the Special Sandwich is the healthier choice. It's made with lots of fresh vegetable and other healthy ingredients.

Suji: But it's much more expensive than the Classic Sandwich.

Brian: I know, but I prefer the Special Sandwich (A)[to / than] the Classic Sandwich. (B)[Eat / Eating] healthy is important to me.

Suji: I prefer the cheaper one. I'll spend my money on books instead.

Brian: I guess our spending habits (C)[is / are] different.

**08** 위 대화에서 다음 영영풀이가 나타내는 말을 찾아 쓰시오.

one of the things from which something is made, especially one of the foods that are used together to make a particular dish

➡ _____

**09** 위 대화의 (A)~(C)에 들어갈 말이 바르게 짝지어진 것은?

| | (A) | (B) | (C) |
|---|---|---|---|
| ① | to | Eat | is |
| ② | to | Eating | are |
| ③ | to | Eating | is |
| ④ | than | Eating | are |
| ⑤ | than | Eat | is |

**10** 위 대화를 읽고 대답할 수 없는 것은?

① Which sandwich does Brian prefer?
② What is the Special Sandwich made with?
③ Which sandwich is cheaper, the Special Sandwich or the Classic Sandwich?
④ What does Suji want to spend more money on?
⑤ Why is eating healthy important to Brian?

**11** 다음 중 어법상 옳지 <u>않은</u> 문장을 <u>모두</u> 고르면?

① Born in America, he can speak fluently.

② Weather permitting, I'll start tomorrow.

③ There being no public transportation service that night, the people had to walk their way home.

④ Worked hard to hand in the paper in time, Thomas fell asleep.

⑤ Being looked much prettier than before, the flowers are in bloom.

**12** 다음 주어진 문장을 분사구문으로 만들 때 가장 적절한 것은?

> When a pet owner is looking for pet sitters, he or she should upload a post.

① A pet owner looking for pet sitters, he or she should upload a post.

② Looking for pet sitters, a pet owner should upload a post.

③ When a pet owner looking for pet sitters, he or she should upload a post.

④ Looking a pet owner for pet sitters, he or she should upload a post.

⑤ Having looked for pet sitters, a pet owner should upload a post.

**13** 다음 중 주어진 문장과 같은 의미로 쓰인 것을 고르시오.

> The deeper we go down into the earth, the hotter it becomes.

① If we keep going down into the earth, it becomes hotter.

② As we go down into the earth, we should feel hotter.

③ Since we go down into the earth, the climate becomes hotter.

④ Though we go down into the earth, it becomes hotter.

⑤ While the air goes down into the earth, we become hotter.

**14** 다음 각 문장의 밑줄 친 분사구문을 부사절로 바꿀 때 어법상 <u>어색한</u> 것은?

① <u>Borrowing a tent,</u> we can find someone to take care of our dog through the mobile sharing service.

→ While we're borrowing a tent,

② <u>It being so cold,</u> Jordan couldn't go out to swim and play on the beach.

→ Although it was so cold,

③ <u>There being nothing to eat,</u> the young couple moved to another restaurant.

→ Since there was nothing to eat,

④ <u>Finishing the final line of the paper,</u> the professor went out for a walk.

→ After she finished the final line of the paper,

⑤ <u>Carefully checked by our service staff,</u> the condition of the product you are borrowing must be the best.

→ As it is carefully checked by our service staff,

**15** 다음 각 문장의 밑줄 친 부사절을 분사구문으로 바꾼 것 중 옳은 것은?

① <u>While Samantha was eating a beef sandwich,</u> her little sisters fell asleep.

→ Eating a beef sandwich,

② <u>As Ann went to bed earlier yesterday,</u> she woke up at 4 this morning.

→ Ann going to bed earlier yesterday,

③ When the towers are seen from outer space, they will look like monsters.
→ Seen from outer space,

④ If we put a coin next to its hand, the toy cat will take it away.
→ Putting a coin next to its hand,

⑤ When you borrow things more often, you can save not only some money but also some resources.
→ You borrowing things more often,

**16** 다음 우리말을 주어진 〈조건〉에 맞게 영작하시오.

┌─── 조건 ───┐
1. 'the 비교급 ~, the 비교급 …' 구문을 사용할 것.
2. 주어와 시제에 유의하고, 괄호 안의 어구를 활용할 것. (내용과 어법에 맞게 변형 가능함.)
3. 글자 수 조건에 맞게 영작할 것.

(1) 더 많은 사람들이 공유 경제를 이해할수록, 더 적은 자원이 지구에서 사용될 것이다. (many, few, will, the sharing economy, understand, use, on Earth, 15 단어)
➡ _____

(2) 비가 더 많이 내릴수록, 그녀는 기분이 더 즐거워졌다. (please, much, it, feel, 9 단어)
➡ _____

(3) 그 가수의 인기가 더 많아질수록, 콘서트는 관객들로 더 붐비게 될 것이다. (the singer, popular, become, crowd, the concert, be, 13 단어)
➡ _____

[17~18] 다음 글을 읽고 물음에 답하시오.

Jasmine: December 12, 2019
I asked for a board game and got one in less than 30 minutes. I love saving money by borrowing things that I don't often need. Also, I think ⓐit's environmentally friendly. ⓑ우리가 제품들을 더 적게 구매할수록, 우리는 더 많은 자원들을 아끼는 거예요.

**17** 위 글의 밑줄 친 ⓐit이 가리키는 것을 본문에서 찾아 쓰시오.
➡ _____

**18** 위 글의 밑줄 친 ⓑ의 우리말에 맞게 주어진 어휘를 알맞게 배열하시오.

we / more / products / the / save / we / fewer / resources / buy / the / , /

➡ _____

[19~20] 다음 글을 읽고 물음에 답하시오.

Cassandra: March 7, 2020
Seeing a lot of positive reviews, I decided to borrow a bike helmet. When I got it, ___ⓐ___, it was broken. I was so upset!

Ask Your Neighbors: March 9, 2020
We're sorry that you had such a negative experience. ⓑTo fix this issue, we are asking lenders to update the pictures of their items regularly. This will let other users know the exact condition of the product.

**19** 위 글의 빈칸 ⓐ에 들어갈 알맞은 말을 고르시오.
① for example      ② therefore
③ that is           ④ however
⑤ in addition

**20** 아래 〈보기〉에서 위 글의 밑줄 친 ⓑTo fix와 to부정사의 용법이 같은 것의 개수를 고르시오.

┌─ 보기 ─┐

① Do you have something interesting to read?

② Everybody was surprised to see him.

③ I got up early to get ready for the game.

④ It is important to read a lot of books.

⑤ He grew up to be a pianist.

① 1개   ② 2개   ③ 3개   ④ 4개   ⑤ 5개

**[21~22]** 다음 글을 읽고 물음에 답하시오.

**I can look after your pet!**

 (①) Pet Sitter Finder is the perfect app for pet lovers and pet owners. (②) It helps pet owners find reliable people to look after their pets. (③) When a pet owner is looking for pet sitters, he or she ____ⓐ____ s a post. (④) The owner checks their reviews and chooses the best person. (⑤)

**21** 주어진 영영풀이를 참고하여 빈칸 ⓐ에 철자 u로 시작하는 단어를 쓰시오.

to transfer data to your computer or from your computer to another computer

➡ _____

**22** 위 글의 흐름으로 보아, 주어진 문장이 들어가기에 가장 적절한 곳은?

Pet sitters or dog walkers can then send messages to the owner.

①     ②     ③     ④     ⑤

**[23~24]** 다음 글을 읽고 물음에 답하시오.

Pet Sitter Finder: November 14, 2019

 We're aware of this issue. We're now developing a system that allows users to communicate freely without showing their personal information.

Samantha: February 22, 2020

 Animals aren't allowed in my apartment, so I don't have any pets. However, by using Pet Sitter Finder, I can experience the joy of walking a dog.

**23** Why does Samantha have no pets? Answer in English beginning with "Because".

➡ _____

**24** According to the passage, which is NOT true?

① Pet Sitter Finder is aware of this issue.

② Pet Sitter Finder is now developing a system that allows users to communicate freely without showing their personal information.

③ Animals aren't allowed in Samantha's apartment.

④ Samantha uses Pet Sitter Finder.

⑤ It's impossible for Samantha to walk a dog.

**[25~27]** 다음 글을 읽고 물음에 답하시오.

Son: What great apps! We can borrow a tent and find someone to take care of our dog.

Dad: That's right. (①) These kinds of services are part of the "sharing economy." (②) People can share their items ____ⓐ____ others and provide services to them ____ⓑ____ a small fee or for free.

Son: (③) Some people left negative reviews about the services.

Dad: (④) Well, I think ⓒthe more people use the services, the more they will improve. (⑤)

**25** 위 글의 빈칸 ⓐ와 ⓑ에 들어갈 전치사가 바르게 짝지어진 것은?

|  | ⓐ | ⓑ |  | ⓐ | ⓑ |
|---|---|---|---|---|---|
| ① | for | at | ② | with | to |
| ③ | in | for | ④ | for | to |
| ⑤ | with | at | | | |

**26** 위 글의 흐름으로 보아, 주어진 문장이 들어가기에 가장 적절한 곳은?

> But these services do have some weaknesses.

①      ②      ③      ④      ⑤

**27** 위 글의 밑줄 친 ⓒ를 접속사 as를 사용하여 고칠 때, 빈칸에 들어갈 알맞은 말을 쓰시오.

➡ as people use the services _____, they will improve _____.

**[28~30]** 다음 글을 읽고 물음에 답하시오.

**I Can Share My Jump Rope with You!**

Here is a jump rope that I can share. It's not new, but it's in good condition. You can borrow it for ⓐup to two days.

There are two rules:
❶ You can borrow it once a week.
❷ You must pay for the item if you lose or break it.

If you are willing to follow the rules above, feel free ____ⓑ____ contact me! I will happily share it with you.

**28** 위 글의 밑줄 친 ⓐup to와 같은 의미로 쓰인 것을 고르시오.

① He is up to the job.
② It's up to you.
③ What are you up to?
④ I can take up to four people in my car.
⑤ Her latest book isn't up to her usual standard.

**29** 위 글의 빈칸 ⓑ에 알맞은 말을 쓰시오.

➡ _____

**30** 위 글의 줄넘기를 빌릴 때의 두 가지 규칙을 우리말로 쓰시오.

➡ (1) _____
(2) _____

# Future Changes through Technology

 **의사소통 기능**

- 설명 요청하기
  **Could you explain** how it works?

- 가능성 정도 표현하기
  **It is likely that** we will have to change how we get our food.

**언어 형식**

- 가정법 과거
  Cooking and cleaning **would be** easier **if** you **had** one.

- '목적'을 나타내는 so that 구문
  It can navigate roads for you **so that** you can relax and enjoy the ride.

교과서

# Words & Expressions

## Key Words

- **artificial**[ὰːrtəfíʃəl] 형 인공적인, 인위적인
- **awesome**[ɔ́ːsəm] 형 굉장한, 아주 멋진
- **bright**[brait] 형 밝은, 희망적인
- **cashier**[kæʃíər] 명 출납원
- **common**[kámən] 형 흔한
- **convenient**[kənvíːnjənt] 형 편리한
- **delivery**[dilívəri] 명 배달, 전달
- **destination**[dèstənéiʃən] 명 목적지, 도착지
- **difference**[dífərəns] 명 차이, 차이점
- **disaster**[dizǽstər] 명 재해, 참사, 재난
- **ensure**[inʃúər] 동 보장하다
- **equip**[ikwíp] 동 ~에 (필요한 것을) 갖추다
- **escape**[iskéip] 동 탈출하다, 달아나다, 벗어나다
- **factory**[fǽktəri] 명 공장
- **forecast**[fɔ́ːrkæst] 명 예측, 예보
- **human**[hjúːmən] 명 인간 형 인간의
- **intelligence**[intélədʒəns] 명 지능, 정보
- **invention**[invénʃən] 명 발명, 발명품
- **lab**[læb] 명 과학 실험실 (= laboratory)
- **likely**[láikli] 형 있음직한, 가능하다고 생각되는, ~할 것 같은
- **navigate**[nǽvəgèit] 동 길을 찾다, 항해하다
- **nutrient**[njúːtriənt] 명 영양소, 영양분
- **outer**[áutər] 형 외부의, 바깥쪽의
- **perceive**[pərsíːv] 동 인지하다, 감지하다

- **perform**[pərfɔ́ːrm] 동 공연하다, 실행하다
- **possible**[pásəbl] 형 가능한
- **praise**[preiz] 명 칭찬
- **present**[préznt] 형 현재의, 존재하는
- **program**[próugræm] 동 프로그램을 짜다
- **reality**[riǽləti] 명 현실
- **recipe**[résəpi] 명 요리법
- **recognize**[rékəgnàiz] 동 인식하다
- **resource**[ríːsɔːrs] 명 자원, 재원
- **route**[ruːt] 명 길, 경로
- **safety**[séifti] 명 안전, 안전한 곳
- **self-driving**[sélfdráiviŋ] 형 자율 주행하는
- **sense**[sens] 동 감지하다
- **sensor**[sénsər] 명 센서, 감지기
- **signal**[sígnəl] 명 신호
- **site**[sait] 명 위치, 장소, 용지, 부지, 현장
- **solution**[səlúːʃən] 명 해법, 해답, 해결책
- **speech**[spiːtʃ] 명 연설, 담화, 언어 능력
- **survivor**[sərváivər] 명 생존자, 살아남은 사람
- **swarm**[swɔːrm] 명 떼, 군중, 벌 떼
- **task**[tæsk] 명 일, 과제, 과업
- **technology**[teknálədʒi] 명 기술, 기계
- **threat**[θret] 명 위협, 협박

## Key Expressions

- **a variety of** 다양한
- **act like** ~처럼 행동하다
- **around the world** 세계 곳곳의
- **as a group** 집단으로
- **be able to** ~할 수 있다
- **deal with** 처리하다, 다루다
- **find solutions** 해결책을 찾다
- **go into** ~에 들어가다
- **keep track of** ~의 자국을 뒤밟다

- **look toward** 앞날을 생각하다
- **make decisions** 결정을 하다
- **search and rescue** 수색 구조
- **so that ~** ~하기 위하여
- **such as** ~와 같은
- **throughout the day** 하루 종일
- **wait in line** 줄을 서서 기다리다
- **with the help of** ~의 도움으로
- **work on** ~에 노력을 들이다, 애쓰다

## Word Power

※ 서로 비슷한 뜻을 가진 어휘

□ **a variety of** ~ 다양한 : **various** 다양한
□ **disaster** 재해, 참사, 재난 : **catastrophe** 재난, 재앙
□ **go into** ~에 들어가다 : **enter** 들어가다
□ **praise** 칭찬 : **compliment** 칭찬
□ **solution** 해법, 해답 : **answer** 답, 해답

□ **bright** 밝은, 희망적인 : **promising** 조짐이 좋은, 유망한
□ **escape** 탈출하다, 달아나다, 벗어나다 : **flee** 도망치다, 피하다
□ **perceive** 인지하다 : **recognize** 인지하다
□ **signal** 신호 : **sign** 신호, 암호
□ **task** 일, 과제, 과업 : **job** 과제, 직무, 역할

※ 서로 반대의 뜻을 가진 어휘

□ **bright** 밝은, 희망적인 ↔ **dark** 어두운, 암울한
□ **convenient** 편리한 ↔ **inconvenient** 불편한
□ **possible** 가능한 ↔ **impossible** 불가능한
□ **present** 현재의, 존재하는 ↔ **absent** 부재의

□ **common** 흔한 ↔ **uncommon** 흔하지 않은
□ **difference** 차이, 차이점 ↔ **similarity** 유사, 유사성
□ **praise** 칭찬 ↔ **criticism** 비평, 비난
□ **recognize** 인식하다 ↔ **ignore** 무시하다, 모른 체하다

## English Dictionary

□ **artificial** 인공적인, 인위적인
→ made by humans 인간에 의해 만들어진

□ **convenient** 편리한, 간편한
→ able to be used easily 쉽게 사용될 수 있는

□ **deal with** 처리하다, 다루다
→ to handle or solve something such as a problem
문제 같은 것을 다루거나 해결하다

□ **disaster** 참사, 재난, 재해
→ an unfortunate event that damages a large area and may harm many people 큰 지역에 손상을 가해 많은 사람들에게 해를 입힐 수도 있는 불행한 사건

□ **escape** 탈출하다, 달아나다, 벗어나다
→ to get free 자유롭게 되다

□ **navigate** 길을 찾다, 항해하다
→ to make one's way through an area 한 지역의 길을 찾다

□ **perceive** 인지하다, 감지하다
→ to notice something with the senses 감각으로 어떤 것을 알아채다

□ **perform** 공연하다, 해 보이다; 실행[수행]하다
→ to complete an action or activity

행동이나 행위를 완결하다

□ **route** 경로
→ a way to go from one place to another
한곳에서 다른 곳으로 가는 길

□ **safety** 안전
→ the state of being safe from harm or danger
피해나 위험으로부터 안전한 상태

□ **sense** 감지하다
→ to be aware of something without seeing or hearing it 보거나 듣지 않고도 어떤 것을 알다

□ **solution** 해법, 해답
→ the answer to a problem 어떤 문제에 대한 답

□ **survivor** 생존자
→ a person who remains alive 살아남은 사람

□ **swarm** 떼, 군중
→ a large number of living things
많은 살아 있는 것들

□ **threat** 협박, 위협
→ a risk or danger 위험이나 우려

**Words & Expressions** 시험대비 실력평가

**서답형**

**01** 다음 짝지어진 단어의 관계가 같도록 빈칸에 알맞은 말을 주어진 철자로 시작하여 쓰시오.

bright : dark = c_____ : praise

**02** 다음 영영풀이가 가리키는 것을 고르시오.

able to be used easily

① convenient     ② artificial

③ disaster     ④ nutrient

⑤ swarm

**중요**

**03** 다음 중 밑줄 친 부분의 뜻풀이가 바르지 <u>않은</u> 것은?

① The light bulb was a great <u>invention</u>. (발명품)

② It changes your voice into an electrical <u>signal</u>. (사인)

③ Although my sister was hiding in her room, I was able to sense her <u>presence</u>. (존재)

④ He finally <u>escaped</u> from his enemies. (도망쳤다)

⑤ It is <u>possible</u> to see the whole city from this roof. (가능한)

**서답형**

**04** 다음 우리말에 맞게 빈칸에 알맞은 말을 주어진 철자로 시작하여 쓰시오.

(1) 모든 차는 에어백을 갖추고 있다.
➡ Every car is e_____ with an airbag.

(2) 나는 한국의 역사적인 장소를 방문하는 것을 좋아한다.
➡ I like visiting historical s_____ in Korea.

(3) 그 아기는 자라면서 사물을 정확히 인지하기 시작했다.
➡ As the baby grew, he started to p_____ objects clearly.

**서답형**

**05** 다음 문장의 빈칸에 들어갈 말을 〈보기〉에서 골라 쓰시오.

┤ 보기 ├

deal with / keep track of / destination / be used in / forecast

(1) Parents can _____ their children using smartphones.

(2) This tool can _____ a variety of ways.

(3) The weather _____ says there will be more snow.

(4) The _____ of our trip is Washington, D.C.

(5) You have to _____ this problem first.

**중요**

**06** 다음 주어진 문장의 밑줄 친 present와 같은 의미로 쓰인 것은?

How do you read the <u>present</u> situation?

① 200 people were <u>present</u> at the meeting.

② Those <u>present</u> were in favour of change.

③ The local MP will start the race and <u>present</u> the prizes.

④ There's no end in sight to the <u>present</u> crisis.

⑤ She chose the <u>present</u> with loving care.

**01** 다음 짝지어진 단어의 관계가 같도록 빈칸에 알맞은 말을 주어진 철자로 시작하여 쓰시오.

> go into : enter = p_____ : recognize

**02** 다음 우리말에 맞게 빈칸에 알맞은 말을 쓰시오.

(1) 그 기원에 관해서는 여러 가지 설이 있다.
➡ There are _____ _____ _____
views about its origin.

(2) 삼촌의 도움으로 그는 암호를 알아낸다.
➡ _____ _____ _____
his uncle, he figures out the password.

(3) 이것과 같은 기회가 매일 찾아오는 것은 아니었다.
➡ Opportunities _____ _____ this
did not come every day.

**03** 다음 우리말에 맞게 주어진 어구를 사용하여 영작하시오.

(1) 이 단어는 일상 대화에서 흔히 쓰는 말이 아니다. (casual conversation)
➡ _____
_____

(2) 전자 레인지는 편리한 요리 기구이다. (a microwave, cooking device)
➡ _____
_____

(3) 어느 길로 가는 것이 가장 좋을까? (take, route)
➡ _____
_____

**04** 다음 제시된 의미에 맞는 단어를 주어진 철자로 시작하여 빈칸에 쓰고, 알맞은 것을 골라 문장을 완성하시오.

> • s_____ : to be aware of something without seeing or hearing it
> • n_____ : to make one's way through an area
> • n_____ : a chemical or food that provides what is needed to live and grow

(1) Travelers usually _____ by the stars in the old days.

(2) She _____ someone watching her at that time.

(3) Vitamins are essential _____ for us.

**05** 다음 우리말과 일치하도록 주어진 어구를 바르게 배열하시오.

(1) 이 개들은 그들의 높은 지능으로 잘 알려져 있다.
(their / these dogs / intelligence / known / high / are / for)
➡ _____
_____

(2) 홍수와 지진과 같은 자연 재해는 매년 수천 명의 사람에게 피해를 입힌다.
(of / natural / every / disasters / affect / such / as / floods / and / earthquakes / thousands / people / year)
➡ _____
_____

# Conversation

**1 설명 요청하기**

**Could you explain** how it works? 이게 어떻게 작동하는 건지 설명해 줄 수 있니?

■ 어떤 사실이나 대상에 대해 설명해 달라고 요청할 때, 'Can you explain ~?'이라는 표현을 쓸 수 있다. 이와 같은 표현으로는 'Can you tell me how to ~?', 'Can you explain how to ~?' 등이 있다. 이때, explain 또는 tell 뒤에는 보통 의문사절이나 '의문사+to 동사원형'을 써서 구체적으로 설명을 요청하는 내용을 제시한다. Can 대신에 Could를 쓰면 보다 정중한 표현이 된다.

■ 상대방에게 설명을 요청 받았을 때 다음과 같이 요청을 수락한다는 의사를 표현할 수 있다.

Yes. / Okay. / Sure. / All right. / No problem. / Of course.

**설명 요청하기**

- Do you know how to ~? ~하는 법을 아니?
- Can[Could] you tell me how to ~? ~하는 법을 말해 주시겠어요?
- Can[Could] you explain how to ~? ~하는 법을 설명해 주시겠어요?
- What do you mean by A? A가 무슨 의미이죠?
- Can[Could] you tell me what A means? A가 무슨 의미인지 말해 줄래요?
- I'd like to know what A means. A가 무슨 의미인지 알고 싶어요.

**핵심 Check**

1. 다음 대화에서 밑줄 친 부분과 바꿔 쓸 수 <u>없는</u> 표현은?

   A: Hey, have you played this game? It's really interesting. The developers used AI technology.

   B: No, I haven't. <u>Can you explain in more detail?</u>

   A: Sure. The AI characters in the game learn from what human players do and develop their skills.

   B: Oh, that's very smart. I'd like to give it a try.

   ① Can you tell me how it works in more detail?
   ② Could you tell me how to play it in more detail?
   ③ Do you know how to learn it in more detail?
   ④ Could you explain how to play it in more detail?
   ⑤ Can you explain how it works in more detail?

## ② 가능성 정도 표현하기

> **It is likely that** we will have to change how we get our food.
> 우리는 식량을 얻는 방법을 바꾸어야 할 가능성이 있다.

- 'It's likely that ~'은 자신이 생각하는 어떤 일에 대한 가능성의 정도를 나타낼 때 사용하는 표현이다. It은 가주어이고 접속사 that이 이끄는 명사절이 진주어 역할을 한다. 보통 절 안에는 미래를 나타내는 조동사를 쓰는 경우가 많다.

  • It's likely that he will cancel his order. 그가 주문을 취소할 가능성이 있습니다.

- 'It is possible to ~', '~ can ~', 'It is probable that ~' 등으로 가능성의 정도를 나타낼 수도 있다.

  • It is possible to get there by bus. 버스로 거기에 가는 것이 가능하다.

  • Dogs can be trained to obey orders. 개는 명령을 따르도록 훈련시킬 수가 있다.

  • It is probable that she will come tomorrow. 그녀가 내일 올 것으로 예상된다.

- 미래를 나타내는 조동사로는 대표적으로 will과 'be going to'가 있다. 이때, 'be going to'는 미래에 어떤 일이 일어날 것임을 확신할 때 쓰는 반면, will은 어떤 일이 일어날 확신보다는 가능성이 있을 때 쓰는 표현이다. 따라서 가능성을 나타내는 'It's likely that ~' 구문에서는 조동사 will을 쓰는 것이 보다 적절하다.

  • It's likely that you or someone you love will suffer from high blood pressure. 당신 또는 사랑하는 사람이 고혈압으로 고생할 수 있습니다.

### 핵심 Check

2. 다음 밑줄 친 우리말을 likely를 이용해 영작하시오.

M: As climate change is going to make farming harder, there may not be enough resources for the increasing number of people on Earth. For this reason, <u>우리가 식량을 얻기 위한 방식을 바꿔야 할 수도 있을 것이다.</u> For example, we won't kill animals for food. Instead, meat will be grown in a lab using animal cells. This will require less land, water, and other resources.

➡ _____

### Listen & Talk 1 A

G: Hey, have you heard of a smart umbrella?

B: No, I haven't. ❶Could you explain ❷what it is?

G: Sure. It's an umbrella ❸that gives you the weather forecast for the day. ❹If it is going to rain, the umbrella makes a sound.

B: That's very convenient.

여: 있잖아. 스마트 우산에 대해 들어 본 적 있니?

남: 아니. 들어 본 적 없어. 그게 무엇인지 설명해 줄 수 있니?

여: 물론이지. 그것은 그날의 일기 예보를 알려주는 우산이야. 만약 비가 올 예정이면, 우산에서 소리가 나.

남: 그거 참 편리하구나.

❶ 설명을 요청하는 표현이다.　　❷ what it is는 간접의문문으로 explain의 목적어이다.
❸ that은 주격 관계대명사이다.　　❹ If는 조건절을 이끄는 접속사이다.

**Check(√) True or False**

(1) The boy has heard of a smart umbrella.　　　　　　　　　　　　　T ☐ F ☐

(2) If it is going to rain, the smart umbrella makes a sound.　　　　　T ☐ F ☐

### Listen & Talk 1 B

G: Look at these. They are the new inventions of the month!

B: They all ❶look great. What is the invention on the first page?

G: It's a new smart refrigerator. ❷It senses the items inside ❷it and suggests ❸recipes.

B: That sounds helpful.

G: It does. What do you think of this flying camera? I want to buy it.

B: A flying camera? ❹Could you explain how it works?

G: Of course. This machine flies to a destination ❺that we have already set. While it's flying, it can take pictures from 500 meters above the location.

B: That ❻sounds awesome. What do you want to take pictures of?

G: I want to take pictures of flying birds!

여: 이것들을 봐. 이달의 새로운 발명품들이야!

남: 모두 멋져 보인다. 첫 번째 쪽에 있는 발명품은 뭐지?

여: 그건 새로 나온 스마트 냉장고야. 이 냉장고는 냉장고 내부의 음식들을 감지해서 요리법을 제시해 줘.

남: 유용하겠다.

여: 맞아. 이 플라잉 카메라에 대해서는 어떻게 생각해? 나는 이 카메라를 사고 싶어.

남: 플라잉 카메라? 이게 어떻게 작동하는 건지 설명해 줄 수 있니?

여: 물론이지. 이 기기는 우리가 미리 설정해 둔 목적지로 날아가. 비행하는 동안 이 기기는 그 지점의 500미터 상공에서 사진을 찍을 수 있어.

남: 정말 멋지다. 너는 무슨 사진을 찍고 싶니?

여: 나는 날고 있는 새들의 사진을 찍고 싶어!

❶ look+형용사: ~해 보이다　　❷ It[it]은 a new smart refrigerator를 가리킨다.　　❸ recipe: 요리법
❹ 설명을 요청하는 표현으로 'Can you tell me how it works?'로 바꿔 쓸 수 있다.
❺ that은 목적격 관계대명사이다.　　❻ sound+형용사: ~하게 들리다

**Check(√) True or False**

(3) The new smart refrigerator senses the items inside it and suggests recipes.　　T ☐ F ☐

(4) The boy wants to take pictures of flying birds with the flying camera.　　T ☐ F ☐

### Listen & Talk 1 C

B: What are you watching?

G: It's a show about a man ❶who lost one of his arms in an accident. Surprisingly, he can play the drums very well.

B: How can he play the drums with only one arm?

G: Actually he uses two arms. One is a robot arm ❷controlled by his brain.

B: That's awesome. ❸Could you explain in more detail?

G: Sure. First, he thinks ❹what he wants to do with his arm. Then those thoughts are turned into electronic signals. The signals travel from his brain to his robot arm and move ❺it.

B: That's amazing! I think this technology can help many people.

❶ who는 주격 관계대명사이다.

❷ controlled가 뒤에서 a robot arm을 수식하고 있다.

❸ 설명을 요청하는 표현이다. in more detail: 더 자세히

❹ what은 선행사를 포함하는 관계대명사로 '~하는 것'으로 해석한다.

❺ it은 his robot arm을 가리킨다.

### Listen & Talk 2 A

G: ❶You know what? Scientists are ❷working on a project to send people to Mars.

B: ❸It is likely that we'll live in outer space in the near future.

❶ You know what?: 그거 아니?, 있잖아.

❷ work on: ~에 노력을 들이다, 애쓰다

❸ 'It's likely that ~'은 자신이 생각하는 어떤 일에 대한 가능성의 정도를 나타낼 때 사용하는 표현이다.

### Listen & Talk 2 B

M: ❶As climate change is going to make farming harder, there may not be enough resources for the increasing number of people on Earth. ❷For this reason, ❸it is likely that we will have to change how we get our food. For example, we won't kill animals for food. Instead, meat will be grown in a ❹lab using animal cells. This will require less land, water, and other resources. Also, bugs ❺such as ants will become part of our daily meals. You might not want to eat them, but they are actually very ❻rich in nutrients!

❶ As는 이유를 나타내는 부사절을 이끌고 있다.

❷ For this reason: 이러한 이유로    ❸ 가능성의 정도를 나타내는 표현이다.

❹ lab: 과학 실험실(= laboratory), cell: 세포

❺ such as: ~와 같은(= like)    ❻ rich: 풍부한 nutrient: 영양소, 영양분

### Listen & Talk 2 C

G: I had to wait in line at the store for almost twenty minutes.

B: That's too bad. Maybe in the future we'll never have to wait in line.

G: What do you mean?

B: I read about a store without cashiers. You take ❶what you want to buy and just walk out.

G: ❷That's it? How do you pay for it?

B: There are cameras and sensors in the store. They ❸keep track of the items you choose and send the information to an app on your smartphone.

G: Then the app pays for ❹them when you leave the store?

B: Exactly. ❺It's likely that these kinds of stores will be more common in the future.

❶ what은 선행사를 포함하는 관계대명사이다.

❷ That's it?: 그게 다야?    ❸ keep track of: ~의 자국을 뒤밟다

❹ the items you choose를 가리킨다.

❺ 가능성의 정도를 나타내는 표현이다. 'It is possible to ~', 'It is probable that ~' 등으로 가능성의 정도를 나타낼 수도 있다.

### Do It Yourself A

B: Hey, have you played this game? It's really exciting.

G: Yes, I ❶have. That game is pretty popular these days.

B: The developers used AI technology in ❷it. The game characters are equipped with AI.

G: Oh, really? ❸Could you explain in more detail?

B: Sure. The AI characters in the game learn from what human players do and develop their skills.

G: Oh! ❹That's why I sometimes felt like they already knew my moves!

B: They're very smart. ❺It is likely that the AI in games will get stronger and stronger.

❶ have는 대동사 역할을 하고 있다.    ❷ it은 'That game'을 가리킨다.

❸ 설명을 요청하는 표현이다.    ❹ That's why ~: 그것이 ~한 이유이다.

❺ 가능성의 정도를 나타내는 표현이다.

● 다음 우리말과 일치하도록 빈칸에 알맞은 말을 쓰시오.

### Listen & Talk 1 A

G: Hey, have you _____ _____ a smart umbrella?

B: No, I haven't. _____ _____ _____ _____ _____ _____?

G: Sure. It's an umbrella _____ gives you the _____ _____ for the day. If it _____ _____ _____ rain, the umbrella _____ a sound.

B: That's very _____.

### Listen & Talk 1 B

G: Look at these. They are the new _____ of the month!

B: They all look _____. What is the invention on the first page?

G: It's a new smart refrigerator. It _____ the items inside _____ and _____ recipes.

B: That sounds _____.

G: It _____. What do you _____ _____ _____ this _____ camera? I want to buy it.

B: A flying camera? Could you explain _____ _____ _____?

G: Of course. This machine flies to a destination _____ we have already _____. _____ _____ _____, it can take pictures from 500 meters above the location.

B: That sounds _____. _____ do you want to take pictures _____?

G: I want to take pictures of _____ birds!

### Listen & Talk 1 C

B: What are you watching?

G: It's a show about a man _____ lost _____ _____ his _____ in an accident. Surprisingly, he can play _____ _____ very well.

B: _____ can he play the drums _____ only one arm?

G: Actually he uses two arms. One is a robot arm _____ by his brain.

B: That's awesome. Could you explain _____ more _____?

G: Sure. First, he thinks _____ he wants to do _____ his arm. Then those thoughts _____ _____ _____ electronic signals. The signals _____ from his brain to his robot arm and move it.

B: That's amazing! I think this _____ can help many people.

여: 있잖아, 스마트 우산에 대해 들어 본 적 있니?

남: 아니, 들어 본 적 없어. 그게 무엇인지 설명해 줄 수 있니?

여: 물론이지. 그것은 그날의 일기 예보를 알려주는 우산이야. 만약 비가 올 예정이면, 우산에서 소리가 나.

남: 그거 참 편리하구나.

여: 이것들을 봐. 이달의 새로운 발명품들이야!

남: 모두 멋져 보인다. 첫 번째 쪽에 있는 발명품은 뭐지?

여: 이건 새로 나온 스마트 냉장고야. 이 냉장고는 냉장고 내부의 음식들을 감지해서 요리법을 제시해 줘.

남: 유용하겠다.

여: 맞아. 이 플라잉 카메라에 대해서는 어떻게 생각해? 나는 이 카메라가 사고 싶어.

남: 플라잉 카메라? 이게 어떻게 작동하는 건지 설명해 줄 수 있니?

여: 물론이지. 이 기기는 우리가 미리 설정해 둔 목적지로 날아가. 비행하는 동안 이 기기는 그 지점의 500미터 상공에서 사진을 찍을 수 있어.

남: 정말 멋지다. 너는 무슨 사진을 찍고 싶니?

여: 나는 날고 있는 새들의 사진을 찍고 싶어!

남: 무엇을 보고 있니?

여: 이건 사고로 한쪽 팔을 잃은 한 남자에 관한 프로야. 놀랍게도 그는 드럼을 매우 잘 쳐.

남: 그는 어떻게 한쪽 팔만으로 드럼을 칠 수 있는 거지?

여: 사실 그는 두 팔을 사용해. 한쪽 팔은 그의 뇌가 제어하는 로봇 팔이야.

남: 그거 정말 멋지다. 좀 더 구체적으로 설명해 줄 수 있니?

여: 물론이지. 먼저, 그는 자신의 팔로 하고 싶은 것을 생각해. 그런 다음 그 생각들이 전기 신호로 바뀌지. 그 신호들은 그의 뇌에서 로봇 팔로 이동해서 그 팔을 움직여.

남: 놀라운데! 이 기술이 많은 사람들에게 도움을 줄 수 있을 것 같아.

### Listen & Talk 2 B

M: _____ climate change is going to make farming _____, there _____ _____ _____ enough resources for the _____ number of people on Earth. _____ _____ _____, _____ _____ _____ _____ we will have to change _____ _____ _____ our food. For example, we won't kill animals for food. _____, meat _____ _____ _____ in a lab _____ animal cells. This will require less land, water, and other resources. Also, bugs _____ _____ ants will become part of our daily meals. You might not want to eat them, but they are actually very _____ in _____!

### Listen & Talk 2 C

G: I _____ _____ wait _____ _____ at the store for almost twenty minutes.

B: That's too bad. Maybe in the future _____ _____ _____ _____ wait in line.

G: What _____ _____ _____?

B: I read about a store without cashiers. You take _____ you want to buy and just walk out.

G: That's it? _____ do you pay _____ it?

B: There are cameras and sensors in the store. They _____ _____ the items you choose and _____ _____ _____ to an app on your smartphone.

G: Then the app pays for _____ when you leave the store?

B: Exactly. _____ _____ _____ these kinds of stores will be more _____ in the future.

### Do It Yourself A

B: Hey, have you played this game? It's really _____.

G: Yes, I _____. That game is pretty _____ these days.

B: The developers used AI technology in _____. The game characters _____ _____ _____ AI.

G: Oh, really? Could you _____ _____ _____ _____?

B: Sure. The AI characters in the game learn from _____ _____ _____ and develop their skills.

G: Oh! That's _____ I sometimes _____ _____ they already knew my moves!

B: They're very smart. _____ _____ _____ the AI in games will get stronger and stronger.

---

해석

남: 기후 변화가 농업을 더 어렵게 만들 것이기 때문에, 지구상의 점점 더 늘어나는 사람들을 위한 자원이 충분하지 않게 될지도 모른다. 이러한 이유로, 우리는 식량을 얻는 방법을 바꾸어야 할 가능성이 높다. 예를 들어, 우리는 식량을 얻기 위해 동물을 죽이지 않게 될 것이다. 대신, 동물 세포를 이용하여 실험실에서 고기가 배양될 것이다. 이는 더 적은 땅과 물, 그리고 다른 자원들을 필요로 할 것이다. 또한, 개미와 같은 곤충들이 우리 끼니의 일부가 될 것이다. 여러분은 먹고 싶지 않을 수도 있지만, 사실 곤충들은 영양분이 매우 풍부하다!

여: 매장에서 거의 20분 동안 줄을 서서 기다려야 했어.

남: 그것 참 안됐다. 어쩌면 미래에는 줄을 서서 기다릴 필요가 전혀 없을지도 몰라.

여: 그게 무슨 말이야?

남: 계산원이 없는 매장에 관한 글을 읽었거든. 사고 싶은 것을 가지고 그냥 걸어나가면 돼.

여: 그게 다야? 지불은 어떻게 해?

남: 매장 내에 카메라와 감지기가 있어. 그것들이 네가 고른 물건들을 계속 파악하면서 그 정보를 네 스마트폰에 있는 앱으로 보내.

여: 그러면 네가 매장을 나갈 때 앱이 물건 값을 지불하는 거고?

남: 바로 그거야. 미래에는 이런 종류의 매장이 더 흔해질 것 같아.

남: 저기, 이 게임 해봤니? 이거 정말 흥미진진해.

여: 응, 해봤어. 그 게임은 요즘 꽤 인기가 있어.

남: 개발자들이 이 게임에 인공지능 기술을 사용했어. 게임 캐릭터들에 인공지능이 탑재되어 있지.

여: 아, 정말? 좀 더 구체적으로 설명해 줄 수 있니?

남: 물론이지. 게임 속 인공지능 캐릭터들은 인간 플레이어가 하는 행동을 통해 배우고 자신의 기술을 발전시켜.

여: 아! 그래서 이따금씩 캐릭터들이 이미 내 움직임을 알고 있는 것처럼 느껴졌던 거구나!

남: 그들은 매우 똑똑해. 게임 속 인공지능은 점점 더 강화될 가능성이 높아.

**[01~02]** 다음 대화를 읽고 물음에 답하시오.

> G: Look at these. They are the new inventions of the month!
> B: They all look great. (①) What is the invention on the first page?
> G: It's a new smart refrigerator. (②)
> B: That sounds helpful. (③)
> G: It does. What do you think of this flying camera? I want to buy it.
> B: A flying camera? (④) Could you explain how it works?
> G: Of course. (⑤) This machine flies to a destination that we have already set. While it's flying, it can take pictures from 500 meters above the location.

**01** 위 대화의 (①)~(⑤) 중 다음 문장이 들어가기에 적절한 곳은?

> It senses the items inside it and suggests recipes.

①      ②      ③      ④      ⑤

**02** 위 대화의 내용과 일치하지 <u>않는</u> 것은?

① G는 새로 나온 스마트 냉장고에 대해 이미 알고 있다.
② 스마트 냉장고는 냉장고 내부의 음식들을 감지해서 요리법을 제시해 준다.
③ G는 플라잉 카메라를 사고 싶어한다.
④ B는 플라잉 카메라의 작동법을 알고 있었다.
⑤ 플라잉 카메라는 500미터 상공에서 사진을 찍을 수 있었다.

**[03~04]** 다음 대화를 읽고 물음에 답하시오.

> G: Hey, have you heard of a smart umbrella?
> B: No, I haven't. (A)Could you explain what it is?
> G: Sure. It's an umbrella that gives you the weather forecast for the day. If it is going to rain, the umbrella makes a sound.
> B: (B)That's very convenient.

**03** 위 대화의 밑줄 친 (A)를 tell을 이용하여 바꿔 쓰시오.

➡ _____

**04** 위 대화의 밑줄 친 (B)That이 가리키는 것을 우리말로 쓰시오.

➡ _____

서답형

**01** 다음 주어진 대화 사이의 (A)~(E)가 자연스럽게 이어지도록 순서대로 배열하시오.

> B: What are you watching?
>
> (A) Actually he uses two arms. One is a robot arm controlled by his brain.
>
> (B) How can he play the drums with only one arm?
>
> (C) It's a show about a man who lost one of his arms in an accident. Surprisingly, he can play the drums very well.
>
> (D) That's awesome. Could you explain in more detail?
>
> (E) Sure. First, he thinks what he wants to do with his arm. Then those thoughts are turned into electronic signals. The signals travel from his brain to his robot arm and move it.
>
> B: That's amazing! I think this technology can help many people.

➡ _____

[02~05] 다음 글을 읽고 물음에 답하시오.

> M: As climate change is going to make farming harder, there may not be enough resources for the ⓐincreased number of people on Earth. For this reason, it is likely that we ⓑwill have to change how we get our food. _____(A)_____, we won't kill animals for food. Instead, meat ⓒwill grow in a lab ⓓused animal cells. This will require less land, water, and other resources. Also, (B)개미와 같은 곤충들이 우리 끼니의 일부가 될 것이다 (meals, bugs, ants, part, such, will, our, become, daily, of, as). You might not want to eat ⓔit, but they are actually very rich in nutrients!

**02** 위 글의 빈칸 (A)에 알맞은 것을 고르시오.

① For example　② Therefore

③ As a result　④ However

⑤ In addition

서답형

**03** 위 글의 밑줄 친 ⓐ~ⓔ 중 어색한 것을 모두 찾아 바르게 고치시오.

➡ _____

_____

중요

**04** 위 글의 내용과 일치하지 않는 것은?

① 기후 변화가 농업을 더 어렵게 만들 것이다.
② 지구상의 점점 더 늘어나는 사람들을 위한 자원이 충분하지 않게 될지도 모른다.
③ 우리는 식량을 얻는 방법을 바꾸어야 할 가능성이 높다.
④ 고기가 동물 세포를 이용하여 실험실에서 배양될 것이다.
⑤ 영양분이 매우 풍부하기 때문에 곤충은 인기 있는 음식이 될 것이다.

서답형

**05** 위 글의 밑줄 친 (B)의 우리말에 맞게 괄호 안에 주어진 어휘를 알맞게 배열하여 영작하시오.

➡ _____

_____

**[06~08]** 다음 대화를 읽고 물음에 답하시오.

G: I had to wait in line at the store for almost twenty minutes.
B: (A)That's too bad. Maybe in the future we'll never have to wait in line.
G: What do you mean?
B: I read about (B)a store without cashiers. You take what you want to buy and just walk out.
G: That's it? How do you pay for it?
B: There are cameras and sensors in the store. They keep track of the items you choose and send the information to an app on your smartphone.
G: Then the app pays for them when you leave the store?
B: Exactly. (C)미래에는 이런 종류의 매장이 더 흔해질 것 같아. (likely, that, common)

**06** 밑줄 친 (A)를 대신하여 쓸 수 있는 것은?

① That depends on you.
② That's cool.
③ I'm sorry to hear that.
④ Don't be so disappointed.
⑤ Can you tell me why you waited in line?

**서답형**

**07** 밑줄 친 (B)a store without cashiers에서는 어떻게 물건 값을 지불하는지 40자 내외의 우리말로 쓰시오.

➡ _____

_____

**서답형**

**08** 위 대화의 밑줄 친 우리말 (C)를 주어진 어휘를 활용하여 영작하시오.

➡ _____

_____

**[09~11]** 다음 대화를 읽고 물음에 답하시오.

B: Hey, have you played this game? It's really exciting.
G: Yes, I (A)[do / have]. That game is pretty popular these days.
B: The developers used AI technology in it. The game characters are equipped with AI.
G: Oh, really? (a)Could you explain in more detail?
B: Sure. The AI characters in the game learn from (B)[that / what] human players do and develop their skills.
G: Oh! That's (C)[because / why] I sometimes felt like they already knew my moves!
B: They're very smart. (b)It is likely that the AI in games will get stronger and stronger. (possible)

**09** 위 대화의 괄호 (A)~(C)에 알맞은 말이 바르게 짝지어진 것은?

| | (A) | (B) | (C) |
|---|---|---|---|
| ① | do | that | because |
| ② | do | what | because |
| ③ | have | what | because |
| ④ | have | what | why |
| ⑤ | have | that | why |

**중요**

**10** 위 대화의 밑줄 친 (a)가 의도하는 것은?

① 소원 묻기          ② 설명 요청하기
③ 궁금증 표현하기      ④ 의견 묻기
⑤ 가능성 정도 표현하기

**서답형**

**11** 위 대화의 밑줄 친 (b)를 주어진 어휘를 이용하여 바꿔 쓰시오.

➡ _____

_____

**01** 다음 대화가 자연스럽게 이어지도록 순서대로 배열하시오.

> (A) How do you think they will change?
> (B) It is likely that there will be 3D printed food in restaurants.
> (C) I think that restaurants will change a lot.
> (D) How will our lives change in the future?

➡ _____

**[02~04]** 다음 대화를 읽고 물음에 답하시오.

G: Look at these. They are the new inventions of the month!

B: They all look great. What is the invention on the first page?

G: It's a new smart refrigerator. It senses the items inside it and suggests recipes.

B: That sounds helpful.

G: It does. What do you think of this flying camera? I want to buy it.

B: A flying camera? (A)이게 어떻게 작동하는 건지 설명해 줄 수 있니? (how, work, could, explain)

G: Of course. This machine flies to a destination that we have already set. While it's flying, it can take pictures from 500 meters above the location.

B: That sounds awesome. What do you want to take pictures of?

G: I want to take pictures of flying birds!

**02** (중요) What does the new smart refrigerator do?

➡ _____

**03** What can we do with the flying camera?

➡ _____
_____

**04** 위 대화의 밑줄 친 우리말 (A)를 주어진 어휘를 활용하여 영작하시오.

➡ _____

**[05~07]** 다음 대화를 읽고 물음에 답하시오.

G: Hey, have you heard of a smart umbrella?

B: No, I haven't. Could you explain what it is?

G: Sure. It's an umbrella that gives you the ____(A)____ for the day. If it is going to rain, the umbrella makes a sound.

B: That's very ____(B)____.

**05** 위 대화의 빈칸 (A)에 알맞은 말을 두 단어로 쓰시오.

➡ _____

**06** (고난이도) 다음 문장의 X에 해당하는 단어를 위 대화의 빈칸 (B)에 쓰시오.

> If a way of doing something is X, it is easy, or very useful or suitable for a particular purpose.

➡ _____

**07** (중요) How does the smart umbrella work? Explain in Korean.

➡ _____

# Grammar

**1** 가정법 과거: 'If+주어+동사 과거형 ~, 주어+would/could+동사원형 …'

- Cooking and cleaning **would be** easier **if** you **had** a robot.
  만약 당신이 로봇 하나를 가지고 있다면, 요리와 청소가 더 쉬워질 텐데.
- **If** I **had** a self-driving car, I **would** not drive. 자율주행차가 있다면, 나는 운전을 안 할 텐데.

■ **가정법 과거**: 현재 사실을 반대로 가정하거나 실현 가능성이 없는 일을 가정한다. 'If+주어+동사 과거형 ~, 주어+would/could+동사원형 …' 형태로, '만약 ~라면 …할 텐데'의 뜻이다.

- **If** I **raise** a pet robot, I **will play** with it. 내가 펫 로봇을 키운다면, 함께 놀 것이다. (조건문)
- **If** I **raised** a pet robot, I **would play** with it. 내가 펫 로봇을 키운다면, 함께 놀 텐데. (가정법)
  = **As** I **don't raise** a pet robot, I **won't play** with it. 내가 펫 로봇을 키우지 않아, 함께 놀 수 없다. (직설법)

■ **가정법 과거완료**: 일어난 과거 사실을 반대로 가정한다. 'If+주어+had+과거분사 ~, 주어+would/could+have+과거분사 …'의 형태이다.

- **If** Foster **had not invented** the robot, Mina **would have ignored** him.
  Foster가 그 로봇을 발명하지 않았더라면, Mina가 그를 무시했을 텐데.

■ 'I wish' 가정법은 현재 사실에 반대되는 소망 또는 현재 사실에 대한 유감을 나타낸다.

- **I wish** I **were** a great musician like Bach. 내가 바흐같은 훌륭한 음악가라면 좋을 텐데.
  = **I'm sorry that** I**'m not** a great musician like Bach.

■ 가정법의 다양한 표현들로 직설법의 의미를 나타낼 수 있다.

- **As** there **is** an AI speaker, he **can** play music for you. (직설법) 인공지능 스피커가 있어서, 그가 당신을 위해 음악을 재생할 수 있다.
  → **If** there **were no** AI speaker, he **couldn't play** music for you. (가정법) 인공지능 스피커가 없다면, 그가 당신을 위해 음악을 재생할 수 없을 텐데.
  → **Were** there **no** AI speaker, he **couldn't play** music for you. (If 생략 후 도치)
  → **Without** an AI speaker, he **couldn't play** music for you.
  → **If it were not for** an AI speaker, **he couldn't play** music for you.
  → **Were it not for** an AI speaker, **he couldn't play** music for you. (If 생략 후 도치)

## 핵심 Check

1. 다음 우리말에 맞게 괄호 안의 어구를 바르게 배열하여 빈칸을 채우시오.

  (1) 내가 로봇이라면, 그녀의 말을 들을 텐데. (her, to, would, were, I, listen, a robot)
  ➡ If I _____.

  (2) 돈이 좀 있으면, 서울에 아파트를 살 텐데. (if, an apartment, money, buy, Seoul, would, had, some, I, in)
  ➡ I _____.

## ② '목적'이나 '의도'를 나타내는 so that

- It can navigate roads for you **so that** you can relax and enjoy the ride.
  그것은 당신이 쉬면서 주행을 즐길 수 있도록, 당신을 위해 길을 찾아갈 수 있다.

- I'll do something **so that** she can cheer up. 나는 그녀가 기운낼 수 있도록, 뭔가 할 것이다.

■ so that은 '~하기 위해', '~하고자', '~하도록'의 의미로 '목적'이나 '의도'를 나타낸다. 일반적으로 '주절 +so that+주어+can/will(조동사)+동사원형 ~'의 구조로 쓰인다.

  - We sat at the front **so that** we **could** see the stage well. 우리는 무대를 잘 볼 수 있도록, 앞에 앉았다.
  - The singer did her best in the performance **so that** she **would** satisfy herself. 그 가수는 스스로 만족할 수 있도록 공연에서 최선을 다했다.

■ so that은 다양한 표현들로 같은 의미를 나타낼 수 있다.

  - He donated money **so that** he **could help** others. 그는 다른 사람들을 돕고자 돈을 기부했다.
    = He donated money **in order that** he **could help** others.
    = He donated money **to help** others. 〈to부정사의 부사적 용법 – 목적〉
    = He donated money **so as to help** others.
    = He donated money **in order to help** others.
  - She studied hard **so that she wouldn't** fail. 그녀는 낙제하지 않으려고 열심히 공부했다.
    = She studied hard **in order that she wouldn't** fail.
    = She studied hard **(in order) not to** fail.
    = She studied hard **so as not to** fail.

■ so that을 기준으로 앞과 뒤의 시제를 일치시킨다.

  - Sujin **works** hard **so that** she **can** support her sisters. 수진이는 동생들을 부양하기 위해 열심히 일한다.
  - Sujin **worked** hard **so that** she **could** support her sisters.

■ so that이 '결과'의 의미를 갖는 접속사로 쓰이기도 한다. 이때는 대개 so that 앞에 쉼표가 온다.

  - Minkyoung overate every day, **so that** she **became** overweight. 민경이는 매일 과식했고, 결국 과체중이 되었다.

■ so ~ that 사이에 수식어가 오면, '너무 ~해서 결국 …하다'라는 뜻이 된다.

  - The road was **so dark that** the drivers could see nothing. 도로가 너무 캄캄해서 운전자들이 아무것도 볼 수 없었다.

### 핵심 Check

**2.** 다음 괄호 안에서 알맞은 말을 고르시오.

(1) Sana came to Korea so (that / where) she could be an idol star.

(2) Be quiet please (for that / so that) the audience can focus on the music.

**01** 다음 각 가정법 문장에서 어법상 어색한 단어를 한 개씩만 찾아 고치시오.

(1) If the robots are smarter, they could think like humans.

_____ ➡ _____

(2) If the machine had AI, it can make decisions.

_____ ➡ _____

(3) It would be better if the patient eats some healthy food.

_____ ➡ _____

(4) I will find solutions if the robots caused problems.

_____ ➡ _____

**02** 다음 두 문장의 의미가 같도록 빈칸에 알맞은 말을 쓰시오.

(1) They built the dam to prevent the flood.

➡ They built the dam so _____ they _____ prevent the flood.

(2) Since it was very cold, Tom turned on the heater.

➡ It was _____ _____ _____ Tom turned on the heater.

(3) Jihun's friends will run in order to save the baby ducks.

➡ Jihun's friends will run so _____ _____ _____ save the baby ducks.

**03** 다음 빈칸에 들어갈 말로 알맞은 것은?

> If the car _____ cameras, sensors, and software, it could navigate the roads for you.

① can have    ② will have    ③ have had    ④ had    ⑤ has had

**04** 다음 각 문장의 빈칸에 공통으로 들어갈 말로 알맞은 것은?

> • People invented search-and-rescue robots _____ that they could go into the dangerous areas.
> • Turn the volume down _____ that I can enjoy the meal.
> • The question is _____ easy that you can answer in two seconds.

① enough    ② too    ③ so    ④ such    ⑤ quite

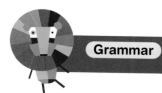 

**01** 다음 중 같은 뜻을 가진 문장끼리 짝지어진 것은?

① The robots would help you do the science homework if they had artificial intelligence.
= The robots didn't have artificial intelligence, so they wouldn't help you do the science homework.

② If it snows tomorrow morning, Nelly would stay in her hotel room.
= It is going to snow tomorrow morning, so Nelly will stay in her hotel room.

③ If Chris could run faster than usual, he would arrive at the meeting in time.
= Chris can't run faster than usual, so he won't arrive at the meeting in time.

④ If my uncle saw the truck coming, he could avoid the accident.
= My uncle didn't see the truck coming, so he couldn't avoid the accident.

⑤ The little girl could write a letter to the composer of the song if she knew his mail address.
= The little girl can't write a letter to the composer of the song though she knows his mail address.

[02~03] 다음 우리말을 어법상 알맞게 영작한 것을 고르시오.

**02**

> 그 노인은 그녀가 기운 낼 수 있도록 나뭇잎 그림을 그렸다.

① The old man drew a picture of the leaf that she so could cheer up.
② The old man drew a picture of the leaf so what she could cheer up.
③ The old man drew a picture of the leaf such that she could cheer up.
④ The old man drew a picture of the leaf so that she could cheer up.
⑤ The old man drew a picture of the leaf so order that she could cheer up.

**03**

> 우리는 무대 위 배우들의 연기를 더 잘 보기 위해서 앞에 앉았다.

① We sat at the front so that we can see the actors' performance on the stage better.
② We sat at the front in order that we can see the actors' performance on the stage better.
③ We sat at the front for that we could see the actors' performance on the stage better.
④ We sat at the front so as we saw the actors' performance on the stage better.
⑤ We sat at the front so that we could see the actors' performance on the stage better.

**04** 다음 중 어법상 어색한 문장은?

① If I knew the truth, I would tell it to you.
② If the fish knew the way to their home, they could go up against the river.
③ If the lady were in Spain, she could attend her father's funeral.
④ If the robot had AI, it won't do the bad thing to human children.
⑤ If it were not for the shoes you bought for me, I would not be able to survive.

서답형
**[05~08]** 다음 우리말과 일치하도록 괄호 안에 주어진 어구들을 바르게 배열하시오.

**05**
> 진호의 반 친구들 모두가 어려운 사람들이 도움을 얻도록, 그들의 용돈을 기부했다.
> → All of Jinho's classmates (in, that, get, their, so, donated, people, could, need, help, allowances).

➡ _____

_____

**06**
> 수업 시간 동안에 집중할 수 있도록 충분히 잠을 자라구!
> → Be sure (sleep, order, to, can, that, you, enough, focus, in, get) during class!

➡ _____

_____

**07**
> 날씨가 맑다면, 우리는 놀이 공원에 갈 수 있을 텐데.
> → If (sunny, the amusement park, go, we, it, to, were, could).

➡ _____

_____

**08**
> 펫 로봇을 키운다면, 그 어린이 환자는 더 이상 심심하지 않을 텐데.
> → If the child patient (bored, wouldn't, she, a pet robot, be, raised) anymore.

➡ _____

_____

**[09~10]** 다음 각 가정법 과거 문장에서 어법상 옳은 것을 고르시오.

**09** ① I wish Sam follows her father's advice when she gets in trouble.
② I wish I had been at her concert playing the songs this coming Sunday.
③ I wish Brian can memorize the form so well that he could pass the test.
④ I wish all my relatives don't live far from the town my family will move to.
⑤ I wish people in my country knew a lot about the heroes in our history.

**중요**
**10** ① If Jessica has the car, she could pick my kids up on her way home.
② If the girl I met yesterday were rich, she could travel all around the world.
③ I wish the new cleaning robots will remove the dirty matter from the river.
④ If the scientists had invented the AI robot, you can deal with it easily.
⑤ I wish I know the correct answers to the final term exam.

서답형
**11** 다음 가정법 과거 문장에서 어법상 <u>어색한</u> 부분을 찾아서 고치시오. (총 4곳)

> If you are a scientist developed robots, what kinds of robots will you be designed?

➡ ① _____ ② _____
③ _____ ④ _____

**12** 다음 두 문장의 의미가 같도록 바꿔 쓸 때 적절하지 <u>않은</u> 것은?

① Lisa works out regularly in order for her daddy not to get worried.
= Lisa works out regularly so that her daddy won't get worried.
② Jinsu left the dance party quite early not to meet his girlfriend.
= Jinsu left the dance party quite early, so he could not meet his girlfriend.
③ Wendy left for London so that she would get a better job in design.
= Wendy left for London so as to get a better job in design.
④ Thomas made cookies for Marianne so that he would feel happy.
= Thomas made cookies for Marianne in order to feel happy.
⑤ Karen waved her hand so that her study members could find her with ease.
= Karen waved her hand in order for her study members to find her with ease.

**13** 다음 문장의 빈칸 (A)~(C)에 들어갈 말로 가장 적절한 것은?

• If the gentleman ___(A)___ some money, he could help you to support the victims.
• Were it not for the sun, all the living things on earth ___(B)___ not survive.
• If the show ___(C)___ early, Frank would come and help me with the project.

| | (A) | (B) | (C) |
|---|---|---|---|
| ① | has | would | ends |
| ② | had | could | ends |
| ③ | had had | could | will end |
| ④ | had | would | ended |
| ⑤ | has | could | ended |

**14** 다음 중 주어진 문장과 의미가 <u>다른</u> 것은?

Scientists try to make the robots able to recognize human emotions so that they can act like real friends.

① Scientists try to make the robots able to recognize human emotions in order that they can act like real friends.
② Scientists try to make the robots able to recognize human emotions in order for them to act like real friends.
③ Scientists try to make the robots able to recognize human emotions to have them act like real friends.
④ Scientists try to make the robots able to recognize human emotions in case that they can act like real friends.
⑤ Scientists try to make the robots able to recognize human emotions so as to have them act like real friends.

**15** 다음 〈보기〉의 밑줄 친 부분과 쓰임이 <u>다른</u> 하나는?

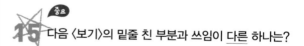

I wish robots <u>could</u> be able to think and act like humans.

① If the officer knew the driver's number, he <u>could</u> make a phone call.
② <u>Could</u> you make me a robot pet for my little daughter?
③ I wish I <u>could</u> speak as many foreign languages as possible.
④ Were it not for your help, they <u>could</u> not complete the assignment.
⑤ The prisoner <u>could</u> get freedom if the witness told the truth to the judge.

**01** 다음 각 가정법 문장에서 어법상 어색한 단어를 한 개씩만 찾아 바르게 고치시오. (고친 부분은 두 단어라도 상관 없음.)

(1) Without artificial intelligence, robots won't be able to think like humans.

_____ ➡ _____

(2) If the police officer is in the driver's situation, he would understand how urgently she should get to the hospital.

_____ ➡ _____

(3) Samuel wouldn't be late for the P.E. class yesterday if his bike had not been broken.

_____ ➡ _____

(4) I wish I make a smarter robot so that it could help me with my homework.

_____ ➡ _____

(5) If robots could recognize the emotions of humans, they can act like real friends.

_____ ➡ _____

(6) If it were not for the effort of the medical staff around the country, we will be in a big trouble from the covid 19.

_____ ➡ _____

(7) I wish the robots can talk with my family members and sense their emotions.

_____ ➡ _____

**02** 다음 우리말과 일치하도록 괄호 안에 주어진 단어들을 바르게 배열하여 문장을 완성하시오.

(1) 그 로봇이 사람의 감정을 느낀다면, 우리는 그것과 친구처럼 지낼 수 있을 텐데.

➡ If the robot _____ _____ with it like a friend. (could, human, along, we, sensed, get, emotions)

(2) 수색-구조 로봇들이 없다면, 사람들이 위험한 재난 현장으로 들어갈 텐데.

➡ If there _____ _____.

(would, areas, search-and-rescue, go, into, humans, robots, disaster, were, no)

(3) 그 발명가는 외로운 사람들을 도울 수 있게 펫 로봇을 만들었다.

➡ The inventor made _____ _____.

(the lonely people, so, could, a pet robot, help, he, that).

**03** 다음 문장과 같은 뜻이 되도록 괄호 안의 주어진 조건에 맞게 빈칸을 채우시오.

> Without cameras and the GPS system, the self-driving cars could not navigate roads.

(1) _____ cameras and the GPS system, the self-driving cars could not navigate roads. (it, be동사 활용, 5 단어)

(2) _____ cameras and the GPS system, the self-driving cars could not navigate roads. (there, no 활용, 4 단어)

(3) _____ cameras and the GPS system, the self-driving cars could not navigate roads. (it, be동사 활용, 4 단어)

(4) _____ _____ navigate roads. (직설법, there, 접속사 as 활용, 12 단어, self-driving은 한 단어로 간주)

**04** 다음 〈보기〉와 같이 두 문장이 같은 의미가 되도록 주어진 단어를 활용하여 다시 쓰시오.

> ─┤ 보기 ├─
>
> Some people exercise regularly to stay healthy. (so, that)
>
> ➡ Some people exercise regularly so that they can stay healthy.

(1) Mom returned home so as to take the umbrella with her. (that, in, could, order)

➡ _____

(2) Abigail runs every day to join his sports club. (that, so, can, she)

➡ _____

_____

(3) Semi left for Italy to learn cooking. (that, in, could, she, order)

➡ _____

_____

(4) Be sure to get enough sleep to focus during class. (that, so, you)

➡ _____

_____

(5) Sean ran fast in order not to be late for the wedding. (that, would, so, he)

➡ _____

_____

**05** 다음 〈보기〉와 같이 직설법 문장을 가정법으로 고치시오.

> ─┤ 보기 ├─
>
> Since Paul isn't an eagle, he can't fly high.
>
> → If Paul were an eagle, he could fly high.

(1) Since the coronavirus isn't in my town, we feel relieved.

➡ _____

_____

(2) As Brian had an invitation, it was easy for them to enter the castle.

➡ _____

(3) Because she is not rich enough, she will sell her books on the street market.

➡ _____

_____

(4) As there is no money left, Mr. Robert won't join the party.

➡ _____

_____

**06** 다음 그림을 보고, 그림에 나온 단어를 활용하여, 우리말에 맞게 가정법 문장으로 빈칸을 채우시오.

> When the last leaf falls, it will be my last day.

마지막 잎이 떨어진다면, 그게 나의 마지막 날이 될 텐데.

→ If _____.

(가정법 과거, If 포함 총 11 단어)

# Reading

## Life with Robots

### Where Do We See Robots?

Robots are not only in movies and books anymore. Around the world, robots are doing a variety of tasks. There are delivery robots flying in the sky, robot arms in factories, and service robots in public places.
앞의 명사 delivery robots를 수식하는 현재분사

- A delivery robot in the sky
- Robot arms in a factory
- A service robot at the PyeongChang Olympics

### Robots Are Becoming Smart

목적격 관계대명사절을 이끌며 선행사 only easy tasks를 수식함.

In the past, robots performed only easy tasks <u>that</u> humans programmed them to do. However, robots are now getting "smarter," and soon they might be able to think like humans. What makes this possible is artificial intelligence (AI).
What은 선행사를 포함하는 관계대명사.
주어 역할을 하는 명사절을 이끈다.

Robots that have AI can perceive environments and make decisions. They can also recognize speech, tell jokes, and play games with humans.

### AI Speakers

They can answer your questions, control machines in your home, and play music for you.

### AI Pets

They act just like real dogs. They walk and play with their owners and recognize praise.

---

a variety of 다양한
task 일, 과제, 과업
delivery 배달
factory 공장
perform 실행하다, 공연하다
program 프로그램을 짜다
artificial 인공적인
intelligence 지능
perceive 인지하다, 감지하다
recognize 알아보다, 인정하다
speech 연설, 말

---

### 확인문제

- 다음 문장이 본문의 내용과 일치하면 T, 일치하지 <u>않으면</u> F를 쓰시오.

1  Around the world, robots are doing a variety of tasks. ☐

2  There are delivery robots in public places. ☐

3  In the past, robots performed only easy tasks that humans programmed them to do. ☐

4  Robots that have AI can recognize speech, tell jokes, and play games with each other. ☐

## Robots around Us – Present and Future

Robots are making things faster and easier. They can help us anywhere—in our homes, on roads, or in disaster areas.

**Home Helper Robot:** This robot helps your family throughout the day. Cooking and cleaning would be easier if you had one. It also talks
<small>가정법 과거: If+주어+동사의 과거형 ~, 주어+조동사의 과거형[would/could/might]+동사원형 …</small>
with family members and can sense emotions.

**Self-Driving Car:** A self-driving car doesn't need a driver. With cameras, sensors, and software, it can navigate roads for you so that you can relax and enjoy the ride.
<small>목적을 나타내는 so that은 부사절을 이끌고 있음: ~하도록, ~하기 위해서</small>

**Robot Swarm:** A robot swarm is a large group of robots that can communicate with one another, like ants or bees. They can be used in a variety of places, including farms or building sites. They work on tasks and find solutions as a group.

**Search-and-Rescue Robot:** Search-and-rescue robots can go into disaster areas that are dangerous for humans. They find survivors, deal
<small>주격 관계대명사절을 이끌며 선행사 disaster areas를 수식</small>
with dangers, and clear routes so that people can escape to safety.
<small>목적을 나타내는 so that은 부사절을 이끌고 있음: ~하도록, ~하기 위해서</small>

## Looking toward the Future

Our future with robots looks bright but not perfect. Some people expect life to become more convenient with the help of robots. However, other people worry about problems they might cause, such
<small>problems와 they might cause 사이에 목적격 관계대명사 that이 생략</small>
as threats to our jobs and safety. The important thing is to find possible
<small>명사적 용법(보어)</small>
solutions and to ensure that robots are only used for good.

---

**present** 현재의
**disaster** 재난, 재해
**sense** 감지하다; 감각
**navigate** 길을 찾다, 항해하다
**swarm** 떼, 군중
**site** 위치, 현장
**solution** 해법, 해결책
**survivor** 생존자, 살아남은 사람
**deal with** ~을 다루다, 처리하다
**route** 길, 경로
**escape** 탈출하다, 달아나다
**safety** 안전(함), 안전한 곳
**look toward** 앞날을 생각하다
**convenient** 편리한, 간편한
**threat** 위협
**possible** 가능한

---

### 확인문제

● 다음 문장이 본문의 내용과 일치하면 T, 일치하지 <u>않으면</u> F를 쓰시오.

1  Robots are making things faster and easier. ☐

2  A home helper robot can help us in disaster areas. ☐

3  A self-driving car doesn't need a driver. ☐

4  The robots in a robot swarm work on tasks and find solutions alone. ☐

5  Search-and-rescue robots can go into disaster areas that are dangerous for humans. ☐

6  Our future with robots looks bright and perfect. ☐

● 우리말을 참고하여 빈칸에 알맞은 말을 쓰시오.

**1** **Life** _____ _____

**2** _____ **Do We See Robots?**

**3** Robots are _____ only in movies and books _____.

**4** Around the world, robots are doing _____ _____ _____ tasks.

**5** There are delivery robots _____ in the sky, robot arms in factories, and service robots _____ _____ _____.

**6** A _____ robot in the sky

**7** Robot arms in a _____

**8** _____ _____ _____ at the PyeongChang Olympics

**9** **Robots Are** _____ _____

**10** In the past, robots performed only easy tasks that humans _____ _____ _____ _____.

**11** However, robots are now _____ "_____," and soon they might be able to think like humans.

**12** _____ _____ _____ _____ is artificial intelligence (AI).

**13** Robots that have AI can _____ _____ and make decisions.

**14** They can also _____ _____, tell jokes, and play games with humans.

**15** **AI Speakers:** They can answer your questions, _____ _____ in your home, and play music for you.

**16** **AI Pets:** They _____ _____ _____ real dogs.

**17** They walk and play with their owners and _____ _____.

**18** **Robots** _____ _____ – **Present and Future**

**19** Robots are making things _____ and _____.

| | |
|---|---|
| 1 | 로봇과 함께하는 삶 |
| 2 | 우리는 어디에서 로봇을 보는 가? |
| 3 | 로봇은 더는 영화와 책 속에만 있는 것은 아니다. |
| 4 | 전 세계적으로 로봇은 다양한 임무를 수행하고 있다. |
| 5 | 하늘에는 날아다니는 배달 로 봇, 공장에는 로봇 팔, 그리고 공공장소에는 서비스 로봇이 있 다. |
| 6 | 하늘에서 날아다니는 배달 로봇 |
| 7 | 공장의 로봇 팔들 |
| 8 | 평창 올림픽의 서비스 로봇 |
| 9 | 로봇이 똑똑해지고 있다 |
| 10 | 과거에 로봇은 인간이 로봇에게 실행하도록 프로그램을 설정한 단순 업무만을 수행했다. |
| 11 | 그러나 로봇은 이제 '더 똑똑'해 지고 있으며, 곧 인간처럼 생각 할 수 있을지도 모른다. |
| 12 | 이러한 것을 가능하게 만드는 것은 인공 지능(AI)이다. |
| 13 | 인공 지능을 가진 로봇은 환경 을 인식하고 의사 결정을 할 수 있다. |
| 14 | 그들은 또한 인간의 말을 인지 하고, 농담을 건네며, 인간과 게 임을 할 수 있다. |
| 15 | 〈인공 지능 스피커〉 그들은 당 신의 질문에 대답할 수 있고, 당 신의 집에 있는 기계들을 조종 할 수 있으며, 당신을 위해 음악 을 재생할 수도 있다. |
| 16 | 〈인공 지능 반려동물〉 그들은 마치 진짜 개처럼 행동한다. |
| 17 | 그들은 그들의 주인과 함께 걷 고 놀며 칭찬을 알아챈다. |
| 18 | 우리 주변의 로봇들 – 현재와 미래 |
| 19 | 로봇은 일을 더 빠르고 더 쉽게 해 주고 있다. |

**20** They can help us _____ — in our homes, on roads, or _____ _____ _____ .

**21** **Home Helper Robot:** This robot helps your family _____ the day.

**22** Cooking and cleaning _____ _____ _____ if you _____ _____ .

**23** It also talks with family members and can _____ _____ .

**24** **Self-Driving Car:** A self-driving car doesn't need _____ _____ .

**25** With cameras, sensors, and software, it can navigate roads for you _____ _____ you _____ relax and enjoy the ride.

**26** **Robot Swarm:** A robot swarm is _____ _____ _____ _____ _____ that can communicate with one another, like ants or bees.

**27** They _____ _____ _____ in a variety of places, _____ farms or building sites.

**28** They work on tasks and find solutions _____ _____ .

**29** **Search-and-Rescue Robot:** Search-and-rescue robots can go into disaster areas that are _____ _____ _____ .

**30** They find survivors, deal with dangers, and clear routes _____ _____ people _____ escape to safety.

**31** _____ _____ the Future

**32** Our future with robots looks bright but _____ _____ .

**33** Some people expect life _____ _____ more convenient with the help of robots.

**34** However, other people worry about problems _____ _____ _____ , such as threats to our jobs and safety.

**35** The important thing is _____ _____ possible solutions and _____ _____ that robots are only used for _____ .

---

**20** 그들은 어디에서나 우리를 도울 수 있다. 우리의 집에서, 길에서 또는 재난 지역에서 말이다.

**21** 〈집안일 도우미 로봇〉 이 로봇은 온종일 당신의 가족을 돕는다.

**22** 만약 당신이 이 로봇 하나를 가지고 있다면 요리와 청소가 더 쉬워질 것이다.

**23** 이 로봇은 또한 가족 모두와 이야기를 나누며 감정을 파악할 수 있다.

**24** 〈자율 주행 자동차〉 자율 주행 자동차는 운전자를 필요로 하지 않는다.

**25** 카메라, 감지기 그리고 소프트웨어를 갖춘 채, 이 자동차는 당신이 쉬면서 주행을 즐길 수 있도록 당신을 위해 길을 찾아갈 수 있다.

**26** 〈로봇 군집〉 로봇 군집은 개미나 벌처럼, 서로 의사소통할 수 있는 로봇의 대규모 집단을 말한다.

**27** 이 로봇들은 농장이나 건설 현장을 포함한 다양한 장소에서 사용될 수 있다.

**28** 그들은 하나의 집단으로서 임무를 완수하고 해결책을 찾는다.

**29** 〈수색 구조 로봇〉 수색 구조 로봇은 사람에게 위험한 재난 지역에 투입될 수 있다.

**30** 그들은 생존자를 찾고 위험한 상황을 처리하며, 사람들이 안전한 곳으로 대피할 수 있도록 길을 확보한다.

**31** 미래에 대한 전망

**32** 로봇과 함께하는 우리의 미래는 밝지만 완벽하지는 않다.

**33** 어떤 사람들은 로봇의 도움으로 삶이 더욱 편리해질 것을 기대한다.

**34** 그러나 다른 사람들은 우리의 일자리와 안전에 대한 위협과 같이, 로봇이 일으킬지 모르는 문제들에 대해 걱정한다.

**35** 중요한 것은 가능한 해결책을 찾아내는 것과 로봇이 오로지 좋은 일을 위해서만 쓰이게 됨을 확실히 하는 것이다.

● 우리말을 참고하여 본문을 영작하시오.

**1** ▶ 로봇과 함께하는 삶

➡ _____

**2** ▶ 우리는 어디에서 로봇을 보는가?

➡ _____

**3** ▶ 로봇은 더는 영화와 책 속에만 있는 것은 아니다.

➡ _____

**4** ▶ 전 세계적으로 로봇은 다양한 임무를 수행하고 있다.

➡ _____

**5** ▶ 하늘에는 날아다니는 배달 로봇, 공장에는 로봇 팔, 그리고 공공장소에는 서비스 로봇이 있다.

➡ _____

**6** ▶ 하늘에서 날아다니는 배달 로봇

➡ _____

**7** ▶ 공장의 로봇 팔들

➡ _____

**8** ▶ 평창 올림픽의 서비스 로봇

➡ _____

**9** ▶ 로봇이 똑똑해지고 있다

➡ _____

**10** ▶ 과거에 로봇은 인간이 로봇에게 실행하도록 프로그램을 설정한 단순 업무만을 수행했다.

➡ _____

**11** ▶ 그러나 로봇은 이제 '더 똑똑'해지고 있으며, 곧 인간처럼 생각할 수 있을지도 모른다.

➡ _____

**12** ▶ 이러한 것을 가능하게 만드는 것은 인공 지능(AI)이다.

➡ _____

**13** ▶ 인공 지능을 가진 로봇은 환경을 인식하고 의사 결정을 할 수 있다.

➡ _____

**14** ▶ 그들은 또한 인간의 말을 인지하고, 농담을 건네며, 인간과 게임을 할 수 있다.

➡ _____

**15** ▶ 〈인공 지능 스피커〉 그들은 당신의 질문에 대답할 수 있고, 당신의 집에 있는 기계들을 조종할 수 있으며, 당신을 위해 음악을 재생할 수도 있다.

➡ _____

➡ _____

**16** ▶ 〈인공 지능 반려동물〉 그들은 마치 진짜 개처럼 행동한다.

➡ _____

**17** ▶ 그들은 그들의 주인과 함께 걷고 놀며 칭찬을 알아챈다.

➡ _____

**18** ▶ 우리 주변의 로봇들 – 현재와 미래

➡ _____

**19** 로봇은 일을 더 빠르고 더 쉽게 해 주고 있다.
➡ _____

**20** 그들은 어디에서나 우리를 도울 수 있다. 우리의 집에서, 길에서 또는 재난 지역에서 말이다.
➡ _____

**21** 〈집안일 도우미 로봇〉 이 로봇은 온종일 당신의 가족을 돕는다.
➡ _____

**22** 만약 당신이 이 로봇 하나를 가지고 있다면 요리와 청소가 더 쉬워질 것이다.
➡ _____

**23** 이 로봇은 또한 가족 모두와 이야기를 나누며 감정을 파악할 수 있다.
➡ _____

**24** 〈자율 주행 자동차〉 자율 주행 자동차는 운전자를 필요로 하지 않는다.
➡ _____

**25** 카메라, 감지기 그리고 소프트웨어를 갖춘 채, 이 자동차는 당신이 쉬면서 주행을 즐길 수 있도록 당신을 위해 길을 찾아갈 수 있다.
➡ _____

**26** 〈로봇 군집〉 로봇 군집은 개미나 벌처럼, 서로 의사소통할 수 있는 로봇의 대규모 집단을 말한다.
➡ _____

**27** 이 로봇들은 농장이나 건설 현장을 포함한 다양한 장소에서 사용될 수 있다.
➡ _____

**28** 그들은 하나의 집단으로서 임무를 완수하고 해결책을 찾는다.
➡ _____

**29** 〈수색 구조 로봇〉 수색 구조 로봇은 사람에게 위험한 재난 지역에 투입될 수 있다.
➡ _____

**30** 그들은 생존자를 찾고 위험한 상황을 처리하며, 사람들이 안전한 곳으로 대피할 수 있도록 길을 확보한다.
➡ _____

**31** 미래에 대한 전망
➡ _____

**32** 로봇과 함께하는 우리의 미래는 밝지만 완벽하지는 않다.
➡ _____

**33** 어떤 사람들은 로봇의 도움으로 삶이 더욱 편리해질 것을 기대한다.
➡ _____

**34** 그러나 다른 사람들은 우리의 일자리와 안전에 대한 위협과 같이, 로봇이 일으킬지 모르는 문제들에 대해 걱정한다.
➡ _____

**35** 중요한 것은 가능한 해결책을 찾아내는 것과 로봇이 오로지 좋은 일을 위해서만 쓰이게 됨을 확실히 하는 것이다.
➡ _____

[01~03] 다음 글을 읽고 물음에 답하시오.

> ⓐ
> Robots are not only in movies and books anymore. Around the world, robots are doing ⓑa variety of tasks. There are delivery robots ⓒflying in the sky, robot arms in factories, and service robots in public places.
> • A delivery robot in the sky
> • Robot arms in a factory
> • A service robot at the PyeongChang Olympics

**01** 위 글의 빈칸 ⓐ에 들어갈 제목으로 알맞은 것을 고르시오.

① Robots Are Becoming Smart
② Looking toward the Future
③ Where Do We See Robots?
④ Robots in Movies
⑤ Robots around Us – Present and Future

**서답형**
**02** 위 글의 밑줄 친 ⓑ의 임무를 수행하는 로봇 세 종류를 우리말로 쓰시오.

➡ (1) _____
　(2) _____
　(3) _____

**03** 위 글의 밑줄 친 ⓒflying과 문법적 쓰임이 같은 것을 모두 고르시오.

① He is good at flying in the sky.
② Two birds are flying in the sky.
③ My dream is flying in the sky.
④ Look at the man flying in the sky.
⑤ Flying in the sky, the eagle looked down at the tree.

[04~06] 다음 글을 읽고 물음에 답하시오.

> **Robots Are Becoming Smart**
> In the past, robots performed only easy tasks that humans programmed (A)them to do. ⓐ , robots are now getting "smarter," and soon they might be able to think like humans. (B)What makes this possible is artificial intelligence (AI).
> Robots that have AI can perceive environments and make decisions. (C)They can also recognize speech, tell jokes, and play games with humans.

**04** 위 글의 빈칸 ⓐ에 들어갈 알맞은 말을 고르시오.

① In addition　② In other words
③ For example　④ Therefore
⑤ However

**서답형**
**05** 다음 빈칸에 위 글의 밑줄 친 (A)them과 (C)They가 가리키는 것을 쓰시오. (한 칸에 한 단어씩 쓸 것.)

➡ (A) _____ of _____
　(C) _____ _____ _____ _____

**06** 위 글의 밑줄 친 (B)What과 문법적 쓰임이 같은 것을 고르시오.

① What is the matter with you?
② What kind of fruit do you like best?
③ What he needs is a good meal.
④ What do you think of that film?
⑤ I know what plan he will try.

**[07~09]** 다음 글을 읽고 물음에 답하시오.

### Search-and-Rescue Robot

ⓐSearch-and-rescue robots can go into disaster areas that are safe for humans. They find survivors, deal with dangers, and clear routes ⓑso that people can escape to safety.

### Looking toward the Future

Our future with robots looks bright but not perfect. Some people expect life to become more convenient with the help of robots. However, other people worry about problems they might cause, such as threats to our jobs and safety. The important thing is to find possible solutions and to ensure that robots are only used for good.

**서답형**

**07** 위 글의 밑줄 친 ⓐ에서 흐름상 어색한 부분을 찾아 고치시오.

➡ _____ ➡ _____

**서답형**

**08** 위 글의 밑줄 친 ⓑ를 다음과 같이 바꿔 쓸 때 빈칸에 들어갈 알맞은 말을 두 단어로 쓰시오.

➡ for people _____ to safety

**09** According to the passage, which is NOT true?

① Search-and-rescue robots find survivors, deal with dangers, and clear routes so that people can escape to safety.

② Our future with robots looks bright and perfect.

③ There are some people who expect life to become more convenient with the help of robots.

④ Other people worry about problems that robots might cause.

⑤ The important thing is finding possible solutions and ensuring that robots are only used for good.

**[10~12]** 다음 글을 읽고 물음에 답하시오.

### Robots around Us – Present and Future

(A)로봇은 일을 더 빠르고 더 쉽게 해 주고 있다. They can help us anywhere — in our homes, on roads, or in disaster areas.

### Home Helper Robot

This robot helps your family throughout the day. Cooking and cleaning would be easier if you ____ⓐ____ one. It also talks with family members and can sense emotions.

**서답형**

**10** 위 글의 빈칸 ⓐ에 have를 알맞은 형태로 쓰시오.

➡ _____

**11** 위 글의 밑줄 친 (A)의 우리말에 맞게 주어진 어휘를 알맞게 배열하시오.

| making / easier / things / robots / and / are / faster |

➡ _____

 **12** According to the passage, which is NOT true?

① Thanks to robots, things are becoming faster and easier.

② It is not easy to use robots in such places as disaster areas.

③ A home helper robot helps your family throughout the day.

④ A home helper robot would make cooking easier.

⑤ A home helper robot talks with family members and can sense emotions.

[13~15] 다음 글을 읽고 물음에 답하시오.

### Robots Are Becoming Smart

In the past, robots performed only easy tasks ____ⓐ____ humans programmed them to do. However, robots are now getting "smarter," and soon they might be able to think like humans. (A)이러한 것을 가능하게 만드는 것은 인공 지능(AI)이다.

Robots ____ⓑ____ have AI can perceive environments and make decisions. They can also recognize speech, tell jokes, and play games with humans.

**13** 위 글의 빈칸 ⓐ와 ⓑ에 공통으로 들어갈 알맞은 말을 모두 고르시오.

① which          ② what

③ who            ④ that

⑤ whom

**서답형**

**14** 위 글의 밑줄 친 (A)의 우리말에 맞게 주어진 어휘를 이용하여 영작하시오.

> what, this, (AI)

➡ _____

**15** According to the passage, which is NOT true?

① In the past, robots performed only easy tasks humans programmed them to do.

② Robots are now getting "smarter."

③ Artificial intelligence can make it possible for robots to think like humans.

④ Every robot can perceive environments and make decisions.

⑤ Robots having AI can also recognize speech, tell jokes, and play games with humans.

[16~18] 다음 글을 읽고 물음에 답하시오.

### Self-Driving Car

A self-driving car doesn't need a driver. With cameras, sensors, and software, ⓐit can navigate roads for you so that you can relax and enjoy the ride.

### Robot Swarm

A robot swarm is a large group of robots that can communicate with one another, like ants or bees. They can be used in a variety of places, including farms or building sites. They work on tasks and find solutions ⓑas a group.

**서답형**

**16** 위 글의 밑줄 친 ⓐit이 가리키는 것을 본문에서 찾아 쓰시오.

➡ _____

**17** 위 글의 밑줄 친 ⓑas와 같은 의미로 쓰인 것을 고르시오.

① As I was tired, I soon fell asleep.

② This box will serve as a table.

③ Do in Rome as the Romans do.

④ Susan is not as pretty as Jane.

⑤ She sang as she walked.

**18** According to the passage, which is NOT true?

① A self-driving car doesn't need a driver.

② A self-driving car can navigate roads for you.

③ A robot swarm is a large group of robots.

④ A robot swarm can communicate with ants or bees.

⑤ A robot swarm works on tasks and finds solutions as a group.

[19~22] 다음 글을 읽고 물음에 답하시오.

### Self-Driving Car

A self-driving car doesn't need a driver. ⓐ_____ cameras, sensors, and software, it can navigate roads for you so that you can relax and enjoy the ride.

### Robot Swarm

A robot swarm is a large group of robots that can communicate ⓑ_____ one another, like ants or bees. ⓒThey can be used in a variety of places, including farms or building sites. They work on tasks and find solutions as a group.

**19** 위 글의 빈칸 ⓐ와 ⓑ에 공통으로 들어갈 알맞은 전치사를 고르시오. (대·소문자 무시)

① On      ② With      ③ For
④ About      ⑤ By

**서답형**

**20** 주어진 영영풀이에 해당하는 단어를 본문에서 찾아 쓰시오.

> It means finding a direction across, along, or over an area of water or land, often by using a map.

➡ _____

**서답형**

**21** 위 글의 밑줄 친 ⓒ를 다음과 같이 바꿔 쓸 때 빈칸에 들어갈 알맞은 말을 두 단어로 쓰시오.

➡ They can be used in a variety of places, _____ _____ farms or building sites.

**22** Which question CANNOT be answered after reading the passage?

① Does a self-driving car need a driver?
② What is a robot swarm?
③ How many robots are there in a robot swarm?
④ Where can a robot swarm be used?
⑤ Does each robot in a robot swarm work alone?

[23~26] 다음 글을 읽고 물음에 답하시오.

### Looking toward the Future

Our future with robots looks bright but not perfect. Some people expect life to become more convenient _____(A)_____ robots. However, other people worry about problems ⓐthey might cause, ⓑsuch as threats to our jobs and safety. The important thing is to find possible solutions and to ensure that robots are only used for good.

**서답형**

**23** 위 글의 빈칸 (A)에 '~의 도움으로'의 뜻을 갖는 4 단어를 쓰시오.

➡ _____

**서답형**

**24** 위 글의 밑줄 친 ⓐthey가 가리키는 것을 본문에서 찾아 쓰시오.

➡ _____

**서답형**

**25** 위 글의 밑줄 친 ⓑsuch as와 바꿔 쓸 수 있는 한 단어를 쓰시오.

➡ _____

**서답형**

**26** What are the problems that robots might cause? Answer in English. (8 words)

➡ _____

[01~04] 다음 글을 읽고 물음에 답하시오.

### Robots Are Becoming Smart

In the past, robots performed only easy tasks that humans programmed them to do. (A)However, robots are now getting "sillier," and soon they might be able to think like humans.  ⓐ  makes this possible is artificial intelligence (AI).

Robots that have AI can perceive environments and make decisions. They can also recognize speech, tell jokes, and play games with humans.

**01** 위 글의 빈칸 ⓐ에 들어갈 알맞은 한 단어를 쓰시오.

➡ _____

**02** 위 글의 밑줄 친 (A)에서 흐름상 어색한 부분을 찾아 고치시오.

_____ ➡ _____

**03** What kinds of tasks did the robots do in the past? Fill in the blanks (A) and (B) with suitable words.

In the past, humans (A)_____ easy tasks that robots would perform, and then robots (B)_____ only those tasks.

**04** 본문의 내용과 일치하도록 다음 빈칸 (A)와 (B)에 공통으로 들어갈 알맞은 단어를 쓰시오.

Robots that can perceive environments and make decisions have (A)_____. Thanks to (B)_____, they can also recognize speech, tell jokes, and play games with humans.

[05~07] 다음 글을 읽고 물음에 답하시오.

### AI Speakers

They can answer your questions, control machines in your home, and play music for you.

### AI Pets

ⓐ그들은 마치 진짜 개처럼 행동한다. They walk and play with their owners and recognize praise.

**05** 위 글의 밑줄 친 ⓐ의 우리말에 맞게 주어진 어휘를 이용하여 6 단어로 영작하시오.

act, just

➡ _____

**06** What activities can AI pets do? Answer in English in a full sentence. (11 words)

➡ _____

_____

**07** 다음 빈칸 (A)와 (B)에 알맞은 단어를 넣어 '인공 지능 스피커'에 대한 소개를 완성하시오.

AI Speakers can reply to (A)_____ _____, manage (B)_____ in your home, and play music for you.

**[08~11]** 다음 글을 읽고 물음에 답하시오.

### Search-and-Rescue Robot

Search-and-rescue robots can go into disaster areas that are dangerous for humans. They find ___ⓐ___, (A)deal with dangers, and clear routes so that people can escape to ___ⓑ___ .

### Looking toward the Future

Our future with robots looks bright but not perfect. Some people expect life to become more convenient with the help of robots. However, other people worry about problems they might cause, such as threats to our jobs and safety. (B)The important thing is to find possible solutions and to ensure that robots are only used for good.

**08** 주어진 영영풀이를 참고하여 빈칸 ⓐ에 철자 s로 시작하는 단어를 쓰시오.

> people who continue to live afterwards in spite of coming close to death

➡ _____

**09** 위 글의 빈칸 ⓑ에 safe를 알맞은 형태로 쓰시오.

➡ _____

**10** 위 글의 밑줄 친 (A)deal with와 바꿔 쓸 수 있는 한 단어를 쓰시오.

➡ _____ 또는 _____

**11** 위 글의 밑줄 친 (B)The important thing에 해당하는 두 가지를 우리말로 쓰시오.

➡ (1) _____
　(2) _____

**[12~15]** 다음 글을 읽고 물음에 답하시오.

### Self-Driving Car

A self-driving car doesn't need a driver. With cameras, sensors, and software, (A)it can navigate roads for you so that you can relax and enjoy the ride.

### Robot Swarm

A robot swarm is a large group of robots that can communicate with one another, like ants or bees. They can be used in a variety of places, including farms or building sites. They work ___ⓐ___ tasks and find solutions as a group.

**12** 위 글의 빈칸 ⓐ에 알맞은 전치사를 쓰시오.

➡ _____

**13** 위 글의 밑줄 친 (A)를 다음과 같이 바꿔 쓸 때 빈칸에 들어갈 알맞은 말을 세 단어로 쓰시오.

➡ it can navigate roads for you _____ _____ _____ you can relax and enjoy the ride

**14** Why does a self-driving car need no driver? Answer in English in a full sentence beginning with "Because".

➡ _____
　 _____

**15** With whom can a robot swarm communicate? Answer in English in a full sentence beginning with "It". (6 words)

➡ _____

**교과서**

# 구석구석

### Presentation Time Step 3

What do you think this painting shows? I think it shows a machine helping
〔machine을 수식하는 현재분사〕
people clean their houses. The machine looks similar to today's robot vacuum
〔help의 목적격보어(= to clean)〕　〔'거리, 시간, 가격, 무게' 등의 경우 무생물이라도 아포스트로피('s)로 소유격을 나타낼 수 있음.〕
cleaners, but they have some differences. For example, unlike today's robot
〔전치사: ～와는 달리〕
vacuum cleaners, the machine in the painting is controlled by a human.
〔the machine이 주어이므로 수동태〕

구문해설　• machine: 기계　• similar: 비슷한　• difference: 차이　• robot vacuum cleaner: 로봇
진공청소기　• unlike: ～와 다른, ～와는 달리　• control: 조정[조절]하다

### After You Read B

**home helper robot:** I tried to cheer up a child of the family I work for. He felt
〔try+to부정사: ～하려고 노력하다〕
sad because of his bad grades.
〔because of 뒤에는 '주어+동사'가 올 수 없다.〕
**search-and-rescue robot:** Last week, after a storm hit, I cleared a route to
help a boy to escape.
〔help+목적어+(to)부정사〕
**robot swarm:** We communicated with one another and built a tower
〔서로〕
by working together.
〔by ～ing: ～하는 것에 의해, ～함으로써〕

구문해설　• cheer up: 기운을 내다, ～을 격려하다　• grade: 성적　• rescue: 구조　• escape: 탈출하다
• communicate with: ～와 연락하다

### Think and Write Step 3

#### School Life in 30 Years

In 30 years, school life will be very different from now. It is likely
〔가주어〕
that there will be a big change in location. Students won't have to go to school.
〔진주어〕　　　　　　　　　　　　　　　　　　　　〔= will not〕
Instead, they will study at home using a variety of apps. One positive effect of
〔분사구문〕　　〔= various〕
such a change would be that students could save time because they would not
〔가정법(미래 상황)〕
have to go to school and come back. However, there could be some negative
〔가정법〕
effects too. For example, students wouldn't be able to meet their friends as
〔가정법〕　　　　〔= can〕　　　　　　　　　　　　　〔원급 비교〕
often. We don't know exactly what school life will be like in the future, but I
〔what A will be like: A가 어떻게 될지〕
hope it will be as fun and meaningful as it is now.
〔원급 비교〕　　　　　　　　　〔지금과 같이〕

구문해설　• a variety of: 다양한　• exactly: 정확하게　• meaningful: 의미 있는

해석

여러분은 이 그림이 무엇을 보여준다고 생각하나요? 저는 이것이 사람들이 집을 청소하는 것을 도와주는 기계를 보여준다고 생각합니다. 그 기계는 오늘날의 로봇 진공청소기와 비슷하게 보이지만 약간의 차이가 있습니다. 예를 들어, 오늘날의 로봇 진공청소기와는 다르게 그림에 있는 기계는 인간에 의해 조종됩니다.

**집안일 도우미 로봇:** 나는 내가 일하는 가족의 한 아이의 기운을 북돋워주려고 했다. 그는 나쁜 점수 때문에 슬픔을 느꼈다.

**수색 구조 로봇:** 지난주에 나는 폭풍이 강타한 뒤에 한 소년이 탈출하는 것을 돕기 위해 길을 청소했다.

**로봇 군집:** 우리는 서로 의사소통하고, 함께 일함으로써 탑을 지었다.

**30년 후의 학교 생활**

30년 후에, 학교 생활은 지금과 많이 달라질 것이다. 장소에 큰 변화가 있을 것이다. 학생들은 학교에 갈 필요가 없게 될 것이다. 대신, 그들은 집에서 다양한 앱을 이용하여 공부할 것이다. 그러한 변화의 한 가지 긍정적인 효과는 학생들이 학교에 다녀올 필요가 없기 때문에 시간을 절약할 수 있다는 것이다. 하지만, 부정적인 효과 또한 있을 수 있다. 예를 들어, 학생들이 전과 같이 자주 친구들을 만날 수 없을 것이다. 우리는 미래에 학교 생활이 어떻게 될지 정확하게 알 수는 없다. 그렇지만, 나는 오늘날과 마찬가지로 재미있고, 의미 있기를 희망한다.

Words & Expressions

**01** 밑줄 친 부분과 바꿔 쓸 수 있는 말을 주어진 철자로 시작하여 쓰시오.

> He is 59 years old, and uses his fake arms well.

➡ a_____

**02** 다음 영영풀이가 가리키는 것을 고르시오.

> an unfortunate event that damages a large area and may harm many people

① delivery  ② intelligence  ③ program
④ signal  ⑤ disaster

**03** 다음 중 밑줄 친 부분의 뜻풀이가 바르지 않은 것은?

① He performs an important role in this group. (공연하다)
② A swarm of bees passed over the field. (떼)
③ The solution to last week's puzzle is on page 12. (해답)
④ You should think of your safety before anything else. (안전)
⑤ The president's speech continued for more than an hour. (연설)

**04** 다음 짝지어진 단어의 관계가 같도록 빈칸에 알맞은 말을 쓰시오.

> praise : compliment = _____ : flee

**05** 다음 문장의 빈칸에 들어갈 말을 〈보기〉에서 골라 쓰시오.

> ┤ 보기 ├
> make decisions / work on / find solutions / look toward / deal with

(1) Moody people are very difficult to _____.
(2) We _____ based on our experiences.
(3) _____ the future and make a plan.
(4) Which subject do you want to _____?
(5) I have to face my problems and learn to _____ for them.

Conversation

**[06~08]** 다음 대화를 읽고 물음에 답하시오.

G: Look at these. They are the new inventions of the month!
B: They all look great. What is the invention on the first page?
G: It's a new smart refrigerator. It senses the items inside it and suggests recipes.
(A) It does. What do you think of this flying camera? I want to buy it.
(B) That sounds awesome. What do you want to take pictures of?
(C) A flying camera? Could you explain how it works?
(D) ⓐThat sounds helpful.
(E) ⓑOf course. This machine flies to a destination that we have already set. While it's flying, it can take pictures from 500 meters above the location.
G: I want to take pictures of flying birds!

**06** 위 대화의 (A~(E)가 자연스럽게 이어지도록 순서대로 배열한 것을 고르시오.

① (B) – (A) – (C) – (E) – (D)
② (C) – (B) – (D) – (A) – (E)
③ (C) – (D) – (A) – (E) – (B)
④ (D) – (A) – (C) – (E) – (B)
⑤ (D) – (B) – (A) – (C) – (E)

**07** 위 대화의 밑줄 친 @That이 가리키는 것을 우리말로 쓰시오.

➡ _____

_____

**08** 위 대화의 밑줄 친 ⓑOf course.와 바꿔 쓸 수 없는 것을 고르시오.

① Yes.
② That's all right.
③ Okay.
④ Sure.
⑤ No problem.

**[09~11]** 다음 대화를 읽고 물음에 답하시오.

B: What are you watching?
G: It's a show about a man who lost one of his @arm in an accident. Surprisingly, he can play the drums very well.
B: How can he play the drums with only one arm?
G: Actually he uses two arms. ⓑOne is a robot arm ⓒcontrolled by his brain.
B: That's awesome. Could you explain in more detail?
G: Sure. First, he thinks @what he wants to do with his arm. Then those thoughts are turned into electronic signals. The signals travel from his brain to his robot arm and move @it.
B: That's amazing! I think this technology can help many people.

**09** 위 대화의 밑줄 친 @~@ 중에서 어법상 어색한 것은?

① @     ② ⓑ     ③ ⓒ     ④ @     ⑤ @

**10** 위 대화에서 다음의 영영풀이가 나타내는 말을 찾아 쓰시오.

> information sent in the form of light, sound, electricity, etc., by a machine

➡ _____

**11** 위 대화의 내용과 일치하도록 다음 빈칸에 알맞은 말을 쓰시오.

➡ He thinks _____ with his arm. → Those thoughts are changed to _____. → The signals are transported from his brain _____.

Grammar

**12** 다음 주어진 문장을 가정법으로 바르게 고친 것은?

> As Anne didn't pay the bill, she couldn't use light and water last year.

① If Anne paid the bill, she could use light and water last year.
② If Anne paid the bill last year, she could have used light and water.
③ If Anne had paid the bill, she couldn't have used light and water last year.
④ If Anne had paid the bill, she could have used light and water last year.
⑤ If Anne had paid the bill, she could have been used light and water last year.

**13** 다음 대화를 참고하여 아래 주어진 빈칸에 적절한 단어를 쓰시오.

> **Tommy:** Did you call me yesterday? Why?
> **Sandy:** To get you ready for the presentation.

➡ Sandy called Tommy yesterday in _____ _____ he might _____ _____ _____ the presentation.

[14~15] 다음 가정법으로 주어진 우리말에 맞게 아래 어구들을 어법상 적절한 형태로 바꿔 배열하고, 직설법 문장으로도 바꾸시오.

**14**

> 비가 세차게 오면, 우리가 응원하러 야구장에 갈 수 없을 텐데. (hard, to, can, go, we, the stadium, it, to, rain, cheer, not)

➡ (1) If _____

_____ .

(2) 직설법: As _____

_____ .

**15**

> 인공지능이 개발되지 않았다면, 컴퓨터가 인간을 이길 수 없었을 텐데. (be developed, can't, win over, artificial intelligence, humans)

➡ (1) If _____

_____ .

(2) 직설법: As _____

_____ .

**16** 다음 우리말을 영작할 때, 어법상 어색한 문장을 모두 고르시오.

> 로봇이 없다면, 많은 사람들이 그 위험한 작업을 해야 할 텐데.

① Without robots, many people should have done the dangerous work.
② If there were no robots, many people would have to do the dangerous work.
③ If it were not for robots, many people would have to do the dangerous work.
④ Were it not for robots, many people would have to do the dangerous work.
⑤ If there are no robots, many people would have to do the dangerous work.

[17~18] 다음 중 어법상 어색한 문장을 고르시오.

**17** ① If he told that to his friends, they would be upset with the teacher.
② If the boy succeeded in catching the school bus this morning, he would not have been late for school.
③ If you were the president, you could make a rule to respect one another.
④ If Mary got up earlier, she could be at the meeting in time.
⑤ If Yuna had put that coat on, she wouldn't have caught a cold.

**18** ① Could you share your method of studying so that the students can improve their scores in a math test?

② Jamie practiced playing the cello hard so that for her to get a scholarship.

③ Julie prepared rice and water so that she could make Juk, the Korean porridge.

④ The genius majored in the computer science so as to make a better machine.

⑤ Mr. Lee got up early so as not to miss the airplane.

**19** 다음 그림을 보고 괄호 안의 어구를 바르게 배열하여 빈칸을 알맞게 채우시오.

(1)

➡ The rescue robot is approaching the burning building _____ _____ of human firefighters.
(the risks, order, can, it, reduce, that, in)

(2)

➡ The robots in a robot swarm communicate with one another _____ _____ .
(tasks, as, on, they, that, so, can, work, a group)

---

**Reading**

[20~22] 다음 글을 읽고 물음에 답하시오.

**Robots around Us – Present and Future**

Robots are making things faster and easier. They can help us anywhere—in our homes, on roads, or in disaster areas.

**Home Helper Robot**

This robot helps your family throughout the day. Cooking and cleaning _____ⓐ_____ be easier if you had ⓑone. It also talks with family members and can sense emotions.

**20** 위 글의 빈칸 ⓐ에 들어갈 알맞은 조동사를 쓰시오.

➡ _____

**21** Where can robots help us? Answer in English in a full sentence.

➡ _____
_____

**22** 위 글의 밑줄 친 ⓑone과 문법적 쓰임이 같은 것을 고르시오.

① There's only one thing we can do.

② They all went off in one direction.

③ She was wearing her new dress, the red one.

④ Do you want one biscuit or two?

⑤ One must obey one's parents.

**[23~24]** 다음 글을 읽고 물음에 답하시오.

_____ ⓐ _____

Our future with robots looks bright but not perfect. Some people expect life to become more convenient with the help of robots. ___ⓑ___, other people worry about problems they might cause, such as threats to our jobs and safety. The important thing is to find possible solutions and to ensure that robots are only used for good.

## 23 위 글의 빈칸 ⓐ에 들어갈 제목으로 알맞은 것을 고르시오.

① Looking toward the Future
② Threats to Our Safety Caused by Robots
③ Robots around Us – Present and Future
④ Robots Are Becoming Smart
⑤ Where Do We See Robots?

## 24 위 글의 빈칸 ⓑ에 들어갈 알맞은 말을 고르시오.

① Similarly     ② However
③ Thus     ④ That is
⑤ As a result

**[25~27]** 다음 글을 읽고 물음에 답하시오.

### School Life in 30 Years

In 30 years, school life will be very different from now. ( ① ) It is likely that there will be ⓐ <u>a big change in location.</u> ( ② ) Students won't have to go to school. ( ③ ) One positive effect of such a change would be that students could save time because they would not have to go to school and come back. ( ④ ) However, there could be some negative effects too. ( ⑤ ) For example, students wouldn't be able to meet their friends as often. We don't know exactly what school life will be like in the future, but I hope it will be as fun and meaningful as it is now.

## 25 위 글의 흐름으로 보아, 주어진 문장이 들어가기에 가장 적절한 곳은?

Instead, they will study at home using a variety of apps.

①     ②     ③     ④     ⑤

## 26 위 글의 밑줄 친 ⓐ의 구체적인 내용을 우리말로 쓰시오.

➡ _____

## 27 According to the passage, which is NOT true?

① In 30 years, school life will be very different from now.
② Students will study at home using a variety of apps.
③ Students could save time because they would not have to go to school and come back.
④ Students wouldn't be able to meet their friends as often.
⑤ School life in the future will be as fun and meaningful as it is now.

**출제율 90%**

**01** 다음 영영풀이가 가리키는 것을 고르시오.

> to attach something or put something on, especially something useful

① escape       ② equip

③ recognize     ④ navigate

⑤ ensure

**출제율 95%**

**02** 다음 주어진 문장의 밑줄 친 common과 같은 의미로 쓰인 것은?

> Jackson is a common English name.

① They combined against a common enemy.

② This decision was taken for the common good.

③ It's a common mistake among learners of English.

④ Just use your common sense!

⑤ We went for a walk on the common.

**출제율 100%**

**03** 다음 문장의 빈칸 (A)~(C)에 들어갈 말로 바르게 짝지어진 것은?

> • It was not an easy ___(A)___, and I couldn't finish it on time.
> • The machine ___(B)___ my question and answered it.
> • There is a ___(C)___ of stormy weather during the flight.

① task – ensured – delivery

② destination – ensured – delivery

③ task – recognized – delivery

④ destination – recognized – threat

⑤ task – recognized – threat

**[04~06]** 다음 대화를 읽고 물음에 답하시오.

G: I had to wait in line at the store for almost twenty minutes.

B: That's too bad. (①) Maybe in the future we'll never have to wait in line.

G: (②) What do you mean?

B: (③) I read about (a)a store without cashiers. You take what you want to buy and just walk out.

G: (④) _____(A)_____

B: There are cameras and sensors in the store. (⑤) They keep track of the items you choose and send the information to an app on your smartphone.

G: Then the app pays for them when you leave the store?

B: Exactly. It's likely that these kinds of stores will be more common in the future.

**출제율 90%**

**04** 위 대화의 (①)~(⑤) 중 다음 문장이 들어가기에 적절한 곳은?

> That's it?

①     ②     ③     ④     ⑤

**출제율 90%**

**05** 위 대화의 빈칸 (A)에 알맞은 것은?

① How do you pay for it?

② How do you think they will change?

③ Have you heard of it before?

④ Could you tell me if they are equipped with AI?

⑤ Could you explain what it is?

**출제율 95%**

**06** 밑줄 친 (a)a store without cashiers의 특징을 45자 내외의 우리말로 서술하시오.

➡ _____

_____

B: Hey, have you played this game? It's really exciting.
G: Yes, I have. That game is pretty popular these days.
B: The developers used AI technology in it. The game characters are equipped with AI.
G: Oh, really? Could you explain in more detail?
B: Sure. The AI characters in the game learn from what human players do and develop their skills.
G: Oh! That's why I sometimes felt like they already knew my moves!
B: They're very smart. (A)It is likely that the AI in games will get stronger and stronger.

출제율 95%

**07** 위 대화의 밑줄 친 (A)와 바꾸어 쓸 수 있는 것을 모두 고르시오.

① It is notable that the AI in games will get stronger and stronger.
② It is probable that the AI in games will get stronger and stronger.
③ It is expected that the AI in games will get stronger and stronger.
④ It is possible that the AI in games will get stronger and stronger.
⑤ It is doubtful that the AI in games will get stronger and stronger.

출제율 100%

**08** 위 대화의 내용과 일치하지 않는 것은?

① G는 그 게임을 해봤다.
② 개발자들이 그 게임에 인공지능 기술을 사용했다.
③ 게임 캐릭터들에 인공지능이 탑재되어 있다.

④ 게임 속 인공지능 캐릭터들은 인간 플레이어가 하는 행동을 통해 배우고 자신의 기술을 발전시킨다.
⑤ B는 이따금씩 캐릭터들이 이미 자신의 움직임을 알고 있는 것처럼 느꼈다.

출제율 95%

**09** 다음 가정법 문장 중 어법상 옳은 것을 고르시오.

① His father would feel proud if David makes it to the finals of the national athletic competition.
② If it had not been for the Chinese characters, it would be difficult for the ancient people to read and write.
③ If the student were not so hungry, he can share his sandwich with you.
④ What would Mr. Kang do if it rained on his daughter's marathon day?
⑤ Mary will feel disappointed if her dogs and cats left the area.

출제율 95%

**10** 다음 각 빈칸에 공통으로 들어갈 단어 중 나머지 넷과 성격이 다른 하나는?

① They woke up early _____ that they could see their mom off.
② Yejin hurried _____ that she couldn't miss the train her husband was in.
③ Carlson Jr. was _____ busy that he couldn't hear my requests.
④ The member of city council talked louder _____ that everyone present could understand.
⑤ Please switch on the light _____ that I can get out of here.

**출제율 90%**

**11** 다음 주어진 우리말을 어법에 맞게 바르게 영작한 것은?

> 비가 충분히 오지 않으면 곡식들이 전보다 덜 자랄 텐데. (사실 비가 충분히 안 온다.)

① If it didn't rain enough, the crops would grow less than before.
② If it had not rained enough, the crops would have grown less than before.
③ Had it not rained enough, the crops would grow less than before.
④ Didn't it rain enough, the crops will grow less than before.
⑤ If it rained not enough, the crops would have grown less than before.

**출제율 100%**

**12** 다음 문장의 밑줄 친 so that의 쓰임이 흐름상 어색한 것은?

① Sumi's father baked some bread for her friends so that they could enjoy.
② The performer played the guitar on the street so that the passers-by could listen to the beautiful music.
③ Minju practiced hard so that she could pass the P.E. test.
④ Wendy failed to get the doctor's certificate so that she had studied harder.
⑤ The actress wore sunglasses so that she could hide her face.

**출제율 100%**

**13** 다음 중 어법상 옳은 문장은?

① Jane has saved changes for 8 months so to buy a pretty doll.
② Bob has been exercising regularly in order that he could lose some weight.
③ The penguin was so sadness that it wouldn't show up above the water.

④ Kate came out earlier so that she not being late for the concert.
⑤ Henderson took the umbrellas in order for his kids could use them.

**출제율 100%**

**14** 다음 우리말을 주어진 어구들과 조건에 맞게 영작하시오.

> 한국의 역사를 배우면, 그들이 독도를 더욱 이해할 수 있을 텐데.
> (learn, understand, much, can, Dokdo, the history of Korea 활용. If로 시작, 단어 변형 가능, 총 12 단어로 할 것)

➡ _____

_____

**출제율 100%**

**15** 다음 주어진 문장과 같은 뜻이 되도록 각각 주어진 조건에 맞게 빈칸을 채우시오.

> Beth watched the movie three times so that she would not forget the touching scenes.

(1) Beth watched the movie three times _____ the touching scenes.
   (to부정사의 부사적 용법 활용, 3 단어)
(2) Beth watched the movie three times _____ the touching scenes.
   (so as 활용, 5 단어)
(3) Beth watched the movie three times _____ she would not forget the touching scenes. (in 활용, 3 단어)

**16** 다음 그림을 보고 자연스러운 문장이 되도록 괄호 안에 주어진 단어를 바르게 배열하여 빈칸을 완성하시오.

(1)

**Self-Driving Car**

➡ Mike bought a self-driving car _____ _____ himself. (would, that, drive, he, not, so)

(2)

➡ Gutenberg invented the printing press _____ and wider. (that, information, in order, spread, faster, could, much)

**[17~18]** 다음 중에서 틀린 문장을 찾아 기호를 쓰고, 바르게 고쳐 문장을 다시 쓰시오.

**17** ① If the professor could be awarded for her work, I would be very proud of her.
② If Sujin told the truth to her mom, she would be touched with what her daughter had been doing for her.
③ If Teresa had got up earlier than usual this morning, she wouldn't have missed the train.
④ If Sehee missed the school bus, she would not have been late for class.

⑤ If Ralph had put on the glasses, he would have noticed the girl.

➡ _____

**18** ① The priest has gone to the poor town so that he would help the kids there.
② The old maid saved some money in order that her son could study abroad.
③ I called the special cleaning service so that my car would get washed.
④ The players tried their best in order to beat the other players.
⑤ The shopper didn't buy a thing so as that she could save money.

➡ _____

**19** 괄호 안의 조건과 가정법을 이용하여 아래 대화의 빈칸을 알맞게 채우시오.

(1) A: Do the girls see the show?
B: No, but if they _____, they _____ happy. (see, will, feel 활용)

(2) A: Does Jenny have my number?
B: No, but if she _____, she _____ you. (know, can, contact 활용)

(3) A: Was the lady healthy?
B: No, but if she _____, she _____ the short marathon last week. (be, complete, can 활용)

**[20~22]** 다음 글을 읽고 물음에 답하시오.

ⓐ _____

(①) In the past, robots performed only easy tasks that humans programmed them to do. (②) However, robots are now getting "smarter," and soon they might be able to think ⓑlike humans. (③)
Robots that have AI can perceive environments and make decisions. (④) They can also recognize speech, tell jokes, and play games with humans. (⑤)

**20** 위 글의 빈칸 ⓐ에 들어갈 제목으로 알맞은 것을 고르시오.

① Robots around Us – Present and Future
② Where Do We See Robots?
③ Humans Programmed Tasks for Robots
④ Looking toward the Future
⑤ Robots Are Becoming Smart

**21** 위 글의 흐름으로 보아, 주어진 문장이 들어가기에 가장 적절한 곳은?

> What makes this possible is artificial intelligence (AI).

①     ②     ③     ④     ⑤

**22** 위 글의 밑줄 친 ⓑlike와 같은 의미로 쓰인 것을 고르시오.

① What's it like studying in Spain?
② He ran like the wind.
③ I didn't like noisy music.
④ No one sings the blues like she did.
⑤ She responded in like manner.

**[23~24]** 다음 글을 읽고 물음에 답하시오.

**Robot Swarm**

A robot swarm is a large group of robots that can communicate with one another, like ants or bees. (A)They can ___ⓐ___ in a variety of places, including farms or building sites. They work on tasks and find solutions as a group.

**23** 위 글의 빈칸 ⓐ에 use를 알맞은 형태로 쓰시오.

➡ _____

**24** 위 글의 밑줄 친 (A)They가 가리키는 것을 본문에서 찾아 쓰시오.

➡ _____

**[25~26]** 다음 글을 읽고 물음에 답하시오.

**The Smartphone**

• When was it invented?
- The smartphone was invented in the United States in 1992.
• What changes did it bring?
- The smartphone allows people to do many different things with just their phone. ⓐIt can be used not only for calls but also for sending messages, taking pictures, and more. Also, it lets people access the Internet any time and anywhere.

*출제율 95%*

**25** 위 글의 밑줄 친 ⓐ를 다음과 같이 바꿔 쓸 때 빈칸에 들어갈 알맞은 말을 세 단어로 쓰시오.

➡ It can be used for sending messages, taking pictures, and more _____ _____ _____ for calls.

*출제율 100%*

**26** 위 글을 읽고 알 수 없는 것을 고르시오.

① When was the smartphone invented?
② Who invented the smartphone?
③ Can people do many different things with just their smartphone?
④ Can people take pictures with their smartphone?
⑤ Can people access the Internet any time and anywhere with the smartphone?

*출제율 100%*

**27** 주어진 문장 다음에 이어질 글의 순서로 가장 적절한 것은?

> In the past, robots performed only easy tasks that humans programmed them to do.
> (A) What makes this possible is artificial intelligence (AI).
> (B) Robots that have AI can perceive environments and make decisions. They can also recognize speech, tell jokes, and play games with humans.
> (C) However, robots are now getting "smarter," and soon they might be able to think like humans.

① (A) – (C) – (B)  ② (B) – (A) – (C)
③ (B) – (C) – (A)  ④ (C) – (A) – (B)
⑤ (C) – (B) – (A)

[28~30] 다음 글을 읽고 물음에 답하시오.

**School Life in 30 Years**

In 30 years, school life will be very different from now. It is likely that there will be ⓐa big change in textbooks. Students won't use paper books anymore. Instead, they will use a tablet PC and files (A)[downloading / downloaded] from the cloud. One positive effect of (B)[so / such] a change would be that students won't have to carry heavy backpacks with books and notebooks. However, there could be some negative effects too. For example, students' eyesight could get (C)[better / worse] because they have to look at the tablet PC screen all day long. We don't know exactly ⓑ학교 생활이 어떤 모습일지 in the future, but I hope it will be as fun and meaningful as it is now.

*출제율 90%*

**28** 위 글의 밑줄 친 ⓐ의 구체적인 내용을 우리말로 쓰시오.

➡ _____

_____

*출제율 100%*

**29** 위 글의 괄호 (A)~(C)에서 문맥이나 어법상 알맞은 낱말을 골라 쓰시오.

➡ (A) _____  (B) _____  (C) _____

*출제율 95%*

**30** 위 글의 밑줄 친 ⓑ의 우리말에 맞게 주어진 어휘를 알맞게 배열하시오.

> will / school life / like / what / be

➡ _____

**[01~03]** 다음 대화를 읽고 물음에 답하시오.

G: I had to wait in line at the store for almost twenty minutes.

B: That's too bad. Maybe in the future we'll never have to wait in line.

G: What do you mean?

B: I read about a store without cashiers. You take what you want to buy and just walk out.

G: That's it? How do you pay for it?

B: There are cameras and sensors in the store. They keep track of the items you choose and send the information to an app on your smartphone.

G: Then the app pays for them when you leave the store?

B: Exactly. It's likely that these kinds of stores will be more common in the future.

**01** What is likely to disappear at stores in the future? Use the phrase "It is likely that".

➡ _____

_____

**02** What will pay for the items you choose at the store without cashiers?

➡ _____

_____

**03** What are there in the store without cashiers?

➡ _____

_____

**04** 다음 우리말을 영작할 때, 〈보기〉의 어구들을 사용하여 빈칸에 알맞게 써 넣으시오. (중복 사용 불가)

┌─ 보기 ─┐
could / would / order / in order to / that / raise / so that / satisfy / show / his thirst / it / I / them
└────────┘

(1) 그는 갈증을 채우기 위해서 시원한 음료수를 주문했다.

➡ He ordered cold beverage _____

_____.

(2) 유진이는 아빠에게 보여드리기 위해서 춤 동작들을 연습했다.

➡ Yujin practiced the dance movements _____ to her daddy.

(3) 나는 강아지를 기를 수 있도록 하기 위해서, 애완 동물 학교에 등록했다.

➡ I signed up for a pet school in _____ _____ a puppy.

**[05~06]** 아래 각 두 문장을 가정법의 한 문장으로 합치되, 주어진 단어로 시작하시오.

**05**
• Jihun doesn't know the actor's name.
• He wants to search him online.

➡ If _____

_____.

**06**
• I'm sorry that I'm not as smart as Bill.
• I want to be as smart as Bill.

➡ I _____.

### Robots Are Becoming Smart

In the past, robots performed only easy tasks (A)[that / what] humans programmed them to do. However, robots are now getting "smarter," and soon they might be able to think like humans. What makes ⓐthis possible (B)[is / are] artificial intelligence (AI).

Robots that have AI can perceive environments and (C)[make / makes] decisions. They can also recognize speech, tell jokes, and play games with humans.

**07** 위 글의 괄호 (A)~(C)에서 어법상 알맞은 낱말을 골라 쓰시오.

➡ (A) _____ (B) _____ (C) _____

**08** 위 글의 밑줄 친 ⓐthis가 가리키는 것을 본문에서 찾아 쓰시오.

➡ _____

_____

**09** 위 글을 읽고, (1) '과거에 로봇이 할 수 있던 일'과 (2) '미래에 인공 지능을 가진 로봇이 할 수 있는 일'을 각각 우리말로 쓰시오.

➡ (1) _____

_____

(2) _____

_____

### Search-and-Rescue Robot

Search-and-rescue robots can go into disaster areas that are dangerous for humans. They find survivors, deal with dangers, and clear routes so that people can escape to safety.

### Looking toward the Future

Our future with robots looks bright but ⓐnot perfect. ⓑSome people expect life becoming more convenient with the help of robots. However, other people worry about problems they might cause, such as threats to our jobs and safety. The important thing is to find possible solutions and to ensure that robots are only used for good.

**10** 위 글의 밑줄 친 ⓐnot perfect를 한 단어로 바꿔 쓰시오.

➡ _____

**11** 위 글의 밑줄 친 ⓑ에서 어법상 틀린 부분을 찾아 고치시오.

_____ ➡ _____

**12** 본문의 내용과 일치하도록 다음 빈칸 (A)와 (B)에 알맞은 단어를 쓰시오.

Search-and-rescue robots can be used in (A)_____ _____ that are dangerous for humans, where they find survivors, deal with dangers, and (B)_____ _____ for people to escape to safety.

**01** 다음 그림을 보고 '가능성 정도 표현하기'를 이용하여 자신의 생각을 쓰시오.

(1)   (2)   (3)

(1) _____

(2) _____

(3) _____

**02** 다음 내용을 바탕으로 30년 후의 학교 생활을 상상하여 쓰시오.

---

**1. How will school life be different in 30 years?**

There will be a big change in location.

**2. Give some details about the change.**

Students won't have to go to school. Instead, they will study at home using a variety of apps.

**3. What would be a positive effect of the change?**

Students could save time because they would not have to go to school and come back.

**4. Would there be any negative effects? If so, describe one.**

Students wouldn't be able to meet their friends as often.

---

**School Life in 30 Years**

In 30 years, school life will be very different from now. It is likely that there will be a big change in (A)_____. Students won't have to go to school. Instead, they will study at home (B)_____. One positive effect of such a change would be that students could (C)_____ because they would not have to go to school and come back. However, there could be some (D)_____ too. For example, students wouldn't be able to (E)_____ as often. We don't know exactly what school life will be like in the future, but I hope it will be as fun and meaningful as it is now.

---

## 단원별 모의고사

**01** 다음 우리말에 맞게 빈칸에 알맞은 말을 쓰시오. (철자가 주어진 것도 있음.)

(1) 그가 그 사고의 유일한 생존자였다.
➡ He was the only _____ of the accident.

(2) 거실에는 몇 개의 조화가 장식용으로 사용되었다.
➡ Some _____ flowers were used to decorate the living room.

(3) 이것이 학교로 가는 가장 짧은 길이다.
➡ This is the shortest r_____ to the school.

(4) 주문하신 상품을 이번 주에 배달해 드릴 것을 약속드립니다.
➡ We guarantee _____ of your order this week.

**02** 다음 문장의 빈칸에 들어갈 말을 〈보기〉에서 골라 쓰시오.

┌─── 보기 ├───
likely / resource / safety / sense / signal
└──────────────

(1) Oil is not a renewable energy _____.
(2) They have a casual attitude towards _____.
(3) The siren was a _____ for everyone to leave the building.
(4) The computer will be able to _____ other cars on the road.
(5) The exchange rate is _____ to fall in the near future.

**03** 다음 제시된 의미에 맞는 단어를 주어진 철자로 시작하여 빈칸에 쓰고, 그 뜻을 마지막의 빈칸에 쓰시오.

(1) d_____ _____ : to handle or solve something such as a problem: _____

(2) s_____ : the answer to a problem: _____

(3) s_____ : the state of being safe from harm or danger: _____

(4) s_____ : a large number of living things: _____

(5) e_____ : to get free: _____

(6) p_____ : to notice something with the senses: _____

**04** 다음 중 짝지어진 대화가 어색한 것은?

① A: The space balloon is an interesting invention.
　B: I haven't heard of it before.

② A: Could you explain how it works in more detail?
　B: Sure. That sounds awesome.

③ A: How will our lives change in the future?
　B: I think that restaurants will change a lot.

④ A: What do you want to take pictures of?
　B: I want to take pictures of flying birds!

⑤ A: Then the app pays for them when you leave the store?
　B: Exactly. It's likely that these kinds of stores will be more common in the future.

**[05~06]** 다음 대화를 읽고 물음에 답하시오.

B: What are you watching?

G: It's a show about a man who lost one of his arms in an accident. Surprisingly, he can play the drums very well.

B: How can he play the drums with only one arm?

G: Actually he uses two arms. One is a robot arm controlled by his brain.

B: That's awesome. Could you explain in more detail?

G: Sure. First, he thinks what he wants to do with his arm. Then those thoughts are turned into electronic signals. The signals travel from his brain to his robot arm and move it.

B: That's amazing! I think this technology can help many people.

**05** What is the show G is watching about?

➡ _____

_____

**06** 위 대화의 내용과 일치하지 않는 것은?

① G는 사고로 한쪽 팔을 잃은 남자에 관한 프로그램을 보고 있다.

② 그 남자는 드럼을 매우 잘 칠 수 있다.

③ 사실 그 남자는 두 팔을 사용해서 드럼을 친다.

④ 그 남자가 자신의 팔로 하고 싶은 것을 생각하면 그 생각들이 전기 신호로 바뀐다.

⑤ 로봇 팔이 바뀐 전기 신호를 뇌로 전달한다.

**[07~08]** 다음 대화를 읽고 물음에 답하시오.

B: Hey, have you played this game? It's really exciting.

G: Yes, I have. That game is pretty popular these days.

B: The developers used AI technology in it. The game characters are equipped with AI.

G: Oh, really? Could you explain in more detail?

B: Sure. The AI characters in the game learn from what human players do and develop their skills.

G: Oh! (a)그래서 이따금씩 그들이 이미 내 움직임을 알고 있는 것처럼 느껴졌던 거구나! (my moves, sometimes, that's, feel, already)

B: They're very smart. It is ___(A)___ that the AI in games will get stronger and stronger.

**07** 위 대화의 빈칸 (A)에 알맞지 않은 것을 모두 고르시오.

① probable　　② possible

③ likely　　④ imaginable

⑤ appropriate

**08** 위 대화의 밑줄 친 우리말 (a)를 주어진 어휘를 활용하여 11 단어로 영작하시오.

➡ _____

_____

**[09~10]** 다음 글을 읽고 물음에 답하시오.

M: As climate change is going to make farming harder, there may not be enough resources for the increasing number of people on Earth. For this reason, ___(A)___. For example, we won't kill animals for food. ___(B)___, meat will be grown in a lab using animal cells. This will require less land, water, and other resources. ___(C)___, bugs such as ants will become part of our daily meals. You might not want to eat them, but they are actually very rich in nutrients!

**09** 〈보기〉에 주어진 어휘를 알맞게 배열하여 위 글의 빈칸 (A)에 들어갈 말을 쓰시오.

> ┤ 보기 ├
>
> we, we, our, it, food, get, change, have, is, will, likely, how, that, to

➡ _____

_____

**10** 위 글의 빈칸 (B)와 (C)에 알맞은 것으로 바르게 짝지어진 것을 고르시오.

|  | (B) | (C) |
|---|---|---|
| ① | Instead | Also |
| ② | Instead | That is |
| ③ | In addition | Also |
| ④ | In addition | That is |
| ⑤ | As a result | However |

**[11~12]** 다음 중 밑줄 친 부분의 쓰임이 나머지와 다른 것은?

**11** ① The ballerina would get a full scholarship to the college if she practiced harder than before.
② If Henry were an actor in the movie, you could find him at least once.
③ The kids in the kinderagarten would go out to play if it stopped raining.
④ Nancy had no idea if the rumor about Jessy would turn out true.
⑤ The secretary could call his boss if he needed advice about the report.

**12** ① My aunt turned off the radio so that she could concentrate on the study.
② Those flowers open up in early spring so that they can avoid the competition.
③ Jordan's friends tried their best so that they could win the final match.
④ Marianne took a taxi so that she wouldn't be late for work.

⑤ She made a great fortune, so that she could buy a big house in New York.

**13** 다음 중 〈보기〉의 밑줄 친 would와 쓰임이 같은 것은?

> ┤ 보기 ├
>
> Lynn would give up the job opportunity from abroad if her family didn't agree on their being apart.

① Would you bring me the red umbrella while I'm holding this dog?
② The math teacher said that he would buy me a good meal the next day.
③ Michael's family would go on a picnic to the lake park when I was young.
④ The students would like to eat the Bulgogi pizza for the birthday party.
⑤ The applicant would get the position if he improved the skill in persuading others.

**14** 다음 주어진 우리말을 영작한 것으로 옳지 않은 것은?

> Paul은 세계적인 가수가 되기 위해 밤낮으로 노래 연습을 했다.

① Paul practiced singing day and night in order to become a world-class singer.
② Paul practiced singing day and night so that he became a world-class singer.
③ Paul practiced singing day and night so as to become a world-class singer.
④ Paul practiced singing day and night so that he could become a world-class singer.
⑤ Paul practiced singing day and night in order that he would become a world-class singer.

**15** 다음 중 내용상 〈보기〉의 밑줄 친 부분과 바꿔 쓸 수 없는 것은?

┤ 보기 ├

If it were not for Artificial Intelligence, the robots could not decide what to do.

① Were it not for Artificial Intelligence,
② Without Artificial Intelligence,
③ Had it not been for Artificial Intelligence,
④ But for Artificial Intelligence,
⑤ If there were no Artificial Intelligence,

**16** 다음 중 〈보기〉의 문장과 의미가 가장 가까운 것을 고르시오.

┤ 보기 ├

If Kobe were in good condition, he would make three times as many clean shots as any other players.

① As Kobe was not in good condition, he didn't make three times as many clean shots as any other players.
② As Kobe is not in good condition, he doesn't make three times as many clean shots as any other players.
③ Though Kobe was not in good condition, he made three times as many clean shots as any other players.
④ As Kobe isn't in good condition, he didn't make three times as many clean shots as any other players.
⑤ As Kobe was in good condition, he made three times as many clean shots as any other players.

**17** 다음 우리말을 주어진 어구들과 조건에 맞게 영작하시오.

로봇들이 인간의 감정을 느낀다면, 우리는 그들과 함께 놀 수 있을 텐데

(can, sense, with, human emotions 활용. If로 시작, 단어 변형 가능, 총 10 단어로 할 것.)

➡ _____

_____

**[18~20]** 다음 글을 읽고 물음에 답하시오.

**Where Do We See Robots?**

Robots are not only in movies and books ⓐ . Around the world, robots are doing (A)a variety of tasks. There are delivery robots ⓑ in the sky, robot arms in factories, and service robots in public places.
• A delivery robot in the sky
• Robot arms in a factory
• A service robot at the PyeongChang Olympics

**18** 위 글의 빈칸 ⓐ에 들어갈 알맞은 말을 모두 고르시오.

① no longer      ② anymore
③ anywhere      ④ no more
⑤ any longer

**19** 위 글의 빈칸 ⓑ에 fly를 알맞은 형태로 쓰시오.

➡ _____

**20** 위 글의 밑줄 친 (A)a variety of와 바꿔 쓸 수 있는 한 단어를 쓰시오.

➡ _____

**[21~23]** 다음 글을 읽고 물음에 답하시오.

ⓐ
_____

Robots are making things faster and easier. They can help us anywhere — in our homes, on roads, or in disaster areas.

**Home Helper Robot**

This robot helps your family throughout the day. Cooking and cleaning would be easier if you had ⓑone. It also talks with family members and can sense emotions.

**21** 위 글의 빈칸 ⓐ에 들어갈 제목으로 알맞은 것을 고르시오.

① Looking toward the Future
② Life with a Home Helper Robot
③ Robots Are Becoming Smart
④ Robots around Us – Present and Future
⑤ Let's Enjoy Talking with Robots

**22** 위 글의 밑줄 친 ⓑone이 가리키는 것을 본문에서 찾아 쓰시오.

➡ _____

**23** 다음 중 '집안일 도우미 로봇'이 할 수 있는 일이 <u>아닌</u> 것을 고르시오.

① 요리
② 재난 지역 복구
③ 청소
④ 가족과 이야기하기
⑤ 가족의 감정을 파악하기

**[24~25]** 다음 글을 읽고 물음에 답하시오.

**Looking toward the Future**

Our future with robots looks bright but not perfect. Some people expect life to become more convenient with the help of robots. However, ___ⓐ___ worry about problems they might cause, such as threats to our jobs and safety. The important thing is ⓑto find possible solutions and to ensure that robots are only used for good.

**24** 위 글의 빈칸 ⓐ에 들어갈 알맞은 말을 고르시오.

① the other        ② another
③ the others       ④ each other
⑤ other people

**25** 아래 〈보기〉에서 위 글의 밑줄 친 ⓑ와 to부정사의 용법이 <u>다른</u> 것의 개수를 고르시오.

┌─── 보기 ───┐
① I need a pencil to write with.
② I have to study hard to pass the exam.
③ He grew up to be a doctor.
④ It is very important to study English hard.
⑤ She must be stupid to marry him.
└──────────┘

① 1개    ② 2개    ③ 3개    ④ 4개    ⑤ 5개

# MEMO

# Lesson 8

# Which Is the Best Way?

## Key Words

- **agree**[əgríː] 동 동의하다, 찬성하다
- **attack**[ətǽk] 동 공격하다
- **bottom**[bátəm] 명 밑, 바닥
- **climb**[klaim] 동 오르다, 올라가다
- **compare**[kəmpɛ́ər] 동 비교하다
- **correct**[kərékt] 형 옳은
- **create**[kriéit] 동 창조하다
- **destination**[dèstənéiʃən] 명 목적지, 도착지
- **disagree**[dìsəgríː] 동 동의하지 않다, 의견이 다르다
- **further**[fə́ːrðər] 부 더 멀리 형 더 먼
- **gone**[gɔ(ː)n] 형 가버린, 떠난
- **guide**[gaid] 명 안내인, 가이드
- **hunger**[hʌ́ŋgər] 명 굶주림
- **hurry**[hə́ːri] 동 서두르다, 서둘러 가다
- **kindness**[káindnis] 명 친절
- **move**[muːv] 동 움직이다, 감동시키다
- **path**[pæθ] 명 길

- **pioneer**[pàiəníər] 명 선구자, 개척자
- **protect**[prətékt] 동 보호하다
- **reach**[riːtʃ] 동 ~에 이르다[닿다], 도착하다
- **realize**[ríːəlàiz] 동 깨닫다, 자각하다
- **separate**[sépərèit] 형 분리된, 서로 다른
- **solve**[salv] 동 (문제, 곤경을) 해결하다, 풀다
- **someday**[sʌ́mdei] 부 (미래의) 언젠가, 훗날
- **straight**[streit] 부 똑바로
- **strongly**[strɔ́ːŋli] 부 강경히, 강하게
- **survival**[sərváivəl] 명 생존
- **take**[teik] 동 (시간이) 걸리다
- **thick**[θik] 형 두꺼운, (나무가) 울창한
- **thief**[θiːf] 명 도둑
- **travel**[trǽvəl] 명 여행 동 여행하다
- **whole**[houl] 형 전체의, 모든
- **wisdom**[wízdəm] 명 지혜, 슬기
- **wise**[waiz] 형 지혜로운, 현명한

## Key Expressions

- **a group of** ~의 집단
- **act on** ~에 따라 행동하다
- **become lost** 길을 잃다
- **die of** ~으로 죽다
- **even though** ~일지라도
- **for a while** 잠시 동안
- **go on forever** 무한정 계속되다
- **in the end** 마침내, 결국

- **keep ~ing** 계속 ~하다
- **make one's way to ~** ~로 나아가다
- **on the way** 가는 길에
- **shake one's head** 고개를 가로젓다
- **thanks to ~** ~ 덕분에
- **the way out** 나가는 길, 출구
- **without ~ing** ~하지 않고

## Word Power

### ※ 서로 비슷한 뜻을 가진 어휘

- ☐ **climb** 오르다, 올라가다 : **ascend** 올라가다, 오르다
- ☐ **in the end** 마침내, 결국 : **finally** 마침내, 결국
- ☐ **move** 옮기다, 감동시키다 : **touch** 마음을 움직이다, 감동시키다
- ☐ **separate** 분리된 : **divided** 분리된
- ☐ **thick** 두꺼운, (나무가) 울창한 : **dense** 밀집한, 빽빽한

- ☐ **hurry** 서두르다 : **rush** 급히 움직이다, 서두르다
- ☐ **kindness** 친절 : **goodwill** 선의, 친절
- ☐ **path** 길 : **way** 길, 도로
- ☐ **someday** (미래의) 언젠가 : **one day** 어느 날, 언젠가
- ☐ **wisdom** 지혜, 슬기 : **knowledge** 지식, 지혜

### ※ 서로 반대의 뜻을 가진 어휘

- ☐ **agree** 동의하다 ↔ **disagree** 동의하지 않다, 의견이 다르다
- ☐ **climb** 오르다, 올라가다 ↔ **descend** 내려가다
- ☐ **separate** 분리된 ↔ **connected** 연결된, 일관된
- ☐ **whole** 전체의 ↔ **partial** 일부의, 부분적인

- ☐ **bottom** 밑, 바닥 ↔ **top** 꼭대기, 정상
- ☐ **kindness** 친절 ↔ **unkindness** 불친절, 몰인정
- ☐ **thick** 두꺼운, (나무가) 울창한 ↔ **thin** 얇은, 가느다란
- ☐ **wisdom** 지혜, 슬기 ↔ **foolishness** 어리석음

### ※ 접두사 dis-

- ☐ **dis-**+use → **disuse** 사용하지 않음
- ☐ **dis-**+like → **dislike** 싫어하다
- ☐ **dis-**+cover → **discover** 발견하다
- ☐ **dis-**+close → **disclose** 밝히다, 폭로하다
- ☐ **dis-**+count → **discount** 할인하다

### ※ 접미사 -ness

- ☐ **bright**+-ness → **brightness** 빛남, 밝음
- ☐ **kind**+-ness → **kindness** 친절함
- ☐ **good**+-ness → **goodness** 선량함
- ☐ **busy**+-ness → **business** 사업, 업무
- ☐ **happy**+-ness → **happiness** 행복
- ☐ **weak**+-ness → **weakness** 약함, 약점
- ☐ **ill**+-ness → **illness** 병

## English Dictionary

- ☐ **agree** 동의하다, 찬성하다
  → to accept an idea suggested by someone else
  다른 어떤 사람이 제안한 아이디어를 받아들이다

- ☐ **attack** 공격하다
  → to try to hurt or damage 피해를 입히거나 다치게 하다

- ☐ **destination** 목적지, 도착지
  → the place where somebody or something is going or being sent
  어떤 사람이나 사물이 가고 있는 혹은 보내지고 있는 장소

- ☐ **hunger** 굶주림
  → the feeling of needing food 음식을 필요로 하는 느낌

- ☐ **kindness** 친절
  → the quality of behaving in a thoughtful, helpful, or friendly way
  사려 깊고, 도움이 되거나 친절한 방식으로 행동하는 성질

- ☐ **move** 감동시키다
  → to cause someone to feel strong emotions
  어떤 사람에게 강렬한 감정을 불러일으키게 하다

- ☐ **pioneer** 선구자, 개척자
  → one of the first people to do something or to travel to a new area
  어떤 일을 하거나 새로운 곳을 여행하는 최초의 사람들 중의 하나

- ☐ **realize** 깨닫다, 자각하다
  → to know and understand that something is true or has happened
  어떤 것이 사실이거나 일어났다는 것을 알고 이해하다

- ☐ **separate** 분리된
  → not together or the same 같이 있지 않거나 같지 않은

- ☐ **survival** 생존
  → the state of continuing to live, after despite difficult conditions
  어려운 상황에도 불구하고 이후에 계속 살아남는 상태

# Reading

## The Five Wise Men

One day, five wise men met on the road. They <u>agreed</u> to travel
to부정사를 목적어로 취하는 동사
together. On the way, however, they became lost in a thick forest.
Before walking any further, they decided <u>to stop and find the best</u>
to stop과 (to) find out이 등위접속사<br>and로 병렬 연결되어 있음.
<u>way out</u>.

After thinking for a while, the first man said, "I strongly feel <u>that</u>
명사절을 이끄는 접속사
we should go left."

The second man said, "We should go right, because *right* also means
'correct.'"

Then the third man said, "Let's walk <u>back</u>. We came that way, so we
뒤돌아서
can leave that way. Then we can walk around the forest."

The fourth man disagreed and said, "<u>I think</u> we should <u>keep</u> walking
동사 think 뒤에 명사절을 이끄는 접속사 that이 생략     동명사를 목적어로 취하는 동사, ~을 계속하다
straight. The forest cannot go on forever. A new path will open."

<u>Looking at them all</u>, the fifth man shook his head and said, "I know
동시동작을 나타내는 분사구문: ~하면서
<u>how to solve this</u>. Just wait."
'의문사+to부정사'가 동사 know의 목적어로 쓰임.

---

**wise** 지혜로운, 현명한

**agree** 동의하다, 찬성하다

**travel** 여행하다

**thick** 두꺼운, (나무가) 울창한

**further** 더 멀리

**correct** 옳은

**disagree** 동의하지 않다, 의견이 다르다

**straight** 똑바로

**path** 길

**shake one's head** 고개를 가로젓다

**solve** (문제·곤경을) 해결하다

---

### 확인문제

● 다음 문장이 본문의 내용과 일치하면 T, 일치하지 <u>않으면</u> F를 쓰시오.

1 One day, five wise men met on the road. ☐

2 Five wise men agreed to travel separately. ☐

3 On the way, they became lost in a thick forest. ☐

4 After thinking for a while, the first man felt that he should go right. ☐

5 The fourth man said he should keep walking straight. ☐

6 The fifth man just kept silent. ☐

He started to climb the tallest tree he could find. As he climbed,
to부정사와 동명사를 모두 목적어로 취하는 동사, ~하기 시작했다          앞에 목적격 관계대명사 that이 생략되었음.

everyone else decided to go their separate ways.
                  to부정사를 목적어로 취함

When the fifth man reached the top, he could see the whole forest.

Looking at all the paths, he found the shortest way out. He hurried

down to tell the others. However, when he got to the bottom, everyone
to부정사 부사적      정해진 범위 안에서 일부를 제외한          때를 나타내는 접속사
용법(목적)         나머지 전부를 가리키는 부정대명사

was gone. He thought to himself, *Where did they go? I found the best*
'가 버리고 없는'이라는 의미의 형용사

*way out.* He thought they were all wrong and he was the only wise
                                모두: they와 동격

man.

climb 오르다, 올라가다

separate 분리된, 서로 다른

reach ~에 이르다[닿다]

whole 전체의, 모든

hurry 서두르다

bottom 밑, 바닥

---

📎 확인문제

● 다음 문장이 본문의 내용과 일치하면 T, 일치하지 않으면 F를 쓰시오.

1   The fifth man started to climb the tallest tree he could find. ☐

2   As the fifth man climbed, everyone else decided to go together. ☐

3   Reaching the top, the fifth man could see the whole forest. ☐

4   Looking at all the paths, the fifth man found the safest way out. ☐

5   When the fifth man got to the bottom, everyone was gone. ☐

6   The fifth man thought he was wrong and the others were wise. ☐

However, he was wrong. Everyone was wise. Each man had chosen

과거완료로 과거 시점을 기준으로 그 이전에 일어난 일이<br>과거의 한 시점까지 영향을 미치는 것을 나타낼 때 씀.

his path and created his future.

The man who went to the left walked deeper into the forest. He was

주격 관계대명사

attacked by wild animals and almost died of hunger. Soon he learned

거의

how to protect himself and find food. In the end, he made his way out

재귀대명사(재귀 용법)

of the forest and taught others survival skills.

수여동사    간접목적어      직접목적어

The man who went to the right met a group of thieves. They took

everything from him and made him join them. While he was with

them, he showed them great kindness. The thieves were moved by his

kindness and learned from his wisdom. Later, they also became wise

men.

The man who walked back created a safe path around the forest.

Using this path, people could get where they were going without

때를 나타내는 분사구문: ~할 때

getting lost, even though the trip took a little longer.

양보의 부사절을 이끄는 접속사: (비록) ~임에도

---

**attack** 공격하다

**die of** ~로 죽다

**hunger** 굶주림

**protect** 보호하다

**make one's way** (to) (~로) 나아가다

**survival** 생존

**thief** 도둑 (*pl.* thieves)

**kindness** 친절함

**move** 움직이다, 감동시키다

**wisdom** 지혜, 슬기

---

📎 **확인문제**

● 다음 문장이 본문의 내용과 일치하면 T, 일치하지 <u>않으면</u> F를 쓰시오.

1   Each man had chosen his path and created his future. ☐

2   The man who went to the right walked deeper into the forest. ☐

3   After the man who went to the left made his way out of the forest, he taught others survival skills. ☐

4   The man who went to the left met a group of thieves. ☐

5   The thieves were moved by the kindness of the man who went to the right and learned from his wisdom. ☐

The man who went straight became a pioneer. He left the forest and

discovered places no one else had been before. Thanks to him, people

places 뒤에 선행사 places를
수식하는 관계부사 where가 생략

과거 시점을 기준으로 그 이전에 일어난 일이 과거의
한 시점까지 영향을 미치는 상태를 나타내는 과거완료

could enjoy these new beautiful lands.

The man who climbed the tree became a guide. Since he had found

과거 시점을 기준으로 그 이전에 있었던 일을 나타낼 때 쓰인 과거완료

many different paths, he was able to teach people how to find the

'의문사+to부정사'는 '의문사+주어+should/can+동사'로 바꿔 쓸 수 있다.

quickest ways to their destinations.

This is how the five men found their own paths. Like them, we are

이것이 (주어)가 ~한 방법이다. the way how(×)

each on our own journey in life, and we cannot compare one journey

각자(we와 동격)

to another. You have to create your own path. Listen to yourself, make

a decision, and act on it. Then, someday, you will realize that you

realize의 목적어 역할을 하는 명사절을 이끄는 접속사

have been living the life that is right for you.

have been V-ing(현재완료 진행형): 과거          주격 관계대명사
부터 현재까지 동작이 계속되고 있음을 나타냄.

pioneer 선구자, 개척자

discover 발견하다

guide 안내인, 가이드

destination 목적지, 도착지

on one's journey 여행 중에

compare 비교하다

create 창조하다

make a decision 결정하다

act on ~에 따라 행동하다

realize 깨닫다

---

 **확인문제**

● 다음 문장이 본문의 내용과 일치하면 T, 일치하지 않으면 F를 쓰시오.

1 The man who went straight became a pioneer and discovered places no one else had been before. ☐

2 Thanks to the man who climbed the tree, people could enjoy the new beautiful lands. ☐

3 The man who climbed the tree was able to teach people how to find the quickest ways to their destinations. ☐

4 We should compare one journey to another. ☐

5 You have to create your own path. ☐

6 If you listen to yourself, make a decision, and act on it, you will realize that you have been living the best life in the world. ☐

● 우리말을 참고하여 빈칸에 알맞은 말을 쓰시오.

**1** The Five _____ Men

**2** One day, five wise men _____ on the road.

**3** They _____ to travel together.

**4** On the way, however, they _____ _____ in a thick forest.

**5** Before walking _____ _____, they decided to stop and find the best way out.

**6** After thinking _____ _____ _____, the first man said, "I strongly feel that we should go left."

**7** The second man said, "We should go right, because *right* also means '_____.'"

**8** Then the third man said, "Let's _____ _____.

**9** We came that way, so we can _____ _____ _____.

**10** Then we can _____ _____ the forest."

**11** The fourth man disagreed and said, "I think we should _____ _____ straight.

**12** The forest cannot _____ _____ _____.

**13** A _____ _____ will open."

**14** Looking at them all, the fifth man _____ _____ _____ and said, "I know how to solve this. Just wait."

**15** He started to climb the tallest tree he _____ _____.

**16** As he climbed, everyone else decided to go their _____ ways.

| | |
|---|---|
| 1 | 5명의 지혜로운 사람들 |
| 2 | 어느 날 5명의 지혜로운 사람들이 길에서 만났다. |
| 3 | 그들은 여행을 함께 하기로 했다. |
| 4 | 그러나 도중에 그들은 울창한 숲속에서 길을 잃게 되었다. |
| 5 | 더 멀리 가기 전에 그들은 멈추고 빠져나갈 최선의 방법을 찾기로 결정했다. |
| 6 | 잠시 동안 생각한 후, 첫 번째 남자는 "우리가 왼쪽으로 가야 한다는 생각이 강하게 들어요."라고 말했다. |
| 7 | 두 번째 남자가 "우리는 오른쪽으로 가야 해요. 왜냐하면 '오른쪽'은 또한 '옳은'이라는 의미이기 때문이죠."라고 말했다. |
| 8 | 그러자 세 번째 남자가 "뒤로 돌아갑시다. |
| 9 | 우리가 그 길로 왔으니 그 길로 나갈 수 있을 겁니다. |
| 10 | 그러면 우리는 숲을 한 바퀴 돌 수 있고요."라고 말했다. |
| 11 | 네 번째 남자가 이의를 제기하며 "나는 우리가 똑바로 계속 걸어 나가야 한다고 생각해요. |
| 12 | 숲이 영원히 계속될 수는 없으니까요. |
| 13 | 새로운 길이 열릴 것입니다."라고 말했다. |
| 14 | 모두를 바라보면서 다섯 번째 남자가 고개를 저으며 "나는 이것을 해결하는 방법을 알아요. 잠깐 기다려 보세요."라고 말했다. |
| 15 | 그는 그가 찾을 수 있는 가장 높은 나무를 오르기 시작했다. |
| 16 | 그가 올라가자 다른 모든 사람들은 각자 서로 다른 길을 가기로 결정했다. |

**17** When the fifth man _____ the top, he could see the _____ forest.

**18** Looking at all the paths, he found the _____ _____ _____.

**19** He _____ _____ to tell the others.

**20** However, when he got to the bottom, everyone _____ _____.

**21** He _____ _____ _____, *Where did they go? I found the* _____ _____ _____.

**22** He thought they were all _____ and he was _____ _____ _____ man.

**23** However, he was _____.

**24** _____ was wise.

**25** Each man had chosen his path and _____ _____ _____.

**26** The man who went to the left _____ _____ into the forest.

**27** He _____ _____ by wild animals and almost _____ _____ hunger.

**28** Soon he learned how to _____ _____ and find food.

**29** In the end, he _____ _____ _____ _____ _____ the forest and taught others survival skills.

**30** The man who went to the right met _____ _____ _____ thieves.

**31** They took everything from him and made him _____ _____.

**32** While he was with them, he showed them _____ _____.

**17** 다섯 번째 남자가 꼭대기에 이르자 그는 전체 숲을 볼 수 있었다.

**18** 모든 길을 바라보며 그는 빠져나갈 가장 짧은 길을 찾았다.

**19** 그는 다른 사람들에게 알리기 위해 급히 내려갔다.

**20** 하지만 그가 밑으로 내려왔을 때, 모든 사람들은 이미 가 버리고 없었다.

**21** 그는 '다들 어디 간 거야? 내가 빠져나갈 최선의 길을 찾았는데.'라고 마음속으로 생각했다.

**22** 그는 그들이 모두 틀렸고 자신이 유일하게 현명한 사람이라고 생각했다.

**23** 그러나 그가 틀렸다.

**24** 모두가 지혜로웠다.

**25** 각자 자신의 길을 선택했고 자신의 미래를 만들었다.

**26** 왼쪽으로 간 남자는 숲속으로 더 깊이 걸어 들어갔다.

**27** 그는 야생 동물들의 습격을 받았고 거의 굶어 죽을 뻔했다.

**28** 머지않아 그는 자신을 지키고 먹을 것을 찾는 방법을 터득했다.

**29** 결국 그는 숲 밖으로 빠져나왔고 다른 사람들에게 생존 기술을 가르쳤다.

**30** 오른쪽으로 간 남자는 도둑 무리를 만났다.

**31** 그들은 그에게서 모든 것을 가져갔고 그를 그들과 합류시켰다.

**32** 그는 그들과 함께 있는 동안 그들에게 많은 친절을 베풀었다.

33 The thieves _____ _____ by his kindness and learned from his wisdom.

34 _____, they also became wise men.

35 The man who walked back created _____ _____ _____ around the forest.

36 Using this path, people could get where they were going _____ _____ _____, even though the trip took a little longer.

37 The man who _____ _____ became a pioneer.

38 He left the forest and discovered places no one else _____ _____ before.

39 _____ _____ him, people could enjoy these new beautiful lands.

40 The man _____ _____ the tree became a guide.

41 Since he had found many different paths, he was able to teach people how to find _____ _____ _____ to their destinations.

42 _____ _____ _____ the five men found their own paths.

43 Like them, we are each on our own journey in life, and we cannot compare _____ _____ to _____.

44 You have to create _____ _____ _____.

45 Listen to yourself, make a decision, and _____ _____ _____.

46 Then, someday, you will realize that you _____ _____ the life that is right for you.

33 그 도둑들은 그의 친절에 감동을 받았고 그의 지혜에서 배우게 되었다.

34 나중에 그들 또한 지혜로운 사람들이 되었다.

35 뒤돌아 간 남자는 숲 주변에 안전한 길을 만들었다.

36 사람들은 이 길을 이용할 때 길을 잃지 않고 자신이 가고자 하는 길에 다다를 수 있었다. 비록 이동 시간이 약간 더 오래 걸려도 말이다.

37 똑바로 간 남자는 개척자가 되었다.

38 그는 숲을 벗어나 아무도 이전에 가 본 적이 없는 곳을 발견했다.

39 그 남자 덕분에, 사람들은 이 새롭고 아름다운 지역을 즐길 수 있었다.

40 나무 위로 올라간 남자는 가이드가 되었다.

41 그는 여러 다양한 길을 발견했었기 때문에, 사람들에게 자신의 목적지에 이르는 가장 빠른 길을 찾는 법을 가르쳐 줄 수 있었다.

42 이런 식으로 다섯 남자는 자신만의 길을 찾아냈다.

43 그들처럼 우리는 각각 인생에서 자기 자신만의 여행을 하고 있고, 우리는 한 여정을 다른 것과 비교할 수 없다.

44 당신은 당신 자신만의 길을 만들어가야 한다.

45 자신의 목소리를 듣고, 결정하고, 그 결정에 따라 행동하라.

46 그러면 언젠가 당신은 당신에게 맞는 삶을 살아가고 있다는 것을 깨닫게 될 것이다.

• 우리말을 참고하여 본문을 영작하시오.

**1** 5명의 지혜로운 사람들

➡ _____

**2** 어느 날 5명의 지혜로운 사람들이 길에서 만났다.

➡ _____

**3** 그들은 여행을 함께 하기로 했다.

➡ _____

**4** 그러나 도중에 그들은 울창한 숲속에서 길을 잃게 되었다.

➡ _____

**5** 더 멀리 가기 전에 그들은 멈추고 빠져나갈 최선의 방법을 찾기로 결정했다.

➡ _____

**6** 잠시 동안 생각한 후, 첫 번째 남자는 "우리가 왼쪽으로 가야 한다는 생각이 강하게 들어요."
라고 말했다.

➡ _____

**7** 두 번째 남자가 "우리는 오른쪽으로 가야 해요. 왜냐하면 '오른쪽'은 또한 '옳은'이라는 의미이기
때문이죠."라고 말했다.

➡ _____

**8** 그러자 세 번째 남자가 "뒤로 돌아갑시다.

➡ _____

**9** 우리가 그 길로 왔으니 그 길로 나갈 수 있을 겁니다.

➡ _____

**10** 그러면 우리는 숲을 한 바퀴 돌 수 있고요."라고 말했다.

➡ _____

**11** 네 번째 남자가 이의를 제기하며 "나는 우리가 똑바로 계속 걸어 나가야 한다고 생각해요.

➡ _____

**12** 숲이 영원히 계속될 수는 없으니까요.

➡ _____

**13** 새로운 길이 열릴 것입니다."라고 말했다.

➡ _____

**14** 모두를 바라보면서 다섯 번째 남자가 고개를 저으며 "나는 이것을 해결하는 방법을 알아요.
잠깐 기다려 보세요."라고 말했다.

➡ _____

**15** 그는 그가 찾을 수 있는 가장 높은 나무를 오르기 시작했다.

➡ _____

**16** ▶ 그가 올라가자 다른 모든 사람들은 각자 서로 다른 길을 가기로 결정했다.

➡ _____

**17** ▶ 다섯 번째 남자가 꼭대기에 이르자 그는 전체 숲을 볼 수 있었다.

➡ _____

**18** ▶ 모든 길을 바라보며 그는 빠져나갈 가장 짧은 길을 찾았다.

➡ _____

**19** ▶ 그는 다른 사람들에게 알리기 위해 급히 내려갔다.

➡ _____

**20** ▶ 하지만 그가 밑으로 내려왔을 때, 모든 사람들은 이미 가 버리고 없었다.

➡ _____

**21** ▶ 그는 '다들 어디 간 거야? 내가 빠져나갈 최선의 길을 찾았는데.'라고 마음속으로 생각했다.

➡ _____

**22** ▶ 그는 그들이 모두 틀렸고 자신이 유일하게 현명한 사람이라고 생각했다.

➡ _____

**23** ▶ 그러나 그가 틀렸다.

➡ _____

**24** ▶ 모두가 지혜로웠다.

➡ _____

**25** ▶ 각자 자신의 길을 선택했고 자신의 미래를 만들었다.

➡ _____

**26** ▶ 왼쪽으로 간 남자는 숲속으로 더 깊이 걸어 들어갔다.

➡ _____

**27** ▶ 그는 야생 동물들의 습격을 받았고 거의 굶어 죽을 뻔했다.

➡ _____

**28** ▶ 머지않아 그는 자신을 지키고 먹을 것을 찾는 방법을 터득했다.

➡ _____

**29** ▶ 결국 그는 숲 밖으로 빠져나왔고 다른 사람들에게 생존 기술을 가르쳤다.

➡ _____

**30** ▶ 오른쪽으로 간 남자는 도둑 무리를 만났다.

➡ _____

**31** ▶ 그들은 그에게서 모든 것을 가져갔고 그를 그들과 합류시켰다.

➡ _____

**32** 그는 그들과 함께 있는 동안 그들에게 많은 친절을 베풀었다.

➡ _____

**33** 그 도둑들은 그의 친절에 감동을 받았고 그의 지혜에서 배우게 되었다.

➡ _____

**34** 나중에 그들 또한 지혜로운 사람들이 되었다.

➡ _____

**35** 뒤돌아 간 남자는 숲 주변에 안전한 길을 만들었다.

➡ _____

**36** 사람들은 이 길을 이용할 때 길을 잃지 않고 자신이 가고자 하는 길에 다다를 수 있었다. 비록 이동 시간이 약간 더 오래 걸려도 말이다.

➡ _____

_____

**37** 똑바로 간 남자는 개척자가 되었다.

➡ _____

**38** 그는 숲을 벗어나 아무도 이전에 가 본 적이 없는 곳을 발견했다.

➡ _____

**39** 그 남자 덕분에, 사람들은 이 새롭고 아름다운 지역을 즐길 수 있었다.

➡ _____

**40** 나무 위로 올라간 남자는 가이드가 되었다.

➡ _____

**41** 그는 여러 다양한 길을 발견했었기 때문에, 사람들에게 자신의 목적지에 이르는 가장 빠른 길을 찾는 법을 가르쳐 줄 수 있었다.

➡ _____

_____

**42** 이런 식으로 다섯 남자는 자신만의 길을 찾아냈다.

➡ _____

**43** 그들처럼 우리는 각각 인생에서 자기 자신만의 여행을 하고 있고, 우리는 한 여정을 다른 것과 비교할 수 없다.

➡ _____

**44** 당신은 당신 자신만의 길을 만들어가야 한다.

➡ _____

**45** 자신의 목소리를 듣고, 결정하고, 그 결정에 따라 행동하라.

➡ _____

**46** 그러면 언젠가 당신은 당신에게 맞는 삶을 살아가고 있다는 것을 깨닫게 될 것이다.

➡ _____

**01** 다음 빈칸에 알맞은 단어를 〈보기〉에서 골라 쓰시오. (필요하면 어형을 바꿀 것.)

┌─ 보기 ┐
move   hunger   discover   wisdom
└─────┘

(1) _____ causes great suffering in the world.

(2) Columbus wasn't the first person to _____ America.

(3) It is good to hear the _____ of great people.

(4) I was _____ by her songs and her beautiful voice.

**02** 주어진 단어의 영영풀이가 잘못된 것을 고르시오.

① agree: to accept an idea suggested by someone else

② attack: to prevent someone or something from being harmed or damaged

③ survival: the state of continuing to live, after despite difficult conditions

④ pioneer: one of the first people to do something or to travel to a new area

⑤ destination: the place where somebody or something is going or being sent

**03** 다음 우리말에 맞게 주어진 어휘를 모두 사용하여 분사구문으로 시작하는 문장을 만드시오. (동사만 변형 가능)

(1) 그들 모두를 바라보며, 다섯 번째 남자가 고개를 저었다. (the fifth man, his head, them all, look at, shake)

➡ _____

_____

(2) 당신 자신의 목소리를 들으면, 당신의 삶이 옳다는 것을 깨닫게 될 것이다. (you, yourself, your life, listen to, is, realize, will, that, right)

➡ _____

_____

(3) 그의 친절에 감동 받아, 도둑들은 그의 지혜에서 배우게 되었다. (the thieves, his kindness, his wisdom, learn, move, by, from)

➡ _____

_____

**04** 다음 글에서 어법상 어색한 부분을 찾아 바르게 고치시오.

┌─────────────────────────────┐
│ Since he has found many different paths, │
│ he was able to teach people how to find │
│ the quickest ways to their destinations. │
└─────────────────────────────┘

➡ _____

_____

**05** 다음 우리말과 일치하도록 괄호 안의 단어를 활용하여 빈칸을 채우시오.

그는 야생 동물들의 습격을 받았고 거의 굶어 죽을 뻔했다. 머지않아 그는 자신을 지키고 먹을 것을 찾는 방법을 터득했다.

➡ He _____ _____ _____ wild animals and almost died of hunger. Soon he learned _____ _____ _____ _____ and find food.

(how, attack, protect, to)

After thinking for a while, the first man said, "I strongly feel that we should go left."

The second man said, "We should go right, because *right* also means 'correct.'"

Then the third man said, "Let's walk back. We came that way, so we can leave that way. Then we can walk around the forest."

The fourth man disagreed and said, "I think we should keep ___ⓐ___ straight. The forest cannot go on forever. A new path will open."

ⓑLooking at them all, the fifth man shook his head and said, "I know how to solve this. Just wait."

**06** 위 글의 빈칸 ⓐ에 walk를 알맞은 형태로 쓰시오.

➡ _____

**07** 위 글의 밑줄 친 분사구문 ⓑ를 부사절로 고치시오.

➡ _____ 또는

_____

**08** 두 번째 남자가 "우리는 오른쪽으로 가야 해요."라고 말한 이유를 우리말로 쓰시오.

➡ _____

The man who went to the right met a group of thieves. They took everything from him and made him join them. While he was with them, he showed ⓐthem great kindness. ⓑThe thieves were moved by his kindness and learned from his wisdom. Later, they also became wise men.

The man who walked back created a safe path around the forest. Using this path, people could get where they were going without getting lost, even though the trip took a little longer.

**09** 위 글의 밑줄 친 ⓐthem이 가리키는 것을 본문에서 찾아 쓰시오.

➡ _____

**10** 위 글의 밑줄 친 ⓑ를 능동태로 고치시오.

➡ _____

ⓐThis is the way how the five men found their own paths. Like them, we are each on our own journey in life, and we cannot compare one journey to another. You have to create your own path. Listen to yourself, make a decision, and act on it. Then, someday, you will realize that you have been living the life that is right for you.

**11** 위 글의 밑줄 친 ⓐ에서 어법상 틀린 부분을 찾아 고치시오.

_____ ➡ _____

_____

**12** 본문의 내용과 일치하도록 다음 빈칸 (A)와 (B)에 알맞은 단어를 쓰시오.

Each of you are on (A)_____ _____ _____ in life, and you cannot compare one journey to another. You have to create (B)_____ _____ _____ by listening to yourself, making a decision, and acting on it.

**01** 출제율 95%

다음 빈칸에 공통으로 들어갈 말을 쓰시오.

> • You'll pass a bank _____ the way to the train station.
> • If you only act _____ instinct, you are an animal.

**02** 출제율 90%

다음 빈칸에 알맞은 단어를 〈보기〉에서 골라 쓰시오. (필요하면 어형을 바꿀 것.)

> ┤ 보기 ├
> climb   realize   compare   disagree

(1) I will _____ the prices of several digital cameras online.

(2) Janet _____ with her parents on everything.

(3) It is not easy to _____ the mountain.

(4) They didn't _____ how creative their work was.

**03** 출제율 95%

다음 짝지어진 단어의 관계가 같도록 빈칸에 알맞은 말을 주어진 철자로 시작하여 쓰시오.

(1) move – touch : separate – d_____

(2) bottom – top : kindness – u_____

(3) agree – disagree : t_____ – thin

**04** 출제율 90%

밑줄 친 부분과 바꿔 쓸 수 있는 말을 고르시오.

> We can't arrive at the airport in time.

① realize   ② compare   ③ disagree
④ solve     ⑤ reach

**05** 출제율 100%

다음 우리말에 맞도록 빈칸에 알맞은 말을 쓰시오. (철자가 주어진 것도 있음.)

(1) 우리는 대기 오염 문제를 해결해야 한다.
➡ We should s_____ the problem of air pollution.

(2) 모든 동물들은 그들만의 생존 방법이 있다.
➡ All animals have their own ways of _____.

(3) 코페르니쿠스는 시대를 앞선 선구자라는 점에서 개척자로 여겨졌다.
➡ Corpernicus was considered a p_____ because he was ahead of his time.

(4) 나는 제시간에 목적지에 도착했다.
➡ I reached my d_____ on time.

**06** 출제율 95%

다음 영영풀이를 보고 빈칸에 알맞은 단어를 주어진 철자로 시작하여 쓰시오.

> to know and understand that something is true or has happened

> I don't think you r_____ how important this is to her.

**07** 출제율 95%

다음 밑줄 친 to부정사들 중 쓰임이 다른 것을 고르시오.

① One day, five wise men agreed to travel together.

② Before walking any further, they decided to stop and find the best way out.

③ The fifth wise man started to climb the tallest tree he could find.

④ The fifth wise man hurried down from the tree to tell the others.

⑤ Each man left there and chose to create his own future.

**08** 다음 중 〈보기〉의 밑줄 친 부분을 같은 의미로 알맞게 바꾼 것은?

┌─ 보기 ├─
He was able to teach people <u>how to find the quickest ways</u> to their destinations.
└─────

① He was able to teach people <u>how they found the quickest ways</u> to their destinations.

② He was able to teach people <u>how they had found the quickest ways</u> to their destinations.

③ He was able to teach people <u>how he had found the quickest ways</u> to their destinations.

④ He was able to teach people <u>how could they find the quickest ways</u> to their destinations.

⑤ He was able to teach people <u>how they should find the quickest ways</u> to their destinations.

**09** 다음 밑줄 친 부분 중 어법상 어색한 것을 고르시오.

① He left the forest and discovered places no one else <u>had been</u> before.

② Since he <u>had found</u> many different paths, he was able to teach people how to find the ways to their destinations.

③ When he got to the bottom of the tree, everyone <u>had already gone</u>.

④ When the fifth man reached the top, he <u>had seen</u> the whole forest.

⑤ He asked himself when and where they <u>had gone</u>.

**10** 다음 중 주어진 〈보기〉의 문장에서 밑줄 친 부분을 분사구문으로 알맞게 바꾼 것을 고르시오.

┌─ 보기 ├─
<u>When he met the thieves,</u> the man gave them his all money.
└─────

① Meeting the thieves, the man gave them his all money.

② He meeting the thieves, the man gave them his all money.

③ His meeting the thieves, the man gave them his all money.

④ Having met the thieves, the man gave them his all money.

⑤ When he meeting the thieves, the man gave them his all money.

**11** 다음 〈보기〉의 두 문장을 하나의 문장으로 만들 때 어법상 옳지 <u>않은</u> 것은?

┌─ 보기 ├─
• This is the way.
• The five men found their own paths in the way.
└─────

① This is the way the five men found their own paths.

② This is the way in which the five men found their own paths.

③ This is the way that the five men found their own paths.

④ This is the way in that the five men found their own paths.

⑤ This is how the five men found their own paths.

**12** 다음 주어진 우리말에 맞게 괄호 안의 단어를 알맞게 배열하여 빈칸에 넣으시오. *출제율 90%*

> 언젠가 당신은 당신에게 맞는 삶을 살아가고 있다는 것을 깨닫게 될 것이다.
>
> (you, that, that, realize, living, right, the life, been, is, have)

➡ Someday, you will ＿＿＿＿＿＿＿＿＿＿
＿＿＿＿＿＿＿＿＿＿＿＿＿＿＿ for you.

**[13~14]** 다음 〈보기〉에 주어진 어구들을 사용하여, 각 번호의 그림에 대한 우리말 설명에 맞게 빈칸을 채우시오.

> ┤ 보기 ├
>
> (중복 사용 가능, 동사 변형 가능)
>
> where / without / find / create / walk / get / even though / who / the / how / quick / they / tree / use / back / be / climb / to

**13** *출제율 95%*

> 나무 위로 올라간 남자는 가이드가 되었다. 그는 여러 다양한 길을 발견했었기 때문에, 사람들에게 자신의 목적지에 이르는 가장 빠른 길을 찾는 법을 가르쳐 줄 수 있었다.
>
> ➡ The man ＿＿＿＿ ＿＿＿＿ ＿＿＿＿
> ＿＿＿＿ became a guide. Since he
> ＿＿＿＿ ＿＿＿＿ many different
> paths, he was able to teach people
> ＿＿＿＿ ＿＿＿＿ ＿＿＿＿
> ＿＿＿＿ ways to their destinations.

**14** *출제율 95%*

> 뒤돌아 간 남자는 숲 주변에 안전한 길을 만들었다. 사람들은 이 길을 이용할 때 길을 잃지 않고 자신이 가고자 하는 길에 다다를 수 있었다. 비록 이동 시간이 약간 더 오래 걸려도 말이다.
>
> ➡ The man ＿＿＿＿ ＿＿＿＿ ＿＿＿＿
> ＿＿＿＿ a safe path around the forest.
> ＿＿＿＿ this path, people could
> ＿＿＿＿ ＿＿＿＿ ＿＿＿＿ ＿＿＿＿
> going ＿＿＿＿ ＿＿＿＿ lost, ＿＿＿＿
> ＿＿＿＿ the trip took a little longer.

**[15~17]** 다음 글을 읽고 물음에 답하시오.

> After thinking for a while, the first man said, "I strongly feel that we should go left."
>
> The second man said, "We should go right, because *right* also means 'correct.'"
>
> Then the third man said, "Let's walk back. We came that way, so we can leave that way. Then we can walk around the forest."
>
> The fourth man disagreed and said, "I think we should keep walking straight. The forest cannot go on forever. A new path will open."
>
> ⓐLooking at them all, the fifth man nodded his head and said, "I know how to solve this. Just wait."

**15** Why did the fourth man suggest that they should keep walking straight? Fill in the blanks (A) and (B) with suitable words.

> Because he believed the forest could not go on (A)_____ and that (B)_____ _____ _____ would open.

**16** 위 글의 밑줄 친 ⓐ에서 흐름상 어색한 부분을 찾아 고치시오.

_____ ➡ _____

**17** According to the passage, which is NOT true?

① The first man strongly felt that they should go left.

② The second man said they should go right.

③ The word 'right' means 'to the right side' and 'correct.'

④ The third man suggested that they should walk straight.

⑤ The fifth man said he knew how to solve the problem.

**[18~20] 다음 글을 읽고 물음에 답하시오.**

He started to climb the tallest tree he could find. (①) As he climbed, everyone else decided to go their separate ways. (②)

When the fifth man reached the top, he could see the whole forest. (③) He hurried down to tell the others. (④) ___ⓐ___, when he got to the bottom, everyone was gone. (⑤) He thought to himself, *Where did* ⓑ*they go? I found the best way out.* He thought they were all wrong and he was the only wise man.

**18** 위 글의 빈칸 ⓐ에 들어갈 알맞은 말을 고르시오.

① For example　② That is

③ Moreover　④ However

⑤ Therefore

**19** 위 글의 흐름으로 보아, 주어진 문장이 들어가기에 가장 적절한 곳은?

> Looking at all the paths, he found the shortest way out.

①　②　③　④　⑤

**20** 위 글의 밑줄 친 ⓑ*they*가 가리키는 것을 본문에서 찾아 쓰시오.

➡ _____

**[21~24] 다음 글을 읽고 물음에 답하시오.**

The man who went to the left walked deeper into the forest. He was attacked by wild animals and almost died ___ⓐ___ hunger. (A) Soon he learned how to protect him and find food. In the end, he made his way out of the forest and taught others survival skills.

The man who went to the right met a group of thieves. They took everything ___ⓑ___ him and made him join them. While he was with them, he showed them great kindness. The thieves were (B)moved by his kindness and learned from his wisdom. Later, they also became wise men.

**21** 위 글의 빈칸 ⓐ와 ⓑ에 들어갈 전치사가 바르게 짝지어진 것은?

　ⓐ　ⓑ　　　ⓐ　ⓑ

① for – from　② of – from

③ from – to　④ for – to

⑤ of – for

**22** 위 글의 밑줄 친 (A)에서 어법상 틀린 부분을 찾아 고치시오.

➡ _____ ➡ _____

**23** 위 글의 밑줄 친 (B)moved와 같은 의미로 쓰인 것을 고르시오.

① Time moved on.

② He moved to Seoul last week.

③ We moved our chairs a little nearer.

④ I moved that the meeting should start.

⑤ The sight moved me to tears.

**24** Which question CANNOT be answered after reading the passage?

① What attacked the man who went to the left?

② What did the man who went to the left do after he made his way out of the forest?

③ Whom did the man who went to the right meet?

④ How long did the man who went to the right live with the thieves?

⑤ How did the thieves become wise?

[25~26] 다음 글을 읽고 물음에 답하시오.

The man who went straight became a pioneer. He left the forest and discovered places no one else ___ⓐ___ before. Thanks to him, people could enjoy these new beautiful lands.

The man who climbed the tree became a guide. Since he had found many different paths, ⓑhe was able to teach people how to find the quickest ways to their destinations.

**25** 위 글의 빈칸 ⓐ에 be를 알맞은 형태로 쓰시오.

➡ _____

**26** 위 글의 밑줄 친 ⓑ를 다음과 같이 바꿔 쓸 때 빈칸에 들어갈 알맞은 말을 두 단어로 쓰시오.

➡ he was able to teach people how _____ _____ find the quickest ways to their destinations

[27~28] 다음 글을 읽고 물음에 답하시오.

This is how the five men found their own paths. Like them, we are each on our own journey in life, and we cannot compare one journey to another. You have to create your own path. Listen to yourself, make a decision, and act on it. Then, someday, you will realize that you have been living the life that is right for you.

**27** 위 글의 분위기로 가장 알맞은 것을 고르시오.

① instructive      ② cynical

③ confusing       ④ skeptical

⑤ festive

**28** 위 글의 주제로 알맞은 것을 고르시오.

① the way the five men found their own paths

② the benefit of comparing one journey to another

③ how to live harmoniously with others

④ living the life that is right for you

⑤ how to make a unique decision

Middle School 3-2
2학기 전과정

중간 + 기말
적중100 plus
영어 기출문제집

영어 중 3
능률 | 김성곤

Best Collection
내용문의 중등영어발전소 적중100 편집부  TEL 070-7707-0457

# INSIGHT
## on the textbook

교과서 파헤치기

영어 기출 문제집

적중100 plus
2학기 전과정

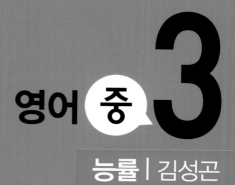

영어 중 3

능률 | 김성곤

# INSIGHT
## on the textbook

교과서 파헤치기

※ 다음 영어를 우리말로 쓰시오.

01 artwork _____

02 bright _____

03 architect _____

04 contain _____

05 architecture _____

06 explanation _____

07 statue _____

08 attract _____

09 grain _____

10 greenery _____

11 hopefully _____

12 climate _____

13 innovation _____

14 additional _____

15 material _____

16 damage _____

17 pollution _____

18 awareness _____

19 unwanted _____

20 prevent _____

21 incredible _____

22 protect _____

23 eco-friendly _____

24 provide _____

25 surface _____

26 theme _____

27 reduce _____

28 reusable _____

29 structure _____

30 separate _____

31 disappear _____

32 encourage _____

33 remind _____

34 resource _____

35 in addition to _____

36 break down _____

37 throw ~ away _____

38 be bored with _____

39 in harmony with _____

40 contribute to _____

41 a variety of _____

42 take care of _____

43 come up with _____

※ 다음 우리말을 영어로 쓰시오.

01 오염 _____

02 추가적인 _____

03 인식, 의식 _____

04 혁신 _____

05 건축가 _____

06 포함하다 _____

07 주제 _____

08 예방하다, 막다, 방지하다 _____

09 내내, 줄곧, 가로질러 _____

10 손상시키다 _____

11 보호하다, 지키다 _____

12 친환경적인 _____

13 자원 _____

14 격려하다, 장려하다 _____

15 끌다, 매혹시키다 _____

16 줄이다 _____

17 사라지다 _____

18 곡물, 알곡 _____

19 수중, 해저 _____

20 유일무이한, 독특한 _____

21 원치 않는, 불필요한 _____

22 재사용할 수 있는 _____

23 믿기 힘든, 굉장한 _____

24 제안 _____

25 (예술적) 작품 _____

26 자연적인 _____

27 의견 _____

28 설명 _____

29 심각하게, 진지하게 _____

30 적절하게 _____

31 깨닫다 _____

32 조각상 _____

33 구조(물) _____

34 분리하다 _____

35 무너지다, 고장 나다 _____

36 회복하다, 좋아지다 _____

37 ~을 돌보다 _____

38 ~을 생각해 내다 _____

39 다양한 _____

40 일리가 있다 _____

41 ~와 조화하여 _____

42 ~에 지루해하다 _____

43 ~ 이외에도 _____

※ 다음 영영풀이에 알맞은 단어를 <보기>에서 골라 쓴 후, 우리말 뜻을 쓰시오.

1 _____ : to harm something: _____

2 _____ : to no longer be seen: _____

3 _____ : the top layer of something: _____

4 _____ : below the water: _____

5 _____ : a person who designs buildings: _____

6 _____ : something that you are trying to do or achieve: _____

7 _____ : plants or vegetation: _____

8 _____ : the general weather of a region: _____

9 _____ : an object made from stone or metal: _____

10 _____ : the introduction of new things, ideas, or ways of doing something:

 _____

11 _____ : the small hard seeds of food plants such as wheat, rice, etc.: _____

12 _____ : something created to be beautiful by a painter, sculptor, etc.: _____

13 _____ : information to help people understand something: _____

14 _____ : one's beliefs, ideas, thoughts, and assumptions about a matter: _____

15 _____ : capable of being used more than once: _____

16 _____ : an area of slight darkness that is produced when something blocks the

 light of the sun: _____

| 보기 | | | |
|---|---|---|---|
| innovation | grain | surface | disappear |
| shade | opinion | climate | goal |
| statue | artwork | damage | underwater |
| reusable | explanation | greenery | architect |

※ 다음 우리말과 일치하도록 빈칸에 알맞은 말을 쓰시오.

해석

## Listen & Talk 1 A

B: I think we're using too many _____ _____.

G: I agree. It's _____ _____ _____ the _____. How can we _____ our use of _____ _____?

B: _____ _____ _____, we _____ _____ _____ when we go shopping.

남: 내 생각엔 우리는 비닐봉지를 너무 많이 쓰는 것 같아.
여: 내 생각도 그래. 그건 환경에 좋지 않아. 우리 비닐봉지 사용을 어떻게 줄일 수 있을까?
남: 내 생각에는 물건을 사러 갈 때 재사용할 수 있는 가방을 가져 가야 해.

## Listen & Talk 1 B

G: Jiho, hurry _____! The elevator is _____ _____ soon.

B: The science room is just on the _____ _____. _____ we _____ _____ _____?

G: I don't want to walk _____ _____ _____ up there.

B: Come on. Elevators use _____ _____ energy. We need to _____ energy to _____ _____ _____.

G: But _____ _____ _____ doesn't use that _____.

B: That's true, but the energy from all the elevator rides _____ _____ over time. _____ _____ _____, _____ _____ _____ the environment starts with the _____ _____.

G: You _____ _____ _____. _____ _____ the stairs.

여: 지호야, 서둘러! 엘리베이터가 곧 올라간다.
남: 과학실은 겨우 3층에 있잖아. 우리 계단을 오르는 건 어때?
여: 그 모든 계단을 올라서 가고 싶진 않아.
남: 잘 생각해 봐. 엘리베이터는 전기를 많이 쓰잖아. 우리는 환경을 보호하려면 에너지를 아껴야 해.
여: 하지만 엘리베이터를 한 번 탄다고 그렇게 많은 에너지를 사용하진 않잖아.
남: 그렇지, 하지만 엘리베이터를 타면서 사용하는 에너지는 시간이 흐르면서 누적될 거야. 내 생각에는, 환경을 보호하는 것은 작은 것부터 시작한다고 생각해.
여: 네 말이 일리가 있네. 계단을 이용하자.

## Listen & Talk 1 C

B: Today, I'd _____ _____ _____ _____ _____ about the trash problem at our school. I've found that many students just _____ things _____ instead _____ _____ them. _____ you know, however, recycling is very important _____ it saves _____ and helps _____ the environment. So, _____ _____, we need to reduce the number of _____ _____ at school _____ _____ _____. Why don't we _____ four different _____ _____ on every floor instead? This will _____ students to _____ the paper, glass, plastic, and cans _____.

남: 오늘 저는 우리 학교의 쓰레기 문제에 대해 제안을 하나 하고자 합니다. 저는 많은 학생들이 쓰레기를 재활용하는 대신에 그냥 버리는 것을 발견했습니다. 하지만, 여러분도 알다시피, 재활용은 자원을 아낄 수 있고 환경을 보호하는 것을 돕기 때문에 재활용하는 것은 정말 중요합니다. 그래서 제 생각에는 재활용을 권장하기 위해 학교에 있는 쓰레기통의 수를 줄이는 것이 필요하다고 생각합니다. 대신에 모든 층에 각기 색이 다른 4개의 재활용 통을 두는 것이 어떨까요? 이는 학생들이 종이, 유리, 플라스틱, 캔을 적절하게 구분할 수 있도록 상기시킬 것입니다.

### Listen & Talk 2 A

B: Our club is _____ a photo contest next week.

G: _____ _____ _____ photos will be in it?

B: The _____ is pollution around the world. We _____ _____ this contest to _____ _____ _____ of environmental problems.

G: That sounds nice. I can't _____ _____ _____ _____!

### Listen & Talk 2 B

G: I read a cool _____ today.

B: _____ was it _____?

G: It was about a new bag. It just _____ _____ a _____ _____, but it's _____ mostly _____ corn.

B: That sounds really _____.

G: Yes, but there's more. The bag _____ _____ in _____ in only three months and _____ in about _____ _____ in warm water!

B: Wow! That will help us _____ _____ _____ by a lot!

G: I know! The _____ will start _____ the bag sometime _____ _____. I can't _____ _____ _____ it!

### Listen & Talk 2 C

B: What _____ we _____ _____ do this weekend, Mihee?

G: Why don't we go to the _____ _____ near my house?

B: A sheep park? How _____! Are there really sheep in the park?

G: Yes. They are there to _____ _____ _____.

B: _____ _____ they help the environment?

G: You know, people usually use _____ to kill _____ _____. The sheep in the park eat those plants, so the _____ are _____.

B: What a _____ idea! I _____ _____ _____ visit the park!

### Do It Yourself

G: I want _____ _____ a new bag.

B: You already have too many bags. _____ _____ _____, you don't need _____ _____.

G: But I'm _____ _____ my old bags.

B: Then how _____ _____ old clothes to make a new bag? You can _____ _____ _____ _____ _____ _____ online.

G: Oh, that sounds _____! I can't wait _____ _____ my own bag.

---

※ 다음 우리말에 맞도록 대화를 영어로 쓰시오.

### Listen & Talk 1 A

B: _____

G: _____

_____

B: _____

남: 내 생각엔 우리는 비닐봉지를 너무 많이 쓰는 것 같아.

여: 내 생각도 그래. 그건 환경에 좋지 않아. 우리 비닐봉지 사용을 어떻게 줄일 수 있을까?

남: 내 생각에는 물건을 사러 갈 때 재사용할 수 있는 가방을 가져 가야 해.

### Listen & Talk 1 B

G: _____

B: _____

G: _____

B: _____

G: _____

B: _____

G: _____

여: 지호야, 서둘러! 엘리베이터가 곧 올라간다.

남: 과학실은 겨우 3층에 있잖아. 우리 계단을 오르는 건 어때?

여: 그 모든 계단을 올라서 가고 싶진 않아.

남: 잘 생각해 봐. 엘리베이터는 전기를 많이 쓰잖아. 우리는 환경을 보호하려면 에너지를 아껴야 해.

여: 하지만 엘리베이터를 한 번 탄다고 그렇게 많은 에너지를 사용하진 않잖아.

남: 그렇지, 하지만 엘리베이터를 타면서 사용하는 에너지는 시간이 흐르면서 누적될 거야. 내 생각에는, 환경을 보호하는 것은 작은 것부터 시작한다고 생각해.

여: 네 말이 일리가 있네. 계단을 이용하자.

### Listen & Talk 1 C

B: _____

_____

_____

_____

_____

_____

_____

남: 오늘 저는 우리 학교의 쓰레기 문제에 대해 제안을 하나 하고자 합니다. 저는 많은 학생들이 쓰레기를 재활용하는 대신에 그냥 버리는 것을 발견했습니다. 하지만, 여러분도 알다시피, 재활용은 자원을 아낄 수 있고 환경을 보호하는 것을 돕기 때문에 재활용하는 것은 정말 중요합니다. 그래서 제 생각에는 재활용을 권장하기 위해 학교에 있는 쓰레기통의 수를 줄이는 것이 필요하다고 생각합니다. 대신에 모든 층에 각기 색이 다른 4개의 재활용 통을 두는 것이 어떨까요? 이는 학생들이 종이, 유리, 플라스틱, 캔을 적절하게 구분할 수 있도록 상기시킬 것입니다.

## Listen & Talk 2 A

B: _____

G: _____

B: _____

_____

G: _____

## Listen & Talk 2 B

G: _____

B: _____

G: _____

B: _____

G: _____

B: _____

G: _____

## Listen & Talk 2 C

B: _____

G: _____

B: _____

G: _____

B: _____

G: _____

_____

B: _____

## Do It Yourself

G: _____

B: _____

G: _____

B: _____

_____

G: _____

---

남: 다음 주에 우리 동아리에서 사진 대회를 개최할 거야.
여: 어떤 종류의 사진들이 출품되니?
남: 주제는 세계의 환경오염이야. 우리는 학생들이 환경 문제에 대해 인식을 높일 수 있도록 이 대회를 개최하는 거야.
여: 그거 참 멋지네. 나도 어서 대회를 보고 싶다!

여: 오늘 굉장한 기사를 읽었어.
남: 무엇에 대한 기사였니?
여: 새로운 봉지에 관한 기사였어. 그것은 비닐봉지처럼 생겼지만, 대부분 옥수수로 만든 거야.
남: 그것 참 놀랍구나.
여: 응, 하지만 놀라운 게 더 있어. 그 봉지는 흙 속에서 3달 만에 분해되고 따뜻한 물속에서는 3분 만에 사라져!
남: 와! 그건 우리가 플라스틱 쓰레기를 줄이는 데 많이 도움이 되겠구나!
여: 내 말이 그 말이야! 그 회사는 올해 중으로 그 봉지를 팔기 시작할 거야. 어서 사용하고 싶어!

남: 이번 주말에 무엇을 할 계획이니, 미희야?
여: 우리 집 근처에 있는 양 공원에 가는 것은 어때?
남: 양 공원? 그것 참 흥미로운데! 공원에 정말로 양이 있는 거야?
여: 응. 양들은 환경을 보호하기 위해 거기에 있어.
남: 그들이 어떻게 환경에 도움을 줄 수 있지?
여: 있지, 사람들은 잡초를 없애기 위해 화학 물질을 사용하잖아. 그 공원에 있는 양들이 그런 잡초들을 먹어서, 화학물질이 필요하지 않게 돼.
남: 그것 참 놀라운 생각이구나! 어서 그 공원에 가보고 싶다!

여: 나 새로운 가방을 사고 싶어.
남: 넌 이미 너무 많은 가방을 가지고 있어. 내 생각에 넌 가방이 더 필요하지 않아.
여: 하지만 난 나의 오래된 가방들에 질렸는걸.
남: 그럼 새로운 가방을 만들기 위해 오래된 옷들을 사용하는 것은 어때? 만드는 방법은 온라인상에서 찾아볼 수 있어.
여: 오, 그것 참 흥미로운데! 어서 나만의 가방을 만들고 싶어!

※ 다음 우리말과 일치하도록 빈칸에 알맞은 것을 골라 쓰시오.

Join Hands, Save the Earth

**1** It is important _____ _____ _____ _____ ways to protect the environment.

    A. to               B. for               C. us               D. find

**2** Some people have found _____ _____ to _____ the _____.

    A. save            B. earth           C. ways          D. creative

**3** One _____ is an _____ _____ in Cancun, Mexico.

    A. underwater       B. example       C. museum

**4** Let's _____ Dr. Rosa Allison, an art _____, and listen to her _____ about the _____ museum.

    A. explanation       B. meet       C. professor       D. special

**5** Rosa: Cancun is a city _____ 4.8 million _____ every year.

    A. tourists          B. where         C. travel

**6** One of the _____ _____ activities to do there is looking _____ the _____ beautiful sea life underwater.

    A. at           B. popular         C. area's        D. most

**7** _____, tourist activities are seriously _____ of the sea _____ Cancun.

    A. near          B. damaging       C. however       D. parts

**8** _____ _____ this, artists did _____ _____.

    A. prevent         B. interesting      C. to         D. something

**9** They thought if they _____ tourists to a different _____ of the sea, the _____ areas could have time to get _____.

    A. dying         B. attracted      C. better        D. part

**10** They made an _____ museum _____ from the places _____ sea life was _____.

    A. underwater       B. dying       C. where       D. away

**11** It's _____ 14 meters _____ the surface and _____ 500 _____.

    A. contains       B. about       C. statues       D. below

**12** The statues are _____ _____ _____ that _____ sea life.

    A. materials       B. made       C. support       D. from

**13** They _____ additional places _____ plants and animals to _____ _____.

    A. on           B. for          C. provide       D. live

**14** Over time, many _____ of sea life will grow on the _____, which will make the _____ _____.

    A. unique         B. statues       C. artwork       D. types

**15** The artists want _____ to see a _____ of sea _____ on the _____.

    A. variety        B. life        C. statues       D. people

함께 손잡고, 지구를 구합시다

1 우리가 환경을 보호할 수 있는 방법을 찾는 것은 중요하다.

2 몇몇 사람들은 지구를 구하기 위한 창의적인 방법을 찾았다.

3 한 예로 멕시코 칸쿤에 있는 수중 박물관이 있다.

4 미술학 교수인 Rosa Allison 박사를 만나서 이 특별한 박물관에 대한 설명을 들어보자.

5 Rosa: 칸쿤은 매년 480만 명의 관광객이 여행하는 도시이다.

6 그곳에서 할 수 있는 가장 인기 있는 활동 중 하나는 그 지역의 바닷속의 아름다운 해양 생물을 관찰하는 것이다.

7 하지만, 관광 활동들이 칸쿤 근처의 바다 일부를 심각하게 훼손시키고 있다.

8 이러한 일을 방지하기 위해서, 예술가들이 흥미로운 생각을 해냈다.

9 그들은 만약 관광객들을 바다의 다른 쪽으로 유인한다면, 그 죽어가는 지역이 호전될 시간을 가질 수 있을 것이라 생각했다.

10 그들은 해양 생물이 죽어가는 지역으로부터 떨어진 해저에 수중 박물관을 만들었다.

11 그 박물관은 해수면에서 14미터 아래에 있으며 500개의 조각상이 있다.

12 그 조각상들은 해양 생물에게 도움이 되는 재료들로 만들어졌다.

13 그것들은 식물과 동물들이 살 수 있는 추가적인 장소를 제공한다.

14 시간이 흐르면, 많은 형태의 바다 생명체들이 그 조각상에서 자라게 될 것이며, 이것이 그 예술 작품을 독특하게 만들 것이다.

15 예술가들은 사람들이 그 조각상들에서 (살고 있는) 다양한 해양 생명체를 보길 원한다.

**16** If people _____ how _____ sea life is, they will understand how _____ it is to _____ the sea.

    A. save          B. rich          C. important        D. realize

**17** In Singapore, people are _____ architecture to _____ the _____ on _____.

    A. protect        B. using         C. land         D. environment

**18** Let's hear _____ Rajesh Khan, an _____, _____ about _____ buildings.

    A. eco-friendly    B. what         C. architect      D. says

**19** Rajesh: Singapore is _____ _____ the _____.

    A. throughout    B. hot         C. year

**20** Most buildings _____ air conditioning, _____ _____ _____ a lot of energy and _____ to climate change.

    A. which        B. need        C. contributes    D. uses

**21** That's _____ architects in Singapore have _____ to design eco-friendly buildings that use _____ air conditioning but are _____ cool inside.

    A. why         B. less        C. still         D. begun

**22** For _____, many buildings in Singapore are _____ to have an _____ _____.

    A. structure     B. example     C. designed     D. open

**23** This structure makes it possible for _____ _____ to _____ _____ a building.

    A. air          B. throughout    C. outside      D. move

**24** This _____ air flow is _____ these buildings _____ _____.

    A. stay         B. natural      C. how         D. cool

**25** In _____ to _____ open _____, architects _____ large gardens.

    A. add         B. making      C. addition     D. structures

**26** This greenery _____ shade and _____ parts of the building from _____ sunlight, which _____ the building cooler.

    A. keeps       B. provides     C. direct       D. protects

**27** Eco-friendly buildings like these not _____ help protect the environment, but _____ people _____ a good quality of life.

    A. also         B. with        C. only         D. provide

**28** Those are the _____ of this _____ _____ of _____.

    A. style        B. goals       C. architecture    D. new

**29** Hopefully, architects will _____ _____ _____ new eco-friendly ideas.

    A. up          B. keep       C. with        D. coming

**30** Every _____ has different _____ of _____ the _____.

    A. ways        B. field       C. environment   D. protecting

**31** _____ more innovation, humans and nature will be _____ to live together in harmony _____ _____ the future.

    A. able        B. far         C. with         D. into

---

**16** 만약 사람들이 해양 생물이 얼마나 풍부한지 깨닫는다면, 그들은 바다를 지키는 것이 얼마나 중요한지 이해할 것이다.

**17** 싱가포르에서는 사람들이 육지의 환경을 보호하기 위해 건축을 이용하고 있다.

**18** 건축가인 Rajesh Khan이 친환경 건물에 대해 말하는 것을 들어보자.

**19** Rajesh: 싱가포르는 연중 더운 곳이다.

**20** 대부분의 건물들은 에어컨 가동이 필요한데, 이로 인해 많은 에너지가 사용되고 있으며 기후 변화의 원인이 되고 있다.

**21** 그것이 싱가포르의 건축가들이 에어컨을 덜 쓰면서도 실내에서 여전히 시원한 느낌이 들 수 있는 친환경적인 건물들을 디자인하기 시작한 이유이다.

**22** 가령, 싱가포르의 많은 건물들은 개방형 구조를 포함하게 디자인되었다.

**23** 이러한 구조는 외부 공기가 건물을 관통하는 것을 가능케 한다.

**24** 이러한 자연적인 공기의 흐름이 이 건물을 시원하게 유지해 주는 방법이다.

**25** 건축가들은 개방형 구조를 만드는 것 외에도 큰 정원을 더한다.

**26** 이러한 녹지 공간은 그늘을 제공하고 직사광선으로부터 건물의 부분들을 지켜주어 건물을 시원하게 유지한다.

**27** 이와 같은 친환경적인 건물들은 환경을 보호하는 것을 도울 뿐만 아니라 사람들에게 양질의 삶을 제공한다.

**28** 그것들이 바로 이러한 새로운 건축 방식의 목표이다.

**29** 바라건대, 건축가들은 새로운 친환경 아이디어를 계속해서 생각해 낼 것이다.

**30** 모든 분야에서 환경을 보호하는 다른 방식이 있다.

**31** 더 나은 혁신으로 인해 먼 미래에 인간과 자연은 함께 조화를 이루며 살아갈 수 있을 것이다.

※ 다음 우리말과 일치하도록 빈칸에 알맞은 것을 골라 쓰시오.

Join Hands, Save the Earth

**1** _____ is important _____ _____ _____ _____ to protect the environment.

**2** Some people have found _____ _____ _____ the earth.

**3** One example is an _____ _____ in Cancun, Mexico.

**4** Let's _____ Dr. Rosa Allison, an art _____, and _____ _____ her _____ about the special museum.

**5** Rosa: Cancun is a city _____ 4.8 million _____ _____ _____.

**6** One of _____ _____ _____ activities _____ there _____ _____ _____ the area's beautiful sea life underwater.

**7** _____, tourist activities _____ _____ _____ _____ of the sea _____ Cancun.

**8** _____ _____ _____ _____, artists did _____ _____.

**9** They thought _____ they _____ tourists _____ a different part of the sea, the _____ _____ could have time _____ _____ _____.

**10** They _____ an _____ museum _____ _____ the places _____ sea life was _____.

**11** It's _____ 14 _____ _____ the _____ and _____ 500 _____.

**12** The statues _____ _____ _____ materials _____ _____ _____ _____.

**13** They _____ _____ _____ _____ _____ plants and animals _____ _____.

**14** Over time, many types of sea life _____ _____ _____ the statues, _____ _____ _____ the artwork _____.

**15** The artists _____ _____ _____ _____ sea life _____ the statues.

---

함께 손잡고, 지구를 구합시다

1 우리가 환경을 보호할 수 있는 방법을 찾는 것은 중요하다.

2 몇몇 사람들은 지구를 구하기 위한 창의적인 방법을 찾았다.

3 한 예로 멕시코 칸쿤에 있는 수중 박물관이 있다.

4 미술학 교수인 Rosa Allison 박사를 만나서 이 특별한 박물관에 대한 설명을 들어보자.

5 Rosa: 칸쿤은 매년 480만 명의 관광객이 여행하는 도시이다.

6 그곳에서 할 수 있는 가장 인기 있는 활동 중 하나는 그 지역의 바닷속의 아름다운 해양 생물을 관찰하는 것이다.

7 하지만, 관광 활동들이 칸쿤 근처의 바다 일부를 심각하게 훼손시키고 있다.

8 이러한 일을 방지하기 위해서, 예술가들이 흥미로운 생각을 해냈다.

9 그들은 만약 관광객들을 바다의 다른 쪽으로 유인한다면, 그 죽어가는 지역이 호전될 시간을 가질 수 있을 것이라 생각했다.

10 그들은 해양 생물이 죽어가는 지역으로부터 떨어진 해저에 수중 박물관을 만들었다.

11 그 박물관은 해수면에서 14미터 아래에 있으며 500개의 조각상이 있다.

12 그 조각상들은 해양 생물에게 도움이 되는 재료들로 만들어졌다.

13 그것들은 식물과 동물들이 살 수 있는 추가적인 장소를 제공한다.

14 시간이 흐르면, 많은 형태의 바다 생명체들이 그 조각상에서 자라게 될 것이며, 이것이 그 예술 작품을 독특하게 만들 것이다.

15 예술가들은 사람들이 그 조각상들에서 (살고 있는) 다양한 해양 생명체들을 보길 원한다.

**16** If people realize _____ _____ _____ _____ _____ _____,
they will understand _____ _____ _____ _____ to
save the sea.

**17** In Singapore, people are _____ _____ _____ _____
the environment _____ _____ .

**18** Let's hear _____ Rajesh Khan, an architect, _____ _____
_____ buildings.

**19** Rajesh: Singapore is hot _____ _____ _____ .

**20** Most buildings _____ air conditioning, _____ _____ a lot
of energy and _____ _____ _____ _____ .

**21** _____ _____ architects in Singapore _____ _____
_____ _____ eco-friendly buildings _____ _____
_____ air conditioning but _____ _____ cool inside.

**22** _____ _____ , many buildings in Singapore _____
_____ _____ _____ an _____ _____ .

**23** This structure makes _____ possible _____ _____
_____ _____ _____ a building.

**24** This _____ air flow is _____ _____ _____ _____
_____ .

**25** _____ _____ _____ _____ open structures, architects
add _____ _____ .

**26** This greenery _____ shade and _____ parts of the building
_____ _____ _____ , which _____ the building cooler.

**27** Eco-friendly buildings like these _____ _____ _____
protect the environment, _____ _____ _____ people
_____ a good _____ _____ .

**28** Those are the _____ of this _____ of _____ .

**29** Hopefully, architects _____ _____ _____ _____
_____ new _____ _____ .

**30** _____ _____ _____ different ways of _____ the
environment.

**31** _____ more _____ , humans and nature _____
_____ _____ _____ in harmony _____
_____ the future.

**16** 만약 사람들이 해양 생물이 얼마나 풍부한지 깨닫는다면, 그들은 바다를 지키는 것이 얼마나 중요한지 이해할 것이다.

**17** 싱가포르에서는 사람들이 육지의 환경을 보호하기 위해 건축을 이용하고 있다.

**18** 건축가인 Rajesh Khan이 친환경 건물에 대해 말하는 것을 들어보자.

**19** Rajesh: 싱가포르는 연중 더운 곳이다.

**20** 대부분의 건물들은 에어컨 가동이 필요한데, 이로 인해 많은 에너지가 사용되고 있으며 기후 변화의 원인이 되고 있다.

**21** 그것이 싱가포르의 건축가들이 에어컨을 덜 쓰면서도 실내에서 여전히 시원한 느낌이 들 수 있는 친환경적인 건물들을 디자인하기 시작한 이유이다.

**22** 가령, 싱가포르의 많은 건물들은 개방형 구조를 포함하게 디자인되었다.

**23** 이러한 구조는 외부 공기가 건물을 관통하는 것을 가능케 한다.

**24** 이러한 자연적인 공기의 흐름이 이 건물을 시원하게 유지해 주는 방법이다.

**25** 건축가들은 개방형 구조를 만드는 것 외에도 큰 정원을 더한다.

**26** 이러한 녹지 공간은 그늘을 제공하고 직사광선으로부터 건물의 부분들을 지켜주어 건물을 시원하게 유지한다.

**27** 이와 같은 친환경적인 건물들은 환경을 보호하는 것을 도울 뿐만 아니라 사람들에게 양질의 삶을 제공한다.

**28** 그것들이 바로 이러한 새로운 건축 방식의 목표이다.

**29** 바라건대, 건축가들은 새로운 친환경 아이디어를 계속해서 생각해 낼 것이다.

**30** 모든 분야에서 환경을 보호하는 다른 방식이 있다.

**31** 더 나은 혁신으로 인해 먼 미래에 인간과 자연은 함께 조화를 이루며 살아갈 수 있을 것이다.

※ 다음 문장을 우리말로 쓰시오.

**1** It is important for us to find ways to protect the environment.

➡ _____

**2** Some people have found creative ways to save the earth.

➡ _____

**3** One example is an underwater museum in Cancun, Mexico.

➡ _____

**4** Let's meet Dr. Rosa Allison, an art professor, and listen to her explanation about the special museum.

➡ _____

**5** Rosa: Cancun is a city where 4.8 million tourists travel every year.

➡ _____

**6** One of the most popular activities to do there is looking at the area's beautiful sea life underwater.

➡ _____

**7** However, tourist activities are seriously damaging parts of the sea near Cancun.

➡ _____

**8** To prevent this, artists did something interesting.

➡ _____

**9** They thought if they attracted tourists to a different part of the sea, the dying areas could have time to get better.

➡ _____

➡ _____

**10** They made an underwater museum away from the places where sea life was dying.

➡ _____

**11** It's about 14 meters below the surface and contains 500 statues.

➡ _____

**12** The statues are made from materials that support sea life.

➡ _____

**13** They provide additional places for plants and animals to live on.

➡ _____

**14** Over time, many types of sea life will grow on the statues, which will make the artwork unique.

➡ _____

**15** The artists want people to see a variety of sea life on the statues.

➡ _____

**16** If people realize how rich sea life is, they will understand how important it is to save the sea.

➡ _____

**17** In Singapore, people are using architecture to protect the environment on land.

➡ _____

**18** Let's hear what Rajesh Khan, an architect, says about eco-friendly buildings.

➡ _____

**19** Rajesh: Singapore is hot throughout the year.

➡ _____

**20** Most buildings need air conditioning, which uses a lot of energy and contributes to climate change.

➡ _____

**21** That's why architects in Singapore have begun to design eco-friendly buildings that use less air conditioning but are still cool inside.

➡ _____

_____

**22** For example, many buildings in Singapore are designed to have an open structure.

➡ _____

**23** This structure makes it possible for outside air to move throughout a building.

➡ _____

**24** This natural air flow is how these buildings stay cool.

➡ _____

**25** In addition to making open structures, architects add large gardens.

➡ _____

**26** This greenery provides shade and protects parts of the building from direct sunlight, which keeps the building cooler.

➡ _____

**27** Eco-friendly buildings like these not only help protect the environment, but also provide people with a good quality of life.

➡ _____

**28** Those are the goals of this new style of architecture.

➡ _____

**29** Hopefully, architects will keep coming up with new eco-friendly ideas.

➡ _____

**30** Every field has different ways of protecting the environment.

➡ _____

**31** With more innovation, humans and nature will be able to live together in harmony far into the future.

➡ _____

※ 다음 괄호 안의 단어들을 우리말에 맞도록 바르게 배열하시오.

Join Hands, Save the Earth

**1** (is / it / important / us / for / find / to / to / ways / protect / environment. / the)
➡ _____

**2** (people / some / found / have / ways / creative / save / to / earth. / the)
➡ _____

**3** (eample / one / an / is / museum / underwater / Cancun, / in / Mexico.)
➡ _____

**4** (meet / let's / Rosa / Dr. / Allison, / art / an / professor, / listen / and / her / to / explanation / about / the / museum. / special)
➡ _____

**5** (Rosa: / is / Cancun / city / a / where / million / 4.8 / travel / tourists / year. / every)
➡ _____

**6** (of / one / most / the / activities / popular / do / to / is / there / at / looking / area's / the / life / beautiful / sea / underwater.)
➡ _____

**7** (tourist / howerver, / are / activities / damaging / seriously / of / parts / sea / the / Cancun. / near)
➡ _____

**8** (prevent / to / artists / this, / something / did / interesting.)
➡ _____

**9** (thought / they / they / if / tourists / attracted / a / to / part / different / of / sea, / the / dying / the / could / areas / have / to / time / better. / get)
➡ _____

**10** (made / they / underwater / an / away / museum / the / from / where / places / life / sea / dying. / was)
➡ _____

**11** (about / it's / meters / 14 / the / below / and / surface / 500 / contains / statues.)
➡ _____

**12** (statues / the / made / are / materials / from / support / that / life. / sea)
➡ _____

**13** (provide / they / places / additional / plants / for / and / to / animals / live / on.)
➡ _____

**14** (time, / over / types / many / sea / of / will / life / on / grow / statues, / the / will / which / make / the / unique. / artwork)
➡ _____

**15** (artists / the / people / want / see / to / of / variety / a / sea / of / on / life / statues. / the)
➡ _____

함께 손잡고, 지구를 구합시다

**1** 우리가 환경을 보호할 수 있는 방법을 찾는 것은 중요하다.

**2** 몇몇 사람들은 지구를 구하기 위한 창의적인 방법을 찾았다.

**3** 한 예로 멕시코 칸쿤에 있는 수중 박물관이 있다.

**4** 미술학 교수인 Rosa Allison 박사를 만나서 이 특별한 박물관에 대한 설명을 들어보자.

**5** Rosa: 칸쿤은 매년 480만 명의 관광객이 여행하는 도시이다.

**6** 그곳에서 할 수 있는 가장 인기 있는 활동 중 하나는 그 지역의 바닷속의 아름다운 해양 생물을 관찰하는 것이다.

**7** 하지만, 관광 활동들이 칸쿤 근처의 바다 일부를 심각하게 훼손시키고 있다.

**8** 이러한 일을 방지하기 위해서, 예술가들이 흥미로운 생각을 해냈다.

**9** 그들은 만약 관광객들을 바다의 다른 쪽으로 유인한다면, 그 죽어가는 지역이 호전될 시간을 가질 수 있을 것이라 생각했다.

**10** 그들은 해양 생물이 죽어가는 지역으로부터 떨어진 해저에 수중 박물관을 만들었다.

**11** 그 박물관은 해수면에서 14미터 아래에 있으며 500개의 조각상이 있다.

**12** 그 조각상들은 해양 생물에게 도움이 되는 재료들로 만들어졌다.

**13** 그것들은 식물과 동물들이 살 수 있는 추가적인 장소를 제공한다.

**14** 시간이 흐르면, 많은 형태의 바다 생명체들이 그 조각상에서 자라게 될 것이며, 이것이 그 예술 작품을 독특하게 만들 것이다.

**15** 예술가들은 사람들이 그 조각상들에서 (살고 있는) 다양한 해양 생명체들을 보길 원한다.

**16** (poeple / if / how / realize / rich / life / sea / is, / will / they / how / understand / important / is / it / save / to / sea. / the)
➡ _____

**17** (Singapore, / in / are / people / architecture / using / protect / to / environment / the / land. / on)
➡ _____

**18** (hear / let's / Rajesh / what / Khan, / architect, / an / about / says / buildings. / eco-friendly)
➡ _____

**19** (Rajesh / is / Singapore / throughout / hot / year. / the)
➡ _____

**20** (buildings / most / air / need / which / conditioning, / a / uses / of / lot / and / energy / to / contributes / change. / climate)
➡ _____

**21** (why / that's / in / architects / Singapore / begun / have / design / to / buildings / eco-friendly / use / that / air / less / but / condtioning / are / inside. / cool / still)
➡ _____

**22** (example, / for / buildings / many / Singapore / in / are / to / designed / an / have / structure. / open)
➡ _____

**23** (structure / this / it / makes / for / possible / air / outside / move / to / a / throughout / building.)
➡ _____

**24** (natural / this / flow / air / how / is / buildings / these / cool. / stay)
➡ _____

**25** (addition / in / making / to / structures, / open / add / architects / gardens. / large)
➡ _____

**26** (greenery / this / shade / provides / and / parts / protects / of / building / the / direct / from / which / sunlight, / keeps / building / the / cooler.)
➡ _____

**27** (buildings / eco-friendly / these / like / only / not / protect / help / environment, / the / also / but / people / provide / a / with / good / of / quality / life.)
➡ _____

**28** (are / those / goals / the / this / of / style / new / architecture. / of)
➡ _____

**29** (architects / hopefully, / keep / will / up / coming / new / with / ideas. / eco-friendly)
➡ _____

**30** (field / every / different / has / of / ways / the / protecting / environment.)
➡ _____

**31** (more / with / innovation, / humans / and / will / nature / able / be / live / to / in / together / far / harmony / into / future. / the)
➡ _____

**16** 만약 사람들이 해양 생물이 얼마나 풍부한지 깨닫는다면, 그들은 바다를 지키는 것이 얼마나 중요한지 이해할 것이다.

**17** 싱가포르에서는 사람들이 육지의 환경을 보호하기 위해 건축을 이용하고 있다.

**18** 건축가인 Rajesh Khan이 친환경 건물에 대해 말하는 것을 들어보자.

**19** Rajesh: 싱가포르는 연중 더운 곳이다.

**20** 대부분의 건물들은 에어컨 가동이 필요한데, 이로 인해 많은 에너지가 사용되고 있으며 기후 변화의 원인이 되고 있다.

**21** 그것이 싱가포르의 건축가들이 에어컨을 덜 쓰면서도 실내에서 여전히 시원한 느낌이 들 수 있는 친환경적인 건물들을 디자인하기 시작한 이유이다.

**22** 가령, 싱가포르의 많은 건물들은 개방형 구조를 포함하게 디자인되었다.

**23** 이러한 구조는 외부 공기가 건물을 관통하는 것을 가능케 한다.

**24** 이러한 자연적인 공기의 흐름이 이 건물을 시원하게 유지해 주는 방법이다.

**25** 건축가들은 개방형 구조를 만드는 것 외에도 큰 정원을 더한다.

**26** 이러한 녹지 공간은 그늘을 제공하고 직사광선으로부터 건물의 부분들을 지켜주어 건물을 시원하게 유지한다.

**27** 이와 같은 친환경적인 건물들은 환경을 보호하는 것을 도울 뿐만 아니라 사람들에게 양질의 삶을 제공한다.

**28** 그것들이 바로 이러한 새로운 건축 방식의 목표이다.

**29** 바라건대, 건축가들은 새로운 친환경 아이디어를 계속해서 생각해 낼 것이다.

**30** 모든 분야에서 환경을 보호하는 다른 방식이 있다.

**31** 더 나은 혁신으로 인해 먼 미래에 인간과 자연은 함께 조화를 이루며 살아갈 수 있을 것이다.

※ 다음 우리말을 영어로 쓰시오.

**1** 우리가 환경을 보호할 수 있는 방법을 찾는 것은 중요하다.

➡ _____

**2** 몇몇 사람들은 지구를 구하기 위한 창의적인 방법을 찾았다.

➡ _____

**3** 한 예로 멕시코 칸쿤에 있는 수중 박물관이 있다.

➡ _____

**4** 미술학 교수인 Rosa Allison 박사를 만나서 이 특별한 박물관에 대한 설명을 들어보자.

➡ _____

**5** Rosa: 칸쿤은 매년 480만 명의 관광객이 여행하는 도시이다.

➡ _____

**6** 그곳에서 할 수 있는 가장 인기 있는 활동 중 하나는 그 지역의 바닷속의 아름다운 해양 생물을 관찰하는 것이다.

➡ _____

**7** 하지만, 관광 활동들이 칸쿤 근처의 바다 일부를 심각하게 훼손시키고 있다.

➡ _____

**8** 이러한 일을 방지하기 위해서, 예술가들이 흥미로운 생각을 해냈다.

➡ _____

**9** 그들은 만약 관광객들을 바다의 다른 쪽으로 유인한다면, 그 죽어가는 지역이 호전될 시간을 가질 수 있을 것이라 생각했다.

➡ _____

_____

**10** 그들은 해양 생물이 죽어가는 지역으로부터 떨어진 해저에 수중 박물관을 만들었다.

➡ _____

**11** 그 박물관은 해수면에서 14미터 아래에 있으며 500개의 조각상이 있다.

➡ _____

**12** 그 조각상들은 해양 생물에게 도움이 되는 재료들로 만들어졌다.

➡ _____

**13** 그것들은 식물과 동물들이 살 수 있는 추가적인 장소를 제공한다.

➡ _____

**14** 시간이 흐르면, 많은 형태의 바다 생명체들이 그 조각상에서 자라게 될 것이며, 이것이 그 예술 작품을 독특하게 만들 것이다.

➡ _____

**15** 예술가들은 사람들이 그 조각상들에서 (살고 있는) 다양한 해양 생명체들을 보길 원한다.

➡ _____

**16** 만약 사람들이 해양 생물이 얼마나 풍부한지 깨닫는다면, 그들은 바다를 지키는 것이 얼마나 중요한지 이해할 것이다.

➡ _____

**17** 싱가포르에서는 사람들이 육지의 환경을 보호하기 위해 건축을 이용하고 있다.

➡ _____

**18** 건축가인 Rajesh Khan이 친환경 건물에 대해 말하는 것을 들어보자.

➡ _____

**19** Rajesh: 싱가포르는 연중 더운 곳이다.

➡ _____

**20** 대부분의 건물들은 에어컨 가동이 필요한데, 이로 인해 많은 에너지가 사용되고 있으며 기후 변화의 원인이 되고 있다.

➡ _____

**21** 그것이 싱가포르의 건축가들이 에어컨을 덜 쓰면서도 실내에서 여전히 시원한 느낌이 들 수 있는 친환경적인 건물들을 디자인하기 시작한 이유이다.

➡ _____

_____

**22** 가령, 싱가포르의 많은 건물들은 개방형 구조를 포함하게 디자인되었다.

➡ _____

**23** 이러한 구조는 외부 공기가 건물을 관통하는 것을 가능케 한다.

➡ _____

**24** 이러한 자연적인 공기의 흐름이 이 건물을 시원하게 유지해 주는 방법이다.

➡ _____

**25** 건축가들은 개방형 구조를 만드는 것 외에도 큰 정원을 더한다.

➡ _____

**26** 이러한 녹지 공간은 그늘을 제공하고 직사광선으로부터 건물의 부분들을 지켜주어 건물을 시원하게 유지한다.

➡ _____

**27** 이와 같은 친환경적인 건물들은 환경을 보호하는 것을 도울 뿐만 아니라 사람들에게 양질의 삶을 제공한다.

➡ _____

_____

**28** 그것들이 바로 이러한 새로운 건축 방식의 목표이다.

➡ _____

**29** 바라건대, 건축가들은 새로운 친환경 아이디어를 계속해서 생각해 낼 것이다.

➡ _____

**30** 모든 분야에서 환경을 보호하는 다른 방식이 있다.

➡ _____

**31** 더 나은 혁신으로 인해 먼 미래에 인간과 자연은 함께 조화를 이루며 살아갈 수 있을 것이다.

➡ _____

※ 다음 우리말과 일치하도록 빈칸에 알맞은 말을 쓰시오.

## Listen & Talk 2 D Talk Together

1. A: _____ you _____ of _____ _____? They're _____!
2. B: _____, I _____. _____ _____ about _____.
3. A: They _____ _____ _____ _____. They will _____
   _____.
4. B: That _____ _____. I _____ _____ _____ _____
   them.

1. A: 먹을 수 있는 수저에 대해 들어봤니? 정말 놀라워!
2. B: 아니, 들어 본 적이 없어. 그것에 대해 이야기해 봐.
3. A: 수저는 곡물로 만들어져. 그것들은 자원을 절약할 거야.
4. B: 정말 멋지다. 나는 그것들을 사용하는 게 정말 기다려져.

## Presentation Time

1. _____ can we _____ _____ _____ _____ _____?
2. _____ _____ _____, we need a green wall.
3. _____ _____ _____ of our school is _____ _____
   _____ for it.
4. A green wall _____ _____ _____ the building _____
   _____ _____ _____.
5. This could _____ _____ _____ _____ _____ _____ _____
   for air conditioning.

1. 우리는 어떻게 우리 학교를 친환경적으로 만들 수 있을까요?
2. 제 의견으로는, 우리는 식물로 덮인 벽이 필요합니다.
3. 우리 학교의 앞 벽은 그것을 위한 훌륭한 공간입니다.
4. 식물로 덮인 벽은 햇빛을 차단함으로써 건물을 시원하게 유지하는 것을 돕습니다.
5. 이것은 에어컨을 위해 사용되는 에너지의 양을 줄일 수 있습니다.

## Think & Write Step 3

1. Eat Your Cup and _____ _____ _____!
2. Here' an _____, _____ _____ _____ _____!
3. It is _____ _____ _____.
4. It's a cookie that _____ _____ _____ _____ _____
   _____ a cup.
5. _____ you use the cup, you _____ _____ _____ _____ _____.
6. _____ _____ _____, you _____ _____ _____ or
   plastic.
7. The cookie cup _____ _____ _____ _____.
8. _____ _____ _____ _____ _____ the change!

1. 컵을 먹고 지구를 구하세요!
2. 여기 혁신적이며 친환경적인 상품이 있습니다!
3. 이것은 과자컵입니다.
4. 이것은 컵 모양으로 만들어진 과자입니다.
5. 컵을 사용한 후에 그냥 그것을 먹을 수 있습니다.
6. 이렇게 함으로서 종이나 플라스틱을 절약할 수 있습니다.
7. 과자컵은 세상을 바꿀 수 있습니다.
8. 변화의 일부가 되십시오!

## 구석구석 지문 Test

※ 다음 우리말을 영어로 쓰시오.

### Listen & Talk 2 D Talk Together

1. A: 먹을 수 있는 수저에 대해 들어봤니? 정말 놀라워!
   ➡ _____

2. B: 아니, 들어 본 적이 없어. 그것에 대해 이야기해 봐.
   ➡ _____

3. A: 수저는 곡물로 만들어져. 그것들은 자원을 절약할 거야.
   ➡ _____

4. B: 정말 멋지다. 나는 그것들을 사용하는 게 정말 기다려져.
   ➡ _____

### Presentation Time

1. 우리는 어떻게 우리 학교를 친환경적으로 만들 수 있을까요?
   ➡ _____

2. 제 의견으로는, 우리는 식물로 덮인 벽이 필요합니다.
   ➡ _____

3. 우리 학교의 앞 벽은 그것을 위한 훌륭한 공간입니다.
   ➡ _____

4. 식물로 덮인 벽은 햇빛을 차단함으로써 건물을 시원하게 유지하는 것을 돕습니다.
   ➡ _____

5. 이것은 에어컨을 위해 사용되는 에너지의 양을 줄일 수 있습니다.
   ➡ _____

### Think & Write Step 3

1. 컵을 먹고 지구를 구하세요!
   ➡ _____

2. 여기 혁신적이며 친환경적인 상품이 있습니다!
   ➡ _____

3. 이것은 과자컵입니다.
   ➡ _____

4. 이것은 컵 모양으로 만들어진 과자입니다.
   ➡ _____

5. 컵을 사용한 후에 그냥 그것을 먹을 수 있습니다.
   ➡ _____

6. 이렇게 함으로서 종이나 플라스틱을 절약할 수 있습니다.
   ➡ _____

7. 과자컵은 세상을 바꿀 수 있습니다.
   ➡ _____

8. 변화의 일부가 되십시오!
   ➡ _____

※ 다음 영어를 우리말로 쓰시오.

| | | | |
|---|---|---|---|
| 01 | refund | 22 | experience |
| 02 | user | 23 | fee |
| 03 | weakness | 24 | choose |
| 04 | issue | 25 | freely |
| 05 | lender | 26 | improve |
| 06 | negative | 27 | return |
| 07 | regularly | 28 | owner |
| 08 | positive | 29 | personal |
| 09 | broken | 30 | download |
| 10 | condition | 31 | economy |
| 11 | provide | 32 | purpose |
| 12 | upset | 33 | reliable |
| 13 | concern | 34 | borrow |
| 14 | reasonable | 35 | for free |
| 15 | upload | 36 | look after |
| 16 | exact | 37 | be aware of |
| 17 | wherever | 38 | out of town |
| 18 | communicate | 39 | take care of |
| 19 | discount | 40 | on sale |
| 20 | resource | 41 | less than |
| 21 | balanced | 42 | What if ~? |
| | | 43 | search for |

※ 다음 우리말을 영어로 쓰시오.

| | | | | |
|---|---|---|---|---|
| 01 | 선택하다, 고르다 | _____ | 22 | 긍정적인 | _____ |
| 02 | 믿을 수 있는 | _____ | 23 | 사용자 | _____ |
| 03 | 향상하다, 개선하다 | _____ | 24 | 빌려주는 사람 | _____ |
| 04 | 정확한, 정밀한 | _____ | 25 | 경험하다 | _____ |
| 05 | 균형 잡힌 | _____ | 26 | 개인의, 개인적인 | _____ |
| 06 | 의사소통하다 | _____ | 27 | 어디든지 | _____ |
| 07 | 다운로드하다 | _____ | 28 | 요금, 수수료 | _____ |
| 08 | 경제 | _____ | 29 | 부정적인, 나쁜 | _____ |
| 09 | 우려, 근심 | _____ | 30 | 주인, 소유주 | _____ |
| 10 | 타당한, 합리적인, (값이) 적당한 | _____ | 31 | 제공하다 | _____ |
| 11 | 빌리다 | _____ | 32 | 목적 | _____ |
| 12 | 약점 | _____ | 33 | 함께 쓰다, 공유하다 | _____ |
| 13 | 할인 | _____ | 34 | 돌려주다, 반납하다 | _____ |
| 14 | 업로드하다, 전송하다 | _____ | 35 | ~보다 적은, ~ 미만의 | _____ |
| 15 | 자유롭게 | _____ | 36 | 무료로 | _____ |
| 16 | 환불 | _____ | 37 | 할인 중인 | _____ |
| 17 | 망가진, 고장 난 | _____ | 38 | ~를 찾다 | _____ |
| 18 | 정기적으로 | _____ | 39 | ~을 요청하다, 필요로 하다 | _____ |
| 19 | 문제(점), 쟁점 | _____ | 40 | ~을 찾아오다 | _____ |
| 20 | 상태, 조건 | _____ | 41 | ~을 돌보다 | _____ |
| 21 | 자원 | _____ | 42 | ~을 알고 있다 | _____ |
| | | | 43 | 도시를 떠나, 다른 곳으로 떠나 | _____ |

※ 다음 영영풀이에 알맞은 단어를 <보기>에서 골라 쓴 후, 우리말 뜻을 쓰시오.

1 _____ : not working properly: _____

2 _____ : many times or in large quantities: _____

3 _____ : to repair or correct something: _____

4 _____ : the state or condition of lacking strength: _____

5 _____ : an amount of money that must be paid: _____

6 _____ : a fact or situation that worries you: _____

7 _____ : unpleasant, depressing, or harmful: _____

8 _____ : to decide which person or thing you want to have: _____

9 _____ : to move data to a smaller computer system from a larger one: _____

10 _____ : an amount of money that is taken off the usual cost of something: _____

11 _____ : to give something that someone needs or wants to them, or make it available: _____

12 _____ : able to be trusted, or consistently good in quality or performance: _____

13 _____ : to bring, give, put, or send something back to someone or something: _____

14 _____ : to achieve or produce something of a better standard or quality than before: _____

15 _____ : the system according to which the money, industry and trade of a country or region are organized: _____

16 _____ : based on or using good judgment and therefore fair, practical and sensible: _____

| 보기 | | | |
|---|---|---|---|
| improve | choose | reasonable | negative |
| discount | freely | provide | broken |
| return | concern | economy | fee |
| reliable | fix | download | weakness |

## 대화문 Test

※ 다음 우리말과 일치하도록 빈칸에 알맞은 말을 쓰시오.

 해석

### Listen & Talk 1 A

**G:** These two _____ of shoes are _____ _____! _____ _____ _____ _____?

**B:** Well, I _____ the white shoes _____ the _____ _____.

**G:** Why is that? The black ones are _____.

**B:** Yes, but I like the _____ of the _____ _____.

여: 이 두 켤레의 신발이 세일 중이네! 어떤 것이 더 좋으니?
남: 음, 나는 검은색 신발보다 흰색 신발이 더 좋아.
여: 왜? 검은색 신발이 더 저렴하잖아.
남: 맞아, 하지만 나는 흰색 신발의 디자인이 더 좋아.

### Listen & Talk 1 B

**G:** _____ do you _____, the Special Sandwich _____ the Classic Sandwich?

**B:** Well, the Special Sandwich is the _____ _____. It's _____ _____ lots of fresh vegetables and _____ healthy _____.

**G:** But it's _____ more _____ _____ the Classic Sandwich.

**B:** I know, but I _____ the Special Sandwich _____ the Classic Sandwich. _____ _____ is important _____ me.

**G:** I prefer the _____ one. I'll _____ my money _____ books _____.

**B:** I guess _____ _____ _____ are _____.

여: 스페셜 샌드위치와 클래식 샌드위치 중 어떤 것이 더 좋으니?
남: 음, 스페셜 샌드위치가 더 건강한 선택이야. 그것은 신선한 야채들과 다른 건강한 재료들로 만들어졌어.
여: 하지만 그건 클래식 샌드위치보다 훨씬 더 비싸잖아.
남: 맞아, 하지만 나는 클래식 샌드위치보다 스페셜 샌드위치가 더 좋아. 나에게는 건강하게 먹는 것이 중요하거든.
여: 나는 더 저렴한 것이 더 좋아. 대신 나는 내 돈을 책 사는 데 쓸래.
남: 우리는 소비 습관이 다른 것 같구나.

### Listen & Talk 1 C

**G1:** I think my hair is too _____. I want to _____ my hair. Can you _____ a _____ _____?

**G2:** Sure. I know two places, Styles Studio and Hair Castle.

**G1:** Is there any _____ _____ the _____?

**G2:** Well, Styles Studio provides _____ _____ _____ your hair _____.

**G1:** That's great. _____ _____ Hair Castle?

**G2:** Hair Castle doesn't _____ treatment _____ _____, but they give _____ _____.

**G1:** Okay. _____ do you _____?

**G2:** I _____ Styles Studio _____ Hair Castle. It's important _____ me _____ get hair treatment _____.

여1: 내 머리가 너무 곱슬곱슬한 것 같아. 머리카락을 곧게 펴고 싶어. 좋은 곳을 추천해 줄 수 있니?
여2: 물론이지. 난 스타일 스튜디오와 헤어 캐슬, 두 군데를 알고 있어.
여1: 두 군데의 차이점이 있니?
여2: 음, 스타일 스튜디오는 머리카락을 건강하게 유지해 주는 트리트먼트를 무료로 제공해 줘.
여1: 그것 좋으네. 헤어 캐슬은 어때?
여2: 헤어 캐슬은 트리트먼트를 무료로 제공해 주지는 않지만, 학생 할인을 해 줘.
여1: 그렇구나. 넌 어느 곳을 선호하니?
여2: 나는 헤어 캐슬보다 스타일 스튜디오를 선호해. 나한텐 헤어 트리트먼트를 규칙적으로 받는 것이 중요해.

### Listen & Talk 2 A

**B:** I'm going to _____ _____ _____ for these clothes this evening. I found I have _____ ones.

**W:** Okay. _____ _____ to bring your _____. Last time you couldn't _____ _____ _____ because you didn't bring it.

**B:** Okay, Mom. I _____ _____ it this time.

저 오늘 저녁에 이 옷들을 환불하려고 해요. 제가 비슷한 옷들을 갖고 있다는 것을 발견했거든요.

여: 그래. 영수증 갖고 가는 것 잊지 마렴. 저번에 네가 영수증을 가지고 가지 않는 바람에 환불을 못 받았잖니.

남: 알겠어요, 엄마. 이번에는 잊지 않을게요.

### Listen & Talk 2 B

**G:** What should we sell at the _____ _____ next month?

**B:** Before we choose anything _____ _____, I think we need to do some _____ _____.

**G:** _____ _____? Why do we need _____?

**B:** _____ it helps us _____ out _____ _____ _____ _____ these days.

**G:** I see. Then we can _____ _____ _____ _____ _____ at the market.

**B:** That's right. It will also help us _____ _____ _____ for our items.

**G:** Cool. Is there _____ _____ we should do?

**B:** Oh, don't forget _____ _____ our names _____ this Friday.

**G:** Right. Thanks for _____ me.

여: 우리 다음 달에 벼룩시장에서 무엇을 판매해야 할까?

남: 우리가 판매할 물건을 선택하기 전에 시장 조사부터 좀 해야 할 것 같아.

여: 시장 조사? 우리가 그게 왜 필요한데?

남: 왜냐하면 우리가 시장 조사를 통해 요즘 어떤 물건이 인기 있는지 알아내는 데 도움이 되기 때문이지.

여: 그렇구나. 그럼 벼룩시장에서 무엇을 판매할지 정할 수 있겠다.

남: 맞아. 그리고 시장 조사를 통해 우리는 판매할 물건에 합리적인 가격을 정하는 데 도움이 될 거야.

여: 좋아. 그 외에 우리가 해야 할 다른 게 있을까?

남: 오, 우리 이름을 이번 주 금요일까지 등록하는 것을 잊지 마.

여: 맞아. 알려 줘서 고마워.

### Listen & Talk 2 C

**G:** I tried Spring Chips recently, and now I want to _____ them.

**B:** That sounds fun. _____ will you do your _____?

**G:** I'll make a video. I want to _____ their delicious taste!

**B:** Okay, but _____ _____ _____ _____ about their _____ _____ too.

**G:** I _____. I want to give a _____ _____.

**B:** Good. Your video will make _____ _____ _____ people _____ _____ _____ _____.

**G:** That's exactly _____ I want. I'd _____ _____ give people more _____ _____ about the product.

여: 내가 요새 스프링 칩스를 먹어봤는데, 이제 그것을 비평해 보고 싶어.

남: 그거 재밌겠다. 어떻게 비평할 거니?

여: 나는 동영상을 만들려고 해. 스프링 칩스의 맛있는 맛에 초점을 맞추고 싶어!

남: 그래, 하지만 그것의 단점에 대해서도 이야기하는 것을 잊지 마.

여: 잊지 않을 거야. 나는 균형 잡힌 비평을 보여주고 싶어.

남: 좋아. 네 동영상 덕분에 사람들이 더 나은 제품을 선택하는 것이 쉬워지겠구나.

여: 그것이 바로 내가 원하는 거야. 나는 사람들에게 제품에 대한 더 유용한 정보를 주고 싶어.

### Do It Yourself

**G:** Jinho, look! These two _____ look _____ _____.

**B:** Yeah, they do. _____ _____ _____ _____, the red one or the _____ _____?

**G:** I prefer the red one _____ the black one. It's only 20 dollars, and it comes with a _____ _____ for music downloads.

**B:** _____ the black one is 40 dollars, I think it's the _____ one for me. I heard it has _____ _____ _____.

여: 진호, 이것 봐! 이 스피커 두 개 꽤 멋져 보이는데.

남: 응, 정말 그러네. 빨간색 스피커와 검은색 스피커 중에서 어떤 것이 더 좋니?

여: 나는 검은색 스피커보다 빨간색 스피커가 더 좋아. 그것은 20달러밖에 안 하고, 음악 다운로드를 할인해 주는 쿠폰도 같이 있잖아.

남: 검은색 스피커가 40달러이지만, 그것이 나한테 맞는 것 같아. 그게 더 나은 음질을 갖고 있다고 들었거든.

※ 다음 우리말에 맞도록 대화를 영어로 쓰시오.

### Listen & Talk 1 A

G: _____

B: _____

G: _____

B: _____

여: 이 두 켤레의 신발이 세일 중이네! 어떤 것이 더 좋으니?

남: 음, 나는 검은색 신발보다 흰색 신발이 더 좋아.

여: 왜? 검은색 신발이 더 저렴하잖아.

남: 맞아, 하지만 나는 흰색 신발의 디자인이 더 좋아.

### Listen & Talk 1 B

G: _____

B: _____

_____

G: _____

B: _____

_____

G: _____

B: _____

여: 스페셜 샌드위치와 클래식 샌드위치 중 어떤 것이 더 좋으니?

남: 음, 스페셜 샌드위치가 더 건강한 선택이야. 그것은 신선한 야채들과 다른 건강한 재료들로 만들어졌어.

여: 하지만 그건 클래식 샌드위치보다 훨씬 더 비싸잖아.

남: 맞아, 하지만 나는 클래식 샌드위치보다 스페셜 샌드위치가 더 좋아. 나에게는 건강하게 먹는 것이 중요하거든.

여: 나는 더 저렴한 것이 더 좋아. 대신 나는 내 돈을 책 사는 데 쓸래.

남: 우리는 소비 습관이 다른 것 같구나.

### Listen & Talk 1 C

G1: _____

_____

G2: _____

G1: _____

G2: _____

G1: _____

G2: _____

G1: _____

G2: _____

여1: 내 머리가 너무 곱슬곱슬한 것 같아. 머리카락을 곧게 펴고 싶어. 좋은 곳을 추천해 줄 수 있니?

여2: 물론이지. 난 스타일 스튜디오와 헤어 캐슬, 두 군데를 알고 있어.

여1: 두 군데의 차이점이 있니?

여2: 음, 스타일 스튜디오는 머리카락을 건강하게 유지해 주는 트리트먼트를 무료로 제공해 줘.

여1: 그것 좋으네. 헤어 캐슬은 어때?

여2: 헤어 캐슬은 트리트먼트를 무료로 제공해 주지는 않지만, 학생 할인을 해 줘.

여1: 그렇구나. 넌 어느 곳을 선호하니?

여2: 나는 헤어 캐슬보다 스타일 스튜디오를 선호해. 나한텐 헤어 트리트먼트를 규칙적으로 받는 것이 중요해.

## Listen & Talk 2 A

B: _____

_____

W: _____

_____

B: _____

## Listen & Talk 2 B

G: _____

B: _____

G: _____

B: _____

G: _____

B: _____

G: _____

B: _____

G: _____

## Listen & Talk 2 C

G: _____

B: _____

G: _____

B: _____

G: _____

B: _____

G: _____

## Do It Yourself

G: _____

B: _____

G: _____

_____

B: _____

_____

---

남: 저 오늘 저녁에 이 옷들을 환불하려고 해요. 제가 비슷한 옷들을 갖고 있다는 것을 발견했거든요.
여: 그래. 영수증 갖고 가는 것 잊지 마렴. 저번에 네가 영수증을 가지고 가지 않는 바람에 환불을 못 받았잖니.
남: 알겠어요, 엄마. 이번에는 잊지 않을게요.

여: 우리 다음 달에 벼룩시장에서 무엇을 판매해야 할까?
남: 우리가 판매할 물건을 선택하기 전에 시장 조사부터 좀 해야 할 것 같아.
여: 시장 조사? 우리가 그게 왜 필요한데?
남: 왜냐하면 우리가 시장 조사를 통해 요즘 어떤 물건이 인기 있는지 알아내는 데 도움이 되기 때문이지.
여: 그렇구나. 그럼 벼룩시장에서 무엇을 판매할지 정할 수 있겠다.
남: 맞아. 그리고 시장 조사를 통해 우리는 판매할 물건에 합리적인 가격을 정하는 데 도움이 될 거야.
여: 좋아. 그 외에 우리가 해야 할 다른 게 있을까?
남: 오, 우리 이름을 이번 주 금요일까지 등록하는 것을 잊지 마.
여: 맞아. 알려 줘서 고마워.

여: 내가 요새 스프링 칩스를 먹어봤는데, 이제 그것을 비평해 보고 싶어.
남: 그거 재밌겠다. 어떻게 비평할 거니?
여: 나는 동영상을 만들려고 해. 스프링 칩스의 맛있는 맛에 초점을 맞추고 싶어!
남: 그래, 하지만 그것의 단점에 대해서도 이야기하는 것을 잊지 마.
여: 잊지 않을 거야. 나는 균형 잡힌 비평을 보여주고 싶어.
남: 좋아. 네 동영상 덕분에 사람들이 더 나은 제품을 선택하는 것이 쉬워지겠구나.
여: 그것이 바로 내가 원하는 거야. 나는 사람들에게 제품에 대한 더 유용한 정보를 주고 싶어.

여: 진호, 이것 봐! 이 스피커 두 개 꽤 멋져 보이는데.
남: 응, 정말 그러네. 빨간색 스피커와 검은색 스피커 중에서 어떤 것이 더 좋니?
여: 나는 검은색 스피커보다 빨간색 스피커가 더 좋아. 그것은 20달러밖에 안 하고, 음악 다운로드를 할인해 주는 쿠폰도 같이 있잖아.
남: 검은색 스피커가 40달러이지만, 그것이 나한테 맞는 것 같아. 그게 더 나은 음질을 갖고 있다고 들었거든.

※ 다음 우리말과 일치하도록 빈칸에 알맞은 것을 골라 쓰시오.

**1** _____ in the _____ _____
　　A. Economy　　B. Life　　C. Sharing

**2** Son: _____ _____ _____ _____ this weekend, Dad?
　　A. do　　B. what　　C. we　　D. should

**3** Dad: _____ _____ _____ go camping?
　　A. we　　B. don't　　C. why

**4** Son: But we _____ _____ a _____.
　　A. tent　　B. have　　C. don't

**5** _____ we _____ _____?
　　A. one　　B. should　　C. buy

**6** _____, who will _____ _____ _____ our dog?
　　A. care　　B. also　　C. of　　D. take

**7** Dad: _____ _____. I know some _____ that can _____ us.
　　A. apps　　B. worry　　C. help　　D. don't

**8** _____ _____ your _____!
　　A. neighbors　　B. borrow　　C. from

**9** Ask Your Neighbors _____ people _____ _____ items that they can borrow from _____.
　　A. others　　B. easily　　C. find　　D. helps

**10** First, users _____ the app and _____ for _____ user that has the _____ they need.
　　A. item　　B. search　　C. download　　D. another

**11** Then they _____ _____ the _____ and _____ it later.
　　A. up　　B. return　　C. pick　　D. item

**12** Jasmine: _____ _____, _____
　　A. 2019　　B. 12　　C. December

**13** I _____ _____ a board game and got one in _____ _____ 30 minutes.
　　A. less　　B. for　　C. than　　D. asked

**14** I love _____ money _____ _____ things that I don't often _____.
　　A. borrowing　　B. saving　　C. by　　D. need

**15** _____, I think it's _____ _____.
　　A. friendly　　B. also　　C. environmentally

**16** The _____ _____ we buy, the _____ _____ we save.
　　A. more　　B. fewer　　C. resources　　D. products

| | |
|---|---|
| **1** | 공유 경제 속 삶 |
| **2** | 아들: 아빠, 우리 이번 주말에 뭐 할 거예요? |
| **3** | 아빠: 캠핑 가는 건 어떠니? |
| **4** | 아들: 그런데 우리 텐트가 없잖아요. |
| **5** | 하나 사야 할까요? |
| **6** | 게다가 우리 개는 누가 돌봐요? |
| **7** | 아빠: 걱정하지 마. 내가 우리를 도와줄 수 있는 몇 개의 앱들을 알고 있지. |
| **8** | 당신의 이웃들로부터 빌려라! |
| **9** | Ask Your Neighbors는 사람들이 다른 사람들로부터 빌릴 수 있는 물건을 쉽게 찾도록 돕는다. |
| **10** | 우선, 사용자들은 그 앱을 내려받고 그들이 필요한 물건을 가지고 있는 또 다른 사용자를 찾는다. |
| **11** | 그리고 나서 그들은 그 물건을 받아서 나중에 반납한다. |
| **12** | Jasmine / 2019년 12월 12일 |
| **13** | 저는 보드게임을 요청했고 30분도 안 되어 하나를 구했어요. |
| **14** | 저는 제가 자주 필요하지 않은 것들을 빌림으로써 돈을 아낄 수 있다는 것이 마음에 들어요. |
| **15** | 게다가 이것이 환경친화적이라고 생각해요. |
| **16** | 우리가 제품들을 더 적게 구매할수록, 우리는 더 많은 자원들을 아끼는 거예요. |

**17** Cassandra: _____ _____ , _____
  A. 7          B. 2020          C. March

**18** _____ a lot of _____ _____ , I decided to _____ a bike helmet.
  A. reviews      B. borrow      C. seeing      D. positive

**19** When I _____ it, _____ , it _____ .
  A. broken      B. got      C. however      D. was

**20** I was _____ _____ !
  A. upset      B. so

**21** Ask Your Neighbors: _____ _____ , _____
  A. March      B. 2020      C. 9

**22** We're sorry that you had _____ _____ _____ _____ .
  A. negative      B. a      C. experience      D. such

**23** To _____ this issue, we are asking _____ to _____ the pictures of their items _____ .
  A. update      B. regularly      C. fix      D. lenders

**24** This will _____ other users _____ the _____ condition of the _____ .
  A. product      B. let      C. exact      D. know

**25** I _____ _____ _____ your pet!
  A. can      B. after      C. look

**26** Pet Sitter Finder is the _____ _____ for pet _____ and pet _____ .
  A. owners      B. perfect      C. lovers      D. app

**27** It helps pet _____ find _____ people to _____ their pets.
  A. after      B. reliable      C. owners      D. look

**28** When a pet _____ is _____ for pet sitters, he or she _____ a _____ .
  A. post      B. looking      C. uploads      D. owner

**29** Pet sitters or dog _____ can then _____ _____ to the _____ .
  A. send      B. walkers      C. owner      D. messages

**30** The owner _____ their _____ and _____ the best _____ .
  A. chooses      B. checks      C. person      D. reviews

**31** George: _____ _____ , _____
  A. 2019      B. 12      C. November

**32** I _____ this app _____ I'm going _____ town.
  A. out      B. use      C. of      D. whenever

**17** Cassandra / 2020년 3월 7일

**18** 많은 긍정적인 후기들을 보고 나서, 저는 자전거 헬멧을 빌리기로 결심했어요.

**19** 그러나 제가 그것을 얻었을 때, 그것은 망가져 있었어요.

**20** 저는 몹시 기분이 상했어요!

**21** Ask Your Neighbors / 2020년 3월 9일

**22** 고객님이 그런 부정적인 경험을 겪게 해 드려 죄송합니다.

**23** 이 문제를 바로잡기 위해서, 저희는 빌려주는 사람들에게 그들의 물건 사진을 정기적으로 업데이트해 줄 것을 요구하고 있습니다.

**24** 이것이 다른 사용자들에게 그 제품의 정확한 상태를 알 수 있도록 해 줄 것입니다.

**25** 제가 당신의 반려동물을 돌볼 수 있어요!

**26** Pet Sitter Finder는 반려동물을 좋아하는 사람들과 반려동물 주인들을 위한 완벽한 앱이다.

**27** 그것은 반려동물 주인들이 그들의 반려동물을 돌보는 데 신뢰할 만한 사람들을 찾도록 돕는다.

**28** 반려동물 주인이 반려동물을 돌보는 사람들을 찾을 때, 그 또는 그녀는 게시물을 올린다.

**29** 그리고 나서 반려동물을 돌보는 사람들이나 개를 산책시키는 사람들이 주인에게 메시지를 보낼 수 있다.

**30** 주인은 그들의 후기들을 확인하고 최고의 사람을 선택한다.

**31** George / 2019년 11월 12일

**32** 저는 교외로 나갈 때마다 이 앱을 사용해요.

**33** I have some _____ about my _____ _____ _____.
A. personal    B. concerns    C. though    D. information

**34** _____ _____ people use my phone number for _____ _____?
A. if    B. other    C. what    D. purposes

**35** Pet Sitter Finder: _____ _____, _____
A. 14    B. November    C. 2019

**36** We're _____ _____ this _____.
A. of    B. aware    C. issue

**37** We're now developing a system that _____ users to _____ freely _____ _____ their personal information.
A. allows    B. showing    C. communicate    D. without

**38** Samantha: _____ _____, _____
A. 22    B. February    C. 2020

**39** Animals _____ _____ _____ in my apartment, so I don't _____ _____ pets.
A. allowed    B. have    C. aren't    D. any

**40** However, _____ _____ Pet Sitter Finder, I can _____ the joy of _____ a dog.
A. using    B. experience    C. walking    D. by

**41** Son: _____ _____ _____!
A. great    B. what    C. apps

**42** We can _____ a tent and find someone to _____ _____ _____ our dog.
A. borrow    B. care    C. take    D. of

**43** Dad: _____ _____.
A. right    B. that's

**44** These _____ of _____ are _____ of the "_____ economy."
A. services    B. kinds    C. part    D. sharing

**45** People can _____ their items _____ others and _____ services to them at a small _____ or for free.
A. with    B. fee    C. share    D. provide

**46** Son: But these _____ do _____ some _____.
A. weaknesses    B. services    C. have

**47** Some people _____ _____ _____ about the _____.
A. services    B. negative    C. left    D. reviews

**48** Dad: Well, I think the _____ people _____ the _____, the more they will _____.
A. improve    B. use    C. more    D. services

---

**33** 하지만 저의 개인 정보에 대한 몇 가지 걱정이 있어요.

**34** 만약 다른 사람들이 제 전화번호를 다른 목적으로 사용하면 어쩌죠?

**35** Pet Sitter Finder / 2019년 11월 14일

**36** 저희는 이 문제를 알고 있습니다.

**37** 저희는 현재 사용자들이 자신의 개인 정보를 보여주지 않으면서 자유롭게 소통할 수 있는 시스템을 개발하는 중입니다.

**38** Samantha / 2020년 2월 22일

**39** 동물들이 제 아파트에서는 허락되지 않아서, 저는 반려동물을 키울 수 없어요.

**40** 그런데 Pet Sitter Finder를 이용하면서, 저는 개를 산책시키는 즐거움을 경험할 수 있어요.

**41** 아들: 정말 좋은 앱들이네요!

**42** 우리는 텐트를 빌리고 우리 개를 돌볼 누군가를 찾을 수 있어요.

**43** 아빠: 그렇지.

**44** 이런 종류의 서비스가 '공유 경제'의 일부란다.

**45** 사람들은 자신의 물건을 다른 사람들과 공유할 수 있고 적은 비용이나 무료로 그들에게 서비스를 제공할 수 있어.

**46** 아들: 하지만 사실 이런 서비스들은 몇 가지 약점들을 가지고 있어요.

**47** 몇몇 사람들이 서비스에 대해 부정적인 후기들을 남겼잖아요.

**48** 아빠: 글쎄, 나는 사람들이 그 서비스들을 더 많이 사용할수록, 그것들이 더 개선될 것이라고 생각해.

※ 다음 우리말과 일치하도록 빈칸에 알맞은 것을 골라 쓰시오.

**1**  _____ in the _____ _____

**2**  Son: _____ _____ _____ _____ this weekend, Dad?

**3**  Dad: _____ _____ _____ go camping?

**4**  Son: But we _____ _____ a tent.

**5**  Should we buy _____ ?

**6**  Also, who will _____ _____ _____ our dog?

**7**  Dad: _____ _____ . I know _____ _____ that can help us.

**8**  _____ **from your** _____ !

**9**  Ask Your Neighbors _____ _____ _____ _____ items that they can _____ _____ others.

**10**  First, users download the app and _____ _____ another user that has _____ _____ _____ _____ .

**11**  Then they pick up the item and _____ _____ _____ .

**12**  Jasmine: _____ _____ , 2019

**13**  I _____ _____ a board game and got _____ in _____ _____ 30 minutes.

**14**  I love saving money _____ _____ things that I don't often need.

**15**  _____ , I think it's _____ _____ .

**16**  _____ _____ _____ we buy, _____ _____ _____ we _____ .

**1**  공유 경제 속 삶

**2**  아들: 아빠, 우리 이번 주말에 뭐 할 거예요?

**3**  아빠: 캠핑 가는 건 어떠니?

**4**  아들: 그런데 우리 텐트가 없잖아요.

**5**  하나 사야 할까요?

**6**  게다가 우리 개는 누가 돌봐요?

**7**  아빠: 걱정하지 마. 내가 우리를 도와줄 수 있는 몇 개의 앱들을 알고 있지.

**8**  당신의 이웃들로부터 빌려라!

**9**  Ask Your Neighbors는 사람들이 다른 사람들로부터 빌릴 수 있는 물건을 쉽게 찾도록 돕는다.

**10**  우선, 사용자들은 그 앱을 내려받고 그들이 필요한 물건을 가지고 있는 또 다른 사용자를 찾는다.

**11**  그러고 나서 그들은 그 물건을 받아서 나중에 반납한다.

**12**  Jasmine / 2019년 12월 12일

**13**  저는 보드게임을 요청했고 30분도 안 되어 하나를 구했어요.

**14**  저는 제가 자주 필요하지 않은 것들을 빌림으로써 돈을 아낄 수 있다는 것이 마음에 들어요.

**15**  게다가 이것이 환경친화적이라고 생각해요.

**16**  우리가 제품들을 더 적게 구매할수록, 우리는 더 많은 자원들을 아끼는 거예요.

**17** Cassandra: _____ 7, 2020

**18** _____ a lot of _____ _____, I decided _____ _____ a bike helmet.

**19** When I got it, _____, it _____ _____.

**20** I was _____ _____!

**21** Ask Your Neighbors: _____ _____, 2020

**22** We're sorry that you had _____ _____ _____ _____ _____.

**23** _____ _____ this issue, we are asking lenders _____ _____ _____ _____ of their items _____.

**24** This will _____ other users _____ the _____ _____ of the product.

**25** **I can _____ _____ your pet!**

**26** Pet Sitter Finder is _____ _____ _____ for pet _____ and pet _____.

**27** It helps pet owners find _____ _____ _____ _____ _____ their pets.

**28** When a pet owner _____ _____ _____ pet sitters, he or she uploads _____ _____.

**29** Pet sitters or dog walkers can then _____ _____ _____ the owner.

**30** The owner _____ their _____ and _____ the best person.

**31** George: _____ 12, 2019

**32** I use this app _____ I'm going _____ _____ _____.

---

**17** Cassandra / 2020년 3월 7일

**18** 많은 긍정적인 후기들을 보고 나서, 저는 자전거 헬멧을 빌리 기로 결심했어요.

**19** 그러나 제가 그것을 얻었을 때, 그것은 망가져 있었어요.

**20** 저는 몹시 기분이 상했어요!

**21** Ask Your Neighbors / 2020년 3월 9일

**22** 고객님이 그런 부정적인 경험을 겪게 해 드려 죄송합니다.

**23** 이 문제를 바로잡기 위해서, 저 희는 빌려주는 사람들에게 그들 의 물건 사진을 정기적으로 업 데이트해 줄 것을 요구하고 있 습니다.

**24** 이것이 다른 사용자들에게 그 제품의 정확한 상태를 알 수 있 도록 해 줄 것입니다.

**25** 제가 당신의 반려동물을 돌볼 수 있어요!

**26** Pet Sitter Finder는 반려동물을 좋아하는 사람들과 반려동물 주 인들을 위한 완벽한 앱이다.

**27** 그것은 반려동물 주인들이 그들 의 반려동물을 돌보는 데 신뢰할 만한 사람들을 찾도록 돕는다.

**28** 반려동물 주인이 반려동물을 돌 보는 사람들을 찾을 때, 그 또는 그녀는 게시물을 올린다.

**29** 그리고 나서 반려동물을 돌보는 사람들이나 개를 산책시키는 사 람들이 주인에게 메시지를 보낼 수 있다.

**30** 주인은 그들의 후기들을 확인하 고 최고의 사람을 선택한다.

**31** George / 2019년 11월 12일

**32** 저는 교외로 나갈 때마다 이 앱 을 사용해요.

**33** I have some _____ about my _____ _____ though.

**34** _____ _____ people use my phone number _____ _____ _____?

**35** Pet Sitter Finder: _____ _____, _____

**36** We're _____ _____ this issue.

**37** We're now developing a system that _____ users _____ _____ freely _____ _____ their personal information.

**38** Samantha: _____ 22, 2020

**39** Animals _____ _____ in my apartment, _____ I don't have any pets.

**40** However, _____ _____ Pet Sitter Finder, I _____ _____ the joy of _____ a dog.

**41** Son: _____ great apps!

**42** We can _____ a tent and find someone _____ _____ _____ _____ our dog.

**43** Dad: That's _____.

**44** These _____ of services are part of the "_____ _____."

**45** People can _____ their items _____ others and _____ services to them _____ _____ _____ _____ or _____ _____.

**46** Son: But these services _____ have some _____.

**47** Some people _____ _____ _____ about the services.

**48** Dad: Well, I think _____ _____ people use _____ _____, the more they _____ _____.

---

**33** 하지만 저의 개인 정보에 대한 몇 가지 걱정이 있어요.

**34** 만약 다른 사람들이 제 전화번호를 다른 목적으로 사용하면 어쩌죠?

**35** Pet Sitter Finder / 2019년 11월 14일

**36** 저희는 이 문제를 알고 있습니다.

**37** 저희는 현재 사용자들이 자신의 개인 정보를 보여주지 않으면서 자유롭게 소통할 수 있는 시스템을 개발하는 중입니다.

**38** Samantha / 2020년 2월 22일

**39** 동물들이 제 아파트에서는 허락되지 않아서, 저는 반려동물을 키울 수 없어요.

**40** 그런데 Pet Sitter Finder를 이용하면서, 저는 개를 산책시키는 즐거움을 경험할 수 있어요.

**41** 아들: 정말 좋은 앱들이네요!

**42** 우리는 텐트를 빌리고 우리 개를 돌볼 누군가를 찾을 수 있어요.

**43** 아빠: 그렇지.

**44** 이런 종류의 서비스가 '공유 경제'의 일부란다.

**45** 사람들은 자신의 물건을 다른 사람들과 공유할 수 있고 적은 비용이나 무료로 그들에게 서비스를 제공할 수 있어.

**46** 아들: 하지만 사실 이런 서비스들은 몇 가지 약점들을 가지고 있어요.

**47** 몇몇 사람들이 서비스에 대해 부정적인 후기들을 남겼잖아요.

**48** 아빠: 글쎄, 나는 사람들이 그 서비스들을 더 많이 사용할수록, 그것들이 더 개선될 것이라고 생각해.

※ 다음 문장을 우리말로 쓰시오.

**1** Life in the Sharing Economy

➡ _____

**2** Son: What should we do this weekend, Dad?

➡ _____

**3** Dad: Why don't we go camping?

➡ _____

**4** Son: But we don't have a tent.

➡ _____

**5** Should we buy one?

➡ _____

**6** Also, who will take care of our dog?

➡ _____

**7** Dad: Don't worry. I know some apps that can help us.

➡ _____

**8** Borrow from your neighbors!

➡ _____

**9** Ask Your Neighbors helps people easily find items that they can borrow from others.

➡ _____

**10** First, users download the app and search for another user that has the item they need.

➡ _____

**11** Then they pick up the item and return it later.

➡ _____

**12** Jasmine: December 12, 2019

➡ _____

**13** I asked for a board game and got one in less than 30 minutes.

➡ _____

**14** I love saving money by borrowing things that I don't often need.

➡ _____

**15** Also, I think it's environmentally friendly.

➡ _____

**16** The fewer products we buy, the more resources we save.

➡ _____

17 ▶ Cassandra: March 7, 2020

➡ _____

18 ▶ Seeing a lot of positive reviews, I decided to borrow a bike helmet.

➡ _____

19 ▶ When I got it, however, it was broken.

➡ _____

20 ▶ I was so upset!

➡ _____

21 ▶ Ask Your Neighbors: March 9, 2020

➡ _____

22 ▶ We're sorry that you had such a negative experience.

➡ _____

23 ▶ To fix this issue, we are asking lenders to update the pictures of their items regularly.

➡ _____

_____

24 ▶ This will let other users know the exact condition of the product.

➡ _____

25 ▶ I can look after your pet!

➡ _____

26 ▶ Pet Sitter Finder is the perfect app for pet lovers and pet owners.

➡ _____

27 ▶ It helps pet owners find reliable people to look after their pets.

➡ _____

28 ▶ When a pet owner is looking for pet sitters, he or she uploads a post.

➡ _____

29 ▶ Pet sitters or dog walkers can then send messages to the owner.

➡ _____

30 ▶ The owner checks their reviews and chooses the best person.

➡ _____

31 ▶ George: November 12, 2019

➡ _____

32 ▶ I use this app whenever I'm going out of town.

➡ _____

**33** I have some concerns about my personal information though.

➡ _____

**34** What if people use my phone number for other purposes?

➡ _____

**35** Pet Sitter Finder: November 14, 2019

➡ _____

**36** We're aware of this issue.

➡ _____

**37** We're now developing a system that allows users to communicate freely without showing their personal information.

➡ _____

**38** Samantha: February 22, 2020

➡ _____

**39** Animals aren't allowed in my apartment, so I don't have any pets.

➡ _____

**40** However, by using Pet Sitter Finder, I can experience the joy of walking a dog.

➡ _____

**41** Son: What great apps!

➡ _____

**42** We can borrow a tent and find someone to take care of our dog.

➡ _____

**43** Dad: That's right.

➡ _____

**44** These kinds of services are part of the "sharing economy."

➡ _____

**45** People can share their items with others and provide services to them at a small fee or for free.

➡ _____

**46** Son: But these services do have some weaknesses.

➡ _____

**47** Some people left negative reviews about the services.

➡ _____

**48** Dad: Well, I think the more people use the services, the more they will improve.

➡ _____

※ 다음 괄호 안의 단어들을 우리말에 맞도록 바르게 배열하시오.

**1** (in / Life / the / Economy / Sharing)
➡ _____

**2** (Son: / should / what / do / we / weekend, / this / Dad?)
➡ _____

**3** (Dad: / don't / why / go / we / camping?)
➡ _____

**4** (Son: / we / but / have / don't / tent. / a)
➡ _____

**5** (we / should / one? / buy)
➡ _____

**6** (who / also, / take / will / of / care / dog? / our)
➡ _____

**7** (Dad: / worry. / don't // know / I / apps / some / can / that / us. / help)
➡ _____

**8** (from / borrow / neighbors! / your)
➡ _____

**9** (people / Ask Your Neighbors / helps / easily / items / find / they / that / borrow / can / others. / from)
➡ _____

**10** (users / first, / the / download / app / search / and / another / for / user / has / that / item / the / need. / they)
➡ _____

**11** (they / then / up / pick / item / the / and / it / return / later.)
➡ _____

**12** (Jasmine: / 12, / December / 2019)
➡ _____

**13** (asked / I / a / for / game / board / and / one / got / less / in / 30 / than / minutes.)
➡ _____

**14** (love / I / money / saving / by / things / borrowing / I / that / often / don't / need.)
➡ _____

**15** (I / also, / it's / think / friendly. / environmentally)
➡ _____

**16** (fewer / the / we / products / buy, / more / the / we / resources / save.)
➡ _____

**1** 공유 경제 속 삶

**2** 아들: 아빠. 우리 이번 주말에 뭐 할 거예요?

**3** 아빠: 캠핑 가는 건 어떠니?

**4** 아들: 그런데 우리 텐트가 없잖아요.

**5** 하나 사야 할까요?

**6** 게다가 우리 개는 누가 돌봐요?

**7** 아빠: 걱정하지 마. 내가 우리를 도와줄 수 있는 몇 개의 앱들을 알고 있지.

**8** 당신의 이웃들로부터 빌려라!

**9** Ask Your Neighbors는 사람들이 다른 사람들로부터 빌릴 수 있는 물건을 쉽게 찾도록 돕는다.

**10** 우선. 사용자들은 그 앱을 내려받고 그들이 필요한 물건을 가지고 있는 또 다른 사용자를 찾는다.

**11** 그리고 나서 그들은 그 물건을 받아서 나중에 반납한다.

**12** Jasmine / 2019년 12월 12일

**13** 저는 보드게임을 요청했고 30분도 안 되어 하나를 구했어요.

**14** 저는 제가 자주 필요하지 않은 것들을 빌림으로써 돈을 아낄 수 있다는 것이 마음에 들어요.

**15** 게다가 이것이 환경친화적이라고 생각해요.

**16** 우리가 제품들을 더 적게 구매할수록, 우리는 더 많은 자원들을 아끼는 거예요.

**17** (Cassandra: / 7, / March / 2020)
➡ _____

**18** (a / seeing / lot / positive / of / reviews, / decided / I / borrow / to / bike / a / helmet.)
➡ _____

**19** (I / when / it, / got / however, / was / it / broken.)
➡ _____

**20** (was / I / upset! / so)
➡ _____

**21** (Ask Your Neighbors: / 2020 / 9, / March)
➡ _____

**22** (sorry / we're / you / that / such / had / negative / a / experience.)
➡ _____

**23** (fix / to / issue, / this / are / we / lenders / asking / update / to / the / of / pictures / their / regularly. / items)
➡ _____

**24** (will / this / other / let / know / users / the / condition / exact / of / product. / the)
➡ _____

**25** (can / I / after / look / pet! / your)
➡ _____

**26** (is / Pet Sitter Finder / the / app / perfect / pet / for / and / lovers / owners. / pet)
➡ _____

**27** (helps / it / owners / pet / reliable / find / to / people / after / look / pets. / their)
➡ _____

**28** (a / when / owner / pet / looking / is / pet / for / sitters, / she / or / he / a / uploads / post.)
➡ _____

**29** (sitters / pet / dog / or / can / walkers / then / messages / send / the / to / owner.)
➡ _____

**30** (owner / the / their / checks / reviews / and / the / chooses / person. / best)
➡ _____

**31** (George: / 12, / November / 2019)
➡ _____

**32** (use / I / app / this / I'm / whenever / out / going / town. / of)
➡ _____

**17** Cassandra / 2020년 3월 7일

**18** 많은 긍정적인 후기들을 보고 나서, 저는 자전거 헬멧을 빌리기로 결심했어요.

**19** 그러나 제가 그것을 얻었을 때, 그것은 망가져 있었어요.

**20** 저는 몹시 기분이 상했어요!

**21** Ask Your Neighbors / 2020년 3월 9일

**22** 고객님이 그런 부정적인 경험을 겪게 해 드려 죄송합니다.

**23** 이 문제를 바로잡기 위해서, 저희는 빌려주는 사람들에게 그들의 물건 사진을 정기적으로 업데이트해 줄 것을 요구하고 있습니다.

**24** 이것이 다른 사용자들에게 그 제품의 정확한 상태를 알 수 있도록 해 줄 것입니다.

**25** 제가 당신의 반려동물을 돌볼 수 있어요!

**26** Pet Sitter Finder는 반려동물을 좋아하는 사람들과 반려동물 주인들을 위한 완벽한 앱이다.

**27** 그것은 반려동물 주인들이 그들의 반려동물을 돌보는 데 신뢰할 만한 사람들을 찾도록 돕는다.

**28** 반려동물 주인이 반려동물을 돌보는 사람들을 찾을 때, 그 또는 그녀는 게시물을 올린다.

**29** 그리고 나서 반려동물을 돌보는 사람들이나 개를 산책시키는 사람들이 주인에게 메시지를 보낼 수 있다.

**30** 주인은 그들의 후기들을 확인하고 최고의 사람을 선택한다.

**31** George / 2019년 11월 12일

**32** 저는 교외로 나갈 때마다 이 앱을 사용해요.

**33** (have / I / concerns / some / my / about / personal / though. / information)

➡ _____

**34** (if / what / use / people / phone / my / for / number / purposes? / other)

➡ _____

**35** (Pet Sitter Finder: / 2019 / 14, / November)

➡ _____

**36** (aware / we're / this / of / issue.)

➡ _____

**37** (now / we're / a / developing / system / allows / that / users / communicate / to / without / freely / their / showing / information. / personal)

➡ _____

**38** (Samantha: / 22, / February / 2020)

➡ _____

**39** (aren't / animals / allowed / my / in / so / apartment, / don't / I / any / have / pets.)

➡ _____

**40** (by / however, / Pet Sitter Finder, / using / can / I / the / experience / joy / the / walking / of / dog. / a)

➡ _____

**41** (Son: / great / what / apps!)

➡ _____

**42** (can / we / a / borrow / tent / and / someone / find / take / to / of / care / dog. / our)

➡ _____

**43** (Dad: / right. / that's)

➡ _____

**44** (kinds / these / services / of / part / are / the / of / economy." / "sharing)

➡ _____

**45** (can / people / their / share / with / items / others / and / services / provide / them / to / a / at / fee / small / for / or / free.)

➡ _____

**46** (Son: / these / but / do / services / some / have / weaknesses.)

➡ _____

**47** (people / some / negative / left / about / reviews / services. / the)

➡ _____

**48** (Dad: / I / well, / the / think / people / more / the / use / the / services, / they / more / improve. / will)

➡ _____

**33** 하지만 저의 개인 정보에 대한 몇 가지 걱정이 있어요.

**34** 만약 다른 사람들이 제 전화번호를 다른 목적으로 사용하면 어쩌죠?

**35** Pet Sitter Finder / 2019년 11월 14일

**36** 저희는 이 문제를 알고 있습니다.

**37** 저희는 현재 사용자들이 자신의 개인 정보를 보여주지 않으면서 자유롭게 소통할 수 있는 시스템을 개발하는 중입니다.

**38** Samantha / 2020년 2월 22일

**39** 동물들이 제 아파트에서는 허락되지 않아서, 저는 반려동물을 키울 수 없어요.

**40** 그런데 Pet Sitter Finder를 이용하면서, 저는 개를 산책시키는 즐거움을 경험할 수 있어요.

**41** 아들: 정말 좋은 앱들이네요!

**42** 우리는 텐트를 빌리고 우리 개를 돌볼 누군가를 찾을 수 있어요.

**43** 아빠: 그렇지.

**44** 이런 종류의 서비스가 '공유 경제'의 일부란다.

**45** 사람들은 자신의 물건을 다른 사람들과 공유할 수 있고 적은 비용이나 무료로 그들에게 서비스를 제공할 수 있어.

**46** 아들: 하지만 사실 이런 서비스들은 몇 가지 약점들을 가지고 있어요.

**47** 몇몇 사람들이 서비스에 대해 부정적인 후기들을 남겼잖아요.

**48** 아빠: 글쎄, 나는 사람들이 그 서비스들을 더 많이 사용할수록, 그것들이 더 개선될 것이라고 생각해.

※ 다음 우리말을 영어로 쓰시오.

**1** 공유 경제 속 삶

➡ _____

**2** 아들: 아빠, 우리 이번 주말에 뭐 할 거예요?

➡ _____

**3** 아빠: 캠핑 가는 건 어떠니?

➡ _____

**4** 아들: 그런데 우리 텐트가 없잖아요.

➡ _____

**5** 하나 사야 할까요?

➡ _____

**6** 게다가 우리 개는 누가 돌봐요?

➡ _____

**7** 아빠: 걱정하지 마. 내가 우리를 도와줄 수 있는 몇 개의 앱들을 알고 있지.

➡ _____

**8** 당신의 이웃들로부터 빌려라!

➡ _____

**9** Ask Your Neighbors는 사람들이 다른 사람들로부터 빌릴 수 있는 물건을 쉽게 찾도록 돕는다.

➡ _____

**10** 우선, 사용자들은 그 앱을 내려받고 그들이 필요한 물건을 가지고 있는 또 다른 사용자를 찾는다.

➡ _____

**11** 그러고 나서 그들은 그 물건을 받아서 나중에 반납한다.

➡ _____

**12** Jasmine / 2019년 12월 12일

➡ _____

**13** 저는 보드게임을 요청했고 30분도 안 되어 하나를 구했어요.

➡ _____

**14** 저는 제가 자주 필요하지 않은 것들을 빌림으로써 돈을 아낄 수 있다는 것이 마음에 들어요.

➡ _____

**15** 게다가 이것이 환경친화적이라고 생각해요.

➡ _____

**16** 우리가 제품들을 더 적게 구매할수록, 우리는 더 많은 자원들을 아끼는 거예요.

➡ _____

**17** Cassandra / 2020년 3월 7일

➡ _____

**18** 많은 긍정적인 후기들을 보고 나서, 저는 자전거 헬멧을 빌리기로 결심했어요.

➡ _____

**19** 그러나 제가 그것을 얻었을 때, 그것은 망가져 있었어요.

➡ _____

**20** 저는 몹시 기분이 상했어요!

➡ _____

**21** Ask Your Neighbors / 2020년 3월 9일

➡ _____

**22** 고객님이 그런 부정적인 경험을 겪게 해 드려 죄송합니다.

➡ _____

**23** 이 문제를 바로잡기 위해서, 저희는 빌려주는 사람들에게 그들의 물건 사진을 정기적으로 업데이트해 줄 것을 요구하고 있습니다.

➡ _____

**24** 이것이 다른 사용자들에게 그 제품의 정확한 상태를 알 수 있도록 해 줄 것입니다.

➡ _____

**25** 제가 당신의 반려동물을 돌볼 수 있어요!

➡ _____

**26** Pet Sitter Finder는 반려동물을 좋아하는 사람들과 반려동물 주인들을 위한 완벽한 앱이다.

➡ _____

**27** 그것은 반려동물 주인들이 그들의 반려동물을 돌보는 데 신뢰할 만한 사람들을 찾도록 돕는다.

➡ _____

**28** 반려동물 주인이 반려동물을 돌보는 사람들을 찾을 때, 그 또는 그녀는 게시물을 올린다.

➡ _____

**29** 그러고 나서 반려동물을 돌보는 사람들이나 개를 산책시키는 사람들이 주인에게 메시지를 보낼 수 있다.

➡ _____

**30** 주인은 그들의 후기들을 확인하고 최고의 사람을 선택한다.

➡ _____

**31** George / 2019년 11월 12일

➡ _____

**32** 저는 교외로 나갈 때마다 이 앱을 사용해요.

➡ _____

**33** 하지만 저의 개인 정보에 대한 몇 가지 걱정이 있어요.

➡ _____

**34** 만약 다른 사람들이 제 전화번호를 다른 목적으로 사용하면 어쩌죠?

➡ _____

**35** Pet Sitter Finder / 2019년 11월 14일

➡ _____

**36** 저희는 이 문제를 알고 있습니다.

➡ _____

**37** 저희는 현재 사용자들이 자신의 개인 정보를 보여주지 않으면서 자유롭게 소통할 수 있는 시스템을 개발하는 중입니다.

➡ _____

_____

**38** Samantha / 2020년 2월 22일

➡ _____

**39** 동물들이 제 아파트에서는 허락되지 않아서, 저는 반려동물을 키울 수 없어요.

➡ _____

**40** 그런데 Pet Sitter Finder를 이용하면서, 저는 개를 산책시키는 즐거움을 경험할 수 있어요.

➡ _____

**41** 아들: 정말 좋은 앱들이네요!

➡ _____

**42** 우리는 텐트를 빌리고 우리 개를 돌볼 누군가를 찾을 수 있어요.

➡ _____

**43** 아빠: 그렇지.

➡ _____

**44** 이런 종류의 서비스가 '공유 경제'의 일부란다.

➡ _____

**45** 사람들은 자신의 물건을 다른 사람들과 공유할 수 있고 적은 비용이나 무료로 그들에게 서비스를 제공할 수 있어.

➡ _____

**46** 아들: 하지만 사실 이런 서비스들은 몇 가지 약점들을 가지고 있어요.

➡ _____

**47** 몇몇 사람들이 서비스에 대해 부정적인 후기들을 남겼잖아요.

➡ _____

**48** 아빠: 글쎄, 나는 사람들이 그 서비스들을 더 많이 사용할수록, 그것들이 더 개선될 것이라고 생각해.

➡ _____

※ 다음 우리말과 일치하도록 빈칸에 알맞은 말을 쓰시오.

### Do It Yourself

1. _____ _____, my family _____ _____ _____ a baseball game.

2. _____ _____ our team, we _____ a really _____ _____ _____.

3. _____, our team _____ _____ _____.

4. _____ _____ about the win, we _____ _____ _____.

5. _____ _____ _____ _____, we _____ _____ the game.

1. 지난 일요일, 우리 가족은 야구 경기를 보러 갔다.
2. 우리 팀을 응원하면서, 우리는 함께 정말 좋은 시간을 가졌다.
3. 행복하게도, 우리 팀이 경기를 이겼다.
4. 승리에 대해 기쁨을 느껴서, 우리는 축하하기로 결정했다.
5. 함께 프라이드치킨을 먹으면서, 우리는 그 경기에 대해 얘기했다.

### After You Read C Get the BIG Picture

1. _____ _____

2. where people _____ _____ their items _____ or _____ services _____ _____

Ask Your Neighbors

3. ⊕ _____ people _____ items _____ _____ _____ _____

4. ⊕ _____ _____ _____ money and _____

5. ⊖ needs _____ _____ on _____ _____ _____

6. <⊕ _____ , ⊖ _____ >

1. 공유 경제
2. 사람들이 자신의 물건을 다른 사람들과 공유하거나 그들에게 서비스를 제공할 수 있는 곳
Ask Your Neighbors
3. ⊕ 사람들이 다른 사람들로부터 빌릴 수 있는 물건을 찾도록 돕는다
4. ⊕ 사람들이 돈과 자원들을 아끼도록 돕는다
5. ⊖ 각 제품의 상태에 관해 정기적인 업데이트가 필요하다
6. 〈⊕ 이점, ⊖ 약점〉

### Culture Link

1. _____ Economies _____ the World

2. I sometimes _____ other people _____ _____ _____ _____ _____ _____ _____ .

3. They can _____ _____ their destinations _____ _____ _____ _____ , and I can make some money.

4. _____ _____ also _____ _____ _____ _____ cars on the road, _____ is _____ _____ .

1. 세계의 공유 경제
2. 나는 때때로 출근길에 다른 사람들을 태워준다.
3. 그들은 적은 요금을 내고 목적지에 도착할 수 있고, 나는 약간의 돈을 벌 수 있다.
4. 출근 공유는 또한 도로 위의 차들의 수를 줄여 주는데, 그것은 환경친화적이다.

※ **다음 우리말을 영어로 쓰시오.**

### Do It Yourself

1. 지난 일요일, 우리 가족은 야구 경기를 보러 갔다.
   ➡ _____

2. 우리 팀을 응원하면서, 우리는 함께 정말 좋은 시간을 가졌다.
   ➡ _____

3. 행복하게도, 우리 팀이 경기에서 이겼다.
   ➡ _____

4. 승리에 대해 기쁨을 느껴서, 우리는 축하하기로 결정했다.
   ➡ _____

5. 함께 프라이드치킨을 먹으면서, 우리는 그 경기에 대해 얘기했다.
   ➡ _____

### After You Read C Get the BIG Picture

1. 공유 경제
   ➡ _____

2. 사람들은 자신의 물건을 다른 사람들과 공유하거나 그들에게 서비스를 제공할 수 있는 곳
   ➡ _____

Ask Your Neighbors

3. ⊕ 사람들이 다른 사람들로부터 빌릴 수 있는 물건을 찾도록 돕는다
   ➡ _____

4. ⊕ 사람들이 돈과 자원들을 아끼도록 돕는다
   ➡ _____

5. ⊖ 각 제품의 상태에 관해 정기적인 업데이트가 필요하다
   ➡ _____

6. 〈⊕ 이점, ⊖ 약점〉
   ➡ _____

### Culture Link

1. 세계의 공유 경제
   ➡ _____

2. 나는 때때로 출근길에 다른 사람들을 태워준다.
   ➡ _____

3. 그들은 적은 요금을 내고 목적지에 도착할 수 있고, 나는 약간의 돈을 벌 수 있다.
   ➡ _____

4. 출근 공유는 또한 도로 위의 차들의 수를 줄여 주는데, 그것은 환경친화적이다.
   ➡ _____

※ 다음 영어를 우리말로 쓰시오.

| | | | |
|---|---|---|---|
| 01 task | | 22 swarm | |
| 02 threat | | 23 praise | |
| 03 cashier | | 24 reality | |
| 04 recipe | | 25 intelligence | |
| 05 common | | 26 disaster | |
| 06 navigate | | 27 survivor | |
| 07 forecast | | 28 ensure | |
| 08 perceive | | 29 escape | |
| 09 resource | | 30 solution | |
| 10 delivery | | 31 present | |
| 11 artificial | | 32 route | |
| 12 awesome | | 33 safety | |
| 13 destination | | 34 invention | |
| 14 recognize | | 35 deal with | |
| 15 sense | | 36 work on | |
| 16 bright | | 37 keep track of | |
| 17 difference | | 38 such as | |
| 18 self-driving | | 39 a variety of | |
| 19 perform | | 40 with the help of | |
| 20 nutrient | | 41 so that ~ | |
| 21 equip | | 42 make decisions | |
| | | 43 look toward | |

※ 다음 우리말을 영어로 쓰시오.

| | |
|---|---|
| 01 지능, 정보 | |
| 02 출납원 | |
| 03 현재의, 존재하는 | |
| 04 기술, 기계 | |
| 05 칭찬 | |
| 06 요리법 | |
| 07 목적지, 도착지 | |
| 08 떼, 군중, 벌 떼 | |
| 09 인공적인, 인위적인 | |
| 10 인지하다, 감지하다 | |
| 11 위협, 협박 | |
| 12 해법, 해답, 해결책 | |
| 13 차이, 차이점 | |
| 14 공연하다, 실행하다 | |
| 15 안전, 안전한 곳 | |
| 16 굉장한, 아주 멋진 | |
| 17 생존자, 살아남은 사람 | |
| 18 밝은, 희망적인 | |
| 19 재해, 참사, 재난 | |
| 20 길을 찾다, 항해하다 | |
| 21 탈출하다, 달아나다, 벗어나다 | |

| | |
|---|---|
| 22 영양소, 영양분 | |
| 23 자율 주행하는 | |
| 24 보장하다 | |
| 25 인식하다 | |
| 26 배달, 전달 | |
| 27 길, 경로 | |
| 28 ~에 (필요한 것을) 갖추다 | |
| 29 자원, 재원 | |
| 30 감지하다 | |
| 31 흔한 | |
| 32 예측, 예보 | |
| 33 편리한 | |
| 34 발명, 발명품 | |
| 35 ~의 도움으로 | |
| 36 처리하다, 다루다 | |
| 37 ~와 같은 | |
| 38 다양한 | |
| 39 앞날을 생각하다 | |
| 40 결정을 하다 | |
| 41 ~하기 위하여 | |
| 42 하루 종일 | |
| 43 ~에 노력을 들이다, 애쓰다 | |

※ 다음 영영풀이에 알맞은 단어를 <보기>에서 골라 쓴 후, 우리말 뜻을 쓰시오.

1 _____ : a risk or danger: _____

2 _____ : to be fully aware of: _____

3 _____ :  to complete an action or activity: _____

4 _____ : the answer to a problem: _____

5 _____ : a person who remains alive: _____

6 _____ : made by humans: _____

7 _____ : a way to go from one place to another: _____

8 _____ : to be aware of something without seeing or hearing it: _____

9 _____ : a piece of work that must be done: _____

10 _____ : the ability to learn or understand things well: _____

11 _____ : something that humans have thought of and made: _____

12 _____ : to make one's way through an area: _____

13 _____ : to notice something with the senses: _____

14 _____ : a chemical or food that provides what is needed to live and grow: _____

15 _____ : the action of taking things such as letters, parcels or goods to a person or place: _____

16 _____ : an unfortunate event that damages a large area and may harm many people: _____

보기

| delivery | survivor | nutrient | sense |
| task | recognize | navigate | threat |
| disaster | perform | perceive | route |
| invention | artificial | intelligence | solution |

※ 다음 우리말과 일치하도록 빈칸에 알맞은 말을 쓰시오.

**Listen & Talk 1 A**

G: Hey, _____ you _____ _____ a smart umbrella?

B: No, I _____. _____ _____ _____ _____ _____ _____ ?

G: Sure. It's an umbrella _____ gives you the _____ _____ for the day. If it _____ _____ _____ _____, the umbrella _____ a _____.

B: That's very _____.

**Listen & Talk 1 B**

G: Look at these. They are the new _____ of the month!

B: They all look _____. What is the _____ on the first page?

G: It's a new smart refrigerator. It _____ the items inside _____ and _____ _____.

B: That sounds _____.

G: It _____. What do you _____ _____ this _____ camera? I want to buy it.

B: A flying camera? Could you explain _____ _____ _____ ?

G: Of course. This machine flies to a _____ _____ we have already _____. _____ _____ _____, it can take pictures from 500 meters above the location.

B: That sounds _____. _____ do you want to take pictures _____ ?

G: I want to _____ _____ _____ _____ birds!

**Listen & Talk 1 C**

B: What are you _____ ?

G: It's a show about a man _____ lost _____ _____ his _____ in an accident. _____, he can play _____ _____ very well.

B: _____ can he play the drums _____ only one arm?

G: _____ he uses two arms. One is a robot arm _____ by his _____.

B: That's _____. Could you _____ _____ _____ _____ ?

G: Sure. First, he thinks _____ he wants to do _____ his arm. Then those thoughts _____ _____ _____ electronic signals. The signals _____ _____ his brain _____ his robot arm and move it.

B: That's amazing! I think this _____ can help many people.

여: 있잖아, 스마트 우산에 대해 들어 본 적 있니?
남: 아니, 들어 본 적 없어. 그게 무엇인 지 설명해 줄 수 있니?
여: 물론이지. 그것은 그날의 일기 예보 를 알려주는 우산이야. 만약 비가 올 예정이면, 우산에서 소리가 나.
남: 그거 참 편리하구나.

여: 이것들을 봐. 이달의 새로운 발명품 들이야!
남: 모두 멋져 보인다. 첫 번째 쪽에 있는 발명품은 뭐지?
여: 이건 새로 나온 스마트 냉장고야. 이 냉장고는 냉장고 내부의 음식들을 감 지해서 요리법을 제시해 줘.
남: 유용하겠다.
여: 맞아. 이 플라잉 카메라에 대해서는 어떻게 생각해? 나는 이 카메라가 사 고 싶어.
남: 플라잉 카메라? 이게 어떻게 작동하 는 건지 설명해 줄 수 있니?
여: 물론이지. 이 기기는 우리가 미리 설 정해 둔 목적지로 날아가. 비행하는 동안 이 기기는 그 지점의 500미터 상공에서 사진을 찍을 수 있어.
남: 정말 멋지다. 너는 무슨 사진을 찍고 싶니?
여: 나는 날고 있는 새들의 사진을 찍고 싶어!

남: 무엇을 보고 있니?
여: 이건 사고로 한쪽 팔을 잃은 한 남자 에 관한 프로야. 놀랍게도 그는 드럼 을 매우 잘 쳐.
남: 그는 어떻게 한쪽 팔만으로 드럼을 칠 수 있는 거지?
여: 사실 그는 두 팔을 사용해. 한쪽 팔은 그의 뇌가 제어하는 로봇 팔이야.
남: 그거 정말 멋지다. 좀 더 구체적으로 설명해 줄 수 있니?
여: 물론이지. 먼저, 그는 자신의 팔로 하 고 싶은 것을 생각해. 그런 다음 그 생각들이 전기 신호로 바뀌지. 그 신 호들은 그의 뇌에서 로봇 팔로 이동 해서 그 팔을 움직여.
남: 놀라운데! 이 기술이 많은 사람에 게 도움을 줄 수 있을 것 같아.

### Listen & Talk 2 B

M: _____ climate change is going to make farming _____, there _____ _____ _____ enough _____ for the _____ number of people on Earth. _____ _____ _____, _____ _____ _____ we will have to change _____ _____ _____ our food. For example, we won't kill animals for food. _____, meat _____ _____ _____ in a lab _____ animal cells. This will require _____ _____, water, and _____ _____. Also, bugs _____ _____ ants will become part of our daily meals. You might not want to eat them, but they are actually very _____ in _____!

남: 기후 변화가 농업을 더 어렵게 만들 것이기 때문에, 지구상의 점점 더 늘어나는 사람들을 위한 자원이 충분하지 않게 될지도 모른다. 이러한 이유로, 우리는 식량을 얻는 방법을 바꾸어야 할 가능성이 높다. 예를 들어, 우리는 식량을 얻기 위해 동물을 죽이지 않게 될 것이다. 대신, 동물 세포를 이용하여 실험실에서 고기가 배양될 것이다. 이는 더 적은 땅과 물, 그리고 다른 자원들을 필요로 할 것이다. 또한, 개미와 같은 곤충들이 우리 끼니의 일부가 될 것이다. 여러분은 먹고 싶지 않을 수도 있지만, 사실 곤충들은 영양분이 매우 풍부하다!

### Listen & Talk 2 C

G: I _____ _____ wait _____ _____ at the store _____ _____ _____ _____.

B: That's too bad. Maybe in the future _____ _____ _____ _____ _____ _____ _____.

G: What _____ _____ _____?

B: I read about a store _____ _____ _____. You take _____ you want to buy and just _____ _____.

G: That's it? _____ do you pay _____ it?

B: There are cameras and _____ in the store. They _____ _____ the items you choose and _____ _____ _____ to an app on your smartphone.

G: Then the app pays for _____ when you leave the store?

B: Exactly. _____ _____ _____ these _____ _____ stores will be more _____ in the future.

여: 매장에서 거의 20분 동안 줄을 서서 기다려야 했어.
남: 그것 참 안됐다. 어쩌면 미래에는 줄을 서서 기다릴 필요가 전혀 없을지도 몰라.
여: 그게 무슨 말이야?
남: 계산원이 없는 매장에 관한 글을 읽었거든. 사고 싶은 것을 가지고 그냥 걸어나가면 돼.
여: 그게 다야? 지불은 어떻게 해?
남: 매장 내에 카메라와 감지기가 있어. 그것들이 네가 고른 물건들을 계속 파악하면서 그 정보를 네 스마트폰에 있는 앱으로 보내.
여: 그러면 네가 매장을 나갈 때 앱이 물건 값을 지불하는 거고?
남: 바로 그거야. 미래에는 이런 종류의 매장이 더 흔해질 것 같아.

### Do It Yourself A

B: Hey, _____ you _____ this game? It's really _____.

G: Yes, I _____. That game is pretty _____ these days.

B: The developers used AI technology in _____. The game characters _____ _____ _____ AI.

G: Oh, really? Could you _____ _____ _____ _____?

B: Sure. The AI characters in the game learn from _____ _____ _____ and _____ _____ _____.

G: Oh! That's _____ I sometimes _____ _____ they already knew my moves!

B: They're very smart. _____ _____ _____ _____ _____ the AI in games will _____ _____ _____.

남: 저기, 이 게임 해봤니? 이거 정말 흥미진진해.
여: 응, 해봤어. 그 게임은 요즘 꽤 인기가 있어.
남: 개발자들이 이 게임에 인공지능 기술을 사용했어. 게임 캐릭터들에 인공지능이 탑재되어 있지.
여: 아, 정말? 좀 더 구체적으로 설명해 줄 수 있니?
남: 물론이지. 게임 속 인공지능 캐릭터들은 인간 플레이어가 하는 행동을 통해 배우고 자신의 기술을 발전시켜.
여: 아! 그래서 이따금씩 캐릭터들이 이미 내 움직임을 알고 있는 것처럼 느껴졌던 거구나!
남: 그들은 매우 똑똑해. 게임 속 인공지능은 점점 더 강화될 가능성이 높아.

※ 다음 우리말에 맞도록 대화를 영어로 쓰시오.

### Listen & Talk 1 A

G: _____

B: _____

G: _____

_____

B: _____

여: 있잖아, 스마트 우산에 대해 들어 본 적 있니?
남: 아니, 들어 본 적 없어. 그게 무엇인지 설명해 줄 수 있니?
여: 물론이지. 그것은 그날의 일기 예보를 알려주는 우산이야. 만약 비가 올 예정이면, 우산에서 소리가 나.
남: 그거 참 편리하구나.

### Listen & Talk 1 B

G: _____

B: _____

G: _____

B: _____

G: _____

B: _____

G: _____

_____

B: _____

G: _____

여: 이것들을 봐. 이달의 새로운 발명품들이야!
남: 모두 멋져 보인다. 첫 번째 쪽에 있는 발명품은 뭐지?
여: 이건 새로 나온 스마트 냉장고야. 이 냉장고는 냉장고 내부의 음식들을 감지해서 요리법을 제시해 줘.
남: 유용하겠다.
여: 맞아. 이 플라잉 카메라에 대해서는 어떻게 생각해? 나는 이 카메라가 사고 싶어.
남: 플라잉 카메라? 이게 어떻게 작동하는 건지 설명해 줄 수 있니?
여: 물론이지. 이 기기는 우리가 미리 설정해 둔 목적지로 날아가. 비행하는 동안 이 기기는 그 지점의 500미터 상공에서 사진을 찍을 수 있어.
남: 정말 멋지다. 너는 무슨 사진을 찍고 싶니?
여: 나는 날고 있는 새들의 사진을 찍고 싶어!

### Listen & Talk 1 C

B: _____

G: _____

_____

B: _____

G: _____

B: _____

G: _____

_____

B: _____

남: 무엇을 보고 있니?
여: 이건 사고로 한쪽 팔을 잃은 한 남자에 관한 프로야. 놀랍게도 그는 드럼을 매우 잘 쳐.
남: 그는 어떻게 한쪽 팔만으로 드럼을 칠 수 있는 거지?
여: 사실 그는 두 팔을 사용해. 한쪽 팔은 그의 뇌가 제어하는 로봇 팔이야.
남: 그거 정말 멋지다. 좀 더 구체적으로 설명해 줄 수 있니?
여: 물론이지. 먼저, 그는 자신의 팔로 하고 싶은 것을 생각해. 그런 다음 그 생각들이 전기 신호로 바뀌어. 그 신호들은 그의 뇌에서 로봇 팔로 이동해서 그 팔을 움직여.
남: 놀라운데! 이 기술이 많은 사람들에게 도움을 줄 수 있을 것 같다.

### Listen & Talk 2 B

M: _____
_____
_____
_____
_____
_____
_____

### Listen & Talk 2 C

G: _____
B: _____
G: _____
B: _____

G: _____
B: _____

G: _____
B: _____

### Do It Yourself A

B: _____
G: _____
B: _____

G: _____
B: _____

G: _____
B: _____

---

남: 기후 변화가 농업을 더 어렵게 만들 것이기 때문에, 지구상의 점점 더 늘어나는 사람들을 위한 자원이 충분하지 않게 될지도 모른다. 이러한 이유로, 우리는 식량을 얻는 방법을 바꾸어야 할 가능성이 높다. 예를 들어, 우리는 식량을 얻기 위해 동물을 죽이지 않게 될 것이다. 대신, 동물 세포를 이용하여 실험실에서 고기가 배양될 것이다. 이는 더 적은 땅과 물, 그리고 다른 자원들을 필요로 할 것이다. 또한, 개미와 같은 곤충들이 우리 끼니의 일부가 될 것이다. 여러분은 먹고 싶지 않을 수도 있지만, 사실 곤충들은 영양분이 매우 풍부하다!

여: 매장에서 거의 20분 동안 줄을 서서 기다려야 했어.
남: 그것 참 안됐다. 어쩌면 미래에는 줄을 서서 기다릴 필요가 전혀 없을지도 몰라.
여: 그게 무슨 말이야?
남: 계산원이 없는 매장에 관한 글을 읽었거든. 사고 싶은 것을 가지고 그냥 걸어나가면 돼.
여: 그게 다야? 지불은 어떻게 해?
남: 매장 내에 카메라와 감지기가 있어. 그것들이 네가 고른 물건들을 계속 파악하면서 그 정보를 네 스마트폰에 있는 앱으로 보내.
여: 그러면 네가 매장을 나갈 때 앱이 물건 값을 지불하는 거고?
남: 바로 그거야. 미래에는 이런 종류의 매장이 더 흔해질 것 같아.

남: 저기, 이 게임 해봤니? 이거 정말 흥미진진해.
여: 응, 해봤어. 그 게임은 요즘 꽤 인기가 있어.
남: 개발자들이 이 게임에 인공지능 기술을 사용했어. 게임 캐릭터들에 인공지능이 탑재되어 있지.
여: 아, 정말? 좀 더 구체적으로 설명해 줄 수 있니?
남: 물론이지. 게임 속 인공지능 캐릭터들은 인간 플레이어가 하는 행동을 통해 배우고 자신의 기술을 발전시켜.
여: 아! 그래서 이따금씩 캐릭터들이 이미 내 움직임을 알고 있는 것처럼 느껴졌던 거구나!
남: 그들은 매우 똑똑해. 게임 속 인공지능은 점점 더 강화될 가능성이 높아.

※ 다음 우리말과 일치하도록 빈칸에 알맞은 것을 골라 쓰시오.

**1** _____ _____ Robots
A. with          B. Life

**2** _____ _____ **We** _____ **Robots?**
A. See          B. Where          C. Do

**3** Robots are _____ _____ in _____ and books _____.
A. anymore          B. only          C. not          D. movies

**4** _____ the world, robots are doing a _____ _____ _____.
A. variety          B. around          C. tasks          D. of

**5** There are _____ robots _____ in the sky, robot arms in factories, and service robots in _____ _____.
A. flying          B. public          C. delivery          D. places

**6** A _____ robot _____ the _____
A. sky          B. delivery          C. in

**7** Robot _____ _____ a _____
A. factory          B. arms          C. in

**8** A _____ _____ _____ the PyeongChang Olympics
A. robot          B. service          C. at

**9** **Robots** _____ _____ _____
A. Becoming          B. Are          C. Smart

**10** In the _____, robots _____ only easy _____ that humans _____ them to do.
A. programmed          B. performed          C. tasks          D. past

**11** However, robots are now _____ "_____," and soon they might be _____ to think like _____.
A. getting          B. able          C. humans          D. smarter

**12** _____ makes this _____ is _____ _____ (AI).
A. artificial          B. what          C. intelligence          D. possible

**13** Robots that have AI can _____ _____ and _____ _____.
A. perceive          B. decisions          C. environments          D. make

**14** They can also _____ _____, tell _____, and play games with _____.
A. speech          B. jokes          C. humans          D. recognize

**15** **AI Speakers:** They can _____ your _____, _____ _____ in your home, and play music for you.
A. control          B. answer          C. machines          D. questions

**16** **AI Pets:** They _____ _____ _____ _____ dogs.
A. real          B. just          C. act          D. like

**17** They _____ and play with their _____ and _____ _____.
A. recognize          B. walk          C. praise          D. owners

**18** **Robots** _____ _____ – _____ **and** _____
A. Present          B. around          C. Future          D. Us

**19** Robots are making _____ _____ and _____.
A. faster          B. things          C. easier

1 로봇과 함께하는 삶

2 우리는 어디에서 로봇을 보는 가?

3 로봇은 더는 영화와 책 속에만 있는 것은 아니다.

4 전 세계적으로 로봇은 다양한 임무를 수행하고 있다.

5 하늘에는 날아다니는 배달 로 봇, 공장에는 로봇 팔, 그리고 공공장소에는 서비스 로봇이 있 다.

6 하늘에서 날아다니는 배달 로봇

7 공장의 로봇 팔들

8 평창 올림픽의 서비스 로봇

9 로봇이 똑똑해지고 있다

10 과거에 로봇은 인간이 로봇에게 실행하도록 프로그램을 설정한 단순 업무만을 수행했다.

11 그러나 로봇은 이제 '더 똑똑'해 지고 있으며, 곧 인간처럼 생각 할 수 있을지도 모른다.

12 이러한 것을 가능하게 만드는 것은 인공 지능(AI)이다.

13 인공 지능을 가진 로봇은 환경 을 인식하고 의사 결정을 할 수 있다.

14 그들은 또한 인간의 말을 인지 하고, 농담을 건네며, 인간과 게 임을 할 수 있다.

15 〈인공 지능 스피커〉 그들은 당 신의 질문에 대답할 수 있고, 당 신의 집에 있는 기계들을 조종 할 수 있으며, 당신을 위해 음악 을 재생할 수도 있다.

16 〈인공 지능 반려동물〉 그들은 마치 진짜 개처럼 행동한다.

17 그들은 그들의 주인과 함께 걷 고 놀며 칭찬을 알아챈다.

18 우리 주변의 로봇들 – 현재와 미래

19 로봇은 일을 더 빠르고 더 쉽게 해 주고 있다.

**20** They can help us _____ — in our homes, on roads, or _____
_____ _____.

    A. disaster      B. anywhere      C. areas      D. in

**21 Home Helper Robot:** This robot _____ your family _____
the _____.

    A. throughout      B. helps      C. day

**22** Cooking and _____ be _____ if you _____
one.

    A. easier      B. had      C. cleaning      D. would

**23** It _____ talks _____ family members and can _____
_____.

    A. emotions      B. also      C. sense      D. with

**24 Self-Driving Car:** A _____ car _____ a _____.

    A. driver      B. self-driving      C. need      D. doesn't

**25** With cameras, _____, and software, it can _____ roads for
you so that you can _____ and enjoy the _____.

    A. relax      B. sensors      C. ride      D. navitgate

**26 Robot Swarm:** A robot _____ is a _____ group of robots
that can communicate with one _____, _____ ants or bees.

    A. like      B. swarm      C. another      D. large

**27** They can be _____ in a _____ of places, _____ farms or
building _____.

    A. including      B. used      C. sites      D. variety

**28** They _____ on _____ and find _____ a group.

    A. as      B. work      C. solutions      D. tasks

**29 Search-and-Rescue Robot:** Search-and-rescue robots can go into
_____ _____ that are _____ for _____.

    A. disaster      B. humans      C. areas      D. dangerous

**30** They find _____, _____ with dangers, and clear _____ so
that people can _____ to safety.

    A. survivors      B. escape      C. deal      D. routes

**31** _____ _____ the _____

    A. toward      B. Looking      C. Future

**32** Our _____ with robots _____ _____ but not _____.

    A. perfect      B. future      C. bright      D. looks

**33** Some people _____ life to _____ more _____ with the
_____ of robots.

    A. help      B. expect      C. convenient      D. become

**34** However, other people _____ about problems they might
_____, such as _____ to our jobs and _____.

    A. threats      B. worry      C. cause      D. safety

**35** The important thing is to _____ possible _____ and to
_____ that robots are only used for _____.

    A. ensure      B. good      C. find      D. solutions

---

**20** 그들은 어디에서나 우리를 도울 수 있다. 우리의 집에서, 길에서 또는 재난 지역에서 말이다.

**21** 〈집안일 도우미 로봇〉 이 로봇은 온종일 당신의 가족을 돕는다.

**22** 만약 당신이 이 로봇 하나를 가지고 있다면 요리와 청소가 더 쉬워질 것이다.

**23** 이 로봇은 또한 가족 모두와 이야기를 나누며 감정을 파악할 수 있다.

**24** 〈자율 주행 자동차〉 자율 주행 자동차는 운전자를 필요로 하지 않는다.

**25** 카메라, 감지기 그리고 소프트웨어를 갖춘 채, 이 자동차는 당신이 쉬면서 주행을 즐길 수 있도록 당신을 위해 길을 찾아갈 수 있다.

**26** 〈로봇 군집〉 로봇 군집은 개미나 벌처럼, 서로 의사소통할 수 있는 로봇의 대규모 집단을 말한다.

**27** 이 로봇들은 농장이나 건설 현장을 포함한 다양한 장소에서 사용될 수 있다.

**28** 그들은 하나의 집단으로서 임무를 완수하고 해결책을 찾는다.

**29** 〈수색 구조 로봇〉 수색 구조 로봇은 사람에게 위험한 재난 지역에 투입될 수 있다.

**30** 그들은 생존자를 찾고 위험한 상황을 처리하며, 사람들이 안전한 곳으로 대피할 수 있도록 길을 확보한다.

**31** 미래에 대한 전망

**32** 로봇과 함께하는 우리의 미래는 밝지만 완벽하지는 않다.

**33** 어떤 사람들은 로봇의 도움으로 삶이 더욱 편리해질 것을 기대한다.

**34** 그러나 다른 사람들은 우리의 일자리와 안전에 대한 위협과 같이, 로봇이 일으킬지 모르는 문제들에 대해 걱정한다.

**35** 중요한 것은 가능한 해결책을 찾아내는 것과 로봇이 오로지 좋은 일을 위해서만 쓰이게 됨을 확실히 하는 것이다.

※ 다음 우리말과 일치하도록 빈칸에 알맞은 것을 골라 쓰시오.

**1** **Life** _____ _____

**2** _____ _____ **We** _____ **Robots?**

**3** Robots are _____ _____ in movies and books _____.

**4** Around the world, robots are doing _____ _____ _____ _____.

**5** There are delivery robots _____ in the sky, robot arms in factories, and service robots _____ _____ _____.

**6** A _____ robot in the sky

**7** Robot _____ in a _____

**8** _____ _____ _____ at the PyeongChang Olympics

**9** **Robots Are** _____ _____

**10** In the past, robots _____ only easy tasks that humans _____ _____ _____ _____.

**11** However, robots are now _____ "_____," and soon they might _____ _____ _____ think like humans.

**12** _____ _____ _____ is artificial intelligence (AI).

**13** Robots that have AI can _____ _____ and make _____.

**14** They can also _____ _____, tell jokes, and play games with humans.

**15** **AI Speakers:** They can answer your questions, _____ _____ in your home, and play music for you.

**16** **AI Pets:** They _____ _____ _____ real dogs.

**17** They walk and play with their _____ and _____ _____.

**18** **Robots** _____ _____ – _____ **and Future**

**19** Robots are making things _____ and _____.

---

**1** 로봇과 함께하는 삶

**2** 우리는 어디에서 로봇을 보는가?

**3** 로봇은 더는 영화와 책 속에만 있는 것은 아니다.

**4** 전 세계적으로 로봇은 다양한 임무를 수행하고 있다.

**5** 하늘에는 날아다니는 배달 로봇, 공장에는 로봇 팔, 그리고 공공장소에는 서비스 로봇이 있다.

**6** 하늘에서 날아다니는 배달 로봇

**7** 공장의 로봇 팔들

**8** 평창 올림픽의 서비스 로봇

**9** 로봇이 똑똑해지고 있다

**10** 과거에 로봇은 인간이 로봇에게 실행하도록 프로그램을 설정한 단순 업무만을 수행했다.

**11** 그러나 로봇은 이제 '더 똑똑'해지고 있으며, 곧 인간처럼 생각할 수 있을지도 모른다.

**12** 이러한 것을 가능하게 만드는 것은 인공 지능(AI)이다.

**13** 인공 지능을 가진 로봇은 환경을 인식하고 의사 결정을 할 수 있다.

**14** 그들은 또한 인간의 말을 인지하고, 농담을 건네며, 인간과 게임을 할 수 있다.

**15** 〈인공 지능 스피커〉 그들은 당신의 질문에 대답할 수 있고, 당신의 집에 있는 기계들을 조종할 수 있으며, 당신을 위해 음악을 재생할 수도 있다.

**16** 〈인공 지능 반려동물〉 그들은 마치 진짜 개처럼 행동한다.

**17** 그들은 그들의 주인과 함께 걷고 놀며 칭찬을 알아챈다.

**18** 우리 주변의 로봇들 – 현재와 미래

**19** 로봇은 일을 더 빠르고 더 쉽게 해 주고 있다.

**20** They can help us _____ — in our homes, on roads, or _____ _____.

**21** **Home Helper Robot:** This robot _____ your family _____ _____.

**22** Cooking and cleaning _____ _____ _____ if you _____ _____.

**23** It also talks with family members and can _____ _____.

**24** **Self-Driving Car:** A _____ _____ doesn't need _____.

**25** With cameras, sensors, and software, it _____ _____ roads for you _____ _____ you _____ relax and enjoy the ride.

**26** **Robot Swarm:** A robot swarm is _____ _____ _____ that can _____ _____, like ants or bees.

**27** They _____ _____ _____ in a variety of places, _____ farms or _____ _____.

**28** They _____ _____ tasks and find solutions _____ _____.

**29** **Search-and-Rescue Robot:** Search-and-rescue robots can go into _____ _____ that are _____ _____.

**30** They find survivors, deal with dangers, and clear routes _____ _____ people _____ _____.

**31** _____ the Future

**32** Our future with robots looks bright but _____ _____.

**33** Some people expect life _____ _____ more convenient _____ _____ _____ robots.

**34** However, other people worry about problems _____ _____ _____, _____ threats to our jobs and safety.

**35** The important thing is _____ _____ possible solutions and _____ _____ that robots are only used for _____.

---

**20** 그들은 어디에서나 우리를 도울 수 있다. 우리의 집에서, 길에서 또는 재난 지역에서 말이다.

**21** 〈집안일 도우미 로봇〉 이 로봇은 온종일 당신의 가족을 돕는다.

**22** 만약 당신이 이 로봇 하나를 가지고 있다면 요리와 청소가 더 쉬워질 것이다.

**23** 이 로봇은 또한 가족 모두와 이야기를 나누며 감정을 파악할 수 있다.

**24** 〈자율 주행 자동차〉 자율 주행 자동차는 운전자를 필요로 하지 않는다.

**25** 카메라, 감지기 그리고 소프트웨어를 갖춘 채, 이 자동차는 당신이 쉬면서 주행을 즐길 수 있도록 당신을 위해 길을 찾아갈 수 있다.

**26** 〈로봇 군집〉 로봇 군집은 개미나 벌처럼, 서로 의사소통할 수 있는 로봇의 대규모 집단을 말한다.

**27** 이 로봇들은 농장이나 건설 현장을 포함한 다양한 장소에서 사용될 수 있다.

**28** 그들은 하나의 집단으로서 임무를 완수하고 해결책을 찾는다.

**29** 〈수색 구조 로봇〉 수색 구조 로봇은 사람에게 위험한 재난 지역에 투입될 수 있다.

**30** 그들은 생존자를 찾고 위험한 상황을 처리하며, 사람들이 안전한 곳으로 대피할 수 있도록 길을 확보한다.

**31** 미래에 대한 전망

**32** 로봇과 함께하는 우리의 미래는 밝지만 완벽하지는 않다.

**33** 어떤 사람들은 로봇의 도움으로 삶이 더욱 편리해질 것을 기대한다.

**34** 그러나 다른 사람들은 우리의 일자리와 안전에 대한 위협과 같이, 로봇이 일으킬지 모르는 문제들에 대해 걱정한다.

**35** 중요한 것은 가능한 해결책을 찾아내는 것과 로봇이 오로지 좋은 일을 위해서만 쓰이게 됨을 확실히 하는 것이다.

※ 다음 문장을 우리말로 쓰시오.

**1** ▸ Life with Robots
➡ _____

**2** ▸ Where Do We See Robots?
➡ _____

**3** ▸ Robots are not only in movies and books anymore.
➡ _____

**4** ▸ Around the world, robots are doing a variety of tasks.
➡ _____

**5** ▸ There are delivery robots flying in the sky, robot arms in factories, and service robots in public places.
➡ _____

**6** ▸ A delivery robot in the sky
➡ _____

**7** ▸ Robot arms in a factory
➡ _____

**8** ▸ A service robot at the PyeongChang Olympics
➡ _____

**9** ▸ Robots Are Becoming Smart
➡ _____

**10** ▸ In the past, robots performed only easy tasks that humans programmed them to do.
➡ _____

**11** ▸ However, robots are now getting "smarter," and soon they might be able to think like humans.
➡ _____

**12** ▸ What makes this possible is artificial intelligence (AI).
➡ _____

**13** ▸ Robots that have AI can perceive environments and make decisions.
➡ _____

**14** ▸ They can also recognize speech, tell jokes, and play games with humans.
➡ _____

**15** ▸ AI Speakers: They can answer your questions, control machines in your home, and play music for you.
➡ _____
_____

**16** ▸ AI Pets: They act just like real dogs.
➡ _____

**17** ▸ They walk and play with their owners and recognize praise.
➡ _____

**18** ▸ Robots around Us – Present and Future
➡ _____

**19** Robots are making things faster and easier.
➡ _____

**20** They can help us anywhere — in our homes, on roads, or in disaster areas.
➡ _____

**21** Home Helper Robot: This robot helps your family throughout the day.
➡ _____

**22** Cooking and cleaning would be easier if you had one.
➡ _____

**23** It also talks with family members and can sense emotions.
➡ _____

**24** Self-Driving Car: A self-driving car doesn't need a driver.
➡ _____

**25** With cameras, sensors, and software, it can navigate roads for you so that you can relax and enjoy the ride.
➡ _____

**26** Robot Swarm: A robot swarm is a large group of robots that can communicate with one another, like ants or bees.
➡ _____

**27** They can be used in a variety of places, including farms or building sites.
➡ _____

**28** They work on tasks and find solutions as a group.
➡ _____

**29** Search-and-Rescue Robot: Search-and-rescue robots can go into disaster areas that are dangerous for humans.
➡ _____

**30** They find survivors, deal with dangers, and clear routes so that people can escape to safety.
➡ _____

**31** Looking toward the Future
➡ _____

**32** Our future with robots looks bright but not perfect.
➡ _____

**33** Some people expect life to become more convenient with the help of robots.
➡ _____

**34** However, other people worry about problems they might cause, such as threats to our jobs and safety.
➡ _____

**35** The important thing is to find possible solutions and to ensure that robots are only used for good.
➡ _____

※ 다음 괄호 안의 단어들을 우리말에 맞도록 바르게 배열하시오.

**1** (with / Robots / Life)
➡ _____

**2** (Do / Where / See / We / Robots?)
➡ _____

**3** (are / Robots / only / not / movies / in / books / and / anymore.)
➡ _____

**4** (the / around / world, / are / robots / a / doing / of / variety / tasks.)
➡ _____

**5** (are / there / robots / delivery / in / flying / sky, / the / arms / robot / factories, / in / and / robots / service / public / in / places.)
➡ _____

**6** (delivery / a / in / robot / sky / the)
➡ _____

**7** (arms / robot / a / in / factory)
➡ _____

**8** (service / a / at / robot / the / Olumpics / PyeongChang)
➡ _____

**9** (Are / Robots / Smart / Becoming)
➡ _____

**10** (the / in / past, / performed / robots / easy / only / that / tasks / programmed / humans / to / them / do.)
➡ _____

**11** (robots / however, / now / are / getting / and / "smarter," / soon / might / they / able / be / think / to / humans. / like)
➡ _____

**12** (makes / what / possible / this / artificial / is / (AI). / intelligence)
➡ _____

**13** (that / robots / have / can / AI / perceive / and / environments / decisions. / make)
➡ _____

**14** (can / they / recognize / also / speech, / jokes, / tell / play / and / with / games / humans.)
➡ _____

**15** (AI Speakers: / can / they / your / answer / questions, / machines / control / your / in / home, / play / and / for / music / you.)
➡ _____

**16** (AI Pets: / act / they / like / just / dogs. / real)
➡ _____

**17** (walk / they / play / and / their / with / and / owners / praise. / recognize)
➡ _____

**18** (around / Robots / Us / – / Future / and / Present)
➡ _____

**19** (are / robots / things / making / easier. / and / faster)
➡ _____

**1** 로봇과 함께하는 삶

**2** 우리는 어디에서 로봇을 보는가?

**3** 로봇은 더는 영화와 책 속에만 있는 것은 아니다.

**4** 전 세계적으로 로봇은 다양한 임무를 수행하고 있다.

**5** 하늘에는 날아다니는 배달 로봇, 공장에는 로봇 팔, 그리고 공공장소에는 서비스 로봇이 있다.

**6** 하늘에서 날아다니는 배달 로봇

**7** 공장의 로봇 팔들

**8** 평창 올림픽의 서비스 로봇

**9** 로봇이 똑똑해지고 있다

**10** 과거에 로봇은 인간이 로봇에게 실행하도록 프로그램을 설정한 단순 업무만을 수행했다.

**11** 그러나 로봇은 이제 '더 똑똑'해지고 있으며, 곧 인간처럼 생각할 수 있을지도 모른다.

**12** 이러한 것을 가능하게 만드는 것은 인공 지능(AI)이다.

**13** 인공 지능을 가진 로봇은 환경을 인식하고 의사 결정을 할 수 있다.

**14** 그들은 또한 인간의 말을 인지하고, 농담을 건네며, 인간과 게임을 할 수 있다.

**15** 〈인공 지능 스피커〉 그들은 당신의 질문에 대답할 수 있고, 당신의 집에 있는 기계들을 조종할 수 있으며, 당신을 위해 음악을 재생할 수도 있다.

**16** 〈인공 지능 반려동물〉 그들은 마치 진짜 개처럼 행동한다.

**17** 그들은 그들의 주인과 함께 걷고 놀며 칭찬을 알아챈다.

**18** 우리 주변의 로봇들 – 현재와 미래

**19** 로봇은 일을 더 빠르고 더 쉽게 해 주고 있다.

**20** (can / they / us / help / anywhere / — / our / in / homes, / roads, / on / or / disaster / in / areas.)
➡ _____

**21** (Home Helper Robot: / robot / this / your / helps / throughout / family / day. / the)
➡ _____

**22** (cooking / cleaning / and / be / would / if / easier / had / you / one.)
➡ _____

**23** (also / it / talks / family / with / members / and / sense / can / emotions.)
➡ _____

**24** (Self-Driving Car: / self-driving / a / doesn't / car / need / driver. / a)
➡ _____

**25** (cameras, / with / and / sensors, / it / software, / navigate / can / for / roads / so / you / that / can / you / relax / enjoy / and / ride. / the)
➡ _____

**26** (Robot Swarm: / robot / a / swarm / a / is / group / large / robots / of / can / that / with / communicate / one / like / another, / or / bees. / ants)
➡ _____

**27** (can / they / used / be / a / in / of / variety / places, / farms / including / or / sites. / building)
➡ _____

**28** (work / they / tasks / on / and / solutions / find / a / as / group.)
➡ _____

**29** (Search-and-Rescue Robot: / robots / search-and-rescue / can / into / go / areas / disaster / are / that / for / dangrous / humans.)
➡ _____

**30** (find / they / deal / survivors, / dangers, / with / clear / and / so / routes / that / can / people / escape / safety. / to)
➡ _____

**31** (toward / Looking / Future / the)
➡ _____

**32** (future / our / robots / with / bright / looks / not / but / perfect.)
➡ _____

**33** (people / some / life / expect / to / more / become / with / convenient / the / of / help / robots.)
➡ _____

**34** (other / however, / worry / people / about / they / problems / might / such / cause, / as / to / threats / jobs / our / safety. / and)
➡ _____

**35** (important / the / thing / to / is / possible / find / and / solutions / ensure / to / that / are / robots / only / for / used / good.)
➡ _____

**20** 그들은 어디에서나 우리를 도울 수 있다. 우리의 집에서, 길에서 또는 재난 지역에서 말이다.

**21** 〈집안일 도우미 로봇〉 이 로봇은 온종일 당신의 가족을 돕는다.

**22** 만약 당신이 이 로봇 하나를 가지고 있다면 요리와 청소가 더 쉬워질 것이다.

**23** 이 로봇은 또한 가족 모두와 이야기를 나누며 감정을 파악할 수 있다.

**24** 〈자율 주행 자동차〉 자율 주행 자동차는 운전자를 필요로 하지 않는다.

**25** 카메라, 감지기 그리고 소프트웨어를 갖춘 채, 이 자동차는 당신이 쉬면서 주행을 즐길 수 있도록 당신을 위해 길을 찾아갈 수 있다.

**26** 〈로봇 군집〉 로봇 군집은 개미나 벌처럼, 서로 의사소통할 수 있는 로봇의 대규모 집단을 말한다.

**27** 이 로봇들은 농장이나 건설 현장을 포함한 다양한 장소에서 사용될 수 있다.

**28** 그들은 하나의 집단으로서 임무를 완수하고 해결책을 찾는다.

**29** 〈수색 구조 로봇〉 수색 구조 로봇은 사람에게 위험한 재난 지역에 투입될 수 있다.

**30** 그들은 생존자를 찾고 위험한 상황을 처리하며, 사람들이 안전한 곳으로 대피할 수 있도록 길을 확보한다.

**31** 미래에 대한 전망

**32** 로봇과 함께하는 우리의 미래는 밝지만 완벽하지는 않다.

**33** 어떤 사람들은 로봇의 도움으로 삶이 더욱 편리해질 것을 기대한다.

**34** 그러나 다른 사람들은 우리의 일자리와 안전에 대한 위협과 같이, 로봇이 일으킬지 모르는 문제들에 대해 걱정한다.

**35** 중요한 것은 가능한 해결책을 찾아내는 것과 로봇이 오로지 좋은 일을 위해서만 쓰이게 됨을 확실히 하는 것이다.

※ **다음 우리말을 영어로 쓰시오.**

**1** 로봇과 함께하는 삶
➡ _____

**2** 우리는 어디에서 로봇을 보는가?
➡ _____

**3** 로봇은 더는 영화와 책 속에만 있는 것은 아니다.
➡ _____

**4** 전 세계적으로 로봇은 다양한 임무를 수행하고 있다.
➡ _____

**5** 하늘에는 날아다니는 배달 로봇, 공장에는 로봇 팔, 그리고 공공장소에는 서비스 로봇이 있다.
➡ _____

**6** 하늘에서 날아다니는 배달 로봇
➡ _____

**7** 공장의 로봇 팔들
➡ _____

**8** 평창 올림픽의 서비스 로봇
➡ _____

**9** 로봇이 똑똑해지고 있다
➡ _____

**10** 과거에 로봇은 인간이 로봇에게 실행하도록 프로그램을 설정한 단순 업무만을 수행했다.
➡ _____

**11** 그러나 로봇은 이제 '더 똑똑'해지고 있으며, 곧 인간처럼 생각할 수 있을지도 모른다.
➡ _____

**12** 이러한 것을 가능하게 만드는 것은 인공 지능(AI)이다.
➡ _____

**13** 인공 지능을 가진 로봇은 환경을 인식하고 의사 결정을 할 수 있다.
➡ _____

**14** 그들은 또한 인간의 말을 인지하고, 농담을 건네며, 인간과 게임을 할 수 있다.
➡ _____

**15** 〈인공 지능 스피커〉 그들은 당신의 질문에 대답할 수 있고, 당신의 집에 있는 기계들을 조종할 수 있으며, 당신을 위해 음악을 재생할 수도 있다.
➡ _____
_____

**16** 〈인공 지능 반려동물〉 그들은 마치 진짜 개처럼 행동한다.
➡ _____

**17** 그들은 그들의 주인과 함께 걷고 놀며 칭찬을 알아챈다.
➡ _____

**18** 우리 주변의 로봇들 – 현재와 미래
➡ _____

**19** 로봇은 일을 더 빠르고 더 쉽게 해 주고 있다.
➡ _____

**20** 그들은 어디에서나 우리를 도울 수 있다. 우리의 집에서, 길에서 또는 재난 지역에서 말이다.
➡ _____

**21** 〈집안일 도우미 로봇〉 이 로봇은 온종일 당신의 가족을 돕는다.
➡ _____

**22** 만약 당신이 이 로봇 하나를 가지고 있다면 요리와 청소가 더 쉬워질 것이다.
➡ _____

**23** 이 로봇은 또한 가족 모두와 이야기를 나누며 감정을 파악할 수 있다.
➡ _____

**24** 〈자율 주행 자동차〉 자율 주행 자동차는 운전자를 필요로 하지 않는다.
➡ _____

**25** 카메라, 감지기 그리고 소프트웨어를 갖춘 채, 이 자동차는 당신이 쉬면서 주행을 즐길 수 있도록 당신을 위해 길을 찾아갈 수 있다.
➡ _____

**26** 〈로봇 군집〉 로봇 군집은 개미나 벌처럼, 서로 의사소통할 수 있는 로봇의 대규모 집단을 말한다.
➡ _____

**27** 이 로봇들은 농장이나 건설 현장을 포함한 다양한 장소에서 사용될 수 있다.
➡ _____

**28** 그들은 하나의 집단으로서 임무를 완수하고 해결책을 찾는다.
➡ _____

**29** 〈수색 구조 로봇〉 수색 구조 로봇은 사람에게 위험한 재난 지역에 투입될 수 있다.
➡ _____

**30** 그들은 생존자를 찾고 위험한 상황을 처리하며, 사람들이 안전한 곳으로 대피할 수 있도록 길을 확보한다.
➡ _____

**31** 미래에 대한 전망
➡ _____

**32** 로봇과 함께하는 우리의 미래는 밝지만 완벽하지는 않다.
➡ _____

**33** 어떤 사람들은 로봇의 도움으로 삶이 더욱 편리해질 것을 기대한다.
➡ _____

**34** 그러나 다른 사람들은 우리의 일자리와 안전에 대한 위협과 같이, 로봇이 일으킬지 모르는 문제들에 대해 걱정한다.
➡ _____

**35** 중요한 것은 가능한 해결책을 찾아내는 것과 로봇이 오로지 좋은 일을 위해서만 쓰이게 됨을 확실히 하는 것이다.
➡ _____

※ 다음 우리말과 일치하도록 빈칸에 알맞은 말을 쓰시오.

**Presentation Time Step 3**

1. _____ _____ _____ _____ this painting shows?

2. I think it shows a machine _____ _____ _____ _____ _____.

3. The machine _____ _____ _____ today's robot _____ _____, but they _____ _____ _____.

4. For example, _____ _____ _____ _____ _____, the machine in the painting _____ _____ _____ a human.

**After You Read B**

1. home helper robot: I _____ _____ _____ _____ a child of the family I _____ _____.

2. He felt sad _____ _____ his _____ _____.

3. search-and-rescue robot: Last week, after a storm _____, I cleared a route to _____ _____ _____ _____ _____ _____.

4. robot swarm: We _____ _____ _____ _____ and built a tower _____ _____ _____.

**Think and Write Step 3**

1. School Life _____ 30 Years

2. In 30 years, school life _____ _____ very _____ _____ now.

3. _____ _____ _____ _____ there will be _____ _____ _____ _____ _____.

4. Students _____ _____ _____ go to school.

5. _____, they will study at home _____ _____ _____ _____ _____.

6. One _____ _____ of such a change _____ _____ that students could save time _____ they would _____ _____ _____ _____ to school and _____ _____.

7. However, there _____ _____ some _____ _____ too.

8. For example, students _____ _____ _____ _____ meet their friends _____ often.

9. We don't know exactly _____ _____ _____ _____ _____ _____ in the future, but I hope it will be _____ fun and meaningful _____ _____ _____ _____.

1. 여러분은 이 그림이 무엇을 보여준다고 생각하나요?
2. 저는 이것이 사람들이 집을 청소하는 것을 도와주는 기계를 보여준다고 생각합니다.
3. 그 기계는 오늘날의 로봇 진공청소기와 비슷하게 보이지만 약간의 차이가 있습니다.
4. 예를 들어, 오늘날의 로봇 진공청소기와는 다르게 그림에 있는 기계는 인간에 의해 조종됩니다.

1. 집안일 도우미 로봇: 나는 내가 일하는 가족의 한 아이의 기운을 북돋워주려고 했다.
2. 그는 나쁜 점수 때문에 슬픔을 느꼈다.
3. 수색 구조 로봇: 지난주에 나는 폭풍이 강타한 뒤에 한 소년이 탈출하는 것을 돕기 위해 길을 청소했다.
4. 로봇 군집: 우리는 서로 의사소통하고, 함께 일함으로써 탑을 지었다.

1. 30년 후의 학교 생활
2. 30년 후에, 학교 생활은 지금과 많이 달라질 것이다.
3. 장소에 큰 변화가 있을 것이다.
4. 학생들은 학교에 갈 필요가 없게 될 것이다.
5. 대신, 그들은 집에서 다양한 앱을 이용하여 공부할 것이다.
6. 그러한 변화의 한 가지 긍정적인 효과는 학생들이 학교에 다녀올 필요가 없기 때문에 시간을 절약할 수 있다는 것이다.
7. 하지만, 부정적인 효과 또한 있을 수 있다.
8. 예를 들어, 학생들이 전과 같이 자주 친구들을 만날 수 없을 것이다.
9. 우리는 미래에 학교 생활이 어떻게 될지 정확하게 알 수 없다. 그렇지만, 나는 오늘날과 마찬가지로 재미있고, 의미 있기를 희망한다.

Step2

※ 다음 우리말을 영어로 쓰시오.

## Presentation Time Step 3

1. 여러분은 이 그림이 무엇을 보여준다고 생각하나요?
➡ _____

2. 저는 이것이 사람들이 집을 청소하는 것을 도와주는 기계를 보여준다고 생각합니다.
➡ _____

3. 그 기계는 오늘날의 로봇 진공청소기와 비슷하게 보이지만 약간의 차이가 있습니다.
➡ _____

4. 예를 들어, 오늘날의 로봇 진공청소기와는 다르게 그림에 있는 기계는 인간에 의해 조종됩니다.
➡ _____

## After You Read B

1. 집안일 도우미 로봇: 나는 내가 일하는 가족의 한 아이의 기운을 북돋워주려고 했다.
➡ _____

2. 그는 나쁜 점수 때문에 슬픔을 느꼈다.
➡ _____

3. 수색 구조 로봇: 지난주에 나는 폭풍이 강타한 뒤에 한 소년이 탈출하는 것을 돕기 위해 길을 청소했다.
➡ _____

4. 로봇 군집: 우리는 서로 의사소통하고, 함께 일함으로써 탑을 지었다.
➡ _____

## Think and Write Step 3

1. 30년 후의 학교 생활
➡ _____

2. 30년 후에, 학교 생활은 지금과 많이 달라질 것이다.
➡ _____

3. 장소에 큰 변화가 있을 것이다.
➡ _____

4. 학생들은 학교에 갈 필요가 없게 될 것이다.
➡ _____

5. 대신, 그들은 집에서 다양한 앱을 이용하여 공부할 것이다.
➡ _____

6. 그러한 변화의 한 가지 긍정적인 효과는 학생들이 학교에 다녀올 필요가 없기 때문에 시간을 절약할 수 있다는 것이다.
➡ _____
_____

7. 하지만, 부정적인 효과 또한 있을 수 있다.
➡ _____

8. 예를 들어, 학생들이 전과 같이 자주 친구들을 만날 수 없을 것이다.
➡ _____

9. 우리는 미래에 학교 생활이 어떻게 될지 정확하게 알 수는 없다. 그렇지만, 나는 오늘날과 마찬가지로 재미있고, 의미 있기를 희망한다.
➡ _____
_____

※ 다음 영어를 우리말로 쓰시오.

| | | |
|---|---|---|
| 01 | thief | |
| 02 | climb | |
| 03 | kindness | |
| 04 | path | |
| 05 | survival | |
| 06 | travel | |
| 07 | whole | |
| 08 | compare | |
| 09 | pioneer | |
| 10 | strongly | |
| 11 | attack | |
| 12 | bottom | |
| 13 | separate | |
| 14 | destination | |
| 15 | correct | |
| 16 | wise | |
| 17 | realize | |
| 18 | further | |
| 19 | gone | |
| 20 | create | |
| 21 | hurry | |

| | | |
|---|---|---|
| 22 | someday | |
| 23 | pioneer | |
| 24 | hunger | |
| 25 | thick | |
| 26 | wisdom | |
| 27 | protect | |
| 28 | reach | |
| 29 | disagree | |
| 30 | guide | |
| 31 | straight | |
| 32 | take | |
| 33 | move | |
| 34 | solve | |
| 35 | thanks to | |
| 36 | in the end | |
| 37 | act on | |
| 38 | make one's way to ~ | |
| 39 | become lost | |
| 40 | the way out | |
| 41 | on the way | |
| 42 | die of | |
| 43 | without ~ing | |

※ 다음 우리말을 영어로 쓰시오.

01 굶주림

02 친절

03 보호하다

04 동의하다, 찬성하다

05 지혜로운, 현명한

06 서두르다, 서둘러 가다

07 생존

08 두꺼운, (나무가) 울창한

09 비교하다

10 도둑

11 지혜, 슬기

12 옳은

13 깨닫다, 자각하다

14 선구자, 개척자

15 분리된, 서로 다른

16 공격하다

17 (문제, 곤경을) 해결하다, 풀다

18 목적지, 도착지

19 똑바로

20 창조하다

21 길

22 안내인, 가이드

23 강경히, 강하게

24 동의하지 않다, 의견이 다르다

25 더 멀리; 더 먼

26 전체의, 모든

27 (시간이) 걸리다

28 가버린, 떠난

29 움직이다, 감동시키다

30 밑, 바닥

31 오르다, 올라가다

32 ～에 이르다[닿다], 도착하다

33 (미래의) 언젠가, 훗날

34 여행; 여행하다

35 나가는 길, 출구

36 ～에 따라 행동하다

37 마침내, 결국

38 길을 잃다

39 가는 길에

40 ～ 덕분에

41 ～으로 죽다

42 ～하지 않고

43 ～로 나아가다

※ 다음 영영풀이에 알맞은 단어를 <보기>에서 골라 쓴 후, 우리말 뜻을 쓰시오.

1  _____ : to try to hurt or damage: _____

2  _____ : to go up something towards the top: _____

3  _____ : the feeling of needing food: _____

4  _____ : not together or the same: _____

5  _____ : to cause someone to feel strong emotions: _____

6  _____ : to have a different opinion: _____

7  _____ : to accept an idea suggested by someone else: _____

8  _____ : the state of continuing to live, after despite difficult conditions: _____

9  _____ : a way or track that is built or is made by the action of people walking: _____

10  _____ : the place where somebody or something is going or being sent: _____

11  _____ : the quality of behaving in a thoughtful, helpful, or friendly way: _____

12  _____ : one of the first people to do something or to travel to a new area: _____

13  _____ : to know and understand that something is true or has happened: _____

14  _____ : to examine people or things to see how they are similar and how they are different: _____

15  _____ : to make sure that somebody/something is not harmed, injured, damaged, etc.: _____

16  _____ : the ability to make sensible decisions and give good advice because of the experience and knowledge that you have: _____

| 보기 | | | |
|---|---|---|---|
| pioneer | survival | kindness | agree |
| wisdom | attack | compare | climb |
| path | disagree | destination | move |
| protect | separate | realize | hunger |

※ 다음 우리말과 일치하도록 빈칸에 알맞은 것을 골라 쓰시오.

**1** The _____ _____ _____
A. Wise        B. Five        C. Men

**2** _____ day, five _____ men _____ _____ the road.
A. on        B. one        C. met        D. wise

**3** They _____ _____ _____ _____.
A. together        B. to        C. agreed        D. travel

**4** On the _____, however, they _____ in a _____ forest.
A. thick        B. way        C. lost        D. became

**5** Before walking _____ _____, they decided to stop and find the best _____ _____.
A. way        B. further        C. out        D. any

**6** After _____ for a _____, the first man said, "I _____ feel that we should go _____."
A. strongly        B. while        C. left        D. thinking

**7** The _____ man said, "We should go _____, _____ right also means '_____.'"
A. because        B. correct        C. right        D. second

**8** Then the _____ man said, "Let's _____ _____.
A. back        B. third        C. walk

**9** We came that _____, _____ we can _____ _____ way.
A. so        B. way        C. leave        D. that

**10** Then we can _____ the _____."
A. forest        B. around        C. walk

**11** The fourth man _____ and said, "I think we should _____ _____ _____.
A. walking        B. disagreed        C. keep        D. straight

**12** The _____ cannot _____ _____ _____.
A. on        B. forest        C. forever        D. go

**13** A _____ _____ will _____."
A. path        B. new        C. open

**14** _____ at them all, the _____ man _____ his head and said, "I know how to _____ this. Just wait."
A. fifth        B. looking        C. solve        D. shook

**15** He started to _____ the _____ tree he _____.
A. tallest        B. climb        C. find        D. could

**16** As he _____, everyone else _____ to go their _____.
A. separate        B. climbed        C. ways        D. decided

1 5명의 지혜로운 사람들
2 어느 날 5명의 지혜로운 사람들이 길에서 만났다.
3 그들은 여행을 함께 하기로 했다.
4 그러나 도중에 그들은 울창한 숲속에서 길을 잃게 되었다.
5 더 멀리 가기 전에 그들은 멈추고 빠져나갈 최선의 방법을 찾기로 결정했다.
6 잠시 동안 생각한 후, 첫 번째 남자는 "우리가 왼쪽으로 가야 한다는 생각이 강하게 들어요."라고 말했다.
7 두 번째 남자가 "우리는 오른쪽으로 가야 해요. 왜냐하면 '오른쪽'은 또한 '옳은'이라는 의미이기 때문이죠."라고 말했다.
8 그러자 세 번째 남자가 "뒤로 돌아갑시다.
9 우리가 그 길로 왔으니 그 길로 나갈 수 있을 겁니다.
10 그러면 우리는 숲을 한 바퀴 돌 수 있고요."라고 말했다.
11 네 번째 남자가 이의를 제기하며 "나는 우리가 똑바로 계속 걸어 나가야 한다고 생각해요.
12 숲이 영원히 계속될 수는 없으니까요.
13 새로운 길이 열릴 것입니다."라고 말했다.
14 모두를 바라보면서 다섯 번째 남자가 고개를 저으며 "나는 이것을 해결하는 방법을 알아요. 잠깐 기다려 보세요."라고 말했다.
15 그는 그가 찾을 수 있는 가장 높은 나무를 오르기 시작했다.
16 그가 올라가자 다른 모든 사람들은 각자 서로 다른 길을 가기로 결정했다.

**17** When the fifth man _____ the _____, he could see the _____ _____.

    A. top          B. forest          C. reached        D. whole

**18** Looking at all the _____, he found the _____ _____ _____.

    A. paths          B. way            C. shortest       D. out

**19** He _____ _____ to tell the _____.

    A. others         B. down          C. hurried

**20** However, when he _____ to the _____, everyone _____ _____.

    A. bottom        B. gone          C. got            D. was

**21** He _____ to _____, *Where did they go? I* _____ *the best way* _____.

    A. himself        B. thought       C. out            D. found

**22** He _____ they were all _____ and he was the _____ man.

    A. wrong         B. wise          C. thought       D. only

**23** _____, he was _____.

    A. wrong         B. however

**24** _____ was _____.

    A. wise           B. everyone

**25** Each man had _____ his _____ and _____ his _____.

    A. created        B. chosen       C. future        D. path

**26** The man who went to the left _____ _____ _____ the _____.

    A. deeper        B. walked       C. forest        D. into

**27** He was _____ by wild animals and almost _____ _____.

    A. died           B. hunger       C. attacked       D. of

**28** Soon he _____ _____ to _____ _____ and find food.

    A. himself        B. learned       C. protect       D. how

**29** In the _____, he made his way out of the _____ and taught others _____ _____.

    A. survival        B. end           C. skills         D. forest

**30** The man who went to the _____ met a _____ _____ _____.

    A. thieves        B. right          C. of           D. group

**31** They _____ everything _____ him and _____ him _____ them.

    A. made         B. join          C. took          D. from

**32** _____ he was _____ them, he showed them _____ _____.

    A. kindness       B. while         C. with          D. great

**17** 다섯 번째 남자가 꼭대기에 이르자 그는 전체 숲을 볼 수 있었다.

**18** 모든 길을 바라보며 그는 빠져나갈 가장 짧은 길을 찾았다.

**19** 그는 다른 사람들에게 알리기 위해 급히 내려갔다.

**20** 하지만 그가 밑으로 내려왔을 때, 모든 사람들은 이미 가 버리고 없었다.

**21** 그는 '다들 어디 간 거야? 내가 빠져나갈 최선의 길을 찾았는데.'라고 마음속으로 생각했다.

**22** 그는 그들이 모두 틀렸고 자신이 유일하게 현명한 사람이라고 생각했다.

**23** 그러나 그가 틀렸다.

**24** 모두가 지혜로웠다.

**25** 각자 자신의 길을 선택했고 자신의 미래를 만들었다.

**26** 왼쪽으로 간 남자는 숲속으로 더 깊이 걸어 들어갔다.

**27** 그는 야생 동물들의 습격을 받았고 거의 굶어 죽을 뻔했다.

**28** 머지않아 그는 자신을 지키고 먹을 것을 찾는 방법을 터득했다.

**29** 결국 그는 숲 밖으로 빠져나왔고 다른 사람들에게 생존 기술을 가르쳤다.

**30** 오른쪽으로 간 남자는 도둑 무리를 만났다.

**31** 그들은 그에게서 모든 것을 가져갔고 그를 그들과 합류시켰다.

**32** 그는 그들과 함께 있는 동안 그들에게 많은 친절을 베풀었다.

**33** The _____ were _____ by his _____ and learned from his _____.

    A. wisdom      B. moved      C. kindness      D. thieves

**34** _____, they also _____ _____ _____.

    A. wise      B. became      C. later      D. men

**35** The man who _____ _____ created a _____ _____ around the forest.

    A. safe      B. back      C. path      D. walked

**36** Using this path, people could get where they were going _____ _____ _____, even though the trip took a little _____.

    A. without      B. longer      C. lost      D. getting

**37** The man who _____ _____ _____ a _____.

    A. straight      B. went      C. pioneer      D. became

**38** He left the _____ and discovered _____ no one else _____ _____ before.

    A. been      B. forest      C. had      D. places

**39** _____ _____ him, people could _____ these new beautiful _____.

    A. lands      B. to      C. enjoy      D. thanks

**40** The man _____ _____ the tree _____ a _____.

    A. climbed      B. became      C. who      D. guide

**41** _____ he had found many different paths, he was _____ to teach people how to find the quickest _____ to their _____.

    A. able      B. destinations      C. ways      D. since

**42** This is _____ the five men _____ their _____.

    A. paths      B. found      C. how      D. own

**43** _____ them, we are each on our own journey in life, and we cannot _____ one _____ to _____.

    A. journey      B. another      C. like      D. compare

**44** You _____ to create _____ _____ _____.

    A. own      B. have      C. path      D. your

**45** Listen to yourself, _____ a _____, and _____ _____ it.

    A. decision      B. make      C. on      D. act

**46** Then, someday, you will _____ that you have _____ the life that is _____ for you.

    A. right      B. realize      C. living      D. been

**33** 그 도둑들은 그의 친절에 감동을 받았고 그의 지혜에서 배우게 되었다.

**34** 나중에 그들 또한 지혜로운 사람들이 되었다.

**35** 뒤돌아 간 남자는 숲 주변에 안전한 길을 만들었다.

**36** 사람들은 이 길을 이용할 때 길을 잃지 않고 자신이 가고자 하는 길에 다다를 수 있었다. 비록 이동 시간이 약간 더 오래 걸려도 말이다.

**37** 똑바로 간 남자는 개척자가 되었다.

**38** 그는 숲을 벗어나 아무도 이전에 가 본 적이 없는 곳을 발견했다.

**39** 그 남자 덕분에, 사람들은 이 새롭고 아름다운 지역을 즐길 수 있었다.

**40** 나무 위로 올라간 남자는 가이드가 되었다.

**41** 그는 여러 다양한 길을 발견했었기 때문에, 사람들에게 자신의 목적지에 이르는 가장 빠른 길을 찾는 법을 가르쳐 줄 수 있었다.

**42** 이런 식으로 다섯 남자는 자신만의 길을 찾아냈다.

**43** 그들처럼 우리는 각각 인생에서 자기 자신만의 여행을 하고 있고, 우리는 한 여정을 다른 것과 비교할 수 없다.

**44** 당신은 당신 자신만의 길을 만들어가야 한다.

**45** 자신의 목소리를 듣고, 결정하고, 그 결정에 따라 행동하라.

**46** 그러면 언젠가 당신은 당신에게 맞는 삶을 살아가고 있다는 것을 깨닫게 될 것이다.

※ 다음 우리말과 일치하도록 빈칸에 알맞은 것을 골라 쓰시오.

1  The Five _____ _____

2  _____, five wise men _____ on the road.

3  They _____ _____ _____ together.

4  On the way, however, they _____ _____ in a _____ _____.

5  Before walking _____ _____, they decided to stop and find the best _____ _____.

6  After thinking _____ _____ _____, the first man said, "I _____ _____ that we should go left."

7  The second man said, "We should go right, _____ *right* also means '_____.'"

8  Then the third man said, "_____ _____ _____.

9  We came that way, _____ we can _____ _____ _____.

10  Then we can _____ _____ the forest."

11  The fourth man _____ and said, "I think we should _____ _____ _____.

12  The forest cannot _____ _____ _____.

13  A _____ _____ will _____."

14  Looking at them all, the fifth man _____ _____ _____ and said, "I know _____ _____ _____ this. Just wait."

15  He started _____ _____ the tallest tree he _____ _____.

16  As he climbed, everyone else decided to go their _____ ways.

1  5명의 지혜로운 사람들

2  어느 날 5명의 지혜로운 사람들이 길에서 만났다.

3  그들은 여행을 함께 하기로 했다.

4  그러나 도중에 그들은 울창한 숲속에서 길을 잃게 되었다.

5  더 멀리 가기 전에 그들은 멈추고 빠져나갈 최선의 방법을 찾기로 결정했다.

6  잠시 동안 생각한 후, 첫 번째 남자는 "우리가 왼쪽으로 가야 한다는 생각이 강하게 들어요." 라고 말했다.

7  두 번째 남자가 "우리는 오른쪽으로 가야 해요. 왜냐하면 '오른쪽'은 또한 '옳은'이라는 의미이기 때문이죠."라고 말했다.

8  그러자 세 번째 남자가 "뒤로 돌아갑시다.

9  우리가 그 길로 왔으니 그 길로 나갈 수 있을 겁니다.

10  그러면 우리는 숲을 한 바퀴 돌 수 있고요."라고 말했다.

11  네 번째 남자가 이의를 제기하며 "나는 우리가 똑바로 계속 걸어 나가야 한다고 생각해요.

12  숲이 영원히 계속될 수는 없으니까요.

13  새로운 길이 열릴 것입니다."라고 말했다.

14  모두를 바라보면서 다섯 번째 남자가 고개를 저으며 "나는 이것을 해결하는 방법을 알아요. 잠깐 기다려 보세요."라고 말했다.

15  그는 그가 찾을 수 있는 가장 높은 나무를 오르기 시작했다.

16  그가 올라가자 다른 모든 사람들은 각자 서로 다른 길을 가기로 결정했다.

**17** When the fifth man _____ the top, he could see the _____ _____.

**18** _____ _____ all the paths, he found the _____ _____ _____.

**19** He _____ _____ to tell _____ _____.

**20** However, when he got to the bottom, everyone _____ _____.

**21** He _____ _____ _____, *Where did they go? I found the* _____ _____ _____.

**22** He thought they were all _____ and he was _____ _____ _____ man.

**23** _____, he was _____.

**24** _____ was _____.

**25** Each man _____ _____ his path and _____ _____ _____.

**26** The man who went to the left _____ _____ _____ the forest.

**27** He _____ _____ by wild animals and almost _____ _____ _____.

**28** Soon he learned _____ _____ _____ _____ and find food.

**29** In the end, he _____ _____ _____ _____ _____ the forest and taught others _____ _____.

**30** The man who went to the right met _____ _____ _____.

**31** They took everything from him and made him _____ _____.

**32** _____ he was with them, he showed them _____ _____.

17 다섯 번째 남자가 꼭대기에 이르자 그는 전체 숲을 볼 수 있었다.

18 모든 길을 바라보며 그는 빠져나갈 가장 짧은 길을 찾았다.

19 그는 다른 사람들에게 알리기 위해 급히 내려갔다.

20 하지만 그가 밑으로 내려왔을 때, 모든 사람들은 이미 가 버리고 없었다.

21 그는 '다들 어디 간 거야? 내가 빠져나갈 최선의 길을 찾았는데.'라고 마음속으로 생각했다.

22 그는 그들이 모두 틀렸고 자신이 유일하게 현명한 사람이라고 생각했다.

23 그러나 그가 틀렸다.

24 모두가 지혜로웠다.

25 각자 자신의 길을 선택했고 자신의 미래를 만들었다.

26 왼쪽으로 간 남자는 숲속으로 더 깊이 걸어 들어갔다.

27 그는 야생 동물들의 습격을 받았고 거의 굶어 죽을 뻔했다.

28 머지않아 그는 자신을 지키고 먹을 것을 찾는 방법을 터득했다.

29 결국 그는 숲 밖으로 빠져나왔고 다른 사람들에게 생존 기술을 가르쳤다.

30 오른쪽으로 간 남자는 도둑 무리를 만났다.

31 그들은 그에게서 모든 것을 가져갔고 그를 그들과 합류시켰다.

32 그는 그들과 함께 있는 동안 그들에게 많은 친절을 베풀었다.

본문 Test **71**

**33** The thieves _____ _____ _____ his _____ and learned from his wisdom.

**34** _____, they also _____ _____ _____.

**35** The man who _____ _____ created _____ _____ _____ around the forest.

**36** Using this path, people could get where they were going _____ _____ _____, _____ _____ the trip took a little longer.

**37** The man who _____ _____ became a _____.

**38** He left the forest and discovered places no one else _____ _____ before.

**39** _____ _____ him, people could enjoy these new beautiful lands.

**40** The man _____ _____ the tree became a guide.

**41** Since he had found many _____ _____, he was able to teach people how to find _____ _____ _____ to _____ _____.

**42** _____ _____ _____ the five men found _____ _____ _____.

**43** _____ them, we are each on our own journey in life, and we cannot compare _____ _____ to _____.

**44** You _____ _____ create _____ _____ _____.

**45** Listen to yourself, _____ a _____, and _____ _____.

**46** Then, someday, you will realize that you _____ _____ _____ the life that is _____ _____ you.

33 그 도둑들은 그의 친절에 감동을 받았고 그의 지혜에서 배우게 되었다.

34 나중에 그들 또한 지혜로운 사람들이 되었다.

35 뒤돌아 간 남자는 숲 주변에 안전한 길을 만들었다.

36 사람들은 이 길을 이용할 때 길을 잃지 않고 자신이 가고자 하는 길에 다다를 수 있었다. 비록 이동 시간이 약간 더 오래 걸려도 말이다.

37 똑바로 간 남자는 개척자가 되었다.

38 그는 숲을 벗어나 아무도 이전에 가 본 적이 없는 곳을 발견했다.

39 그 남자 덕분에, 사람들은 이 새롭고 아름다운 지역을 즐길 수 있었다.

40 나무 위로 올라간 남자는 가이드가 되었다.

41 그는 여러 다양한 길을 발견했었기 때문에, 사람들에게 자신의 목적지에 이르는 가장 빠른 길을 찾는 법을 가르쳐 줄 수 있었다.

42 이런 식으로 다섯 남자는 자신만의 길을 찾아냈다.

43 그들처럼 우리는 각각 인생에서 자기 자신만의 여행을 하고 있고, 우리는 한 여정을 다른 것과 비교할 수 없다.

44 당신은 당신 자신만의 길을 만들어가야 한다.

45 자신의 목소리를 듣고, 결정하고, 그 결정에 따라 행동하라.

46 그러면 언젠가 당신은 당신에게 맞는 삶을 살아가고 있다는 것을 깨닫게 될 것이다.

※ 다음 문장을 우리말로 쓰시오.

**1** The Five Wise Men

➡ _____

**2** One day, five wise men met on the road.

➡ _____

**3** They agreed to travel together.

➡ _____

**4** On the way, however, they became lost in a thick forest.

➡ _____

**5** Before walking any further, they decided to stop and find the best way out.

➡ _____

**6** After thinking for a while, the first man said, "I strongly feel that we should go left."

➡ _____

**7** The second man said, "We should go right, because *right* also means 'correct.'"

➡ _____

**8** Then the third man said, "Let's walk back.

➡ _____

**9** We came that way, so we can leave that way.

➡ _____

**10** Then we can walk around the forest."

➡ _____

**11** The fourth man disagreed and said, "I think we should keep walking straight.

➡ _____

**12** The forest cannot go on forever.

➡ _____

**13** A new path will open."

➡ _____

**14** Looking at them all, the fifth man shook his head and said, "I know how to solve this. Just wait."

➡ _____

**15** He started to climb the tallest tree he could find.

➡ _____

**16** As he climbed, everyone else decided to go their separate ways.

➡ _____

**17** When the fifth man reached the top, he could see the whole forest.

➡ _____

**18** Looking at all the paths, he found the shortest way out.

➡ _____

**19** He hurried down to tell the others.

➡ _____

**20** However, when he got to the bottom, everyone was gone.

➡ _____

**21** He thought to himself, *Where did they go? I found the best way out.*

➡ _____

**22** He thought they were all wrong and he was the only wise man.

➡ _____

**23** However, he was wrong.

➡ _____

**24** Everyone was wise.

➡ _____

**25** Each man had chosen his path and created his future.

➡ _____

**26** The man who went to the left walked deeper into the forest.

➡ _____

**27** He was attacked by wild animals and almost died of hunger.

➡ _____

**28** Soon he learned how to protect himself and find food.

➡ _____

**29** In the end, he made his way out of the forest and taught others survival skills.

➡ _____

**30** The man who went to the right met a group of thieves.

➡ _____

**31** They took everything from him and made him join them.

➡ _____

**32** While he was with them, he showed them great kindness.

➡ _____

**33** The thieves were moved by his kindness and learned from his wisdom.

➡ _____

**34** Later, they also became wise men.

➡ _____

**35** The man who walked back created a safe path around the forest.

➡ _____

**36** Using this path, people could get where they were going without getting lost, even though the trip took a little longer.

➡ _____

_____

**37** The man who went straight became a pioneer.

➡ _____

**38** He left the forest and discovered places no one else had been before.

➡ _____

**39** Thanks to him, people could enjoy these new beautiful lands.

➡ _____

**40** The man who climbed the tree became a guide.

➡ _____

**41** Since he had found many different paths, he was able to teach people how to find the quickest ways to their destinations.

➡ _____

**42** This is how the five men found their own paths.

➡ _____

**43** Like them, we are each on our own journey in life, and we cannot compare one journey to another.

➡ _____

**44** You have to create your own path.

➡ _____

**45** Listen to yourself, make a decision, and act on it.

➡ _____

**46** Then, someday, you will realize that you have been living the life that is right for you.

➡ _____

※ 다음 괄호 안의 단어들을 우리말에 맞도록 바르게 배열하시오.

**1** (Five / The / Men / Wise)
➡ _____

**2** (day, / one / wise / five / met / men / the / on / road.)
➡ _____

**3** (agreed / they / to / togehter. / travel)
➡ _____

**4** (the / on / way, / they / however, / became / in / lost / a / forest. / thick)
➡ _____

**5** (walking / before / further, / any / decided / they / stop / to / and / the / find / best / out. / way)
➡ _____

**6** (thinking / after / a / for / while, / first / the / said, / man / strongly / "I / that / feel / should / we / left." / go)
➡ _____

**7** (second / the / said, / man / should / "we / right, / go / *right* / because / also / 'correct.'"/ means)
➡ _____

**8** (the / then / man / third / said, / walk / "let's / back.)
➡ _____

**9** (came / we / way, / that / we / so / leave / can / way. / that)
➡ _____

**10** (we / then / walk / can / the / around / forest.")
➡ _____

**11** (fourth / the / disagreed / man / said, / and / think / "I / should / we / walking / keep / straight.)
➡ _____

**12** (forest / the / go / cannot / forever. / on)
➡ _____

**13** (new / a / will / path / open.")
➡ _____

**14** (at / looking / all, / them / fifth / the / shook / man / head / his / said, / and / know / "I / to / how / this. // solve / wait." / just)
➡ _____
➡ _____

**15** (started / he / climb / to / tallest / the / he / tree / find. / could)
➡ _____

**16** (he / as / climbed, / else / everyone / to / decided / go / separate / their / ways.)
➡ _____

**1** 5명의 지혜로운 사람들

**2** 어느 날 5명의 지혜로운 사람들이 길에서 만났다.

**3** 그들은 여행을 함께 하기로 했다.

**4** 그러나 도중에 그들은 울창한 숲속에서 길을 잃게 되었다.

**5** 더 멀리 가기 전에 그들은 멈추고 빠져나갈 최선의 방법을 찾기로 결정했다.

**6** 잠시 동안 생각한 후, 첫 번째 남자는 "우리가 왼쪽으로 가야 한다는 생각이 강하게 들어요." 라고 말했다.

**7** 두 번째 남자가 "우리는 오른쪽으로 가야 해요. 왜냐하면 '오른쪽'은 또한 '옳은'이라는 의미이기 때문이죠."라고 말했다.

**8** 그러자 세 번째 남자가 "뒤로 돌아갑시다.

**9** 우리가 그 길로 왔으니 그 길로 나갈 수 있을 겁니다.

**10** 그러면 우리는 숲을 한 바퀴 돌 수 있고요."라고 말했다.

**11** 네 번째 남자가 이의를 제기하며 "나는 우리가 똑바로 계속 걸어 나가야 한다고 생각해요.

**12** 숲이 영원히 계속될 수는 없으니까요.

**13** 새로운 길이 열릴 것입니다."라고 말했다.

**14** 모두를 바라보면서 다섯 번째 남자가 고개를 저으며 "나는 이것을 해결하는 방법을 알아요. 잠깐 기다려 보세요."라고 말했다.

**15** 그는 그가 찾을 수 있는 가장 높은 나무를 오르기 시작했다.

**16** 그가 올라가자 다른 모든 사람들은 각자 서로 다른 길을 가기로 결정했다.

**17** (the / when / man / fifth / the / reached / top, / could / he / the / see / forest. / whole)

➡ _____

**18** (at / looking / the / all / paths, / found / he / shortest / the / out. / way)

➡ _____

**19** (hurried / he / to / down / tell / others. / the)

➡ _____

**20** (when / however, / he / to / got / bottom, / the / was / everyone / gone.)

➡ _____

**21** (thought / he / himself, / to / *did / where / go? / they // found / I / best / the / out. / way*)

➡ _____

**22** (thought / he / were / they / wrong / all / and / was / he / only / the / man. / wise)

➡ _____

**23** (he / however, / wrong. / was)

➡ _____

**24** (was / everyone / wise.)

➡ _____

**25** (man / each / chosen / had / path / his / and / his / created / future.)

➡ _____

**26** (man / the / went / who / the / to / left / deeper / walked / the / into / forest.)

➡ _____

**27** (was / he / by / attacked / wild / and / animals / died / almost / hunger. / of)

➡ _____

**28** (he / soon / how / learned / protect / to / himself / and / food. / find)

➡ _____

**29** (the / in / end, / made / he / way / his / of / out / forest / the / and / others / taught / skills. / survival)

➡ _____

➡ _____

**30** (man / the / went / who / the / to / right / a / met / of / group / thieves.)

➡ _____

**31** (took / they / from / everything / him / made / and / join / him / them.)

➡ _____

**32** (he / while / with / was / them, / showed / he / great / them / kindness.)

➡ _____

**17** 다섯 번째 남자가 꼭대기에 이르자 그는 전체 숲을 볼 수 있었다.

**18** 모든 길을 바라보며 그는 빠져나갈 가장 짧은 길을 찾았다.

**19** 그는 다른 사람들에게 알리기 위해 급히 내려갔다.

**20** 하지만 그가 밑으로 내려왔을 때. 모든 사람들은 이미 가 버리고 없었다.

**21** 그는 '다들 어디 간 거야? 내가 빠져나갈 최선의 길을 찾았는데.'라고 마음속으로 생각했다.

**22** 그는 그들이 모두 틀렸고 자신이 유일하게 현명한 사람이라고 생각했다.

**23** 그러나 그가 틀렸다.

**24** 모두가 지혜로웠다.

**25** 각자 자신의 길을 선택했고 자신의 미래를 만들었다.

**26** 왼쪽으로 간 남자는 숲속으로 더 깊이 걸어 들어갔다.

**27** 그는 야생 동물들의 습격을 받았고 거의 굶어 죽을 뻔했다.

**28** 머지않아 그는 자신을 지키고 먹을 것을 찾는 방법을 터득했다.

**29** 결국 그는 숲 밖으로 빠져나왔고 다른 사람들에게 생존 기술을 가르쳤다.

**30** 오른쪽으로 간 남자는 도둑 무리를 만났다.

**31** 그들은 그에게서 모든 것을 가져갔고 그를 그들과 합류시켰다.

**32** 그는 그들과 함께 있는 동안 그들에게 많은 친절을 베풀었다.

**33** (thieves / the / moved / were / his / by / kindness / and / from / learned / wisdom. / his)

➡ _____

**34** (they / later, / became / also / men. / wise)

➡ _____

**35** (man / the / walked / who / created / back / safe / a / path / the / around / forest.)

➡ _____

**36** (this / using / path, / could / people / where / get / they / going / were / getting / without / lost, / though / even / trip / the / a / took / longer. / little)

➡ _____

_____

**37** (man / the / went / who / became / straight / pioneer. / a)

➡ _____

**38** (left / he / forest / the / and / places / discovered / one / no / else / been / had / before.)

➡ _____

**39** (to / thanks / him, / could / people / these / enjoy / beautiful / new / lands.)

➡ _____

**40** (man / the / climbed / who / tree / the / a / became / guide.)

➡ _____

**41** (he / since / found / had / different / many / paths, / was / he / to / able / people / teach / how / find / to / quickest / the / to / ways / destinations. / their)

➡ _____

_____

**42** (is / this / the / how / five / men / their / found / paths. / own)

➡ _____

**43** (them, / like / are / we / each / our / on / journey / own / life, / in / and / cannot / we / one / compare / to / journey / another.)

➡ _____

_____

**44** (have / you / create / to / own / your / path.)

➡ _____

**45** (to / listen / yourself, / a / make / decision, / act / and / it. / on)

➡ _____

**46** (someday, / then, / will / you / that / realize / have / you / living / been / life / the / is / that / for / right / you.)

➡ _____

_____

**33** 그 도둑들은 그의 친절에 감동을 받았고 그의 지혜에서 배우게 되었다.

**34** 나중에 그들 또한 지혜로운 사람들이 되었다.

**35** 뒤돌아 간 남자는 숲 주변에 안전한 길을 만들었다.

**36** 사람들은 이 길을 이용할 때 길을 잃지 않고 자신이 가고자 하는 길에 다다를 수 있었다. 비록 이동 시간이 약간 더 오래 걸려도 말이다.

**37** 똑바로 간 남자는 개척자가 되었다.

**38** 그는 숲을 벗어나 아무도 이전에 가 본 적이 없는 곳을 발견했다.

**39** 그 남자 덕분에, 사람들은 이 새롭고 아름다운 지역을 즐길 수 있었다.

**40** 나무 위로 올라간 남자는 가이드가 되었다.

**41** 그는 여러 다양한 길을 발견했기 때문에, 사람들에게 자신의 목적지에 이르는 가장 빠른 길을 찾는 법을 가르쳐 줄 수 있었다.

**42** 이런 식으로 다섯 남자는 자신만의 길을 찾아냈다.

**43** 그들처럼 우리는 각각 인생에서 자기 자신만의 여행을 하고 있고, 우리는 한 여정을 다른 것과 비교할 수 없다.

**44** 당신은 당신 자신만의 길을 만들어가야 한다.

**45** 자신의 목소리를 듣고, 결정하고, 그 결정에 따라 행동하라.

**46** 그러면 언젠가 당신은 당신에게 맞는 삶을 살아가고 있다는 것을 깨닫게 될 것이다.

※ 다음 우리말을 영어로 쓰시오.

**1** 5명의 지혜로운 사람들

➡ _____

**2** 어느 날 5명의 지혜로운 사람들이 길에서 만났다.

➡ _____

**3** 그들은 여행을 함께 하기로 했다.

➡ _____

**4** 그러나 도중에 그들은 울창한 숲속에서 길을 잃게 되었다.

➡ _____

**5** 더 멀리 가기 전에 그들은 멈추고 빠져나갈 최선의 방법을 찾기로 결정했다.

➡ _____

**6** 잠시 동안 생각한 후, 첫 번째 남자는 "우리가 왼쪽으로 가야 한다는 생각이 강하게 들어요." 라고 말했다.

➡ _____

**7** 두 번째 남자가 "우리는 오른쪽으로 가야 해요. 왜냐하면 '오른쪽'은 또한 '옳은'이라는 의미이기 때문이죠."라고 말했다.

➡ _____

**8** 그러자 세 번째 남자가 "뒤로 돌아갑시다.

➡ _____

**9** 우리가 그 길로 왔으니 그 길로 나갈 수 있을 겁니다.

➡ _____

**10** 그러면 우리는 숲을 한 바퀴 돌 수 있고요."라고 말했다.

➡ _____

**11** 네 번째 남자가 이의를 제기하며 "나는 우리가 똑바로 계속 걸어 나가야 한다고 생각해요.

➡ _____

**12** 숲이 영원히 계속될 수는 없으니까요.

➡ _____

**13** 새로운 길이 열릴 것입니다."라고 말했다.

➡ _____

**14** 모두를 바라보면서 다섯 번째 남자가 고개를 저으며 "나는 이것을 해결하는 방법을 알아요. 잠깐 기다려 보세요."라고 말했다.

➡ _____

**15** 그는 그가 찾을 수 있는 가장 높은 나무를 오르기 시작했다.

➡ _____

**16** 그가 올라가자 다른 모든 사람들은 각자 서로 다른 길을 가기로 결정했다.

➡ _____

**17** 다섯 번째 남자가 꼭대기에 이르자 그는 전체 숲을 볼 수 있었다.

➡ _____

**18** 모든 길을 바라보며 그는 빠져나갈 가장 짧은 길을 찾았다.

➡ _____

**19** 그는 다른 사람들에게 알리기 위해 급히 내려갔다.

➡ _____

**20** 하지만 그가 밑으로 내려왔을 때, 모든 사람들은 이미 가 버리고 없었다.

➡ _____

**21** 그는 '다들 어디 간 거야? 내가 빠져나갈 최선의 길을 찾았는데.'라고 마음속으로 생각했다.

➡ _____

**22** 그는 그들이 모두 틀렸고 자신이 유일하게 현명한 사람이라고 생각했다.

➡ _____

**23** 그러나 그가 틀렸다.

➡ _____

**24** 모두가 지혜로웠다.

➡ _____

**25** 각자 자신의 길을 선택했고 자신의 미래를 만들었다.

➡ _____

**26** 왼쪽으로 간 남자는 숲속으로 더 깊이 걸어 들어갔다.

➡ _____

**27** 그는 야생 동물들의 습격을 받았고 거의 굶어 죽을 뻔했다.

➡ _____

**28** 머지않아 그는 자신을 지키고 먹을 것을 찾는 방법을 터득했다.

➡ _____

**29** 결국 그는 숲 밖으로 빠져나왔고 다른 사람들에게 생존 기술을 가르쳤다.

➡ _____

**30** 오른쪽으로 간 남자는 도둑 무리를 만났다.

➡ _____

**31** 그들은 그에게서 모든 것을 가져갔고 그를 그들과 합류시켰다.

➡ _____

**32** 그는 그들과 함께 있는 동안 그들에게 많은 친절을 베풀었다.

➡ _____

**33** 그 도둑들은 그의 친절에 감동을 받았고 그의 지혜에서 배우게 되었다.

➡ _____

**34** 나중에 그들 또한 지혜로운 사람들이 되었다.

➡ _____

**35** 뒤돌아 간 남자는 숲 주변에 안전한 길을 만들었다.

➡ _____

**36** 사람들은 이 길을 이용할 때 길을 잃지 않고 자신이 가고자 하는 길에 다다를 수 있었다. 비록 이동 시간이 약간 더 오래 걸려도 말이다.

➡ _____

_____

**37** 똑바로 간 남자는 개척자가 되었다.

➡ _____

**38** 그는 숲을 벗어나 아무도 이전에 가 본 적이 없는 곳을 발견했다.

➡ _____

**39** 그 남자 덕분에, 사람들은 이 새롭고 아름다운 지역을 즐길 수 있었다.

➡ _____

**40** 나무 위로 올라간 남자는 가이드가 되었다.

➡ _____

**41** 그는 여러 다양한 길을 발견했었기 때문에, 사람들에게 자신의 목적지에 이르는 가장 빠른 길을 찾는 법을 가르쳐 줄 수 있었다.

➡ _____

_____

**42** 이런 식으로 다섯 남자는 자신만의 길을 찾아냈다.

➡ _____

**43** 그들처럼 우리는 각각 인생에서 자기 자신만의 여행을 하고 있고, 우리는 한 여정을 다른 것과 비교할 수 없다.

➡ _____

**44** 당신은 당신 자신만의 길을 만들어가야 한다.

➡ _____

**45** 자신의 목소리를 듣고, 결정하고, 그 결정에 따라 행동하라.

➡ _____

**46** 그러면 언젠가 당신은 당신에게 맞는 삶을 살아가고 있다는 것을 깨닫게 될 것이다.

➡ _____

# MEMO

MEMO

# MEMO

2학기 전과정

# 적중100 plus

영어 기출 문제집

영어 기출 문제집

2학기

# 정답 및 해설

능률 | 김성곤

중 3

적중100

영어 기출 문제집

적중100

2학기

# 정답 및 해설

능률 | 김성곤

중 3

# Environmental Innovations

## 시험대비 실력평가
p.08

01 disappear 02 ① 03 ②
04 (1) materials (2) support (3) additional
(4) artwork (5) unique
05 ⑤ 06 ①

01 주어진 단어는 반의어 관계를 나타낸다. appear: 나타나다, disappear: 사라지다

02 '건물을 디자인하는 사람'을 가리키는 말은 architect(건축가)이다.

03 suggestion: 제안

04 support: 지지하다, material: 재료, additional: 추가적인, unique: 독특한, artwork: 예술 작품

05 보기에 주어진 bright은 '똑똑한, 영리한'을 의미하며 이와 같은 의미로 쓰인 것은 ⑤번이다. 나머지는 모두 '밝은, 빛나는, 근사한'을 뜻한다.

06 in harmony: 조화하여, in addition to: ~ 이외에도, in my view: 내 생각에는

## 서술형 시험대비
p.09

01 incredible
02 (1) explanation (2) damage (3) prevent
(4) surface (5) statue
03 (1) hold a cooking contest
(2) (r)aise (a)wareness (3) make a suggestion
(4) (b)ored with
04 (1) *Hanok* is a Korean traditional structure made of wood.
(2) We are going to learn how the direction of water flow has changed.
(3) Creativity and innovation are keys to success.
(4) Don't throw away the trash on the street.

01 주어진 단어는 반의어 관계를 나타낸다. credible: 믿을 만한, incredible: 믿기 힘든

02 surface: 표면, statue: 조각상, explanation: 설명, damage: 손상시키다, prevent: 막다, 예방하다

03 hold a contest: 대회를 개최하다. raise awareness: 인식을

높이다; make a suggestion: 제안을 하다, get bored with: ~에 지루해지다

05 structure: 구조(물), flow: 흐름, innovation: 혁신, throw away: 버리다

교과서
## Conversation

핵심 Check
p.10~11

**1** In my opinion, we should bring reusable bags when we go shopping.

**2** ③

## 교과서 대화문 익히기

Check(√) True or False
p.12

1 T 2 F 3 T 4 F

## 교과서 확인학습
p.14~15

**Listen & Talk 1 A**

plastic bags / environment, plastic bags / In my opinion, reusable bags

**Listen & Talk 1 B**

up, going up / take the stairs / all the way / save, protect the environment / one elevator ride / adds up, In my opinion, taking care of / have a point

**Listen & Talk 1 C**

make a suggestion, throw, away, recycling, resources, protect, in my opinion, trash cans, place, colored recycling bins, remind, separate

**Listen & Talk 2 A**

holding / What kinds of / theme, raise students' awareness / wait to see it

**Listen & Talk 2 B**

article / plastic bag, made, of / amazing / breaks down, soil, disappears / reduce plastic waste / company, wait to use

**Listen & Talk 2 C**

sheep park / interesting / protect the environment / How can / chemicals, unwanted plants / chemicals / bright, wait to

In my opinion, any more / bored with / using / how to do it / interesting, to make

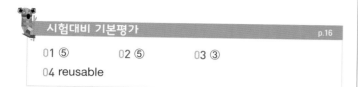

### 시험대비 기본평가 p.16

01 ⑤    02 ⑤    03 ③
04 reusable

01 밑줄 친 (A)는 희망이나 기대를 표현하지만, ⑤번은 지루함을 나타낸다.

03 ③번을 제외하고는 모두 동의의 표현이다.

04 '한 번 이상 사용될 수 있는'을 가리키는 말은 reusable(재사용할 수 있는)이다.

### 시험대비 실력평가 p.17~18

01 (C) → (B) → (D) → (A)    02 ④
03 네 말이 일리가 있다.
04 ②    05 ①    06 ⑤
07 ⓐ The (cool) article  ⓑ the (new) bag
08 ③    09 ③    10 ④    11 ⑤

01 (C) 사진 대회 개최 계획 설명 → (B) 대회에 대한 구체적 질문 → (D) 주제 설명 및 대회 개최 이유 설명 → (A) 기대감 표현

02 (A)는 목적을 나타내는 부사적 용법의 to protect, (B)는 주어가 the energy로 3인칭 단수이므로 adds, (C)는 주어로 동명사 taking이 적절하다.

04 수진은 지호에게 엘리베이터를 타고 갈 것을 제안했다.

05 앞 문장과 상반되는 내용이 이어지므로 '그러나, 하지만'을 뜻하는 however가 적절하다.

06 위 대화에서 학생들이 종이는 어느 색의 분리수거함에 버려야 하는지 알 수 없다.

08 (A) amazing: 놀라운, amazed: 깜짝 놀란, (B) 주어가 The bag으로 3인칭 단수이므로 disappears, (C)는 help의 목적보어로 원형부정사 reduce가 알맞다.

09 따뜻한 물속에서는 3분 만에 사라진다.

10 (A) pollute: 오염시키다, pollution: 오염, (B) raise: 올리다, 끌어올리다, rise: 일어나다, (C) I can't wait to+동사원형: ~이 기대된다

### 서술형 시험대비 p.19

01 (A) seeing  the photo contest  (B) Minsu's club
   (C) raise students' awareness of environmental problems

02 It is mostly made of corn.

03 It breaks down in soil in only three months.

04 It helps protect the environment by reducing the amount of plastic waste.

05 C. cold → warm

06 (B) → (C) → (A) → (E) → (D)

01 소라는 사진 대회를 보기를 기대하고 있다. 이것은 민수의 동아리에 의해 다음 주에 개최될 것이다. 주제는 세계의 환경오염이다. 그것은 환경 문제에 대한 학생들의 인식을 향상시키기 위해 계획되었다.

02 새로운 봉지는 주로 옥수수로 만들어진다.

03 새로운 봉지는 흙 속에서 3달 만에 분해된다.

04 새로운 봉지는 플라스틱 쓰레기를 줄이는 데 도움이 된다.

06 (B) 계단 이용 제안에 대한 거절 → (C) 설득 및 에너지 절약의 필요성을 설명 → (A) 상대방의 의견에 반박 → (E) 인정 및 자신의 의견 설명 → (D) 상대방의 주장에 동의

### 교과서
## Grammar

### 핵심 Check p.20~21

1 (1) to   (2) for   (3) of
2 (1) when   (2) where   (3) why

### 시험대비 기본평가 p.22

01 ④    02 ③    03 ③
04 (1) to write  (2) her  (3) for  (4) why  (5) where
   (6) when

01 It을 가주어로 하고 to부정사를 진주어로 하며 의미상의 주어로 'for him'을 쓴 ④번이 적절하다.

02 관계부사 how는 선행사 the way와 함께 쓰지 않고 반드시 둘 중의 하나만 써야 한다.

03 to부정사의 의미상의 주어가 일반적인 사람일 경우는 보통 생략한다.

04 (1) 진주어로 to부정사가 적절하다. (2), (3) to부정사의 의미상의 주어는 to부정사 바로 앞에 'for+목적격'으로 나타낸다. (4) 선행사가 the reason이므로 관계부사 why가 적절하다. (5) 선행사가 a village이므로 관계부사 where가 적절하다. (6) 선행사가 the day이므로 관계부사 when이 적절하다.

01 ④     02 ②     03 ③

04 (1) to wake   (2) for   (3) of   (4) why   (5) when

    (6) which   (7) how

05 where     06 ①     07 ②     08 ⑤

09 It was hard for them to make Gimchi.

10 ④     11 ③     12 ⑤

13 (1) the time 또는 when   (2) the reason 또는 why

14 (1) For him to live without her even for a single day

     was really hard.

   (2) I suppose it was rude of me to listen to a

     private conversation.

   (3) It is very important for him to make a decision

     soon.

   (4) We should find a place where we can be safe!

   (5) Do you know the reason why John left so

     early?

   (6) I have to say I like the way he solved the

     situation.

15 ① , ④     16 (1) ⓑ, ⓒ, ⓔ (2) ⓐ, ⓓ, ⓕ     17 ⑤

01 ① It was very kind of you to meet me. ② It is easy to catch a disease in winter. ③ It's good for children to do things on their own sometimes. ⑤ It was great for Kevin to rest for a week.

02 선행사가 'the reason'이므로 관계부사 why가 적절하다.

03 선행사로 'the year'가 있으므로 '시간'을 나타내는 when이 적절하다. 가주어로 It이 나와 있고 진주어로 to부정사가 나와 있으므로 빈칸에는 to부정사의 의미상의 주어가 나와야 한다. 사람의 성향이나 성격을 나타내는 형용사가 아니므로 for가 적절하다.

04 (1) 진주어로 to부정사가 적절하다. (2) to부정사의 의미상의 주어는 to부정사 바로 앞에 'for+대명사의 목적격'으로 나타낸다. (3) 문장에 쓰인 형용사가 사람의 성향이나 성격을 나타내는 말일 때는 'for+목적격'이 아니라 'of+목적격'으로 쓴다. (4) 선행사로 the reason이 나왔으므로 관계부사 why가 적절하다. (5) 선행사로 the day가 나왔으므로 관계부사 when이 적절하다. (6) 선행사로 the house가 나왔지만 관계사절에서 in의 목적어가 없으므로 관계대명사 which가 적절하다. (7) 선행사 the way와 how를 함께 쓰지 않으므로 how가 적절하다.

05 'a small town'을 선행사로 하는 관계부사 where가 적절하다.

06 It is very important for me to make the fans happy.
*cane: 지팡이

07 주어진 문장과 ②번은 시간을 선행사로 하는 관계부사이다. ① 의문부사, ③ 의문대명사, ④ 명사, ⑤ 접속사

08 선행사가 'the house'이므로 관계부사 where를 쓰거나 'in which'로 쓰는 것이 적절하며 in은 관계절의 마지막에 써도 좋

다. 'This is the house. + I used to live in the house.'를 관계부사를 이용하여 한 문장으로 만든 것이다.

09 'It ~ for ... to부정사' 구문을 이용하여 쓴다.

10 선행사가 the beach이므로 장소를 나타내는 관계부사 where를 이용한다.

11 가주어로 It을 쓰고 to부정사의 의미상의 주어로 사람의 성향이나 성격을 나타내는 형용사가 아니므로 for를 쓴다.

12 to부정사의 의미상의 주어는 to부정사 바로 앞에 'for+목적격'으로 나타내지만 사람의 성품·성격을 나타내는 형용사가 보어로 쓰이면 의미상의 주어로 'of+목적격'을 쓴다.

13 선행사가 'the time', 'the place', 'the reason'처럼 일반적인 뜻을 나타낼 때 선행사나 관계부사 중 하나를 생략할 수 있다.

14 (1) 의미상의 주어로 For him을 쓴다. (2) 보어로 쓰인 형용사가 사람의 성향, 성격을 나타내는 말이므로 'for+목적격'이 아니라 'of+목적격'으로 쓴다. (3) 의미상의 주어로 'for+목적격'이 나왔으므로 진주어로 to부정사를 쓴다. (4) a place가 선행사로 나왔고 관계사에 이끌리는 절이 완전하므로 관계부사 where로 고치거나 전치사 in을 which 앞이나 관계사절의 끝에 써 주어야 한다. (5) 'The reason'이 선행사이므로 which를 why로 고치는 것이 적절하다. (6) 'the way how'를 쓸 수 없으므로 the way 또는 how를 생략하거나 how를 that이나 'in which'로 고쳐야 한다.

15 ① of her로 의미상의 주어가 나와 있으므로 to부정사가 적절하다. ④ 관계사에 이끌리는 절이 완전하므로 which를 where로 고쳐야 한다.

16 ⓑ, ⓒ, ⓔ: '가주어 It, 진주어 to부정사' 구문 ⓐ, ⓓ, ⓕ: 'It ~ that 강조' 구문 ⓕ는 what을 강조한 'It was what that he wanted you to do.'를 의문문으로 한 것이다.

17 'the reason'이 선행사이므로 관계부사 why가 적절하다.

01 (1) us to   (2) of them to

02 (1) I like the café where we had tea yesterday.

   (2) May I ask you the reason why you decided to

     leave Seoul?

   (3) The bags were too heavy for us to carry.

   (4) It took a few weeks for the workers to repair

     the street.

   (5) It was brave of her to go abroad alone.

03 (1) the way she could solve

   (2) where I want to go

04 (1) for me to wake   (2) of you to remember

05 (1) They made an underwater museum away from

     the places where sea life was dying.

   (2) I can't forget the day when I won the class

     election.

(3) They talked about how he scored the goal in the final match.

(4) That is the reason why I like documentaries.

06 (1) of us → for us    (2) for you → of you

(3) for him → of him    (4) to not → not to

07 (1) where → when

(2) which → why 또는 for which

(3) the way how → the way 또는 how, 또는 the way that 또는 the way in which

(4) in 생략 또는 when → which

08 (1) I explained the reason why I left the party early. / I explained the reason for which I left the party early.

(2) He regrets the way he lived his life. / He regrets how he lived his life. / He regrets the way that he lived his life.

01 'It(가주어) ~ for[of] ...(의미상의 주어) 진주어(to부정사)' 구문을 이용한다.

02 (1) 선행사 'the café'에 맞는 관계부사 where를 이용하여 배열한다. (2) 선행사 'the reason'에 맞는 관계부사 why를 이용하여 배열한다. (3)~(5) 'It(가주어) ~ for(of) …(의미상의 주어) 진주어(to부정사)' 구문을 이용한다.

03 (1) 'the way'가 선행사로 나왔으므로 how를 쓰면 안 되는 것에 주의한다. (2) 'the place'를 선행사로 하는 관계부사 where를 이용한다.

04 'It(가주어) ~ for[of] ...(의미상의 주어) 진주어(to부정사)' 구문을 이용한다.

05 (1) 선행사 'the places'에 맞는 관계부사 where를 이용하여 연결한다. (2) 선행사 'the day'에 맞는 관계부사 when을 이용하여 연결한다. (3) 선행사가 'the way'이므로 how를 이용하여 연결한다. (4) 선행사 'the reason'에 맞는 관계부사 why를 이용하여 연결한다.

06 (1) to부정사의 의미상의 주어는 to부정사 바로 앞에 'for+목적격'으로 나타낸다. (2) 문장에 쓰인 형용사가 사람의 성향, 성격을 나타내는 말일 때는 의미상의 주어로 'of+목적격'으로 쓴다. (3) 의미상의 주어로 'of+목적격'이 적절하다. (4) to부정사의 부정은 to부정사 앞에 not이나 never를 써서 'not[never]+to부정사'로 나타낸다.

07 (1) 'the day'가 선행사이므로 where를 when으로 고치는 것이 적절하다. (2) 'The reason'이 선행사이므로 which를 why나 'for which'로 고치는 것이 적절하다. (3) 'the way how'는 쓸 수 없으므로 the way나 how를 생략하거나 how를 that이나 'in which'로 고쳐야 한다. (4) 관계사절의 마지막에 있는 in을 생략하거나 when을 which로 고쳐 쓴다.

08 (1) 선행사가 '이유'를 나타낼 때 관계부사는 why를 쓰며 여기서 why는 'for which'로 바꿔 쓸 수 있다. for를 관계사절 끝에

쓸 수도 있다. (2) 선행사가 '방법'을 나타낼 때 관계부사는 how를 쓰며 이때 how와 함께 the way를 쓰지 않는다는 것을 주의한다. the way나 how 또는 the way that이나 the way in which를 쓴다.

## Reading

**확인문제**                                                      p.28

1 F   2 F   3 T   4 F

**확인문제**                                                      p.29

1 T   2 T   3 F   4 F

### 교과서 확인학습 A                                            p.30~31

01 for us to find ways          02 creative, to save

03 underwater museum

04 meet, professor, listen to

05 where, tourists travel

06 the most popular, to do, is, at

07 However, are, damaging parts, near

08 To prevent this, something interesting

09 if, attracted, to, dying areas, to get better

10 made, underwater, away from, where, dying

11 about, meters below, contains, statues

12 are made from, that support

13 provide, for, to live on

14 will grow on, which will make, unique

15 want people to see, on

16 how rich sea life is, how important it is

17 using, to protect, on land

18 what, says about          19 throughout the year

20 need, which uses, contributes to

21 That's why, have begun to, that use less, are still

22 For example, are designed to have

23 it, for outside air to move

24 natural, how these buildings stay cool

25 In addition to making

26 provides, protects, from direct sunlight, keeps

27 not only help, but also provide, with

28 goals, new style, architecture

29 will keep coming up with

30 Every field has, protecting

31 With, will be able to live together, far into

1 It is important for us to find ways to protect the environment.

2 Some people have found creative ways to save the earth.

3 One example is an underwater museum in Cancun, Mexico.

4 Let's meet Dr. Rosa Allison, an art professor, and listen to her explanation about the special museum.

5 Rosa: Cancun is a city where 4.8 million tourists travel every year.

6 One of the most popular activities to do there is looking at the area's beautiful sea life underwater.

7 However, tourist activities are seriously damaging parts of the sea near Cancun.

8 To prevent this, artists did something interesting.

9 They thought if they attracted tourists to a different part of the sea, the dying areas could have time to get better.

10 They made an underwater museum away from the places where sea life was dying.

11 It's about 14 meters below the surface and contains 500 statues.

12 The statues are made from materials that support sea life.

13 They provide additional places for plants and animals to live on.

14 Over time, many types of sea life will grow on the statues, which will make the artwork unique.

15 The artists want people to see a variety of sea life on the statues.

16 If people realize how rich sea life is, they will understand how important it is to save the sea.

17 In Singapore, people are using architecture to protect the environment on land.

18 Let's hear what Rajesh Khan, an architect, says about eco-friendly buildings.

19 Rajesh: Singapore is hot throughout the year.

20 Most buildings need air conditioning, which uses a lot of energy and contributes to climate change.

21 That's why architects in Singapore have begun to design eco-friendly buildings that use less air conditioning but are still cool inside.

22 For example, many buildings in Singapore are designed to have an open structure.

23 This structure makes it possible for outside air to move throughout a building.

24 This natural air flow is how these buildings stay cool.

25 In addition to making open structures, architects add large gardens.

26 This greenery provides shade and protects parts of the building from direct sunlight, which keeps the building cooler.

27 Eco-friendly buildings like these not only help protect the environment, but also provide people with a good quality of life.

28 Those are the goals of this new style of architecture.

29 Hopefully, architects will keep coming up with new eco-friendly ideas.

30 Every field has different ways of protecting the environment.

31 With more innovation, humans and nature will be able to live together in harmony far into the future.

01 ③     02 museum    03 ⑤

04 4.8 million tourists visit Cancun every year.

05 ③       06 ④

07 The artists want people to see a variety of sea life on the statues.

08 ④       09 ②

10 Most buildings in Singapore need air conditioning.

11 ②       12 ③

13 Every field has different ways of protecting the environment.

14 ④       15 ⑤

16 Many types of sea life will grow on the statues over time.

17 ②

18 They are made from materials that support sea life.

19 ⑤     20 ②     21 ⑤     22 ③

23 ⑤

01 멕시코 칸쿤에 있는 수중 박물관을 가리키는 말이다. 따라서 ③번이 적절하다.

02 많은 예술 작품 혹은 역사적 물건들과 같은 귀중하고 흥미로운 물건들이 보관되고 연구되고 대중에게 전시되는 건물은 '박물관 (museum)'이다.

03 칸쿤에서 할 수 있는 가장 인기 있는 활동 중 하나는 바닷속의

아름다운 해양 생물을 관찰하는 것이지만 이러한 관광 활동들이 칸쿤 근처의 바다 일부를 심각하게 훼손시킨다는 연결이 자연스럽다.

04 칸쿤은 매년 480만 명의 관광객이 여행하는 도시라고 하였다.

05 해양 생물이 죽어가는 지역으로부터 떨어진 곳에 만들었다고 하였다.

06 예술작품이 독특한 것이므로 make를 5형식 동사로 썼음을 알 수 있다. 따라서 목적격 보어로 형용사를 써야 한다.

07 예술가들은 사람들이 그 조각상에서 살고 있는 다양한 해양 생명체들을 보길 원한다.

08 주어진 문장의 This structure는 an open structure를 의미한다. 따라서 ④번에 들어가는 것이 가장 자연스럽다.

09 싱가포르는 연중 더운 곳이라고 하였다.

10 싱가포르에 있는 대부분의 건물들은 에어컨 가동이 필요하다고 하였다.

11 이어지는 문장에서 '이러한 녹지 공간(this greenery)'이 그늘을 제공한다고 하였으므로 ②번이 가장 적절하다.

12 글의 내용으로 보아 친환경 건물에 관한 글이 선행했음을 알 수 있다.

13 of의 목적어로 동명사 protecting을 쓰는 것에 유의한다.

14 빈칸 (A)에는 진주어를 이끄는 to find가 들어가는 것이 적절하다. ④번에는 enjoy의 목적어인 동명사 finding이 적절하다.

15 몇몇 사람들이 지구를 구하기 위한 창의적인 방법을 찾았다고 말하며, 그 예로 멕시코 칸쿤에 있는 수중 박물관을 들고 있다. 따라서 ⑤번이 가장 적절하다.

16 시간이 흐르면서 많은 형태의 바다 생명체들이 그 조각상에서 자라게 될 것이라고 하였다.

17 칸쿤 근처의 바다 일부는 관광 활동들로 인해 훼손되었다고 하였다. 따라서 ②번이 가장 적절하다.

18 해저 박물관에 있는 조각상들은 해양 생물에게 도움이 되는 재료들로 만들어졌다고 하였다.

19 칸쿤 근처의 바다 일부가 심각하게 훼손되어 예술가들은 그곳에서 멀리 떨어진 곳에 해저 박물관을 만들어 사람들을 유인하려 하였다.

20 건축가들은 개방형 구조를 만드는 것 외에도 큰 정원을 더한다는 의미가 자연스럽다. 따라서 '~에 더하여, ~일 뿐만 아니라'라는 의미로 쓰이는 ②번이 가장 적절하다. regardless of: ~에 상관없이

21 글의 내용에 따르면 먼 미래에 인간과 자연이 함께 조화를 이루며 살아갈 수 있을 것이라고 말하는 것이 자연스럽다. 따라서 isolation을 harmony라고 쓰는 것이 적절하다.

22 사람들에게 양질의 삶을 제공하면서 동시에 환경을 보호하는 것을 돕는 친환경적인 건축 양식을 의미한다.

23 친환경적인 건물들이 사람들에게 양질의 삶을 제공한다고 하였다.

01 It is important for us to find ways to protect the environment.

02 It is located in Mexico.

03 It is looking at the area's beautiful sea life underwater.

04 관광 활동들이 칸쿤 근처의 바다 일부를 심각하게 훼손시키는 것

05 It was to give the dying areas time to get better.

06 materials that support sea life, additional places, plants and animals can live

07 It contains 500 statues.

08 Many types of sea life will make the statues unique.

09 eco-friendly

10 It uses a lot of energy and contributes to climate change.

11 outside air, move throughout a building

12 개방형 구조의 건물, 큰 정원이 있는 건물

13 Hopefully, architects will keep coming up with new eco-friendly ideas.

14 They provide shade and protect parts of the building from direct sunlight.

01 '환경을 보호할 수 있는 방법을 찾는 것'의 주체는 '우리'이므로 의미상의 주어로 'for+목적격'을 쓰는 것에 유의한다.

02 칸쿤은 멕시코에 위치해 있다.

03 칸쿤에서 할 수 있는 가장 인기 있는 활동 중 하나는 그 지역의 바닷속 아름다운 해양 생물을 관찰하는 것이다.

04 앞 문장을 가리키는 말이다.

05 해저 박물관을 만든 목적은 해양 생물이 죽어가는 지역에 호전될 시간을 주는 것이었다.

06 해석: 해양 생물에게 도움이 되는 재료들로 만들어진 것에 더하여, 조각상은 식물과 동물이 살 수 있는 추가적인 장소를 제공할 수 있다.

07 해저 박물관에는 500개의 조각상이 있다고 하였다.

08 많은 형태의 바다 생명체들이 그 조각상에서 자라게 될 것이며, 이것이 그 예술 작품을 독특하게 만들 것이라고 하였다.

09 육지의 환경을 보호하기 위한 건축물을 설명하면서 친환경적인 건물들을 소개하고 있으므로 eco-friendly라고 쓰는 것이 가장 적절하다.

10 많은 에너지를 사용하고 기후 변화의 원인이 되는 것이 에어컨 사용의 문제이다.

11 건물의 개방형 구조는 외부 공기가 건물을 관통하는 것을 가능케 한다. enable+목적어+to V: 목적어가 V하는 것을 가능하게 하다

12 앞서 소개한 개방형 구조의 건물과 큰 정원이 있는 건물을 가리키

는 말이다.

13 '계속해서 ~하다'는 keep+Ving이며, come up with는 '~을 생각해 내다'라는 의미이다. 따라서 keep coming up with라고 쓰는 것에 유의한다.

14 건물의 큰 정원은 그늘을 제공하고 직사광선으로부터 건물의 부분들을 지켜준다고 하였다.

## 영역별 핵심문제                    p.41~45

01 environmental　　　　02 ①　　　　03 ②
04 (1) architect　(2) architecture　(3) additional
　　(4) plastic bag
05 ④　　　　　　　06 ③
07 (1) You have a point.
　　(2) What do you think have contributed to your good health?
　　(3) We should live in harmony with other people.
08 ④　　　　　09 ⑤　　　　10 ⓓ → needed
11 (A) a sheep park　(B) unwanted plants
　　(C) chemicals
12 I can't wait to see it!
13 It's pollution around the world.
14 It's because they want to raise students' awareness of environmental problems.
15 It's because elevators use lots of energy and he believes that they need to save energy to protect the environment.
16 They are going to the science room.
17 ④　　　　　18 the way she has to follow
19 ②　　　　　20 ④
21 (1) I want to go to a place where I can breathe fresh air.
　　(2) Lunch break at school is the time when Junho can play soccer with his friends.
　　(3) I know the reason why the manhole covers are round.
　　(4) My mom doesn't like how my sister drives.
22 how rich sea life is
23 ③　　　　24 ③　　　　25 ⑤
26 ②번 → That's why　　　27 with　　　28 ③
29 Eat Your Cup and Save the Earth!
30 컵을 사용한 후 먹는 것

01 주어진 단어는 명사와 형용사 관계를 나타낸다. environmental: 환경적인

02 '어느 지역의 전체적인 날씨'를 가리키는 말은 climate(기후)이다.

03 incredible: 믿기 힘든, 믿을 수 없는

04 architect: 건축가, architecture: 건축, additional: 추가적인, plastic bag: 비닐봉지

05 보기와 나머지 company는 '회사'를 뜻하지만, ④번은 '친구, 동료'를 뜻한다.

06 ride: 타다; 탑승

07 contribute to: ~에 기여하다, (~의) 원인이 되다, in harmony with: ~와 조화하여

08 주어진 문장은 오래된 가방들이 지겹다는 말에 해 줄 조언으로 적절하므로 (D)가 적절하다.

10 화학 물질이 필요하지 않다는 의미로 수동태가 알맞다.

11 나는 미희네 집 근처에 있는 양 공원에 갔었다. 동물들을 보는 것이 즐거웠다. 더욱이, 그들은 잡초를 먹는다. 이것은 잡초를 없애기 위해 화학 물질을 사용하는 것을 줄이는데 도움이 될 수 있다.

12 I can't wait to+동사원형

13 사진 대회의 주제는 세계의 환경 오염이다.

14 학생들의 환경 문제에 대한 인식을 높이기 위해 대회를 개최한다.

15 지호는 수진에게 엘리베이터가 많은 에너지를 사용하고 그들이 에너지를 절약하고 환경을 보호해야 한다고 생각하기 때문에 계단으로 갈 것을 제안했다.

16 수진과 지호는 과학실에 가고 있다.

17 to부정사의 의미상의 주어는 to부정사 바로 앞에 'for+목적격'으로 나타내지만 보어로 쓰인 형용사가 사람의 성향, 성격을 나타내는 말일 때는 'for+목적격'이 아니라 'of+목적격'으로 쓴다.

18 'the way'가 선행사로 나왔으므로 how를 쓰면 안 되는 것에 주의한다.

19 ②에는 사람의 성격이나 성질을 나타내는 형용사(foolish)가 왔으므로 의미상의 주어로 'of+목적격'이 적절하다. 나머지는 모두 'for+목적격'이 적절하다.

20 의미상의 주어 앞에 전치사 for가 있으므로 빈칸에는 사람의 성격을 나타내는 형용사인 brave는 알맞지 않다.

21 (1) 선행사 'a place'에 맞는 관계부사 where를 이용하여 연결한다. (2) 선행사 'the time'에 맞는 관계부사 when을 이용하여 연결한다. (3) 선행사 'the reason'에 맞는 관계부사 why를 이용하여 연결한다. (4) 선행사가 'the way'이므로 how를 이용하여 연결한다.

22 간접의문문의 어순은 '의문사+주어+동사'이며, how는 rich를 수식하고 있으므로 'how rich sea life is'라고 쓰는 것이 적절하다.

23 관광객들을 바다의 다른 쪽으로 유인하기 위해 만든 것이 주어진 문장에 제시된 해저 박물관이며 이것은 해수면에서 14미터 아래에 있다는 연결이 자연스러우므로 ③번이 가장 적절하다.

24 (A)는 to부정사의 형용사적 용법이다. ①, ② 부사적 용법 중 목적 ③ 형용사적 용법 ④ 명사적 용법 중 진주어 ⑤ 명사적 용법 중 보어

25 예술가들은 사람들이 조각상들에서 살고 있는 다양한 해양 생명체들을 보고 해양 생물이 얼마나 풍부한지 인지한다면 바다를 지키는 것이 얼마나 중요한지 이해할 것이라고 하였다. 따라서 ⑤번이 글의 내용과 일치한다.

26 앞 문장에 대한 결과를 이끌고 있으므로 That's why라고 쓰는 것이 적절하다.

27 provide A with B: A에게 B를 제공하다, come up with: ~을 생각해 내다

28 개방형 구조는 외부 공기가 건물을 관통하는 것을 가능하게 한다.

29 글의 내용은 먹을 수 있는 컵을 사용하여 지구를 구하라는 것이다.

30 앞 문장의 내용을 가리키는 말이다.

## 단원별 예상문제
p.46~49

01 (B) → (C) → (A)　　02 ⑤　　03 ⑤
04 ⑤　　　　05 ④　　　06 ④
07 separate
08 I'm looking forward to visiting the park!
09 ④　　　　10 when　　11 ④　　12 ③
13 ⓒ, ⓔ, ⓖ
14 (1) He grew up in a city where violence was rare.
　 (2) It took three hours for me to write the report.
15 An underwater museum is used to protect the environment.
16 ②　　　17 ④　　　18 ⑤　　　19 ②
20 ⑤　　　21 They add large gardens.

01 (B) 의견 언급 → (C) 동의 및 비닐봉지 사용을 줄이기 위한 방법 질문 → (A) 의견 말하기

02 의견을 묻는 질문에 기대감을 표현하는 것은 어색하다.

03 주어진 문장은 수진의 '엘리베이터를 한 번 탄다고 그렇게 많은 에너지를 사용하지 않는다'는 주장에 반박하는 말로 적절하므로 (E)에 들어가야 한다.

04 대화를 통해 한 번 엘리베이터를 타는 것이 얼마나 많은 에너지를 사용하는지는 알 수 없다..

05 (A) instead는 부사, instead of+명사구, (B) 주어 역할을 하는 동명사 recycling, (C) 부사가 적절하므로 properly가 알맞다.

06 소년은 재활용을 권장하기 위해 학교에 있는 쓰레기통의 개수를 줄이는 것이 필요하다고 생각한다.

07 '무언가를 다른 부분이나 다른 그룹으로 나누다'라는 뜻을 나타내는 말은 separate(분리하다)이다.

08 can't wait to+동사원형 = look forward to+ing

10 'the day'를 선행사로 하는 관계부사 when이 적절하다.

11 ① It is easy for children to learn foreign languages. ② This structure makes it possible for outside air to move throughout a building. ③ It was boring for her to ride a bike. ⑤ They don't have enough food to eat.

12 첫 번째 문장에서는 'the reason'이 선행사이므로 why가 적절하다. 두 번째 문장에서는 to부정사의 의미상의 주어를 to부정사 바로 앞에 'for+목적격'으로 나타낸다.

13 ⓐ which → where ⓑ where → when ⓓ of → for ⓕ getting → to get

14 (1) 선행사 'a city'를 수식하는 관계부사 where를 이용한다.
(2) 'It(가주어) ~ for ...(의미상의 주어) 진주어(to부정사)' 구문을 이용한다.

15 지구를 구하기 위한 창의적인 방법으로 칸쿤에서는 해저 박물관을 사용하였다.

16 Rosa Allison 교수가 칸쿤에 있는 수중 박물관에 대해 설명할 것이라고 하였으므로 ②번이 가장 적절하다.

17 ⓐ, ⓑ, ⓒ는 예술가들을, ⓓ는 조각상들을 가리키는 말이다.

18 현재 많은 관광객들로 인해 훼손된 칸쿤 근처의 바다가 회복할 시간을 갖도록 하기 위해 해저 박물관을 지었다.

19 앞 문장에 대한 예시를 제공하고 있으므로 ②번이 가장 적절하다.

20 ⑤ 녹지 공간이 그늘을 제공하고 직사광선으로부터 건물의 부분들을 지켜주어 건물을 더 시원하게 유지한다고 말하는 것이 자연스럽다. warmer → cooler

21 건축가들은 개방형 구조를 만드는 것 외에도 큰 정원을 더한다고 하였다.

## 서술형 실전문제
p.50~51

01 Many students just throw things away instead of recycling them.

02 He suggests reducing the number of trash cans at school.

03 He wants to place four different colored recycling bins on every floor.

04 (1) He was born in the year when the war ended.
(2) I know the reason why Jane didn't come here yet.
(3) This is the city where I lived 10 years ago.
(4) This is how he caught the big fish.

05 (1) for them to live　(2) for me to visit
(3) of her to kee

06 (1) for a baby to cry　(2) considerate of Jane to let
(3) of him to show

07 We can save paper or plastic.

08 It looks like a cup.

09 It's because Singapore is hot throughout the year.

10 It is providing people with a good quality of  life as well as helping protect the environment.

11 (1) air conditioning  (2) a lot of energy
(3) climate change  (4) an open structure
(5) cool  (6) gardens  (7) from direct sunlight

01 소년에 따르면 많은 학생들이 쓰레기를 재활용하는 대신에 그냥 버리는 것이 문제이다.

02 소년은 학교에 쓰레기통의 수를 줄일 것을 제안한다.

03 소년은 모든 층에 각기 색이 다른 4개의 재활용 통을 두기를 원한다.

04 (1) 선행사 'the year'에 맞는 관계부사 when을 이용하여 연결한다. (2) 선행사 'the reason'에 맞는 관계부사 why를 이용하여 연결한다. (3) 선행사 'the city'에 맞는 관계부사 where를 이용하여 연결한다. (4) 선행사가 'the way'이므로 how를 이용하여 연결한다.

05 to부정사의 의미상의 주어는 to부정사 바로 앞에 'for+목적격'으로 나타낸다. 이때 보어로 쓰인 형용사가 사람의 성향, 성격을 나타내는 말일 때는 'of+목적격'으로 쓴다.

06 'It(가주어) ~ for[of] ...(의미상의 주어) 진주어(to부정사)' 구문을 이용한다. to부정사의 의미상의 주어를 'for+목적격'으로 나타내지만, 보어로 쓰인 형용사가 사람의 성향, 성격을 나타내는 말일 때는 'of+목적격'을 쓴다.

07 쿠키 컵을 사용함으로써 우리는 종이나 플라스틱을 절약할 수 있다.

08 쿠키 컵은 컵처럼 생겼다고 하였다.

09 싱가포르에 있는 대부분의 건물들이 에어컨 가동이 필요한 이유는 싱가포르가 연중 더운 곳이기 때문이다.

10 친환경적인 건물들의 목표는 환경을 보호하는 것을 도울 뿐만 아니라 사람들에게 양질의 삶을 제공하는 것이라고 했다.

11 싱가포르에서 대부분의 건물들은 에어컨을 필요로 하며, 이로 인해 많은 에너지가 사용되고 기후 변화의 원인이 되고 있다. 개방형 구조 덕분에 외부 공기가 건물을 관통하여 건물을 시원하게 유지할 수 있다. 또한 큰 정원을 더하여 직사광선으로부터 건물의 부분들을 지켜주어 건물을 더 시원하게 유지한다.

### 창의사고력 서술형 문제　p.52

|모범답안|

01 (A) the 3rd floor  (B) taking the stairs
(C) take all the way up there
(D) that much energy
(E) take care of the environment

02 (1) It is dangerous for her to ride a bike.
(2) It's necessary for him to learn German.

(3) It is rude of him to talk loudly like that.

(4) It is difficult for her to take care of the children.

01 나는 오늘 반성을 했다. 나는 3층에 있는 과학실에 갈 때 엘리베이터를 타곤 했다. 내가 그곳에 가려고 했을 때, 지호는 계단으로 갈 것을 제안 했다. 사실 나는 그 모든 계단을 올라서 가고 싶진 않았다. 하지만 지호는 내가 계단으로 가야 한다고 설득했다. 나는 한 번 엘리베이터를 타는 것이 그렇게 많은 에너지를 사용하지 않는다고 생각했지만 지호는 내게 환경을 보호하기 위해 작은 것부터 시작해야 하는 것의 중요성을 상기 시켜주었다. 환경을 보호하기 위해 나는 작은 것들을 하며 에너지를 절약하기로 결심했다.

### 단원별 모의고사　p.53~57

01 ⑤　　　　02 (1) shade  (2) climate, temperatures

03 (1) a variety of  (2) break down  (3) contribute to
(4) would like to  (5) take the stairs

04 ④　　　05 ⑤　　　06 ④

07 (A) the number of trash cans  (B) every floor
(C) Separate

08 (C) → (D) → (A) → (E) → (B)

09 reduce our use of plastic bags, bring reusable bags

10 (1) We should protect the environment for future generations.
(2) A creative person is good at coming up with new ideas.
(3) China's underwater city attracts divers from all over the world.

11 ②　　　12 ②　　　13 ③

14 (1) the way how → the way 또는 how 또는 the way in which 또는 the way that
(2) which → where, 또는 which → at which, 또는 문장의 끝에 at 삽입
(3) of → for　　　(4) for → of

15 (1) for her to study English diligently every day
(2) of her to explain the process of making a newspaper

16 ①

17 (1) She sometimes thinks about the time when she was healthy.
(2) What was the name of the restaurant where we had pizza last week?
(3) It seems impossible for some people to live without their smartphones.
(4) It won't be easy for us to win the game tomorrow.

01 '새롭거나 더 나은 생각, 방법, 또는 장치'를 가리키는 말은 innovation(혁신)이다.

02 shade: 그늘, climate: 기후, temperature: 온도

03 contribute to: ~에 기여하다, a variety of: 다양한, break down: 고장나다, take the stairs: 계단을 오르다, would like to: ~하고 싶다

04 플라스틱 쓰레기를 줄이는 데 도움을 주므로 reduce 또는 decrease가 알맞다.

05 대화를 통해 Brian이 기대하고 있는 것이 무엇인지는 알 수 없다.

06 주어진 문장은 (D)에 이어지는 문장에서 This가 가리키는 내용이 되므로 (D)가 적절하다.

08 (C) 희망 사항 언급 → (D) 의견 표현 → (A) 반박 → (E) 조언 및 의견 제시 → (B) 수용 및 기대 표현

09 환경을 보호하기 위해 우리는 비닐봉지 사용을 줄일 필요가 있다. 예를 들어 우리가 물건을 사러 갈 때, 재사용할 수 있는 가방을 들고 가는 것이 한 가지 방법이 될 수 있다.

10 environment: 환경, creative: 창의적인, underwater: 수중의, 물속의

11 to부정사의 의미상의 주어로 보어로 쓰인 형용사가 사람의 성향, 성격을 나타내는 말일 때는 'of+목적격'으로 쓴다.

12 'the way how'는 쓸 수 없으므로 'the way'나 how만 쓰는 것이 적절하다.

13 첫 번째 빈칸에는 의미상의 주어로 for가 적절하고, 두 번째 빈칸에는 관계부사 how가 적절하다.

14 (1) 'the way how'는 쓸 수 없으므로 'the way'나 how만 쓰거나 'the way in which' 또는 'the way that' 등으로 고치는 것이 적절하다. (2) 관계사절이 완전하므로 which를 where로 고치거나 which 앞이나 문장의 끝에 at을 넣어주는 것이 적절하다. (3) to부정사의 의미상 주어는 to부정사 바로 앞에 'for+목적격'의 형태로 쓴다. (4) to부정사의 의미상의 주어로 보어로 쓰인 형용사가 사람의 성향, 성격을 나타내는 말일 때는 'of+목적격'으로 쓴다.

15 'It(가주어) ~ of ...(의미상의 주어) 진주어(to부정사)' 구문을 이용하며, to부정사의 의미상의 주어를 'for+목적격'으로 나타낸다. 이때 보어로 쓰인 형용사가 사람의 성향, 성격을 나타내는 말일 때는 'of+목적격'으로 쓴다.

16 <보기>와 ①의 when은 관계부사이다. ② 대명사 ③ 접속사 ④ 의문부사 ⑤ 접속사

17 (1)~(2) 선행사에 맞는 관계부사를 이용한다. (3)~(4) 'It(가주어) ~ for[of] ...(의미상의 주어) 진주어(to부정사)' 구문을 이용한다.

18 ④번에 이어지는 조각상들은 주어진 문장에 나오는 500개의 조각상들을 가리키는 것이다.

19 understand의 목적어로 간접의문문이 쓰인다. 따라서 '의문사+주어+동사' 어순임에 유의하자.

20 예술가들은 죽어가는 지역이 호전될 시간을 가질 수 있도록, 해양 생물이 죽어가는 지역으로부터 떨어진 해저에 수중 박물관을 만들었다.

21 위 글은 칸쿤의 환경을 보호하기 위한 창의적인 방법으로 해저 수중 박물관을 건설한 것에 관한 글이다. 따라서 ②번이 가장 적절하다.

22 싱가포르는 연중 더워서 대부분의 건물들은 기후 변화의 원인이 되는 에어컨 가동이 필요하고 (C) 그 결과 건축가들이 친환경적인 건물들을 디자인하기 시작함 (B) 친환경적인 건물들은 외부 공기가 건물을 관통하는 것을 가능케 함 (A) 이러한 자연적인 공기의 흐름이 건물을 시원하게 유지해 줌

23 관계대명사 that은 계속적 용법으로 쓰일 수 없다. that → which

24 각각 ① innovation ② eco-friendly ③ climate ④ architect를 풀이한 말이다. ⑤번은 tourist를 의미한다.

25 개방형 구조는 외부 공기가 건물을 관통하게 하는 것이다.

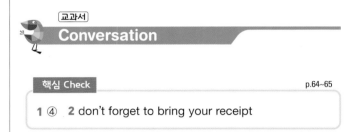

# Take Part in the Economy

## 시험대비 실력평가                                    p.62

01 unreliable          02 ①          03 ①
04 (1) policy   (2) product   (3) allowance
05 (1) looked after   (2) looked for
   (3) environmentally friendly   (4) asked for
   (5) less than
06 ④

01 주어진 관계는 반의어 관계를 나타낸다. reliable: 믿을 수 있는,
   unreliable: 믿을 수 없는
02 '장점이 부족한 상태나 조건'을 나타내는 말은 weakness(약점)
   이다.
03 reasonable: 합리적인
04 policy: 정책, product: 상품, allowance: 용돈
05 environmentally friendly: 친환경적인, look for: ~을 찾
   다, look after: ~을 돌보다, less than: ~보다 적은, ~ 미만의,
   ask for: ~을 요청하다
06 주어진 문장에서 fix는 '고치다'를 의미하며 이와 같은 의미로 쓰
   인 것은 ④번이다. 나머지는 '박다, 고정시키다'를 의미한다.

## 서술형 시험대비                                      p.63

01 negative
02 (1) for free   (2) focused on   (3) aware of
03 (1) fee   (2) weaknesses   (3) improve   (4) spend
   (5) discount
04 (1) He should register the birth of his son as soon
       as possible.
   (2) She doesn't want to open up about her
       weakness to anyone.
   (3) Wise consumers always try to save money.
05 (1) My sister prefers rock music to pop music.
   (2) The cashier gave the student a discount.
   (3) The salesperson didn't give me a refund.

01 주어진 관계는 반의어 관계를 나타낸다. positive: 긍정적인,
   negative: 부정적인
02 for free: 무료로, focus on: 초점을 맞추다. be aware of: ~
   을 알다, 알아차리다
03 weakness: 약점, spend: 쓰다, improve: 향상시키다,

discount: 할인, fee: 요금
04 register: 등록하다, weakness: 약점, consumer: 소비자
05 prefer A to B: A를 B보다 더 좋아하다, cashier: 계산원,
   discount: 할인, refund: 환불

## 교과서
## Conversation

### 핵심 Check                                         p.64~65

1 ④   2 don't forget to bring your receipt

## 교과서 대화문 익히기

### Check(√) True or False                             p.66

1 T   2 F   3 T   4 F

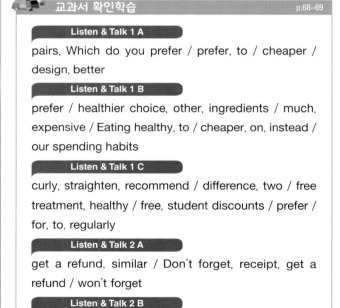

## 교과서 확인학습                                       p.68~69

**Listen & Talk 1 A**
pairs, Which do you prefer / prefer, to / cheaper /
design, better

**Listen & Talk 1 B**
prefer / healthier choice, other, ingredients / much,
expensive / Eating healthy, to / cheaper, on, instead /
our spending habits

**Listen & Talk 1 C**
curly, straighten, recommend / difference, two / free
treatment, healthy / free, student discounts / prefer /
for, to, regularly

**Listen & Talk 2 A**
get a refund, similar / Don't forget, receipt, get a
refund / won't forget

**Listen & Talk 2 B**
flea market / market research / Market research,
that / find, what items are popular / decide what to
sell / set reasonable / anything else / register, by /
reminding

**Listen & Talk 2 C**
review / How, review / focus on / to talk, bad points
/ balanced review / it easier for, to choose better
products / useful information

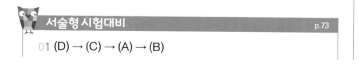

**Do It Yourself**

speakers / Which do you prefer / to, discount coupon / better sound quality

---

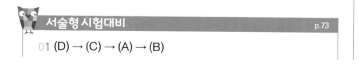
## 시험대비 기본평가　　　　　　　　　p.70

01 ①　　　　02 to　　　　03 the receipt　　04 ③

---

02 prefer A to B: B보다 A를 더 좋아하다 / be important to: ~에게 중요하다

03 영수증(receipt)을 가리킨다.

04 (A)는 clothes를 가리키는 ones, (B) forget to: ~할 것을 잊어버리다

---

## 시험대비 실력평가　　　　　　　　　p.71~72

01 (C) → (B) → (D) → (A) → (E)

02 ⓔ → to register　　　　03 ④

04 ⑤　　　　05 ③

06 She is asking him to remember to bring his receipt.

07 It's because he found he has similar ones.

08 It was because he didn't bring the receipt.

09 (A) straighten　(B) healthy　(C) for　　10 ⑤

---

01 (C) 두 군데 장소 추천 → (B) 두 장소의 차이점 질문 → (D) Styles Studio의 특징 설명 → (A) Hair Castle에 대한 특징 질문 → (E) Hair Castle의 특징 설명

02 forget to ~: ~할 것을 잊다

03 요즘 어떤 물건들이 인기 있는지는 대화를 통해 알 수 없다.

04 Sujin은 시장 조사 후에 벼룩시장에서 무엇을 판매할지 정할 수 있다고 생각한다.

05 (A)는 잊지 않을 것이라는 대답이므로 won't, (B) balanced: 균형 잡힌, (C) 선행사를 포함한 관계대명사 what이 적절하다.

06 엄마는 Jack에게 영수증을 가져갈 것을 기억하라고 요청하였다.

07 Jack은 비슷한 옷을 갖고 있는 것을 발견하여 환불하고 싶어 한다.

08 Jack은 영수증을 가져가지 않아 환불을 받지 못했다.

09 (A) straight: 곧은, straighten: 곧게 펴다, (B) keep+목적어+목적격보어 형태로 '건강한'을 의미하는 healthy, (C) for free: 무료로

10 Gina는 스타일 스튜디오를 선호한다.

---

## 서술형 시험대비　　　　　　　　　p.73

01 (D) → (C) → (A) → (B)

---

02 It's made with lots of fresh vegetables and other healthy ingredients.

03 It's because eating healthy is important to him.

04 It's because she'll spend her money on books instead.

05 register

06 (A) what items are popular
   (B) set reasonable prices

---

01 (D) 선호하는 신발 묻기 → (C) 선호하는 신발 대답 → (A) 이유 질문 → (B) 이유 대답

02 스페셜 샌드위치는 신선한 야채들과 다른 건강한 재료들로 만들어졌다.

03 Brian에게 건강하게 먹는 것이 중요하기 때문에 스페셜 샌드위치를 더 선호한다.

04 수지는 돈을 책을 사는 데 쓸 것이므로 더 저렴한 샌드위치를 더 좋아한다.

05 '당신의, 누군가의, 무언가의 이름을 공식적인 목록에 기록하다'를 의미하는 말은 register(등록하다)이다.

06 시장 조사를 통해, Tom과 수진은 무슨 물건이 요즘 인기 있는지를 알아낼 수 있다. 게다가 그들은 물건에 합리적인 가격을 정할 수 있다.

---

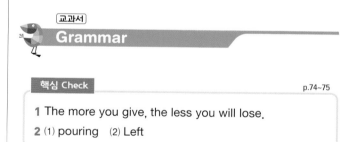
**교과서**
## Grammar

### 핵심 Check　　　　　　　　　　p.74~75

1 The more you give, the less you will lose.

2 (1) pouring　(2) Left

---

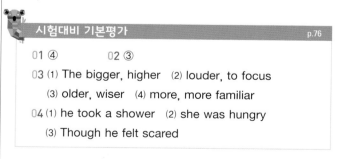
## 시험대비 기본평가　　　　　　　　　p.76

01 ④　　　　02 ③

03 (1) The bigger, higher　(2) louder, to focus
   (3) older, wiser　(4) more, more familiar

04 (1) he took a shower　(2) she was hungry
   (3) Though he felt scared

---

01 tired의 비교급은 more 또는 less를 앞에 붙인다. tired의 비교급으로 tireder도 있으나 잘 쓰지 않는다.

02 부사절을 분사구문으로 바꿀 때, 주어가 같으면 주어를 생략하고 분사를 쓴다. ④, ⑤는 수동태의 분사구문을 만들 때 사용한다.

03 'The+비교급 ~, the+비교급 …' 구문이다. 형용사 또는 부사

의 비교급에 대해 정확하게 공부해야 하며, big, high 등은 er 을 뒤에 쓰지만, familiar는 more/less를 앞에 쓰고, much나 many는 아예 more가 된다. (2)번 문장은 내용상 가주어-진주어 구문이므로 동사 focus를 to부정사로 변형하는 것에 유의한다.

04 분사구문은 분사를 활용하여 부사절을 부사구로 줄인 표현이다. 대개 양보, 동시동작, 이유, 시간, 조건 등의 부사절이며, 절과 구의 전환시 동사의 시제 등에 유의해야 한다. (3)은 내용상 양보이므로 Though 외에도 Although, Even though 등의 접속사가 가능하다.

시험대비 실력평가      p.77~79

| | | | |
|---|---|---|---|
| 01 ④ | 02 ④ | 03 ③ | 04 ③ |
| 05 ④ | 06 ④ | 07 ① | 08 ⑤ |
| 09 ④ | 10 ④ | 11 ④ | 12 ② |
| 13 ③ | | | |

14 The more often you use the sharing economy services, the less resources

15 The higher the price of some products gets, the more people want to buy them.

16 ④

01 'Sally가 추위를 느껴서, 옷을 더 입었다.'는 문장이다. 접속사와 주어를 생략하고, -ing형의 분사구문으로 만든다.

02 'The+비교급 ~, the+비교급 …' 구문이다. '당신이 더 열심히 일할수록 결과가 더 좋아질 것이다.'

03 'The+비교급 ~, the+비교급 …' 구문이다. '그녀의 병이 더 악화될수록, 더 많은 고통을 느낄 것이다.'

04 접속사가 있는 부사절로 영작하면, 'While she played[was playing] the piano,'가 된다. 종속절과 주절의 주어가 같으므로, 접속사와 주어를 생략하고, 동사를 분사로 만든 ③이 적절하다.

05 부사절로 영작하면, 'As he used[was using] the sharing economy apps,'이다. 종속절과 주절의 주어가 같으므로 접속사와 주어를 생략하고, 알맞은 분사형으로 바꾼 ④가 적절하다.

06 '우리가 여러 종류의 제품들을 덜 구매할수록, 우리는 더욱 많은 자원을 아낄 수 있다.'라는 내용이다. 사회와 환경에 도움이 되고, 금전적으로도 절약인데, 판매자에게는 반갑지 않다. ①, ②, ③, ⑤는 의미가 반대가 되는 셈이어서 어색하다.

07 '당신이 더 많은 제품을 대여할수록, 공유 경제는 더 활성화될 것이다.'라는 내용이다. ② become이 있으므로 부사 actively 를 형용사 active로 바꿔야 한다. 반대로 ③, ④는 do, work를 수식해야 하므로 actively가 더 적절하다. ⑤ active의 비교급은 more active

08 <보기>와 ⑤는 '이유'를 나타내는 분사구문이다. ① '양보' ②

'양보' ③ '조건' ④ '동시 동작, 부대상황'

09 <보기>와 ④는 '조건'을 나타내는 분사구문이다. ① '시간' ② '이유' ③ '이유' ⑤ '시간'

10 <보기>와 ④는 '양보' 의미의 분사구문이다. ① '조건' ② '이유' ③ '이유' ⑤ '이유'

11 부사절로 쓰면, 'As there were no seats available in the bus'가 된다. 주어가 다르므로, 유도부사 there는 생략할 수 없다. 'Being'을 'There being'으로 고쳐야 한다.

12 '보기'의 문장을 내용상 부사절을 이용해서 바꿔보면, 'As animals aren't allowed in my apartment'가 된다. 주절과 종속절의 주어가 다르므로, 독립분사구문을 써야 하고, 종속절 주어 Animals 뒤에 not (being) allowed를 쓰는 것이 적절하다.

13 <보기>는 '더 많은 사람들이 공유 경제 서비스를 이용함에 따라, 더 많이 개선될 것이다'라는 뜻이다. 'The+비교급 ~, the+비교급 …' 구문을 사용해서 정확하게 표현한 문장은 ③이다. '더 많은 사람들이 공유 경제 서비스를 이용할수록, 더 많이 개선될 것이다.' 나머지는 모두 어법상 옳지 않은 문장들이다.

14 'The+비교급 ~, the+비교급 …' 구문을 사용한 문장이다.

15 'The+비교급 ~, the+비교급 …' 구문을 사용한 문장이다. '더 많은 사람들'은 'the more people'로 나타낸다.

16 내용상 though의 역접관계가 아닌, and 또는 so와 같은 순접관계의 접속사가 적절하다. '공유경제가 빠르게 확장하여, 많은 자원들이 절약되도록 한다.'

서술형 시험대비      p.80~81

01 (1) The bigger money she makes, the more her family want.

(2) The more often we use the service, the faster we will promote the sharing economy.

(3) The harder she works, the brighter her future will be.

(4) The more closely we know the system, the stronger our trust in the sharing economy becomes.

(5) The more frequently the app is used, the greater the concern about the personal information gets.

02 (1) When he looked through the window of the restaurant,

(2) and it makes resources less used

(3) If you have trouble that you cannot talk to your loved ones,

(4) Because he did not want to disturb his daughter,

(5) While we use various kinds of apps,

(6) Though there are some weaknesses with the services,

03 The less trash we throw away, the cleaner

04 (1) Borrowing things that she doesn't often need

(2) Though having been built only two years ago

(3) Not having any tents, we borrowed one

(4) Though there being sharing economy service apps available

05 (1) The more, the wiser

(2) The farther, the healthier

(3) The older, the more

(4) The louder, the more confident

01 'The+비교급 ~, the+비교급 …' 구문 문장이다.

02 문제에 쓰인 분사구문은 다음과 같다. (1) 시간 '그가 식당 창문을 통해 봤을 때,' (2) 병렬 '그리고 그것은 자원들이 덜 사용되도록 한다.' (3) 조건 '만약 당신이 사랑하는 사람들에게 말할 수 없는 어려움이 있다면,' (4) 이유 '자신의 딸을 방해하고 싶지 않았기 때문에,' (5) 동시 동작 '우리가 다양한 종류의 앱을 사용하여,' (6) 양보 '비록 그 서비스에는 몇 가지 단점들이 있지만,'

03 'The+비교급 ~, the+비교급 …' 구문이다. less에 유의한다.

04 (1) 'Because she borrows things that she doesn't often need,'의 부사절을 분사구문으로 만들었다. (2) 주절보다 종속절 시제가 앞서고, 수동태이므로 완료분사구문의 수동형인 'Having been p.p.'를 활용한다. 접속사의 의미를 명확히 하기 위해 분사구문 앞에 접속사를 쓸 수 있으며, 여기서는 though를 문두에 사용했다. *leak: 물이 새다 (3) 분사구문의 부정은 분사 앞에 not이나 never를 쓴다. 'As we didn't have any tents,'의 부사절을 분사구문으로 만들었다. (4) 주절과 종속절의 주어가 다른 독립분사구문 중에서 유도부사 there가 이끄는 부사절은 분사구문으로 전환할 때에도 there를 분사 앞에 쓴다. 원래의 부사절은 'Though there are sharing economy service apps available,'이다.

05 (1) 그 학생들이 더 많은 책을 읽을수록, 그들은 더 지혜로워질 것이다. (2) 그 할머니가 매일 더 멀리 걸을수록, 그녀는 더욱 건강해질 것이다. (3) 그 소녀가 나이를 먹을수록, 그녀의 할머니와 더 닮았다. (4) 그 소년이 더욱 크게 말하기를 연습할수록 더 많은 자신감을 느낀다.

## 교과서 Reading

확인문제 p.82

1 T  2 F  3 T  4 F  5 T  6 F

확인문제 p.83

1 T  2 F  3 T  4 F  5 F

확인문제 p.84

1 T  2 F  3 T  4 F  5 T

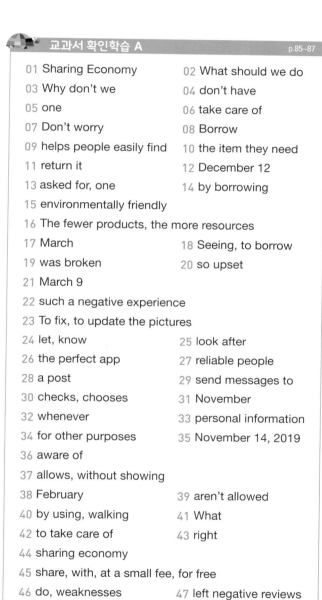

## 교과서 확인학습 A
p.85~87

01 Sharing Economy
02 What should we do
03 Why don't we
04 don't have
05 one
06 take care of
07 Don't worry
08 Borrow
09 helps people easily find
10 the item they need
11 return it
12 December 12
13 asked for, one
14 by borrowing
15 environmentally friendly
16 The fewer products, the more resources
17 March
18 Seeing, to borrow
19 was broken
20 so upset
21 March 9
22 such a negative experience
23 To fix, to update the pictures
24 let, know
25 look after
26 the perfect app
27 reliable people
28 a post
29 send messages to
30 checks, chooses
31 November
32 whenever
33 personal information
34 for other purposes
35 November 14, 2019
36 aware of
37 allows, without showing
38 February
39 aren't allowed
40 by using, walking
41 What
42 to take care of
43 right
44 sharing economy
45 share, with, at a small fee, for free
46 do, weaknesses
47 left negative reviews
48 the more, the services

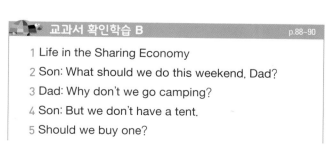

## 교과서 확인학습 B
p.88~90

1 Life in the Sharing Economy
2 Son: What should we do this weekend, Dad?
3 Dad: Why don't we go camping?
4 Son: But we don't have a tent.
5 Should we buy one?

6 Also, who will take care of our dog?

7 Dad: Don't worry. I know some apps that can help us.

8 Borrow from your neighbors!

9 Ask Your Neighbors helps people easily find items that they can borrow from others.

10 First, users download the app and search for another user that has the item they need.

11 Then they pick up the item and return it later.

12 Jasmine: December 12, 2019

13 I asked for a board game and got one in less than 30 minutes.

14 I love saving money by borrowing things that I don't often need.

15 Also, I think it's environmentally friendly.

16 The fewer products we buy, the more resources we save.

17 Cassandra: March 7, 2020

18 Seeing a lot of positive reviews, I decided to borrow a bike helmet.

19 When I got it, however, it was broken.

20 I was so upset!

21 Ask Your Neighbors: March 9, 2020

22 We're sorry that you had such a negative experience.

23 To fix this issue, we are asking lenders to update the pictures of their items regularly.

24 This will let other users know the exact condition of the product.

25 I can look after your pet!

26 Pet Sitter Finder is the perfect app for pet lovers and pet owners.

27 It helps pet owners find reliable people to look after their pets.

28 When a pet owner is looking for pet sitters, he or she uploads a post.

29 Pet sitters or dog walkers can then send messages to the owner.

30 The owner checks their reviews and chooses the best person.

31 George: November 12, 2019

32 I use this app whenever I'm going out of town.

33 I have some concerns about my personal information though.

34 What if people use my phone number for other purposes?

35 Pet Sitter Finder: November 14, 2019

36 We're aware of this issue.

37 We're now developing a system that allows users to communicate freely without showing their personal information.

38 Samantha: February 22, 2020

39 Animals aren't allowed in my apartment, so I don't have any pets.

40 However, by using Pet Sitter Finder, I can experience the joy of walking a dog.

41 Son: What great apps!

42 We can borrow a tent and find someone to take care of our dog.

43 Dad: That's right.

44 These kinds of services are part of the "sharing economy.

45 People can share their items with others and provide services to them at a small fee or for free.

46 Son: But these services do have some weaknesses.

47 Some people left negative reviews about the services.

48 Dad: Well, I think the more people use the services, the more they will improve.

### 시험대비 실력평가

| | | | |
|---|---|---|---|
| 01 ③ | 02 a tent | 03 ④ | 04 ② |
| 05 (A) positive reviews | (B) condition | | |
| 06 download → update | | 07 ② | 08 ② |
| 09 a board game | | 10 chooses | |
| 11 ②, ⑤ | | 12 (A) reviews | (B) send messages |
| 13 ② | 14 ①, ④ | 15 ④ | |
| 16 ①, ③, ④ | 17 ② | 18 ③ | 19 ⑤ |
| 20 ② | 21 ③ | 22 sharing | 23 ③ |
| 24 ④ | 25 ④ | | |
| 26 such a negative experience | | 27 ① | |

01 ③은 '캠핑을 가라, 알겠니?'(명령문의 부가의문문), 나머지는 모두 '~하는 게 어때?'

02 '텐트'를 가리킨다.

03 아빠가 "걱정하지 마. 내가 우리를 도와줄 수 있는 몇 개의 앱들을 알고 있지."라고 말했기 때문에, 뒤에 올 내용으로는 '아들의 걱정을 해결하기 위한 몇 개의 앱들에 대한 소개'가 적절하다.

04 자전거 헬멧을 얻었을 때, 그것은 망가져 있었으므로, 몹시 '기분이 상했다'고 하는 것이 적절하다. upset: 속상한, ① excited: 흥분한, ③ 초조한, ④ 기쁜, ⑤ 부끄러운

05 사용자들이 많은 '긍정적인 후기들'을 보고 나서 빌리기로 결심한 물건을 얻었을 때, 물건의 '상태'가 좋지 않다는 것을 발견하

게 된다.

06 Ask your Neighbors는 빌려주는 사람들에게 그들의 물건 사진을 정기적으로 '업데이트'해 줄 것을 요구하고 있다고 해야 하므로, download를 update로 고치는 것이 적절하다. download: (데이터를) 다운로드하다[내려받다]

07 이 글의 첫 단락은 '앱을 사용하여 다른 사람들로부터 빌릴 수 있는 물건을 쉽게 찾고 그 물건을 받은 다음 나중에 반납하는 것'에 관한 글이므로, 제목으로는 ②번 '당신의 이웃들로부터 빌려라!'가 적절하다.

08 주어진 문장의 Then에 주목한다. ②번 앞 문장의 내용을 하고 난 다음을 가리키므로 ②번이 적절하다.

09 '보드게임'을 가리킨다.

10 동사 checks와 병렬구문을 이루도록 'chooses'로 쓰는 것이 적절하다.

11 look after = care for = take care of: ~을 보살피다[돌보다], ① ~을 알아차리다, 주의하다, ③ ~을 이용하다, ④ ~을 닮다

12 반려동물 주인이 게시물을 올리고 나서 그나 그녀에게 '메시지를 보낸' 반려동물을 돌보는 사람들이나 개를 산책시키는 사람들에 대한 '후기들'을 확인한다. 그러면 반려동물 주인은 그들 중에서 최고의 사람을 선택할 수 있다.

13 동물들이 아파트에 허락되지 않아서, 반려동물을 키울 수 없지만, Pet Sitter Finder를 이용하면서, '강아지를 산책시키는' 즐거움을 경험할 수 있다고 하는 것이 적절하다.

14 (A)와 ②, ③, ⑤: 동명사, ①, ④: 현재분사

15 ⓐ search for: ~를 찾다, ⓑ in: (시간의 경과를 나타내어) ~ 후에[~ 만에/~ 있으면]

16 ⓒ와 ①, ③, ④: 동명사, ②, ⑤: 현재분사

17 ② 우선, 사용자들은 그 앱을 내려받고 '그들이 필요한 물건을 가지고 있는' 또 다른 사용자를 찾을 필요가 있다.

18 앞에 나오는 내용과 상반되는 내용이 뒤에 이어지므로 However가 가장 적절하다. ① 다시 말해서, ② 게다가, 더욱이, ④ 똑같이, 비슷하게, ⑤ 그 결과

19 저희는 이 문제를 알고 있다고 한 다음에 사용자들이 자신의 개인 정보를 보여주지 않으면서 자유롭게 소통할 수 있는 시스템을 개발하는 중이라고 했으므로, 앞에 올 내용으로는 '개인 정보가 알려지는 문제'가 나왔을 것이라고 하는 것이 적절하다.

20 ⓐ와 ②: (문장 끝에 와서) 그렇지만[하지만](부사), ①, ③, ④, ⑤: ~이지만, ~에도 불구하고(접속사)

21 '반려동물 주인이 자신의 반려동물을 돌봐줄 신뢰할 만한 사람을 찾는 데 얼마나 오래 걸리는지'는 대답할 수 없다. ① It is the perfect app for pet lovers and pet owners. ② They send messages to the owner when he or she uploads a post. ④ He uses it whenever he's going out of town. ⑤ He has some concerns about his personal information.

22 앱들을 통해 텐트를 빌리고 개를 돌볼 누군가를 찾는 서비스는 '공유 경제'의 일부이다. sharing economy: 공유 경제

23 이 글은 '앱들을 사용하여 사람들은 자신의 물건을 다른 사람들과 공유할 수 있고 적은 비용이나 무료로 그들에게 서비스를 제공할 수 있지만, 이런 서비스들은 몇 가지 단점들을 가지고 있다'는 내용의 글이므로, 주제로는 ③번 '공유 경제의 혜택과 약점'이 적절하다. benefits: 혜택, weaknesses: 단점

24 ④ (C)의 It이 주어진 글의 Pet Sitter Finder를 가리키므로 제일 먼저 오고 (B)의 their가 (A)의 Pet sitters or dog walkers를 가리키므로 (A) 다음에 (B)가 와야 한다. 그러므로 (C)-(A)-(B)의 순서가 적절하다.

25 전반부의 'Seeing a lot of positive reviews, I decided to borrow a bike helmet.'을 통해 'expectant'를, 후반부의 'I was so upset!'을 통해 'disappointed'를 찾을 수 있다. expectant: (특히 좋거나 신나는 일을) 기대하는, disappointed: 실망한, ① bored: 지루한, ② puzzled: 어리둥절해하는, upset: 속상한, ③ amazed: 놀란, ⑤ nervous: 초조한, satisfied: 만족한

26 'such+a+형용사+명사'의 순서로 쓰는 것이 적절하다.

23 ⓑ와 ①: 바로잡다, 고치다, ②, ④: (움직이지 않게) 고정시키다[박다], ③ 결정하다, ⑤ <시선·주의 등을> (~에) 집중시키다, 모으다

01 camping

02 (1) 그들은 텐트가 없으므로 텐트를 하나를 사야 하는 것일까?
   (2) 개는 누가 돌봐줄 것인가?

03 free of charge 또는 for nothing 또는 at no cost

04 the more people use the services, the more they will improve

05 (A) positive  (B) lenders  (C) users

06 빌려주는 사람들이 그들의 물건 사진을 정기적으로 업데이트하는 것

07 (A) Cassandra  (B) negative

08 I saw  09 (A) the pictures  (B) lenders

10 개인 정보에 대한 몇 가지 걱정이 있을 수 있다는 문제 또는 다른 사람들이 앱 사용자의 전화번호를 다른 목적으로 사용할 수도 있다는 문제

11 communicate

12 (A) pets  (B) by using Pet Sitter Finder

01 go ~ing: ~하러 가다

02 'Why don't we go camping?'이라는 아빠의 물음에 대한 아들의 대답을 쓰는 것이 적절하다.

03 for free = free of charge = for nothing = at no cost: 무

료로

04 the+비교급 …, the+비교급 ~: …하면 할수록 더 ~하다

05 (A) 많은 '긍정적인' 후기들을 보고 나서 빌리기로 결심했고 해야 하므로 positive가 적절하다. positive: 긍정적인, negative: 부정적인, (B) '빌려주는 사람들'에게 그들의 물건 사진을 정기적으로 업데이트해 줄 것을 요구한다고 해야 하므로 lenders가 적절하다. lenders: 빌려주는 사람들, users: 사용자들, (C) 다른 '사용자들'에게 그 제품의 정확한 상태를 알 수 있도록 해준다고 해야 하므로 users가 적절하다.

06 앞 문장에서 Ask Your Neighbors가 빌려주는 사람들에게 요구하는 내용을 가리킨다.

07 Ask Your Neighbors는 'Cassandra'에게 매우 '부정적인' 경험을 준 것에 대해 사과한다. apologize to A for B: B에 대해 A에게 사과하다, Cassandra에게 사과하는 것보다 부정적인 경험을 준 것이 더 먼저 일어난 일이므로, for having given으로 쓰는 것이 적절하다.

08 Seeing은 시간을 나타내는 분사구문으로, '~한 후에'라는 의미로 해석한다.

09 '빌려주는 사람들'에 의해 물건 '사진'이 정기적으로 업데이트된다면, 다른 사용자들은 그 제품의 정확한 상태를 알 수 있을 것이다.

10 George가 말한 'I have some concerns about my personal information.' 또는 'What if people use my phone number for other purposes?'을 가리킨다.

11 allow+목적어+to부정사 = let+목적어+원형부정사

12 Samantha는 '반려동물'을 키울 수 없지만 'Pet Sitter Finder를 이용하면서' 개를 산책시키는 즐거움을 경험할 수 있다.

### 영역별 핵심문제
p.99~103

01 upload 02 ⑤ 03 ① 04 ⑤
05 (B) → (C) → (A)
06 Styles Studio provides free treatment to keep their hair healthy.
07 Students can get discounts.
08 She likes it more because it's important for her to get hair treatment regularly.
09 don't forget to talk about their bad points too
10 ⑤    11 (D) → (B) → (E) → (C) → (A)
12 ④    13 ④    14 ⑤    15 ⑤
16 ④    17 ③    18 ④    19 ④
20 another user that has the item they need
21 fewer products, more resources
22 ④    23 to know → know 또는 let → allow
24 ②    25 ③    26 ④    27 ⑤
28 a week → up to two days

01 주어진 관계는 반의어 관계를 나타낸다. download: 다운로드하다, upload: 업로드하다

02 '누군가가 필요로 하거나 원하는 무언가를 주거나 이용할 수 있게 하다'를 가리키는 말은 provide(제공하다)이다.

03 wherever: 어디든지

04 on sale: 할인 중인, out of town: 도시를 떠나, 다른 곳으로 떠나, search for: ~를 찾다

05 (B) 계획 설명 → (C) 영수증 지참을 상기시키기 → (A) 대답 및 반응

06 Styles Studio는 손님들에게 머리카락을 건강하게 유지해주는 트리트먼트를 무료로 제공해 준다.

07 학생들이 Hair Castle로부터 할인을 받을 수 있다.

08 Gina는 헤어 트리트먼트를 정기적으로 받는 게 중요하기 때문에 Styles Studio를 더 좋아한다.

10 Jane은 상품에 대해 더 유용한 정보를 사람들에게 주고 싶어 한다.

11 (D) 선호하는 샌드위치 선택 및 이유 설명 → (B) 상대방이 선택한 샌드위치의 비싼 가격을 설명 → (E) 비싸지만 선택한 이유 설명 → (C) 가격과 관련하여 선호하는 샌드위치 선택 및 이유 설명 → (A) 소비 습관이 다르다는 것을 설명

12 '인터넷으로 수많은 부정적인 후기들을 보고서, 그 연구원은 그 제품들을 사지 않기로 결심했다.'라는 문장이다. '이유' 의미의 접속사 As를 이용하는 부사절이 적절하다.

13 There가 있는 '독립분사구문'이다. 해석을 하면 '그녀의 친구들이 만든 Pet Sitter Finder앱이 있음에도, 그녀는 그 서비스를 이용하지 않았다.'라는 문장으로, '양보'의 부사절이다. '양보'의 접속사 Even though가 쓰인 문장이 적절하다.

14 ⑤ '더 높이 올라갈수록, 당신은 숨 쉬는 것이 더 어려워진다.'는 문장이다. 'the more it is difficult'가 아니라, 'the more difficult it is'의 어순이 적절하다.

15 분사구문의 부정은 분사 앞에 not을 쓴다. 접속사를 앞에 쓸 경우, 접속사 뒤에 주어를 쓰면, 분사구문이 아니라 절을 만들어야 한다.

16 ① the more faster → the faster ② More → The more, more → the more ③ do → are 또는 will be ⑤ the more they will be careful → the more careful they will be

17 분사구문의 능동과 수동을 구분하는 문제이다. ① '감기에 걸리다'를 수동으로 착각하지 않도록 유의한다. Caught → Catching ② Turned → Turning ④ Interesting → Interested ⑤ Educating → Educated

18 'Anne과 시간을 보낼 때마다, 그는 전보다 더 좋게 느낀다.'라는 문장은 'Anne과 더 많은 시간을 보낼수록, 그는 더 행복해진다.'와 가장 유사하며, 'The+비교급, the+비교급' 구문을 통해 표현된다. ①, ②, ③은 그가 아닌 다른 주어가 행복을 느끼는 것이며, ⑤는 does가 어법상 부적절하다.

19 Ask Your Neighbors는 사람들이 다른 사람들로부터 '빌릴

수 있는' 물건을 쉽게 찾도록 돕는다.

**20** 주격 관계대명사 that을 사용하고, 목적격 관계대명사는 생략하여 8 단어로 영작하는 것이 적절하다.

**21** 'the+비교급 …, the+비교급 ~' 구문을 접속사 As를 사용하여 고칠 때는, 비교급 앞의 the를 생략한 다음에 As 뒤로 적절한 자리를 찾아 옮겨 쓰는 것이 적절하다. the+비교급 …, the+비교급 ~: …하면 할수록, 더 ~하다

**22** ④번 다음 문장의 This에 주목한다. 주어진 문장에서 'Ask Your Neighbors가 빌려주는 사람들에게 요구하는 내용'을 받고 있으므로 ④번이 적절하다.

**23** let+목적어+원형부사, allow+목적어+to부정사

**24** 이 글은 '사용자들이 쓴 많은 긍정적인 후기들을 보고 나서 물건을 빌리기로 결심했는데, 상태가 좋지 않은 물건을 얻게 되어 기분이 상하게 되는 문제를 해결하기 위한 Ask Your Neighbors의 해결책'에 관한 글이므로, 주제로는 ②번 '앱을 사용하여 물건을 빌릴 때의 문제점과 해결책'이 적절하다. ③ unreliable: 믿을[신뢰할] 수 없는

**25** ⓐ와 ③: 강조의 조동사, ① 의문문의 조동사, ② (어떤 동작이나 행위를) 하다(본동사), ④ 부정문의 조동사, ⑤ 대동사(문장의 동사를 반복하지 않기 위해 그 대신에 씀.)

**26** 이런 종류의 서비스들은 '몇 가지 약점들을 가지고 있다.

**27** 위 글은 '안내문'이다. notice: (보통 공공장소에 붙이는) 공고문[안내문], ① 수필, ② (신문·잡지의) 글, 기사, ③ (특히 기계 등을 사면 따라 나오는) 설명서, ④ (책·연극·영화 등에 대한) 논평[비평], 감상문

**28** 사용자들은 '이틀까지' 줄넘기를 빌릴 수 있다.

---

### 단원별 예상문제                               p.104~107

01 ②          02 ②

03 (1) The coat was on sale last week.

   (2) She took care of her friend's pet during
       vacation.

   (3) These pancakes were made with organic eggs.

04 ③          05 ④          06 ②, ③

07 (A) Hair Castle   (B) student discounts

08 (A) cheaper   (B) design          09 ⓒ → to

10 ⑤        11 ④        12 ①        13 ⑤

14 ②

15 (1) Wanting to protect the environment we live in

   (2) Though not knowing what the students wanted

16 the item

17 The less products → The fewer products /
   the less resources → the more resources

18 (1) **사용자들은 Ask Your Neighbors 앱을 내려받고
       그들이 필요한 물건을 가지고 있는 또 다른 사용자를
       찾는다.**

---

(2) **그러고 나서 그들은 그 물건을 받아서 나중에
       반납한다.**

19 ③          20 ②          21 ③

---

**01** '한 나라나 지역의 화폐, 산업 및 무역이 구조화되는 체계'는 economy(경제)이다.

**02** 주어진 문장에서 condition은 '상태'를 의미하며 이와 같은 의미로 쓰인 것은 ②번이다. 나머지는 모두 '조건'을 뜻한다.

**03** on sale: 할인 중인, take care of: 돌보다, be made with: ~로 만들어지다 organic: 유기 비료의

**06** A와 B 두 가지 중에서 어떤 것을 선호하는지 물을 때 'Which (one) do you prefer?'로 표현한다. 같은 표현으로 'Which (one) do you like better[more]?를 쓸 수 있다.

**09** prefer A to B: B보다 A를 더 선호하다

**10** 소녀가 신발을 구매하겠다는 내용은 없다.

**11** 종속절이 주절보다 앞선 시제이므로, 완료분사구문이 필요하다. 준동사의 부정은 not을 앞에 쓴다.

**12** 부사절과 종속절의 주어가 같으므로, 접속사와 주어를 생략하고 동사를 현재분사로 바꾼다. ②, ③, ④ 접속사와 주어를 쓰면 분사구문을 만들 수 없다. ⑤ 능동/수동도 맞지 않고, 독립분사구문으로 표현하려면 the sharing economy가 문두로 와야 한다.

**13** The+비교급 ~, the+비교급 …' 구문과 특수한 경우를 제외하고는 비교급 앞에 the를 쓰지 않는다. 접속사 As와 When이 있는 ①, ② 문장에서 the 비교급은 맞지 않고, ④는 어법상 불가능한 구조이다. ③ less 앞에 more가 부적절하다.

**14** 'The+비교급 ~, the+비교급 …' 구문이다. 형용사 hot은 ①과 ④처럼 more hotter 또는 more hot으로 비교급을 쓰지 않는다. ③은 are needed가 틀렸다, ⑤는 내용상 better보다 more를 쓰는 것이 적절하다.

**15** 주어진 어휘에 접속사들이 없으므로, 분사구문을 배열하는 문제이다. 각각 (1) '이유', (2) '양보'의 부사절을 분사구문으로 만든 것이다.

**16** '그 물건'을 가리킨다.

**17** 우리가 제품들을 더 '적게' 구매할수록, 우리는 '더 많은' 자원들을 아끼는 것이다. products는 셀 수 있는 명사이기 때문에 fewer로 고치고, 더 많은 자원들을 아끼는 것이라고 해야 하므로 the more resources로 고치는 것이 적절하다.

**18** 첫 번째 단락의 First, 다음 부분을 쓰는 것이 적절하다.

**19** 이 글의 첫 단락은 '반려동물을 좋아하는 사람들과 반려동물 주인들을 위한 완벽한 앱인 Pet Sitter Finder를 통해 반려동물 주인들이 그들의 반려동물을 돌보는 데 신뢰할 만한 사람들을 찾는 것'에 관한 글이므로, 제목으로는 ③번 '제가 당신의 반려동물을 돌볼 수 있어요!'가 적절하다.

**20** whenever = every time: ~할 때는 언제든지, ① ~하는 동안, ③ 곧, ④ ~하는 바로 그 순간[~하자마자], ⑤ ~하자마자

**21** 반려동물 주인은 반려동물을 돌보는 사람들이나 개를 산책시키는 사람들의 '후기들을 확인하고' 최고의 사람을 선택한다.

01 He wants to do some market research.

02 She should remember to register their names by this Friday.

03 It is going to be held next month.

04 (1) older, wiser    (2) smaller, shorter

     (3) sooner, better    (4) harder, better

     (5) fewer, happier

05 (1) Not having a car,    (2) Frankly speaking,

     (3) It having snowed the day before,

     (4) Being a little tired,

     (5) Finding the purse Jenny had lost,

06 pet sitters or dog walkers

07 What if people use my phone number for other purposes?

08 (A) look after their pets    (B) personal information

09 (A) find    (B) download    (C) save

10 (A) borrow    (B) app

01 Tom은 요즘 인기 있는 물품을 알아내기 위해 시장 조사를 하고 싶어 한다.

02 수진은 이번 주 금요일까지 그들의 이름을 등록하는 것을 기억해야 한다.

03 벼룩시장은 다음 달에 열릴 것이다.

04 (1) 그 청년은 나이를 먹을수록, 더 지혜로워졌다. (2) 동영상의 크기가 더 작을수록, 게시하는 데 더 짧게 걸릴 것이다. (3) 그녀가 최종 보고서를 일찍 마무리할수록, 협상에서 더 유리한 위치를 차지할 수 있다. (4) 더 열심히 공부할수록, 당신은 더 좋은 성적을 받을 것이다. (5) 중간고사 직후에 수업이 더 적을수록, 학생들은 더 행복하게 느낀다.

05 (1) 분사구문의 부정은 Not을 분사 앞에 쓴다. (2) 비인칭 독립분사구문이므로, We를 쓸 필요가 없다. (3) 원래의 부사절에서 비인칭주어 it이 있으므로, 'It having snowed'와 같이 독립분사구문 형태로 표현하는 것이 적절하다. (4) 내용상 부사 a little은 tired를 수식하기 때문에, 분사 being 앞에 쓰지 않는다. (5) 능동이므로 Found → Finding이 적절하다.

06 '반려동물을 돌보는 사람들이나 개를 산책시키는 사람들'을 가리킨다.

07 'if'를 보충하면 된다. What if ~?: ~라면 어쩌지?

08 'Pet Sitter Finder'라는 앱의 장점은 그것이 반려동물 주인들이 '그들의 반려동물을 돌보는 데' 신뢰할 만한 사람들을 찾도록 돕는다는 것이고, 단점은 '개인 정보'에 대한 몇 가지 걱정이 있다는 것이다. advantage: 장점, disadvantage: 단점

09 (A) 'help+목적어+원형부정사'이므로 find가 적절하다. (B) 사용자들은 그 앱을 '내려받고' 그들이 필요한 물건을 가지고 있는 또 다른 사용자를 찾는다고 해야 하므로 download가 적절하다. download: (데이터를) 다운로드하다[내려받다],

upload: 업로드하다(더 큰 컴퓨터 시스템으로 데이터를 보내는 것), (C) 우리가 제품들을 더 적게 구매할수록, 우리는 더 많은 자원들을 '아끼는 것'이라고 해야 하므로 save가 적절하다. waste: 낭비하다

10 Ask Your Neighbors라는 '앱' 덕분에 사람들은 그들이 다른 사람들로부터 '빌릴 수' 있는 것을 쉽게 찾을 수 있다.

|모범답안|

01 (A) the Special Sandwich

     (B) the Classic Sandwich    (C) eating healthy

     (D) cheaper    (E) books    (F) spending

02 (1) The more she sees, the more she wants.

     (2) The less the baby eats, the more worried her mom becomes.

     (3) The slower the student answers, the angrier his teacher gets.

02 표의 단어들을 적절히 조합하여 어법에 맞게 영작한 답이면 된다.

01 (1) download    (2) natural resources

     (3) negative reviews    (4) exact meaning

02 (1) owner    (2) reliable    (3) concerns    (4) personal

     (5) provide

03 (1) What if it rains tomorrow?

     (2) I'll search for the recipe on the Internet.

     (3) How can we send messages to other children?

04 ①       05 ③       06 ①, ③       07 ⑤

08 ingredient             09 ②       10 ⑤

11 ④, ⑤       12 ②       13 ①       14 ②

15 ③

16 (1) The more people understand the sharing economy, the fewer resources will be used on Earth.

     (2) The more it rained, the more pleased she felt.

     (3) The more popular the singer becomes, the more crowded the concert will be.

17 borrowing things that I don't often need

18 The fewer products we buy, the more resources we save.

19 ④       20 ③       21 upload       22 ④

23 Because animals aren't allowed in her apartment.

24 ⑤       25 ⑤       26 ③

27 more, more        28 ④        29 to

30 (1) 일주일에 한 번 빌릴 수 있다.

(2) 잃어버리거나 망가뜨리면 물건 값을 지불해야 한다.

01 resource: 자원, review: 비평, 서평, negative: 부정적인, exact: 정확한

02 personal: 개인적인, provide: 제공하다, owner: 주인, reliable: 믿을 수 있는, concern: 근심

03 What if ~?: ~하면 어쩌지?, ~라면 어떻게 될까?, search for ~: ~를 찾다, send messages to ~: ~에게 메시지를 보내다

04 이어지는 대화에서 추천하는 장소를 설명하고 있는 (A)가 적절하다.

05 위 대화에서 Judy가 선호하는 곳은 알 수 없다.

06 be sure to: 확실히 ~하다

07 Jack은 영수증을 갖고 가는 것을 잊지 않을 것이다.

08 '무언가를 구성하는 것들 중 하나로 특히 특정한 요리를 만들기 위해 함께 사용하는 음식의 하나'를 가리키는 말은 ingredient(재료)이다.

09 (A) prefer A to B: B보다 A를 선호하다, (B) 주어 역할을 하는 동명사 Eating, (C) 주어가 habits이므로 are가 적절하다.

10 위 대화를 통해 건강하게 먹는 것이 Brain에게 왜 중요한지 알 수 없다.

11 ④ '논문을 제시간에 제출하기 위해 열심히 일해서 곯아 떨어졌다.'는 내용이므로, 능동의 분사구문이 되어야 한다. 'Worked → Working' ⑤ 'look'이 자동사로 쓰였으므로 수동태로 쓸 수 없다. 'Being looked → Looking'

12 주절과 종속절의 주어가 같으므로, 보통 분사구문을 만들면 되는데, 종속절에 명확히 주어의 정체성이 나타나 있으므로, 주절의 he or she 대신 종속절의 a pet owner를 주절에 쓰는 것이 적절하다.

13 '땅속으로 더 깊이 들어갈수록, 온도가 더 뜨거워진다.'라는 문장이다. '조건'을 나타내는 부사절로 바꿀 수 있다. ① '당신이 계속 땅 속으로 들어간다면, 온도가 더 뜨거워진다.'

14 '날씨가 너무 추웠다.'는 내용과, '해변에 수영과 놀이를 하러 나가지 못했다.'는 내용은 '양보'가 아니라 '이유'로 표현하는 것이 맞다. Although → Because 또는 As/Since

15 ①, ④는 주절과 종속절의 주어가 다르므로, 분사구문의 주어를 쓰는 것이 좋다. '독립분사구문' ① Eating → Samantha eating ④ Putting → We putting ②, ⑤는 주절과 종속절의 주어가 같기 때문에, 반대로 주어를 생략해야 한다. ④ Putting → We putting, ⑤ You borrowing → Borrowing

16 (1) many, few의 비교급과 수동태 표현 등에 유의한다. (2) please를 more pleased로 활용하는 것에 유의한다. (3) crowd를 crowded로 활용하는 것에 유의한다.

17 '제가 자주 필요하지 않은 것들을 빌리는 것'을 가리킨다.

18 the+비교급 …, the+비교급 ~: …하면 할수록, 더 ~하다

19 앞에 나오는 내용과 상반되는 내용이 뒤에 이어지므로 however가 가장 적절하다. ② 그러므로, ③ 즉[말하자면], ⑤ 게다가, 더욱이

20 ⓑ와 ②, ③, ⑤: 부사적 용법, ①: 형용사적 용법, ④: 명사적 용법

21 당신의 컴퓨터로 자료를 옮기거나 또는 당신의 컴퓨터로부터 다른 컴퓨터로 자료를 옮기다, upload: 올리다, 업로드하다

22 ④번 다음 문장의 their에 주목한다. 주어진 문장의 Pet sitters or dog walkers를 받고 있으므로 ④번이 적절하다.

23 동물들이 그녀의 아파트에서는 허락되지 않기 때문이다.

24 Samantha는 Pet Sitter Finder를 이용하면서 '개를 산책시키는 즐거움을 경험할 수 있다.'

25 ⓐ share A with B: A를 B와 공유하다, ⓑ at: [수량·값] ~으로, ~에

26 ③번 다음 문장의 Some people left negative reviews ~.에 주목한다. 주어진 문장의 some weaknesses에 해당하는 것이므로 ③번이 적절하다.

27 'the+비교급 …, the+비교급 ~' 구문을 접속사 as를 사용하여 고칠 때는, 비교급 앞의 the를 생략한 다음에 as 뒤의 적절한 자리를 찾아 옮겨 쓰는 것이 적절하다. the+비교급 …, the+비교급 ~: …하면 할수록, 더 ~하다

28 ⓐ와 ④: (특정한 수·정도 등)까지, 내 차에는 네 사람까지 태울 수 있다. ① 일을 감당하는, ② ~에게 달려 있는, ③ (특히 나쁜 짓을) 하고 있는, ⑤ (특정한 기준·수준)만큼, 그녀의 최신 책은 그녀의 평상시 수준만큼 안 된다[수준에 못 미친다].

29 feel free to: 자유롭게 ~하다

30 (1) You can borrow it once a week. (2) You must pay for the item if you lose or break it.

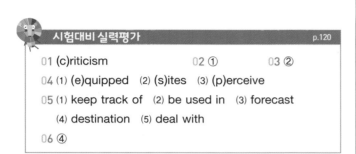

# Future Changes through Technology

## 시험대비 실력평가
p.120

01 (c)riticism　　02 ①　　03 ②
04 (1) (e)quipped　(2) (s)ites　(3) (p)erceive
05 (1) keep track of　(2) be used in　(3) forecast
　　(4) destination　(5) deal with
06 ④

01 주어진 관계는 반의어 관계를 나타낸다. bright: 밝은, 희망적인 - dark: 어두운, 암울한, criticism: 비평, 비난 - praise: 칭찬
02 '쉽게 사용될 수 있는'을 나타내는 말은 convenient(편리한, 간편한)이다.
03 signal: 신호, autograph: 사인, signature: 서명
04 equip: ~에 (필요한 것) 갖추다, site: 위치, 장소, 용지, 부지, 현장, perceive: 인지하다, 감지하다
05 deal with: 처리하다, 다루다, keep track of: ~을 놓치지 않다, ~의 자국을 뒤밟다, destination: 목적지, 도착지, be used in: ~으로 사용되다, forecast: 예측, 예보
06 주어진 문장과 ④: 현재의, ①, ② 있는, 참석[출석]한, ③ 수여[증정]하다, ⑤ 선물

## 서술형 시험대비
p.121

01 (p)erceive
02 (1) a variety of　(2) With the help of　(3) such as
03 (1) This word is not common in casual conversation.
　　(2) A microwave is a convenient cooking device.
　　(3) Which is the best route to take?
04 (s)ense / (n)avigate / (n)utrient
　　(1) navigated　(2) sensed　(3) nutrients
05 (1) These dogs are known for their high intelligence.
　　(2) Natural disasters, such as floods and earthquakes, affect thousands of people every year.

01 주어진 관계는 동의어 관계를 나타낸다. go into: ~에 들어가다 - enter: 들어가다, perceive: 인지하다, 감지하다 -

02 a variety of: 다양한, with the help of: ~의 도움으로, such as: ~와 같은
03 common: 흔한, convenient: 편리한, 간편한, route: 경로, 길
04 (1) navigate: 길을 찾다, 항해하다 / 한 지역의 길을 찾다 / 예전에는 여행자들이 대개 별을 보며 길을 찾았다. (2) sense: 감지하다 / 보거나 듣지 않고도 어떤 것을 알다 / 그녀는 그때 누군가가 자신을 지켜보고 있다는 걸 깨달았다. (3) nutrient: 영양소, 영양분 / 살아가고 성장하기 위해 필요한 것을 제공하는 음식이나 화학 물질 / 비타민은 우리에게 필수적인 영양소이다.
05 be known for: ~로 알려지다 intelligence: 지능, disaster: 재해, 참사, 재난 such as: ~와 같은 floods: 홍수, earthquake: 지진, affect: 영향을 미치다 thousands of people: 수천 명

## Conversation
교과서

### 핵심 Check
p.122~123

1 ③　2 it is likely that we will have to change how we get our food.

## 교과서 대화문 익히기

### Check(√) True or False
p.124

1 F　2 T　3 T　4 F

## 교과서 확인학습
p.126~127

**Listen & Talk 1 A**

heard of / Could you explain what it is / that, weather forecast, is going to, makes / convenient

**Listen & Talk 1 B**

inventions / great / senses, it, suggests / helpful / does, think of, flying / how it works / that, set, While it's flying / awesome, What, of / flying

**Listen & Talk 1 C**

who, one of, arms, the drums / How, with / controlled / in, detail / what, with, are turned into, travel / technology

recognize: 인지하다, 알아보다

**Listen & Talk 2 B**

As, harder, may not be, increasing, For this reason, it is likely that, how we get, Instead, will be grown, using, such as, rich, nutrients

**Listen & Talk 2 C**

had to, in line / we'll never have to / do you mean / what / How, for / keep track of, send the information / them / It's likely that, common

**Do It Yourself A**

exciting / have, popular / it, are equipped with / explain in more detail / what human players do / why, felt like / It is likely that

## 시험대비 기본평가

p.128

01 ②　　　　02 ④

03 Could you tell me what it is?

04 만약 비가 올 예정이면, 우산에서 소리가 나는 것.

01 ②번 다음에 나오는 That이 주어진 문장의 내용을 받고 있으므로 ②번이 적절하다.

02 B는 플라잉 카메라의 작동법을 몰라서 G에게 묻고 있다.

03 'Could you explain what it is?'는 'Could you tell me what it is?'로 바꿔 쓸 수 있다.

04 밑줄 친 (B)의 That은 앞 문장의 내용을 받고 있다.

## 시험대비 실력평가

p.129~130

01 (C) → (B) → (A) → (D) → (E)

02 ①

03 ⓐ increased → ⓐ increasing, ⓒ will grow → ⓒ will be grown, ⓓ used → ⓓ using, ⓔ it → ⓔ them

04 ⑤

05 bugs such as ants will become part of our daily meals

06 ③

07 사고 싶은 것을 가지고 그냥 걸어나가면 매장을 나갈 때 스마트폰에 있는 앱이 물건 값을 지불한다.

08 It's likely that these kinds of stores will be more common in the future.

09 ④　　　　10 ②

11 It is possible that the AI in games will get stronger and stronger.

01 (C)에서 주어진 질문에 답하며 내용을 설명하고 (B)에서 궁금한 것을 묻고 (A)에서 질문에 답한다. (D)의 That이 (A)의 내용을 받고 있으므로 (D)가 다음에 나오고 마지막의 That이 (E)

의 내용을 받고 있으므로 (E)가 마지막에 연결되는 것이 적절하다.

02 앞에 나온 내용의 예를 들고 있으므로 For example이 적절하다.

03 ⓐ 사람들이 계속 늘어나고 있는 것이므로 increased를 increasing으로 고쳐야 한다. ⓒ 고기가 배양되는 것이므로 수동태가 적절하다. ⓓ animal cells라는 목적어가 있으므로 using이 적절하다. ⓔ bugs를 받고 있으므로 them이 적절하다.

04 '여러분은 먹고 싶지 않을 수도 있지만, 사실 곤충들은 영양분이 매우 풍부하다!'라고 하고 있을 뿐이다.

05 such as: ~와 같은 (= like), A such as B: B와 같은 A

06 밑줄 친 (A)는 '그것 참 안됐다.'는 말이므로 ③번으로 대신하여 쓸 수 있다.

07 매장 내의 카메라와 감지기가 고객이 고른 물건들을 계속 파악하면서 그 정보를 스마트폰에 있는 앱으로 보내면 고객이 매장을 나갈 때 앱이 물건 값을 지불한다.

08 'It's likely that ~'은 자신이 생각하는 어떤 일에 대한 가능성의 정도를 나타낼 때 사용하는 표현이다.

09 (A) 현재완료로 물은 질문에 대한 답이므로 have, (B) from과 do의 목적어 역할을 할 수 있는 what, (C) 뒤에 '결과'가 이어지므로 why가 적절하다. That's because 뒤에는 '원인'이 이어진다. That's why ~.: 그것이 ~한 이유이다.

10 'Could you explain ~?'이라는 표현은 어떤 사실이나 대상에 대해 설명을 해달라고 요청할 때 쓸 수 있다.

11 'It's likely that ~'은 자신이 생각하는 어떤 일에 대한 가능성의 정도를 나타낼 때 사용하는 표현으로 'It's possible that ~'으로 쓸 수 있다.

## 서술형 시험대비

p.131

01 (D) → (C) → (A) → (B)

02 It senses the items inside it and suggests recipes.

03 We can take pictures from 500 meters above the location.

04 Could you explain how it works?

05 weather forecast　　　06 convenient

07 만약 비가 올 예정이면, 우산에서 소리가 난다.

01 (D) 미래에 우리 삶이 어떻게 변할지 묻고 (C) 식당들이 변할 것이라고 대답하고 (A) 식당들이 어떻게 변할지 질문하고 (B) 이에 대답하는 순서가 적절하다. (A)의 they가 (D)의 our lives가 아니라 (C)의 restaurants임에 유의한다.

02 스마트 냉장고는 냉장고 내부의 음식들을 감지해서 요리법을 제시해 준다.

03 플라잉 카메라는 미리 설정해 둔 목적지로 날아가서 비행하는

동안 그 지점의 500미터 상공에서 사진을 찍을 수 있다.

04 'how it works'를 explain의 목적어로 하는 간접의문문으로 영작한다.

05 뒤에서 '만약 비가 올 예정이면, 우산에서 소리가 나.'라고 하고 있으므로 weather forecast(일기 예보)가 적절하다.

06 '무언가를 하는 방법이 X라면, 그것은 쉽거나 매우 유용하거나 특정 목적에 적합하다'에 해당하는 것은 convenient(편리한, 간편한)이다.

07 'If it is going to rain, the umbrella makes a sound.'라고 하고 있다.

## Grammar 교과서

### 핵심 Check  p.132~133

1 (1) were a robot, I would listen to her
　(2) would buy an apartment in Seoul if I had some money
2 (1) that　(2) so that

### 시험대비 기본평가  p.134

01 (1) are → were　(2) can → could　(3) eats → ate
　(4) will → would
02 (1) that, could　(2) so cold that　(3) that they can
03 ④　　　04 ③

01 문제에서 모든 문장이 가정법 문장이라고 했고, 모든 문장들의 구조는 '가정법 과거' 형태로 볼 수 있으므로, 조건절의 동사를 과거로, 주절의 조동사도 과거형으로 고치는 것이 적절하다.

02 '목적'을 나타내는 'so that'과 '결과'를 나타내는 'so+수식어(형/부)+that'을 이해하고, 적용하는 문제이다. that을 기준으로 앞, 뒤 문장에 나타난 동사의 시제를 일치시키는 데 유의하여, so that을 활용하도록 한다.

03 주절에 조동사의 과거형이 나왔으므로, 가정법 문장이다. 가정법 과거에서 동사의 과거형 또는 조동사의 과거형을 사용하는 것이 적절하다.

04 'so that ~ 주어 can'은 '~하기 위해서', 'so 형용사 that 주어 V'는 '너무 ~해서 …하다'라는 의미이다.

### 시험대비 실력평가  p.135~137

01 ③　　02 ④　　03 ⑤　　04 ④

05 donated their allowances so that people in need could get help
06 to get enough sleep in order that you can focus
07 it were sunny, we could go to the amusement park
08 raised a pet robot, she wouldn't be bored
09 ⑤　　　　10 ②
11 ① are → were ② developed → developing
　③ will → would ④ be designed → design
12 ②　　　13 ④　　　14 ④　　　15 ②

01 가정법 과거로서 '반대' 개념의 직설법 현재 시제와 적절하게 전환된 문장은 ③번뿐이다.

02 'so that+주어+조동사'가 적절히 사용된 것을 고른다. ⑤의 경우 so를 in으로 바꾸면 in order that이 되어 바르게 된다.

03 'so that+주어+조동사'가 적절히 사용된 것을 찾는다. ④의 so as는 절이 아닌, 'so as to V' 형태로 사용된다.

04 가정법 문장이라면 won't를 wouldn't로, 직설법 문장이라면 had를 has로 쓰는 것이 적절하다.

05 '목적'을 나타내는 'so that'을 활용하는 문제이다. '어려운 사람들'은 'people in need'로 표현한다. * allowance: 용돈

06 '목적'을 나타내는 'so that'과 같은 의미인 'in order that'을 활용하는 문제이다.

07 가정법 과거 시제의 문장이다. If 절에 과거동사 were가 오고, 주절에 조동사의 과거형 could를 쓰는 것에 유의하여 알맞게 배열한다.

08 가정법 과거 시제의 문장이다. If 절에 과거동사 raised가 오고, 주절에 조동사의 과거형 would와 not을 결합한 wouldn't를 쓰는 것에 유의하여 알맞게 배열한다.

09 ① follows → followed ② had been → could be ③ can → could ④ don't → didn't

10 ① has → had ③ will → would ④ had invented → invented, can → could ⑤ know → knew

11 '만약 당신이 로봇을 개발하는 과학자라면, 어떤 종류의 로봇을 설계할 것입니까?'라는 의미의 문장이다. 문제의 조건에서 가정법 과거 문장으로 제한했으므로, if절의 be동사를 were로 고치고, 주절의 will도 과거형 would로 고친다. 또한 a scientist를 후치 수식하는 develop은 현재분사를 쓰며, 로봇을 설계하는 것은 수동이 아닌, 능동의 원형동사 design이다.

12 다른 문장들은 모두 '목적'을 나타내는 표현 형태인데, ②의 두 번째 문장은 '결과'를 나타낸다. 보통, '결과'의 so (that)는 앞 문장의 끝에 콤마(쉼표)를 붙인다.

13 가정법 과거 형태의 문장들이다. If절에는 동사의 과거형을, 주절에는 조동사의 과거형을 쓰는 것이 적절하다.

14 '로봇들이 진짜 친구처럼 행동하도록, 인간의 감정을 인식할 수 있는 로봇을 과학자들이 만들려고 노력한다.'는 문장들로서 모두

'목적'을 나타내는데, ④만 '진짜 친구처럼 행동할 수 있을 경우에'라는 '조건'이다. 'in case that'은 '만약 ~가 …할 경우'라는 뜻이다.

15 ②는 '공손한 질문'을 위한 조동사 Could이다. 나머지 다른 문장들과, <보기>에 주어진 could는 가정법의 주절에 사용된 can의 과거시제형이다.

서술형 시험대비                                    p.138~139

01 (1) won't → wouldn't   (2) is → were[was]
   (3) be → have been   (4) make → made
   (5) can → could   (6) will → would
   (7) can → could

02 (1) sensed human emotions, we could get along
   (2) were no search-and-rescue robots, humans
       would go into disaster areas
   (3) a pet robot so that he could help the lonely
       people

03 (1) If it were not for   (2) If there were no
   (3) Were it not for
   (4) As there are cameras and the GPS system,
       the self-driving cars can

04 (1) Mom returned home in order that she could
       take the umbrella with her.
   (2) Abigail runs every day so that she can join his
       sports club.
   (3) Semi left for Italy in order that she could learn
       cooking.
   (4) Be sure to get enough sleep so that you can
       focus during class.
   (5) Sean ran fast so that he would not be late for
       the wedding.

05 (1) If the coronavirus were[was] in my town, we
       wouldn't feel relieved.
   (2) If Brian had not had an invitation, it would not
       have been easy for them to enter the castle.
   (3) If she were[was] rich enough, she would not
       sell her books on the street market.
   (4) If there were[was] money left, Mr. Robert would
       join the party.

06 the last leaf fell, it would be my last day

01 문제에서 각 문장이 가정법이라고 했으므로, 'if절' 또는 'I wish' 뒤의 동사를 과거형으로, be동사는 were 또는 was로 고친다. (3) 내용상 과거 시제이므로 '가정법 과거완료'로 표현한다. 가정법 과거완료의 주절에는 '조동사+have+p.p.'를 쓴다.

02 (1), (2) 가정법의 동사 구조에 유의하여, 주어진 단어들을 적절히 배열한다. (3) '목적'을 나타내는 부사절에 'so that 주어

could'를 사용한다.

03 '카메라와 GPS 시스템이 없으면, 자율 주행 자동차는 길을 찾아갈 수 없을 텐데.' 직설법은, '카메라와 GPS 시스템이 있어서, 자율 주행 자동차가 길을 찾아갈 수 있다.'가 된다. 가정법 표현, 'Without = If it were not for = Were it not for'를 기억하는 것이 좋다.

04 '목적'을 나타내는 to부정사 또는 'in order to', 'so as to' 등의 표현은 'so[in order]+that+주어+조동사'로 바꿔 쓸 수 있다.

05 가정법 과거는 직설법 현재의 반대, 가정법 과거완료는 직설법 과거의 반대를 나타낸다. (2)는 가정법 과거완료이다

06 그림의 문장은, '마지막 잎이 떨어지면, 나의 마지막 날이 될 것이다.'라는 의미의 직설법이다. 가정법 과거시제를 활용해서 falls를 fell로, will을 would로 변형하는 것에 유의하여 영작한다.

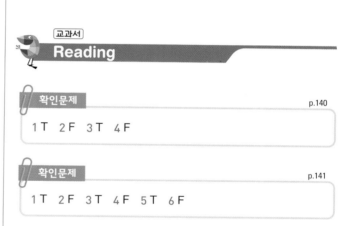

교과서
Reading

확인문제                                          p.140

1 T   2 F   3 T   4 F

확인문제                                          p.141

1 T   2 F   3 T   4 F   5 T   6 F

교과서 확인학습 A                                  p.142~143

01 with Robots                02 Where
03 not, anymore              04 a variety of
05 flying, in public places  06 delivery
07 factory                   08 A service robot
09 Becoming Smart
10 programmed them to do     11 getting, smarter
12 What makes this possible
13 perceive environments     14 recognize speech
15 control machines          16 act just like
17 recognize praise          18 around Us
19 faster, easier
20 anywhere, in disaster areas
21 throughout
22 would be easier, had one   23 sense emotions
24 a driver                   25 so that, can
26 a large group of robots
27 can be used, including      28 as a group
29 dangerous for humans       30 so that, can
31 Looking toward             32 not perfect

33 to become
34 they might cause
35 to find, to ensure, good

1 Life with Robots

2 Where Do We See Robots?

3 Robots are not only in movies and books anymore.

4 Around the world, robots are doing a variety of tasks.

5 There are delivery robots flying in the sky, robot arms in factories, and service robots in public places.

6 A delivery robot in the sky

7 Robot arms in a factory

8 A service robot at the PyeongChang Olympics

9 Robots Are Becoming Smart

10 In the past, robots performed only easy tasks that humans programmed them to do.

11 However, robots are now getting "smarter," and soon they might be able to think like humans.

12 What makes this possible is artificial intelligence (AI)

13 Robots that have AI can perceive environments and make decisions.

14 They can also recognize speech, tell jokes, and play games with humans.

15 AI Speakers: They can answer your questions, control machines in your home, and play music for you.

16 AI Pets: They act just like real dogs.

17 They walk and play with their owners and recognize praise.

18 Robots around Us — Present and Future

19 Robots are making things faster and easier

20 They can help us anywhere — in our homes, on roads, or in disaster areas.

21 Home Helper Robot: This robot helps your family throughout the day.

22 Cooking and cleaning would be easier if you had one.

23 It also talks with family members and can sense emotions.

24 Self-Driving Car: A self-driving car doesn't need a driver.

25 With cameras, sensors, and software, it can navigate roads for you so that you can relax and enjoy the ride.

26 Robot Swarm: A robot swarm is a large group of robots that can communicate with one another, like ants or bees.

27 They can be used in a variety of places, including farms or building sites.

28 They work on tasks and find solutions as a group.

29 Search-and-Rescue Robot: Search-and-rescue robots can go into disaster areas that are dangerous for humans.

30 They find survivors, deal with dangers, and clear routes so that people can escape to safety.

31 Looking toward the Future

32 Our future with robots looks bright but not perfect.

33 Some people expect life to become more convenient with the help of robots.

34 However, other people worry about problems they might cause, such as threats to our jobs and safety.

35 The important thing is to find possible solutions and to ensure that robots are only used for good.

01 ③

02 (1) 하늘에서 날아다니는 배달 로봇 (2) 공장의 로봇 팔 (3) 공공장소의 서비스 로봇

03 ②, ④, ⑤      04 ⑤

05 (A) robots, the past (C) Robots that have AI

06 ③      07 safe → dangerous

08 to escape    09 ②    10 had

11 Robots are making things faster and easier.

12 ②      13 ①, ④

14 What makes this possible is artificial intelligence (AI).

15 ④    16 a self-driving car    17 ②

18 ④    19 ②    20 navigate

21 which include    22 ③

23 with the help of    24 robots   25 like

26 They are threats to our jobs and safety.

01 이 글은 '로봇이 하늘, 공장, 공공장소에서 다양한 임무를 수행하고 있다'는 내용의 글이므로, 제목으로는 ③번 '우리는 어디에서 로봇을 보는가?'가 적절하다.

02 (1) delivery robots flying in the sky, (2) robot arms in factories, (3) service robots in public places를 쓰는 것이 적절하다.

03 ⓒ와 ②, ④, ⑤: 현재분사, ①, ③: 동명사

04 앞에 나오는 내용과 상반되는 내용이 뒤에 이어지므로 However가 가장 적절하다. ① 게다가, 더욱이, ② 다시 말해서, ④ 그러므로

05 (A) '과거의 로봇' (C) '인공 지능을 가진 로봇'을 가리킨다.

06 (B)와 ③: 관계대명사, ①과 ④: 의문대명사, ②와 ⑤: 의문형용사

07 수색 구조 로봇은 사람에게 '위험한' 재난 지역에 투입될 수 있다고 하는 것이 적절하다.

08 목적을 나타내는 so that 부사절을 'to부정사'로 바꾸는 것이 적절하다.

09 로봇과 함께하는 우리의 미래는 밝지만 '완벽하지는 않다.'

10 가정법 과거 시제이므로, 'had'로 쓰는 것이 적절하다.

11 동사 'are making'의 목적어 'things'를 쓴 다음에 목적격보어 'faster and easier'를 쓰는 것이 적절하다.

12 로봇은 '어디에서나' 우리를 도울 수 있다.

13 ⓐ에는 목적격 관계대명사를, ⓑ에는 주격 관계대명사를 쓰는 것이 적절하다.

14 선행사를 포함하는 관계대명사 What을 주어로 하여 쓰는 것이 적절하다.

15 ④ '인공 지능을 가진 로봇'이 환경을 인식하고 의사 결정을 할 수 있다. 모든 로봇이 가능한 것은 아니다.

16 '자율 주행 자동차'를 가리킨다.

17 ⓑ와 ②: [역할·자격·기능·성질 따위를 나타내어] ~으로서(전치사), ① ~이기 때문에(접속사), ③ ~와 같이(접속사), ④ [보통 as ~ as ...로 형용사·부사 앞에서] …와 같은 정도로(as ~ as ...에서, 앞의 as는 지시부사, 뒤의 as는 접속사), ⑤ ~하고 있을 때(접속사)

18 로봇 군집은 '개미나 벌처럼, 서로 의사소통할 수 있는' 로봇의 대규모 집단을 말한다.

19 ⓐ With cameras, sensors, and software: 카메라, 감지기 그리고 소프트웨어를 '갖춘 채', ⓑ communicate with one another: 서로 의사소통하다

20 navigate: 길을 찾다, 항해하다, 그것은 종종 지도를 사용하여 바다나 육지의 지역을 가로지르거나 따라서 가는, 혹은 너머 가서 방향을 찾는 것을 의미한다.

21 'a variety of+복수 명사'는 복수 취급이므로, which include로 바꿔 쓰는 것이 적절하다.

22 로봇 군집 안에 몇 개의 로봇이 있는지는 대답할 수 없다. ① No, it doesn't. ② It is a large group of robots. ④ It can be used in a variety of places, including farms or building sites. ⑤ No, it doesn't. It works on tasks and finds solutions as a group.

23 with the help of: ~의 도움으로

24 '로봇'을 가리킨다.

25 such as = like: ~와 같은

26 로봇이 일으킬지 모르는 문제들에는 '우리의 일자리와 안전에 대한 위협'이 있다.

---

**서술형 시험대비** p.150~151

01 What    02 sillier → smarter
03 (A) programmed    (B) performed
04 (A) AI    (B) AI
05 They act just like real dogs.
06 They can walk and play with their owners and recognize praise.
07 (A) your questions    (B) machines
08 survivors    09 safety    10 treat 또는 handle
11 (1) 가능한 해결책을 찾아내는 것
   (2) 로봇이 오로지 좋은 일을 위해서만 쓰이게 됨을 확실히 하는 것
12 on    13 in order that
14 Because with cameras, sensors, and software, it can navigate roads for you (so that you can relax and enjoy the ride).
15 It can communicate with one another.

---

01 선행사를 포함하는 관계대명사 What을 쓰는 것이 적절하다.

02 앞에 나오는 내용과 상반되는 내용이 뒤에 이어지는 However로 문장이 시작하고 있으므로, 로봇은 이제 '더 똑똑해'지고 있으며, 곧 인간처럼 생각할 수 있을지도 모른다라고 고치는 것이 적절하다. sillier: 더 어리석은

03 과거에는 로봇이 실행할 단순 업무들을 인간이 '프로그램으로 짠' 다음에 로봇은 오직 그 업무들만을 '실행했다.'

04 환경을 인식하고 의사 결정을 할 수 있는 로봇은 '인공 지능'을 가지고 있다. '인공 지능' 덕분에 그들은 또한 인간의 말을 인지하고, 농담을 건네며, 인간과 게임을 할 수 있다.

05 like: …처럼(전치사)

06 그들은 그들의 주인과 함께 걷고 놀며 칭찬을 알아챈다.

07 그들은 '당신의 질문'에 대답할 수 있고, 당신의 집에 있는 '기계들'을 조종할 수 있으며, 당신을 위해 음악을 재생할 수도 있다. reply to = answer, manage: 다루다, 조종하다

08 survivor: 생존자, 살아남은 사람, 죽음 가까이 갔지만 계속 살아남은 사람들

09 전치사 to 다음이므로, safe의 명사 형태로 쓰는 것이 적절하다.

10 deal with = treat: ~을 다루다, 처리하다

11 중요한 것은 '가능한 해결책을 찾아내는 것'과 '로봇이 오로지 좋은 일을 위해서만 쓰이게 됨을 확실히 하는 것'이다.

12 work on: (해결·개선하기 위해) ~에 노력을 들이다, 착수하다

13 목적을 나타내는 부사절에서 so that 대신에 in order that을 쓸 수도 있다.

14 자율 주행 자동차는 '카메라, 감지기 그리고 소프트웨어를 갖춘 채, 당신이 쉬면서 주행을 즐길 수 있도록 당신을 위해 길을 찾아갈 수 있기 때문에' 운전자를 필요로 하지 않는다.

15 로봇 군집은 '서로' 의사소통할 수 있다.

01 (a)rtificial    02 ⑤    03 ①    04 escape

05 (1) deal with   (2) make decisions   (3) Look toward
    (4) work on   (5) find solutions

06 ④

07 스마트 냉장고가 냉장고 내부의 음식들을 감지해서
    요리법을 제시해 주는 것.

08 ②        09 ①        10 signal

11 what he wants to do, electronic signals, to his
    robot arm and move it

12 ④            13 order that, get ready for

14 (1) it rained hard, we could not go to the stadium
       to cheer
    (2) it doesn't rain hard, we can go to the stadium
       to cheer

15 (1) artificial intelligence had not been developed,
       computers couldn't have won over humans
    (2) artificial intelligence was developed, computers
       could win over humans

16 ①, ⑤     17 ②     18 ②

19 (1) in order that it can reduce the risks
    (2) so that they can work on tasks as a group

20 would

21 They can help us anywhere—in our homes, on
    roads, or in disaster areas.

22 ③     23 ①     24 ②     25 ③

26 학생들은 학교에 갈 필요가 없고 집에서 공부할 것이다.

27 ⑤

---

01 artificial: 인공적인, 인위적인, fake: 가짜의, 인조의 / 그는 59살이고 인공 팔을 잘 사용한다.

02 '큰 지역에 손상을 가해 많은 사람들에게 해를 입힐 수도 있는 불행한 사건'을 가리키는 말은 disaster(참사, 재난, 재해)이다.

03 여기서 perform은 '실행[수행]하다'의 뜻으로 쓰였다.

04 주어진 관계는 동의어 관계를 나타낸다. praise: 칭찬 - compliment: 칭찬, escape: 탈출하다, 달아나다, 벗어나다 - flee: 도망치다, 피하다

05 make decisions: 결정을 하다, work on: ~에 노력을 들이다, 애쓰다, find solutions: 해결책을 찾다, look toward: 앞날을 생각하다, deal with: 처리하다, 다루다

06 (D)의 That이 (D) 앞 문장의 내용을 받고 있으므로 제일 먼저 나오고, (C)에서 'A flying camera?'라고 (A)의 내용을 묻고 있으므로 (A) 다음에 (C)가 이어지고, (B)의 That이 (E)의 내용을 받고 있으므로 (E) 다음에 (B)가 이어지는 순서가 자연스럽다.

07 여자가 '이 냉장고는 냉장고 내부의 음식들을 감지해서 요리법을 제시해 줘.'라고 하자, 남자가 '유용하겠다.'라고 하고 있다.

08 상대방에게 설명을 요청 받았을 때 Of course. / Yes. / Okay.

---

/ Sure. / All right. / No problem. 등으로 요청을 수락한다는 의사를 먼저 표현할 수 있다.

09 'one of+복수 명사'로 '~ 중의 하나'라는 뜻이므로 arms로 복수 형태가 되어야 한다.

10 '기계에 의해 빛, 소리, 전기 등의 형태로 전해지는 정보'를 가리키는 말은 signal(신호)이다.

11 자신의 팔로 하고 싶은 것을 생각하고, 그 생각들이 전기 신호로 바뀌고, 그 신호들이 그의 뇌에서 로봇 팔로 이동해서 그 팔을 움직인다.

12 '과거 시제의 직설법 문장'을 가정법으로 고치면 '가정법 과거완료'가 된다. If절에 'had+p.p.', 주절에 '조동사 과거+have+p.p.'를 쓰되, 직설법과 반대되도록 not을 뺀다. ⑤는 수동태 문장이라서 틀렸다.

13 'Sandy가 어제 Tommy에게 전화한 것은 발표를 준비시키도록 하기 위해서'였다. 'in' 뒤에 절이 와야 하므로 'in order that 주어 might 동사' 형태가 적절하며, might 대신 would 또는 could도 가능하다.

14 가정법 과거에는 동사의 과거형이 온다. 이 경우 비인칭 주어 it과 동사 rained를 쓴다는 것에 유의한다.

15 내용상 '가정법 과거완료' 문장이다. If절에 'had p.p.'형태, 주절에는 '조동사 과거형+have p.p.' 형태를 쓰기 때문에 주어진 can't를 'couldn't have p.p.'로 쓰고, 직설법으로 바꿀 때는 not이 없는 과거 시제 could로 고친다.

16 '~가 없다면'이라는 가정법 표현은 'If there were no ~'로 나타내며, without 또는 'If it were not for ~'로 대체할 수 있다. 'If it were not for'는 if를 생략해서 'were it not for ~'로 표현 가능하다. 주절에는 조동사의 과거형을 쓴다. ①의 'should have done'은 '~했어야 했는데'라는 의미이다. ⑤ are → were가 적절하다.

17 ② this morning으로 봐서 내용상 가정법 과거완료 문장이다. If절에 'had+p.p.', 주절에는 '조동사 과거+have+p.p.' 형태가 와야 한다. 'succeeded'를 'had succeeded'로 고치는 것이 적절하다.

18 so that 뒤에는 절을 써야 한다. 'for her to get'을 'she could[would/might] get'으로 고치는 것이 적절하다. 아니면, 'so that'을 'in order'로 바꾸거나, 'so that for her'를 아예 삭제해도 무방하다.

19 (1) 구조 로봇이 인간 소방관들의 위험을 줄이기 위해 불타는 건물을 향해 다가가는 중이다. (2) 무리 로봇 안의 로봇들은 집단으로서 일하기 위해 서로 소통한다.

20 가정법 과거의 주절이므로 조동사의 과거형 would가 적절하다. 가정법 과거: If+주어+동사의 과거형 ~, 주어+조동사의 과거형 [would/could/might]+동사원형 …

21 그들은 어디에서나 우리를 도울 수 있다. 우리의 집에서, 길에서 또는 재난 지역에서 말이다.

22 ⓑ와 ③: 앞에서 이미 언급했거나 상대방이 알고 있는 사람·사물을 가리킬 때 명사의 반복을 피하기 위해 쓰는 부정대명사, ① (강조의 의미로) 단 하나(의)(수사), ② 같은, 한(수사), ④ 하나

의(수사), ⑤ [총칭 인칭으로; 복수형 없음] (일반적으로) 사람 (대명사)

23 이 글은 '로봇과 함께하는 우리의 미래'에 관한 글이므로, 제목으로는 ①번 '미래에 대한 전망'이 적절하다.

24 앞에 나오는 내용과 상반되는 내용이 뒤에 이어지므로 However가 가장 적절하다. ① 비슷하게, 마찬가지로, ③ 따라서, 그러므로, ④ 즉[말하자면], ⑤ 그 결과

25 주어진 문장의 Instead에 주목한다. ③번 앞 문장의 내용을 부연 설명하고 있으므로 ③번이 적절하다.

26 학생들은 학교에 갈 필요가 없고 집에서 다양한 앱을 사용하여 공부할 것이다.

27 미래의 학교 생활이 지금만큼 재미있고 의미 있기를 바란다고 했을 뿐이다.

## 단원별 예상문제

p.158~163

01 ②  02 ③  03 ⑤  04 ④
05 ①

06 줄을 서서 기다릴 필요가 없이 사고 싶은 것을 가지고 그냥 걸어나가면 스마트폰에 있는 앱이 물건 값을 지불한다.

07 ②, ④  08 ④  09 ④  10 ③
11 ①  12 ④  13 ②

14 If they learned the history of Korea, they could understand Dokdo more.

15 (1) not to forget  (2) so as not to forget
   (3) in order that

16 (1) so that he would not drive
   (2) in order that information could spread much faster

17 ④ / ④ If Sehee missed the school bus, she would be late for class. 또는 If Sehee had missed the school bus, she would have been late for class.

18 ⑤ / ⑤ The shopper didn't buy a thing so that she could save money.

19 (1) saw the show, would feel
   (2) knew your number, could contact
   (3) had been healthy, could have completed

20 ⑤  21 ③  22 ②  23 be used

24 a large group of robots / a robot swarm

25 as well as  26 ②  27 ④

28 학생들은 종이책을 더 이상 사용하지 않고 태블릿 피시나 클라우드에서 내려 받은 파일을 사용할 것이다.

29 (A) downloaded  (B) such  (C) worse

30 what school life will be like

01 '특히 유용한 어떤 것을 달거나 부착하다'는 equip(~에 (필요한 것을) 갖추다)이다.

02 주어진 문장, ③: 흔한 ① 공통의 ② 공공의 ④ 일반적인 ⑤ 공

원

03 task: 일, 과제, 과업, recognize: 인식하다, threat: 위협, 협박, destination: 목적지, 도착지, ensure: 보장하다, delivery: 배달, 전달

04 주어진 문장은 '그게 다야?'라고 묻는 것으로 ④번 앞에 나오는 내용에 대해 묻고 있으므로 ④번이 적절하다.

05 빈칸 다음에서 결재 방법에 대해 언급하고 있으므로 '어떻게 지불하는지' 묻는 것이 적절하다.

07 'It's likely that ~'은 가능성의 정도를 나타는 표현으로 'It is possible[probable] that ~' 등으로 나타낼 수도 있다.

08 B가 아니라 G가 느꼈다.

09 ① makes → made ② 가정법 과거완료이므로 would be → would have been ③ can → could ⑤ will → would

10 모든 빈칸에 들어갈 수 있는 단어는 so이다. 다만, ③은 '너무 ~해서 결국 …하다'라는 '결과'를 나타내는 접속사 'so ~ that'이다. 나머지는 모두 '목적'의 'so that'이다.

11 가정법 과거에 맞게 동사의 과거형을 쓰되, 이 예문의 경우 비인칭 주어 it과 부정문의 조동사 didn't rain을 활용하는 것에 유의한다.

12 ④ so that을 (al)though와 같은 '양보'의 접속사로 바꾸는 것이 적절하고, 그렇게 할 경우, 'Wendy는 더 열심히 공부했음에도 불구하고, 의사 자격증 획득에 실패했다.'라는 자연스런 문장이 된다.

13 ① so → so as 또는 in order 또는 so 삭제 ③ sadness → sad ④ not being → would not be ⑤ could → to 또는 for → that

14 내용상 가정법의 형태로 문장이 구성될 수밖에 없다. if절에 learn 동사의 과거형과, 주절에 조동사 can의 과거형을 사용하되, much의 비교급 more를 쓰는 것에 유의한다.

15 so that = in order that = so as to = in order to를 활용한다.

16 '목적'을 나타내는 부사절 'so that', 'in order that' 뒤의 문장 구조에 유의한다. (1) Mike는 직접 운전하지 않으려고 자율 주행차를 샀다. (2) Gutenberg는 정보가 더 빠르게, 더 넓게 퍼져나가도록 인쇄기를 발명했다.

17 ④ '세희가 스쿨 버스를 놓친다면, 수업에 지각하지 않았을 텐데.'라는 문장은 어법과 의미에서 모두 어색하다. 가정법 과거 또는 가정법 과거 완료 둘 중 하나에 맞게 고치되, 내용상으로도 '버스를 놓치면 지각할 텐데' 또는 '버스를 놓쳤다면, 지각했을 텐데'와 같이 표현하는 것에 유의한다.

18 so as that은 '목적'을 나타내는 부사절을 이끌 수 없다. as를 삭제하고 so that을 쓴다.

19 (1), (2)는 가정법 과거, (3)은 가정법 과거완료이다. (4)의 경우, Yes라고 대답한 후에 but이 왔으므로, 뒤에 오는 문장은 '부정적 의미'가 필요하므로 가정법의 If절과 주절 모두에 not이 와야 하는 것에 유의한다.

20 이 글은 '이제 로봇은 '더 똑똑'해지고 있으며, 인공 지능(AI) 덕

분에 곧 인간처럼 생각할 수 있을지도 모른다.'는 내용의 글이므로, 제목으로는 ⑤번 '로봇이 똑똑해지고 있다'가 적절하다.

21 주어진 문장의 this에 주목한다. ③번 앞 문장의 내용을 받고 있으므로 ③번이 적절하다.

22 ⓑ와 ②: ~처럼(전치사), ① ~와 같은(무엇에 대해 남의 의견을 물을 때 씀, 전치사), 스페인에서 공부하는 건 어때요? ③ (~을) 좋아하다(동사), ④ ~하는 것처럼(접속사), ⑤ 비슷한(형용사)

23 다양한 장소에서 '사용될 수 있다'고 해야 하므로 수동태로 쓰는 것이 적절하다.

24 a large group of robots를 가리킨다. a group of+집합명사: 단수 취급, a group of+군집명사(구성원): 복수 취급

25 not only A but also B = B as well as A: A뿐만 아니라 B도

26 '누가 스마트폰을 발명했는지'는 알 수 없다. ① It was invented in 1992. ③ Yes, they can. ④ Yes, they can. ⑤ Yes, they can.

27 (C)의 However 다음에 주어진 글의 내용과 상반되는 내용이 뒤에 이어지므로 제일 먼저 오고 (A)의 this가 (C)의 내용을 가리키므로 (C) 다음에 (A)가 이어지고 (B)의 AI가 (A)의 마지막에 나오는 artificial intelligence (AI)를 가리키므로 (A) 다음에 (B)가 와야 한다. 그러므로 (C)-(A)-(B)의 순서가 적절하다.

29 (A) '다운로드된(내려 받은)' 파일이라고 해야 하므로 downloaded가 옳다. (B) 'such a+(형용사)+명사'의 순서이므로 such가 옳다. so+형용사/부사, 또는 so+형용사+a+명사, (C) 시력이 '나빠질 수 있다'고 해야 하므로 worse가 옳다.

30 know의 목적어이므로 간접의문문(의문사+주어+동사)의 순서로 쓰는 것이 적절하다.

## 서술형 실전문제
p.164~165

01 It is likely that cashiers will disappear at stores in the future.

02 The app on your smartphone will pay for the items you choose when you leave the store.

03 There are cameras and sensors in the store without cashiers.

04 (1) so that it would satisfy his thirst
   (2) in order to show them
   (3) order that I could raise

05 Jihun knew the actor's name, he would[could] search him online

06 wish I were[was] as smart as Bill

07 (A) that   (B) is   (C) make

08 robots are now getting "smarter," and soon they might be able to think like humans

09 (1) 인간이 로봇에게 실행하도록 프로그램을 설정한 단순 업무만을 수행했다.
   (2) 환경을 인식하고 의사 결정을 할 수 있고, 인간의 말을 인지하고, 농담을 건네며, 인간과 게임을 할 수 있다.

10 imperfect        11 becoming → to become

12 (A) disaster areas    (B) clear routes

01 계산원이 없는 매장에 관한 이야기를 하면서 마지막에 '미래에는 이런 종류의 매장이 더 흔해질 것 같아.'라고 하고 있다.

02 '네가 매장을 나갈 때 앱이 물건 값을 지불하는 거고?'라는 질문에 '바로 그거야.'라고 답하고 있다.

03 계산원이 없는 매장에는 매장 내에 카메라와 감지기가 있다.

04 '목적'의 의미를 표현할 때, 'so[in order] that' 부사절과 'in order to V' 부사구를 어디에 쓰는 것이 좋을지 결정하는 것에 유의한다. *satisfy thirst: 갈증을 채우다

05 직설법 문장을 해석해 보면, '지훈이가 그 배우의 이름을 모르는데, 인터넷으로 검색을 하고 싶어한다.'이므로, 가정법 과거 시제 '지훈이가 그 배우의 이름을 알면, 인터넷으로 검색할 텐데.'라고 표현하는 것이 적절하다.

06 직설법에서 'Bill과 같이 머리가 좋으면 좋겠다'고 했으므로, 가정법으로는 'Bill처럼 머리가 좋으면 좋을 텐데'를 표현하는 'I wish 가정법'이 적절하다.

07 (A) 선행사 easy tasks를 수식하는 '목적격 관계대명사'를 써야 하므로 that이 옳다. (B) What 다음의 동사가 makes여서 What이 'The thing which'임을 알 수 있으므로, 그에 맞춰 동사를 is로 하는 것이 적절하다. (C) 조동사 can 다음에 '동사원형'을 써야 하므로 make가 옳다.

08 앞 문장의 내용을 가리킨다.

09 과거에 로봇은 인간이 로봇에게 실행하도록 프로그램을 설정한 단순 업무만을 수행했지만, 이제 인공 지능을 가진 로봇은 '더 똑똑'해지고 있으며, 곧 인간처럼 생각할 수 있을지도 모른다고 하며 예로 든 것을 쓰는 것이 적절하다.

10 perfect의 반의어인 'imperfect'를 쓰는 것이 적절하다.

11 'expect+목적어+to부정사'로 쓰는 것이 적절하다.

12 수색 구조 로봇은 사람에게 위험한 '재난 지역'에서 사용될 수 있는데, 그곳에서 그들은 생존자를 찾고 위험한 상황을 처리하며, 사람들이 안전한 곳으로 대피할 수 있도록 '길을 확보한다.'

## 창의사고력 서술형 문제
p.166

|모범답안|

01 (1) It's likely that we can live under the sea in the near future.
   (2) It's possible for us to have a personal airplane in the near future.
   (3) It's probable that we will live in outer space in the near future.

02 (A) location　(B) using a variety of apps
　　(C) save time　(D) negative effects
　　(E) meet their friends

### 단원별 모의고사

01 (1) survivor　(2) artificial　(3) (r)oute　(4) delivery
02 (1) resource　(2) safety　(3) signal　(4) sense
　　(5) likely
03 (1) (d)eal with, 처리하다, 다루다
　　(2) (s)olution, 해법, 해답　(3) (s)afety, 안전
　　(4) (s)warm, 떼, 군중
　　(5) (e)scape, 탈출하다, 달아나다, 벗어나다
　　(6) (p)erceive, 인지하다, 감지하다
04 ②
05 It is about a man who lost one of his arms in an
　　accident.
06 ⑤　　　　　　　　　　　07 ④, ⑤
08 That's why I sometimes felt like they already
　　knew my moves!
09 it is likely that we will have to change how we get
　　our food
10 ①　　　　11 ④　　　　12 ⑤　　　　13 ⑤
14 ②　　　　15 ③　　　　16 ②
17 If robots sensed human emotions, we could play
　　with them.
18 ②, ⑤　　　19 flying　　　20 various　　　21 ④
22 a home helper robot　　　23 ②
24 ⑤　　　　25 ④

01　survivor: 생존자, artificial flower: 조화, route: 경로, 길, delivery: 배달, 전달
02　likely: 있음직한, 가능하다고 생각되는, ~할 것 같은, resource: 자원, 재원, safety: 안전, 안전한 곳, sense: 감지하다, signal: 신호
03　(1) deal with: 처리하다, 다루다. 문제 같은 것을 다루거나 해결하다 (2) solution: 해법, 해답. 어떤 문제에 대한 답 (3) safety: 안전. 피해나 위험으로부터 안전한 상태 (4) swarm: 떼, 군중. 많은 살아 있는 것들 (5) escape: 탈출하다, 달아나다, 벗어나다. 자유롭게 되다 (6) perceive: 인지하다, 감지하다. 감각으로 어떤 것을 알아채다
04　'어떻게 작동하는 건지 더 구체적으로 설명해 줄 수 있니?'라는 질문에 '물론이지.'라고 하고서 설명을 하는 것이 아니라 '정말 멋지다.'라고 말하는 것은 어색하다.
06　전기 신호들이 그의 뇌에서 로봇 팔로 이동한다.
07　'It's likely that ~'은 가능성의 정도를 나타낼 때 사용하는 표현으로 'It is possible[probable] that ~' 등으로 가능성의 정도를 나타낼 수도 있다. appropriate: (~에) 적합한, 적절(적당)한

08　That's why ~.: 그것이 ~한 이유이다, feel like: ~처럼 느끼다
09　'It's likely that ~'은 자신이 생각하는 어떤 일에 대한 가능성의 정도를 나타낼 때 사용하는 표현이다.
10　(A) 앞에는 '동물을 죽이지 않게 될 것'이라는 내용이 나오고 뒤에는 '동물 세포를 이용하여 실험실에서 고기가 배양될 것'이라는 내용이 나오고 있으므로 Instead(대신에)가 적절하다. (B) 앞에 나온 내용에 추가하고 있으므로 Also(또한)가 적절하다.
11　④를 제외한 모든 문장은 가정법 과거 시제이다. ④의 if는 의문사가 없는 간접의문문의 명사절을 이끄는 접속사이며, 나머지는 모두 가정법의 부사절을 이끄는 종속접속사이다.
12　⑤를 제외한 나머지 so that은 '목적'을 나타내는 부사절을 이끈다. ⑤의 so that은 '결과'를 나타내며, 보통 앞에 콤마(,)가 온다.
13　<보기>의 would는 가정법의 주절에서 쓰이는 조동사이다. 'Lynn은 가족들이 떨어지는 것에 동의하지 않으면, 해외에서의 그 일자리를 포기할 텐데.' 보기와 같은 가정법의 조동사 would는 ⑤이다. '그 지원자가 타인을 설득하는 기술을 발전시키면, 그 직위를 얻을 텐데.' ① 공손한 질문 ② will의 과거시제 ③ 과거의 습관적 행위 ④ would like to = want to
14　②'~하기 위해서'라는 목적의 부사절을 만들 때, so that 또는 in order that 절 뒤에 can 또는 could 등의 조동사를 쓴다. became을 could[would] become으로 고치는 것이 적절하다.
15　'인공지능이 없다면, 로봇들은 무엇을 해야 할지 결정할 수 없을 텐데.'라는 문장이다. '~가 없다면'은 'If it were not for = Were it not for = Without = But for' 등으로 표현하며, ③ 'Had it not been for'는 'If it had not been for'에서 if를 생략하고 도치된 표현으로 가정법 과거완료시제에 사용한다.
16　주어진 문장은 'Kobe가 상태가 좋으면, 다른 선수들보다 세 배의 클린슛을 성공시킬 텐데.'라는 가정법 과거 문장이다. 직설법으로는 반대의 현재시제이므로, As가 이끄는 종속절과 주절에 모두 현재시제가 있는 ②가 정답이다.
17　가정법 과거시제에 맞게 If절에 sense의 과거형을, 주절에 can의 과거형을 써서 알맞게 영작한다.
18　앞부분에 not이 있으므로 ① no longer와 ④ no more는 적절하지 않다.
19　앞의 명사 delivery robots를 수식하도록 현재분사 형태인 flying으로 쓰는 것이 적절하다.
20　a variety of = various: 다양한
21　이 글은 '로봇이 어디에서나 우리를 도울 수 있으며, 일을 더 빠르고 더 쉽게 해 주고 있다'는 내용의 글이므로, 제목으로는 ④번 '우리 주변의 로봇들 - 현재와 미래'가 적절하다.
22　'집안일 도우미 로봇'을 가리킨다.
23　'재난 지역 복구'는 '집안일 도우미 로봇'이 할 수 있는 일에 언급되어 있지 않다.
24　'어떤 사람들은 ~하고', '다른 사람들은 ~하다'라고 할 때는 'some people'과 'other people'을 사용하는 것이 적절하다. ① 둘 중 나머지 하나, ② 또 하나(셋 이상 중에서 두 번째 것을 언급할 때 사용, 항상 단수 취급), ③ 나머지 전체, ④ 서로
25　ⓑ와 ④: 명사적 용법, ①: 형용사적 용법, ②, ③, ⑤: 부사적 용법

# 8

# Which Is the Best Way?

## Reading 교과서

### 확인문제 p.176

1 T  2 F  3 T  4 F  5 T  6 F

### 확인문제 p.177

1 T  2 F  3 T  4 F  5 T  6 F

### 확인문제 p.178

1 T  2 F  3 T  4 F  5 T

### 확인문제 p.179

1 T  2 F  3 T  4 F  5 T  6 F

## 교과서 확인학습 A p.180~182

| | |
|---|---|
| 01 Wise | 02 met |
| 03 agreed | 04 became lost |
| 05 any further | 06 for a while |
| 07 correct | 08 walk back |
| 09 leave that way | 10 walk around |
| 11 keep walking | 12 go on forever |
| 13 new path | 14 shook his head |
| 15 could find | 16 separate |
| 17 reached, whole | 18 shortest way out |
| 19 hurried down | 20 was gone |
| 21 thought to himself, best way out | |
| 22 wrong, the only wise | 23 wrong |
| 24 Everyone | 25 created his future |
| 26 walked deeper | 27 was attacked, died of |
| 28 protect himself | 29 made his way out of |

| | |
|---|---|
| 30 a group of | 31 join them |
| 32 great kindness | 33 were moved |
| 34 Later | 35 a safe path |
| 36 without getting lost | 37 went straight |
| 38 had been | 39 Thanks to |
| 40 who climbed | 41 the quickest ways |
| 42 This is how | 43 one journey, another |
| 44 your own path | 45 act on it |
| 46 have been living | |

## 교과서 확인학습 B p.183~185

1 The Five Wise Men

2 One day, five wise men met on the road.

3 They agreed to travel together

4 On the way, however, they became lost in a thick forest.

5 Before walking any further, they decided to stop and find the best way out.

6 After thinking for a while, the first man said, "I strongly feel that we should go left."

7 The second man said, "We should go right, because *right* also means 'correct.'"

8 Then the third man said, "Let's walk back.

9 We came that way, so we can leave that way.

10 Then we can walk around the forest."

11 The fourth man disagreed and said, "I think we should keep walking straight.

12 The forest cannot go on forever.

13 A new path will open."

14 Looking at them all, the fifth man shook his head and said, "I know how to solve this. Just wait."

15 He started to climb the tallest tree he could find.

16 As he climbed, everyone else decided to go their separate ways.

17 When the fifth man reached the top, he could see the whole forest.

18 Looking at all the paths, he found the shortest way out.

19 He hurried down to tell the others.

20 However, when he got to the bottom, everyone was gone.

21 He thought to himself, *Where did they go? I found the best way out.*

22 He thought they were all wrong and he was the only wise man.

23 However, he was wrong.

24 Everyone was wise.

25 Each man had chosen his path and created his future.

26 The man who went to the left walked deeper into the forest.

27 He was attacked by wild animals and almost died of hunger.

28 Soon he learned how to protect himself and find food.

29 In the end, he made his way out of the forest and taught others survival skills.

30 The man who went to the right met a group of thieves.

31 They took everything from him and made him join them.

32 While he was with them, he showed them great kindness.

33 The thieves were moved by his kindness and learned from his wisdom.

34 Later, they also became wise men.

35 The man who walked back created a safe path around the forest.

36 Using this path, people could get where they were going without getting lost, even though the trip took a little longer.

37 The man who went straight became a pioneer.

38 He left the forest and discovered places no one else had been before.

39 Thanks to him, people could enjoy these new beautiful lands.

40 The man who climbed the tree became a guide.

41 Since he had found many different paths, he was able to teach people how to find the quickest ways to their destinations.

42 This is how the five men found their own paths.

43 Like them, we are each on our own journey in life, and we cannot compare one journey to another.

44 You have to create your own path.

45 Listen to yourself, make a decision, and act on it.

46 Then, someday, you will realize that you have been living the life that is right for you.

---

서술형 실전문제     p.186~187

01 (1) Hunger   (2) discover   (3) wisdom   (4) moved

02 ②

03 (1) Looking at them all, the fifth man shook his head.

   (2) Listening to yourself, you will realize that your life is right.

   (3) Moved by his kindness, the thieves learned from his wisdom.

04 has found → had found, 또는 he was able to → he is able to

05 was attacked by, how to protect himself

06 walking

07 While[As] he was looking at them all 또는 While[As] he looked at them all

08 '오른쪽'은 또한 '옳은'이라는 의미이기 때문이다.

09 a group of thieves

10 His kindness moved the thieves

11 the way how → the way나 how 또는 the way in which나 the way that

12 (A) your own journey   (B) your own path

---

01 (1) hunger: 굶주림. 굶주림은 세상에 큰 고통을 야기한다. (2) discover: 발견하다, 찾다. 콜럼버스는 아메리카를 발견한 최초의 사람이 아니었다. (3) wisdom: 지혜, 슬기. 위대한 사람들의 지혜를 듣는 것은 좋은 일이다. (4) move: 감동시키다. 나는 그녀의 노래와 아름다운 목소리에 감동 받았다.

02 ②의 영영풀이는 protect(보호하다)의 영영풀이이다. ① agree: 동의하다, 찬성하다. 다른 사람이 제안한 아이디어를 받아들이다 ② attack: 공격하다. to try to hurt or damage(피해를 입히거나 다치게 하다) ③ survival: 생존. 어려운 상황에도 불구하고 이후에 계속 살아남는 상태. ④ pioneer: 선구자, 개척자. 어떤 일을 하거나 새로운 곳을 여행하는 최초의 사람들 중의 하나. ⑤ destination: 목적지, 도착지. 어떤 사람이나 사물이 가고 있는 혹은 보내지고 있는 장소

03 분사구문이 들어가는 다양한 문장들이다. (3)은 수동태에서 온 분사구문으로, move를 moved로 고치는 것에 유의한다.

04 내용상 '그가 여러 다양한 길을 발견했(었)기 때문에, 사람들에게 목적지에 이르는 가장 빠른 길을 찾는 법을 가르쳐줄 수 있(었)다.'는 내용이므로, 종속절과 주절의 시제가 일치해야 한다. has found를 had found로 과거완료시제로 고쳐서 주절의 was에 일치시키거나, he was able to를 he is able to로 고쳐서 종속절의 has found와 일치시키면 시제가 서로 맞게 된다.

05 야생동물들의 습격을 받은 것은 수동태로 표현한다. was

33

attacked by, 자신을 지키는 방법은 how to protect himself 이다.

06 keep ~ing: 계속해서 ~하다

07 'Looking at them all'은 동시동작을 나타내는 분사구문으로, 접속사 'while'이나 'as'를 사용하여 고치는 것이 적절하다.

08 'right'는 또한 'correct'라는 의미이기 때문이다.

09 '도둑 무리'를 가리킨다. a group of+집합명사: 단수 취급, a group of+군집명사(구성원): 복수 취급

10 His kindness를 주어로 하여 능동태로 고치는 것이 적절하다.

11 the way와 관계부사 how는 같이 쓸 수 없으므로 둘 중 하나만 쓰거나 the way in which 또는 the way that으로 쓰는 것이 적절하다.

12 여러분 각각은 인생에서 '자기 자신만의 여행'을 하고 있고, 한 여정을 다른 것과 비교할 수 없다. 당신은 자신의 목소리를 듣고, 결정하고, 그 결정에 따라 행동함으로써 '당신 자신만의 길'을 만들어가야 한다.

### 단원별 예상문제
p.188~192

01 on, on
02 (1) compare  (2) disagrees  (3) climb  (4) realize
03 (1) (d)ivided  (2) (u)nkindness  (3) (t)hick
04 ⑤
05 (1) (s)olve  (2) survival  (3) (p)ioneer
   (4) (d)estination
06 (r)ealize   07 ④   08 ⑤   09 ④
10 ①   11 ④
12 realize that you have been living the life that is right
13 who climbed the tree, had found, how to find the quickest
14 who walked back created, Using, get where they were, without getting, even though
15 (A) forever  (B) a new path
16 nodded → shook   17 ④   18 ④
19 ③   20 the others   21 ②
22 him → himself   23 ⑤   24 ④
25 had been   26 they should
27 ①   28 ④

01 • on the way to ~: ~에 가는 길에. 너는 기차역으로 가는 길에 은행을 지나가게 된다. • act on: ~에 따라 행동하다. 단지 본능에 따라서만 행동한다면 당신은 동물입니다.

02 (1) compare: 비교하다, 견주다. 나는 인터넷으로 여러 디지털

카메라의 가격을 비교할 것이다. (2) disagree: 동의하지 않다, 의견이 다르다. Janet은 모든 것에 있어서 부모님과 의견이 다르다. (3) climb: 오르다, 올라가다. 그 산을 오르는 것은 쉽지 않다. (4) realize: 깨닫다, 자각하다. 그들은 자신들의 작품이 얼마나 창의적인지 자각하지 못했다.

03 (1) 동의어 관계이다. move: 감동시키다, touch: 감동시키다, separate: 분리된, divided: 분리된 (2) 반의어 관계이다. bottom: 밑, 바닥, top: 꼭대기, 정상, kindness: 친절, unkindness: 불친절 (3) 반의어 관계이다. agree: 동의하다, 찬성하다, disagree: 동의하지 않다, thick: 두꺼운, (나무가) 울창한, thin: 얇은, 가느다란

04 arrive at: 도착하다. 우리는 제시간에 공항에 도착하지 못했다. ① realize: 깨닫다, 자각하다 ② compare: 비교하다 ③ disagree: 동의하지 않다 ④ solve: (문제, 곤경을) 해결하다, 풀다 ⑤ reach: ~에 이르다, 도착하다

05 (1) solve: (문제, 곤경을) 해결하다 (2) survival: 생존 (3) pioneer: 선구자, 개척자 (4) destination: 목적지, 도착지

06 realize: 깨닫다, 자각하다. 어떤 것이 사실이거나 일어났다는 것을 알고 이해하다. 당신은 이것이 그녀에게 얼마나 중요한지 인식하지 못하고 있는 것 같다.

07 ④의 'to부정사'는 '부사적' 용법으로 쓰여서 '목적'(~하기 위해서)을 나타낸다. 나머지는 모두 '명사적' 용법으로, 동사의 '목적어'로 사용되었다.

08 보기의 'how to부정사'는 '명사구'로 '어떻게 ~할지'라는 뜻이다. 일반적으로 'how+주어+should+V' 형태로 바꿔 쓸 수 있으며, 내용상 주어는 they가 되어야 한다.

09 과거완료시제의 적절한 사용에 관한 질문이다. ④의 과거완료는 '다섯 번째 남자가 꼭대기에 도달했을 때, 그는 전체 숲을 (이미) 봤었다.'는 내용이 되어, 어법상 어색하다. had seen을 could see로 바꾸는 것이 자연스럽다.

10 분사구문은 '부사절'을 '부사구'로 전환한 것이다. 일반적으로 '부사절'은 '접속사+주어+동사'가 기본인데, 주절과 종속절의 주어가 같으면, 접속사와 주어를 생략하고, 동사를 분사로 전환하면 된다.

11 방법을 나타내는 선행사 the way가 있을 때, 두 문장을 관계부사 how로 연결할 수 있는데 the way와 how를 동시에 쓰는 것은 불가능하다. 그러므로 둘 중 하나만 쓰거나 선행사 뒤에 how 대신 관계부사 역할이 가능한 that 또는 '전치사+관계대명사 in which' 등을 쓸 수 있다. 관계대명사로 쓰인 that 앞에 전치사를 쓸 수 없으므로 in that은 부적절하다.

12 접속사 that과 관계대명사 that이 둘 다 나오고, 현재완료진행시제가 나오는 문장이다. 주격 관계대명사 that의 선행사가 the life임에 유의하여, 적절히 영작한다.

13 중복 사용이 가능하므로 **the**는 자주 사용된다. '나무 위로 올라간 남자'는 '관계대명사' who와 동사 climbed를 활용하고, '발견했었기 때문'은 '과거완료시제 had found'를, '~를 찾는 법'은 'how to부정사'를 이용한다. 형용사 quick의 '최상급' 'the quickest'를 쓰는 것에도 유의한다.

14 '분사구문' 표현 Using과, '가고자 하는 길에 다다르다'를 'get where they were going'으로 표현하는 것에 유의하여 알맞게 빈칸을 채운다.

15 숲이 '영원히' 계속될 수는 없고 '새로운 길'이 열릴 것이라고 믿었기 때문이다.

16 다섯 번째 남자가 "나는 이것을 해결하는 방법을 알아요. 잠깐 기다려 보세요."라고 말한 것은 앞의 말들에 동의한 것이 아니므로 'nodded'를 'shook'으로 고치는 것이 적절하다. nod one's head: 고개를 끄덕이다; 찬성[승인, 인정]하다, shake one's head: 고개를 가로 젓다; 부정[거부]하다

17 세 번째 남자는 '뒤로 돌아가자'고 제안했고, 똑바로 계속 걸어 나가야 한다고 생각한 사람은 '네 번째 남자'이다.

18 앞에 나오는 내용과 상반되는 내용이 뒤에 이어지므로 However가 가장 적절하다. ② 즉[말하자면], ③ 게다가, 더욱이, ⑤ 그러므로

19 주어진 문장의 'Looking at all the paths'에 주목한다. ③번 앞 문장의 결과에 해당하므로 ③번이 적절하다.

20 '다른 사람들'을 가리킨다. the others: 정해진 범위 안에서 일부를 제외한 나머지 전부를 가리키는 부정대명사

21 ⓐ die of: ~으로 죽다, ⓑ take A from B: B에게서 A를 가져가다

22 주어와 목적어가 같으므로 '재귀대명사'로 고치는 것이 적절하다.

23 (B)와 ⑤: 감동시키다, ① (~의 길, 방향으로) 나아가다[진행되다], ② 이사하다, ③ (몸 등을) 움직이다, (사물을) 옮기다, ④ <~할 것을> (동의로서) 제의[제안]하다

24 '오른쪽으로 간 남자가 도둑들과 얼마나 오래 살았는지'는 대답할 수 없다. ① Wild animals attacked him. ② He taught others survival skills. ③ He met a group of thieves. ⑤ They were moved by the kindness of the man who went to the right, and they learned from his wisdom.

25 과거 시점을 기준으로 그 이전에 일어난 일이 과거의 한 시점까지 영향을 미치는 상태를 나타내는 과거완료 had been으로 쓰는 것이 적절하다.

26 '의문사+to부정사'는 '의문사+주어+should+동사원형'으로 바꿔 쓸 수 있다.

27 ① 교훈적인, 이 글은 '우리는 각각 인생에서 자기 자신만의 여행을 하고 있고, 우리는 한 여정을 다른 것과 비교할 수 없으며 당신은 당신 자신만의 길을 만들어가야 한다.'는 내용의 글이므로, '교훈적인' 분위기라고 하는 것이 적절하다. ② 냉소적인, ③ 혼란스러운, ④ 의심 많은, 회의적인, ⑤ 축제 분위기의

28 이 글은 '우리는 각각 인생에서 자기 자신만의 여행을 하고 있고, 우리는 한 여정을 다른 것과 비교할 수 없으며 당신은 당신 자신만의 길을 만들어가야 한다.'는 내용의 글이므로, 주제로는 ④번 '당신에게 맞는 삶을 살아가기'가 적절하다.

# 교과서 파헤치기

Lesson 5

1 damage, 손상시키다   2 disappear, 사라지다
3 surface, 표면   4 underwater, 수중에, 해저에
5 architect, 건축가   6 goal, 목표, 목적
7 greenery, 푸른 잎, 푸른 나무   8 climate, 기후
9 statue, 조각상   10 innovation, 혁신
11 grain, 곡물, 알곡   12 artwork, (예술적) 작품
13 explanation, 설명   14 opinion, 의견
15 reusable, 재사용할 수 있는   16 shade, 그늘

## 단어 TEST Step 1                p.02

01 (예술적) 작품   02 영리한, 똑똑한   03 건축가
04 포함하다   05 건축(술)   06 설명
07 조각, 조각상   08 끌다, 매혹시키다   09 곡물, 알곡
10 푸른 잎, 푸른 나무   11 바라건대   12 기후
13 혁신   14 추가적인   15 자료, 소재, 재료
16 손상시키다   17 오염   18 인식, 의식
19 원치 않는, 불필요한
20 예방하다, 막다, 방지하다   21 믿기 힘든, 굉장한
22 보호하다, 지키다   23 친환경적인
24 제공하다   25 표면   26 주제
27 줄이다   28 재사용할 수 있는   29 구조(물)
30 분리하다   31 사라지다
32 격려하다, 장려하다   33 상기시키다
34 자원   35 ~ 이외에도
36 무너지다, 고장 나다, (썩어서) ~이 되다   37 ~을 버리다
38 ~에 지루해하다   39 ~와 조화하여
40 ~에 기여하다, (~의) 원인이 되다   41 다양한
42 ~을 돌보다   43 ~을 생각해 내다

## 단어 TEST Step 2                p.03

01 pollution   02 additional   03 awareness
04 innovation   05 architect   06 contain
07 theme   08 prevent   09 throughout
10 damage   11 protect   12 eco-friendly
13 resource   14 encourage   15 attract
16 reduce   17 disappear   18 grain
19 underwater   20 unique   21 unwanted
22 reusable   23 incredible   24 suggestion
25 artwork   26 natural   27 opinion
28 explanation   29 seriously   30 properly
31 realize   32 statue   33 structure
34 separate   35 break down   36 get better
37 take care of   38 come up with   39 a variety of
40 have a point   41 in harmony with
42 be bored with   43 in addition to

## 대화문 TEST Step 1                p.05~06

**Listen & Talk 1 A**

plastic bags / not good for, environment, reduce, plastic bags / In my opinion, should bring reusable bags

**Listen & Talk 1 B**

up, going up / third floor, Why don't, take the stairs / all the way / lots of, save, protect the environment / one elevator ride, much energy / adds up, In my opinion, taking care of, little things / have a point, Let's take

**Listen & Talk 1 C**

like to make a suggestion, throw, away, of recycling, As, because, resources, protect, in my opinion, trash cans, to encourage recycling, place, colored recycling bins, remind, separate, properly

**Listen & Talk 2 A**

holding / What kinds of / theme, are holding, raise students' awareness / wait to see it

**Listen & Talk 2 B**

article / What, about / looks like, plastic bag, made, of / amazing / breaks down, soil, disappears, three minutes / reduce plastic waste / company, selling, this year, wait to use

**Listen & Talk 2 C**

are, going to / sheep park / interesting / protect the environment / How can / chemicals, unwanted plants, chemicals, not needed / bright, can't wait to

**Do It Yourself**

to buy / In my opinion, any more / bored with / about using / find out how to do it / interesting, to make

### Listen & Talk 1 A

B: I think we're using too many plastic bags.

G: I agree. It's not good for the environment. How can we reduce our use of plastic bags?

B: In my opinion, we should bring reusable bags when we go shopping.

### Listen & Talk 1 B

G: Jiho, hurry up! The elevator is going up soon.

B: The science room is just on the third floor. Why don't we take the stairs?

G: I don't want to walk all the way up there.

B: Come on. Elevators use lots of energy. We need to save energy to protect the environment.

G: But one elevator ride doesn't use that much energy.

B: That's true, but the energy from all the elevator rides adds up over time. In my opinion, taking care of the environment starts with the little things.

G: You have a point. Let's take the stairs.

### Listen & Talk 1 C

B: Today, I'd like to make a suggestion about the trash problem at our school. I've found that many students just throw things away instead of recycling them. As you know, however, recycling is very important because it saves resources and helps protect the environment. So, in my opinion, we need to reduce the number of trash cans at school to encourage recycling. Why don't we place four different colored recycling bins on every floor instead? This will remind students to separate the paper, glass, plastic, and cans properly.

### Listen & Talk 2 A

B: Our club is holding a photo contest next week.

G: What kinds of photos will be in it?

B: The theme is pollution around the world. We are holding this contest to raise students' awareness of environmental problems.

G: That sounds nice. I can't wait to see it!

### Listen & Talk 2 B

G: I read a cool article today.

B: What was it about?

G: It was about a new bag. It just looks like a plastic bag, but it's made mostly of corn.

B: That sounds really amazing.

G: Yes, but there's more. The bag breaks down in soil in only three months and disappears in about

three minutes in warm water!

B: Wow! That will help us reduce plastic waste by a lot!

G: I know! The company will start selling the bag sometime this year. I can't wait to use it!

### Listen & Talk 2 C

B: What are we going to do this weekend, Mihee?

G: Why don't we go to the sheep park near my house?

B: A sheep park? How interesting! Are there really sheep in the park?

G: Yes. They are there to protect the environment.

B: How can they help the environment?

G: You know, people usually use chemicals to kill unwanted plants. The sheep in the park eat those plants, so the chemicals are not needed.

B: What a bright idea! I can't wait to visit the park!

### Do It Yourself

G: I want to buy a new bag.

B: You already have too many bags. In my opinion, you don't need any more.

G: But I'm bored with my old bags.

B: Then how about using old clothes to make a new bag? You can find out how to do it online.

G: Oh, that sounds interesting! I can't wait to make my own bag.

01 for us to find

02 creative ways, save, earth

03 example, underwater museum

04 meet, professor, explanation, special

05 where, tourists travel

06 most popular, at, area's

07 However, damaging parts, near

08 To prevent, something interesting

09 attracted, part, dying, better

10 underwater, away, where, dying

11 about, below, contains, statues

12 made from materials, support

13 provide, for, live on

14 types, statues, artwork unique

15 people, variety, life, statues

16 realize, rich, important, save

17 using, protect, environment, land

18 what, architect, says, eco-friendly

19 hot throughout, year

20 need, which uses, contributes

21 why, begun, less, still

22 example, designed, open structure

23 outside air, move throughout

24 natural, how, stay cool

25 addition, making, structures, add

26 provides, protects, direct, keeps

27 only, also provide, with

28 goals, new style, architecture

29 keep coming up with

30 field, ways, protecting, environment

31 With, able, far into

29 will keep coming up with, eco-friendly ideas

30 Every field has, protecting

31 With, innovation, will be able to live together, far into

01 It, for us to find ways

02 creative ways to save

03 underwater museum

04 meet, professor, listen to, explanation

05 where, tourists travel every year

06 the most popular, to do, is looking at

07 However, are seriously damaging parts, near

08 To prevent this, something interesting

09 if, attracted, to, dying areas, to get better

10 made, underwater, away from, where, dying

11 about, meters below, surface, contains, statues

12 are made from, that support sea life

13 provide additional places for, to live on

14 will grow on, which will make, unique

15 want people to see a variety of, on

16 how rich sea life is, how important it is

17 using architecture to protect, on land

18 what, says about eco-friendly

19 throughout the year

20 need, which uses, contributes to climate change

21 That's why, have begun to design, that use less, are still

22 For example, are designed to have, open structure

23 it, for outside air to move throughout

24 natural, how these buildings stay cool

25 In addition to making, large gardens

26 provides, protects, from direct sunlight, keeps

27 not only help, but also provide, with, quality of life

28 goals, new style, architecture

1 우리가 환경을 보호할 수 있는 방법을 찾는 것은 중요하다.

2 몇몇 사람들은 지구를 구하기 위한 창의적인 방법을 찾았다.

3 한 예로 멕시코 칸쿤에 있는 수중 박물관이 있다.

4 미술학 교수인 Rosa Allison 박사를 만나서 이 특별한 박물관에 대한 설명을 들어보자.

5 Rosa: 칸쿤은 매년 480만 명의 관광객이 여행하는 도시이다.

6 그곳에서 할 수 있는 가장 인기 있는 활동 중 하나는 그 지역의 바닷속의 아름다운 해양 생물을 관찰하는 것이다.

7 하지만, 관광 활동들이 칸쿤 근처의 바다 일부를 심각하게 훼손시키고 있다.

8 이러한 일을 방지하기 위해서, 예술가들이 흥미로운 생각을 해냈다.

9 그들은 만약 관광객들을 바다의 다른 쪽으로 유인한다면, 그 죽어가는 지역이 호전될 시간을 가질 수 있을 것이라 생각했다.

10 그들은 해양 생물이 죽어가는 지역으로부터 떨어진 해저에 수중 박물관을 만들었다.

11 그 박물관은 해수면에서 14미터 아래에 있으며 500개의 조각상이 있다.

12 그 조각상들은 해양 생물에게 도움이 되는 재료들로 만들어졌다.

13 그것들은 식물과 동물들이 살 수 있는 추가적인 장소를 제공한다.

14 시간이 흐르면, 많은 형태의 바다 생명체들이 그 조각상에서 자라게 될 것이며, 이것이 그 예술 작품을 독특하게 만들 것이다.

15 예술가들은 사람들이 그 조각상들에서 (살고 있는) 다양한 해양 생명체들을 보길 원한다.

16 만약 사람들이 해양 생물이 얼마나 풍부한지 깨닫는다면, 그들은 바다를 지키는 것이 얼마나 중요한지 이해할 것이다.

17 싱가포르에서는 사람들이 육지의 환경을 보호하기 위해 건축을 이용하고 있다.

18 건축가인 Rajesh Khan이 친환경 건물에 대해 말하는 것을 들어보자.

19 Rajesh: 싱가포르는 연중 더운 곳이다.

20 대부분의 건물들은 에어컨 가동이 필요한데, 이로 인해 많은 에너지가 사용되고 있으며 기후 변화의 원인이 되고 있다.

21 그것이 싱가포르의 건축가들이 에어컨을 덜 쓰면서도 실내에서 여전히 시원한 느낌이 들 수 있는 친환경적인 건물들을 디자인하기 시작한 이유이다.

22 가령, 싱가포르의 많은 건물들은 개방형 구조를 포함하게 디자인되었다.

23 이러한 구조는 외부 공기가 건물을 관통하는 것을 가능케 한다.

24 이러한 자연적인 공기의 흐름이 이 건물을 시원하게 유지해 주는 방법이다.

25 건축가들은 개방형 구조를 만드는 것 외에도 큰 정원을 더한다.

26 이러한 녹지 공간은 그늘을 제공하고 직사광선으로부터 건물의 부분들을 지켜주어 건물을 시원 하게 유지한다.

27 이와 같은 친환경적인 건물들은 환경을 보호하는 것을 도울 뿐만 아니라 사람들에게 양질의 삶을 제공한다.

28 그것들이 바로 이러한 새로운 건축 방식의 목표이다.

29 바라건대, 건축가들은 새로운 친환경 아이디어를 계속해서 생각해 낼 것이다.

30 모든 분야에서 환경을 보호하는 다른 방식이 있다.

31 더 나은 혁신으로 인해 먼 미래에 인간과 자연은 함께 조화를 이루며 살아갈 수 있을 것이다.

## 본문 TEST Step 4~Step 5 p.15~18

1 It is important for us to find ways to protect the environment.

2 Some people have found creative ways to save the earth.

3 One example is an underwater museum in Cancun, Mexico.

4 Let's meet Dr. Rosa Allison, an art professor, and listen to her explanation about the special museum.

5 Rosa: Cancun is a city where 4.8 million tourists travel every year.

6 One of the most popular activities to do there is looking at the area's beautiful sea life underwater.

7 However, tourist activities are seriously damaging parts of the sea near Cancun.

8 To prevent this, artists did something interesting.

9 They thought if they attracted tourists to a different part of the sea, the dying areas could have time to get better.

10 They made an underwater museum away from the places where sea life was dying.

11 It's about 14 meters below the surface and contains 500 statues.

12 The statues are made from materials that support sea life.

13 They provide additional places for plants and animals to live on.

14 Over time, many types of sea life will grow on the statues, which will make the artwork unique.

15 The artists want people to see a variety of sea life on the statues.

16 If people realize how rich sea life is, they will understand how important it is to save the sea.

17 In Singapore, people are using architecture to protect the environment on land.

18 Let's hear what Rajesh Khan, an architect, says about eco-friendly buildings.

19 Rajesh: Singapore is hot throughout the year.

20 Most buildings need air conditioning, which uses a lot of energy and contributes to climate change.

21 That's why architects in Singapore have begun to design eco-friendly buildings that use less air conditioning but are still cool inside.

22 For example, many buildings in Singapore are designed to have an open structure.

23 This structure makes it possible for outside air to move throughout a building.

24 This natural air flow is how these buildings stay cool.

25 In addition to making open structures, architects add large gardens.

26 This greenery provides shade and protects parts of the building from direct sunlight, which keeps the building cooler.

27 Eco-friendly buildings like these not only help protect the environment, but also provide people with a good quality of life.

28 Those are the goals of this new style of architecture.

29 Hopefully, architects will keep coming up with new eco-friendly ideas.

30 Every field has different ways of protecting the environment.

31 With more innovation, humans and nature will be able to live together in harmony far into the future.

## 구석구석지문 TEST Step 1 p.19

**Listen & Talk 2 D Talk Together**

1. Have, heard, edible spoons, amazing
2. No, haven't, Tell me, them
3. are made of grain, save resources
4. sounds awesome, can't wait to use

**Presentation Time**

1. How, make our school eco-friendly
2. In my opinion
3. The front wall, a great place
4. helps to keep, cool by blocking sunlight

5. reduce the amount of energy used

**Think & Write Step 3**

1. Save the Earth

2. innovative, environmentally friendly item

3. a cookie cup

4. is made in the shape of

5. After, can just eat it

6. By doing this, can save paper

7. can chage the world

8. Be a part of

## 구석구석지문 TEST Step 2      p.20

**Listen & Talk 2 D Talk Together**

1. A: Have you heard of edible spoons? They're amazing!

2. B: No, I haven't. Tell me about them.

3. A: They are made of grain. They will save resources.

4. B: That sounds awesome. I can't wait to use them.

**Presentation Time**

1. How can we make our school eco-friendly?

2. In my opinion, we need a green wall.

3. The front wall of our school is a great place for it.

4. A green wall helps to keep the building cool by blocking sunlight.

5. This could reduce the amount of energy used for air conditioning.

**Think & Write Step 3**

1. Eat Your Cup and Save the Earth!

2. Here' an innovative, environmentally friendly item!

3. It is a cookie cup.

4. It's a cookie that is made in the shape of a cup.

5. After you use the cup, you can just eat it.

6. By doing this, you can save paper or plastic.

7. The cookie cup can chage the world.

8. Be a part of the change!

Lesson 6

## 단어 TEST Step 1      p.21

| | | |
|---|---|---|
| 01 환불 | 02 사용자 | 03 약점 |
| 04 문제(점), 쟁점 | 05 빌려주는 사람 | 06 부정적인, 나쁜 |
| 07 정기적으로 | 08 긍정적인 | 09 망가진, 고장 난 |
| 10 상태, 조건 | 11 제공하다 | 12 화난, 속상한 |
| 13 우려, 근심 | 14 타당한, 합리적인, (값이) 적당한 | |
| 15 업로드하다, 전송하다 | | 16 정확한, 정밀한 |
| 17 어디든지 | 18 의사소통하다 | 19 할인 |
| 20 자원 | 21 균형 잡힌 | 22 경험하다 |
| 23 요금, 수수료 | 24 선택하다, 고르다 | 25 자유롭게 |
| 26 향상하다, 개선하다 | | 27 돌려주다, 반납하다 |
| 28 주인, 소유주 | 29 개인의, 개인적인 | 30 다운로드하다 |
| 31 경제 | 32 목적 | 33 믿을 수 있는 |
| 34 빌리다 | 35 무료로 | 36 ~을 돌보다 |
| 37 ~을 알고 있다 | 38 도시를 떠나, 다른 곳으로 떠나 | |
| 39 ~을 돌보다 | 40 할인 중인 | |
| 41 ~보다 적은, ~ 미만의 | | |
| 42 ~하면 어쩌지?, ~라면 어떻게 될까? | | 43 ~을 찾다 |

## 단어 TEST Step 2      p.22

| | | |
|---|---|---|
| 01 choose | 02 reliable | 03 improve |
| 04 exact | 05 balanced | 06 communicate |
| 07 download | 08 economy | 09 concern |
| 10 reasonable | 11 borrow | 12 weakness |
| 13 discount | 14 upload | 15 freely |
| 16 refund | 17 broken | 18 regularly |
| 19 issue | 20 condition | 21 resource |
| 22 positive | 23 user | 24 lender |
| 25 experience | 26 personal | 27 wherever |
| 28 fee | 29 negative | 30 owner |
| 31 provide | 32 purpose | 33 share |
| 34 return | 35 less than | 36 for free |
| 37 on sale | 38 search for | 39 ask for |
| 40 pick up | 41 take care of = look after | |
| 42 be aware of | 43 out of town | |

## 단어 TEST Step 3      p.23

1 broken, 고장 난    2 freely, 자유롭게    3 fix, 고치다

4 weakness, 약점    5 fee, 요금    6 concern, 우려, 근심

7 negative, 부정적인, 나쁜    8 choose, 선택하다, 고르다

9 download, 다운로드하다    10 discount, 할인

11 provide, 제공하다　12 reliable, 믿을 수 있는
13 return, 돌려주다, 반환하다
14 improve, 향상하다, 개선하다　15 economy, 경제
16 reasonable, 타당한, 합리적인, (값이) 적당한

## 대화문 TEST Step 1　　　　　p.24~25

### Listen & Talk 1 A

pairs, on sale, Which do you prefer / prefer, to, black ones / cheaper / design, white ones better

### Listen & Talk 1 B

Which, prefer, or / healthier choice, made with, other, ingredients / much, expensive than / prefer, to / Eating healthy, to / cheaper, spend, on, instead / our spending habits, different

### Listen & Talk 1 C

curly, straighten, recommend, good place / difference between, two / free treatment to keep, healthy / What about / provide, for free, student discounts / Which, prefer / prefer, to, for, to, regularly

### Listen & Talk 2 A

get a refund, similar / Don't forget, receipt / get a refund / won't forget

### Listen & Talk 2 B

flea market / to sell, market research / Market research, that / Because, find, what items are popular / decide what to sell / set reasonable prices / anything else / to register, by / reminding

### Listen & Talk 2 C

review / How, review / focus on / don't forget to talk, bad points / won't, balanced review / it easier for, to choose better products / what, like to, useful information

### Do It Yourself

speakers, pretty cool / Which do you prefer, black one / to, discount coupon / Although, right, better sound quality

## 대화문 TEST Step 2　　　　　p.26~27

### Listen & Talk 1 A

G: These two pairs of shoes are on sale! Which do you prefer?

B: Well, I prefer the white shoes to the black ones.

G: Why is that? The black ones are cheaper.

B: Yes, but I like the design of the white ones better.

### Listen & Talk 1 B

G: Which do you prefer, the Special Sandwich or the Classic Sandwich?

B: Well, the Special Sandwich is the healthier choice. It's made with lots of fresh vegetables and other healthy ingredients.

G: But it's much more expensive than the Classic Sandwich.

B: I know, but I prefer the Special Sandwich to the Classic Sandwich. Eating healthy is important to me.

G: I prefer the cheaper one. I'll spend my money on books instead.

B: I guess our spending habits are different.

### Listen & Talk 1 C

G1: I think my hair is too curly. I want to straighten my hair. Can you recommend a good place?

G2: Sure. I know two places, Styles Studio and Hair Castle.

G1: Is there any difference between the two?

G2: Well, Styles Studio provides free treatment to keep your hair healthy.

G1: That's great. What about Hair Castle?

G2: Hair Castle doesn't provide treatment for free, but they give student discounts.

G1: Okay. Which do you prefer?

G2: I prefer Styles Studio to Hair Castle. It's important for me to get hair treatment regularly.

### Listen & Talk 2 A

B: I'm going to get a refund for these clothes this evening. I found I have similar ones.

W: Okay. Don't forget to bring your receipt. Last time you couldn't get a refund because you didn't bring it.

B: Okay, Mom. I won't forget it this time.

### Listen & Talk 2 B

G: What should we sell at the flea market next month?

B: Before we choose anything to sell, I think we need to do some market research.

G: Market research? Why do we need that?

B: Because it helps us find out what items are popular these days.

G: I see. Then we can decide what to sell at the market.

B: That's right. It will also help us set reasonable prices for our items.

G: Cool. Is there anything else we should do?

B: Oh, don't forget to register our names by this Friday.

G: Right. Thanks for reminding me.

G: I tried Spring Chips recently, and now I want to review them.

B: That sounds fun. How will you do your review?

G: I'll make a video. I want to focus on their delicious taste!

B: Okay, but don't forget to talk about their bad points too.

G: I won't. I want to give a balanced review.

B: Good. Your video will make it easier for people to choose better products.

G: That's exactly what I want. I'd like to give people more useful information about the product.

G: Jinho, look! These two speakers look pretty cool.

B: Yeah, they do. Which do you prefer, the red one or the black one?

G: I prefer the red one to the black one. It's only 20 dollars, and it comes with a discount coupon for music downloads.

B: Although the black one is 40 dollars, I think it's the right one for me. I heard it has better sound quality.

01 Life, Sharing Economy
02 What should we do
03 Why don't we
04 don't have, tent
05 Should, buy one
06 Also, take care of
07 Don't worry, apps, help
08 Borrow from, neighbors
09 helps, easily find, others
10 download, search, another, item
11 pick up, item, return
12 December 12, 2019
13 asked for, less than
14 saving, by borrowing, need
15 Also, environmentally friendly
16 fewer products, more resources
17 March 7, 2020
18 Seeing, positive reviews, borrow
19 got, however, was broken   20 so upset
21 March 9, 2020
22 such a negative experience

23 fix, lenders, update, regularly
24 let, know, exact, product   25 can look after
26 perfect app, lovers, owners
27 owners, reliable, look after
28 owner, looking, uploads, post
29 walkers, send messages, owner
30 checks, reviews, chooses, person
31 November 12, 2019
32 use, whenever, out of
33 concerns, personal information though
34 What if, other purposes   35 November 14, 2019
36 aware of, issue
37 allows, communicate, without showing
38 February 22, 2020
39 aren't allowed, have any
40 by using, experience, walking
41 What great apps   42 borrow, take care of
43 That's right
44 kinds, services, part, sharing
45 share, with, provide, fee
46 services, have, weaknesses
47 left negative reviews, services
48 more, use, services, improve

01 Life, Sharing Economy
02 What should we do
03 Why don't we
04 don't have
05 one
06 take care of
07 Don't worry, some apps   08 Borrow, neighbors
09 helps people easily find, borrow from
10 search for, the item they need
11 return it later
12 December 12
13 asked for, one, less than   14 by borrowing
15 Also, environmentally friendly
16 The fewer products, the more resources, save
17 March
18 Seeing, positive reviews, to borrow
19 however, was broken   20 so upset
21 March 9
22 such a negative experience
23 To fix, to update the pictures, regularly
24 let, know, exact product   25 look after
26 the perfect app, lovers, owners
27 reliable people to look after
28 is looking for, a post   29 send messages to

30 checks, reviews, chooses　31 November

32 whenever, out of town

33 concerns, personal information

34 What if, for other purposes

35 November 14, 2019　　36 aware of

37 allows, to communicate, without showing

38 February　　　　　39 aren't allowed, so

40 by using, can experience, walking

41 What

42 borrow, to take care of　43 right

44 kinds, sharing economy

45 share, with, provide, at a small fee, for free

46 do, weaknesses　　　47 left negative reviews

48 the more, the services, will improve

---

## 본문 TEST Step 3　　　　　　　　p.34~36

1 공유 경제 속 삶

2 아들: 아빠, 우리 이번 주말에 뭐 할 거예요?

3 아빠: 캠핑 가는 건 어떠니?

4 아들: 그런데 우리 텐트가 없잖아요.

5 하나 사야 할까요?

6 게다가 우리 개는 누가 돌봐요?

7 아빠: 걱정하지 마. 내가 우리를 도와줄 수 있는 몇 개의 앱들을 알고 있지.

8 당신의 이웃들로부터 빌려라!

9 Ask Your Neighbors는 사람들이 다른 사람들로부터 빌릴 수 있는 물건을 쉽게 찾도록 돕는다.

10 우선, 사용자들은 그 앱을 내려받고 그들이 필요한 물건을 가지고 있는 또 다른 사용자를 찾는다.

11 그리고 나서 그들은 그 물건을 받아서 나중에 반납한다.

12 Jasmine / 2019년 12월 12일

13 저는 보드게임을 요청했고 30분도 안 되어 하나를 구했어요.

14 저는 제가 자주 필요하지 않은 것들을 빌림으로써 돈을 아낄 수 있다는 것이 마음에 들어요.

15 게다가 이것이 환경친화적이라고 생각해요.

16 우리가 제품들을 더 적게 구매할수록, 우리는 더 많은 자원들을 아끼는 거예요.

17 Cassandra / 2020년 3월 7일

18 많은 긍정적인 후기들을 보고 나서, 저는 자전거 헬멧을 빌리기로 결심했어요.

19 그러나 제가 그것을 얻었을 때, 그것은 망가져 있었어요.

20 저는 몹시 기분이 상했어요!

21 Ask Your Neighbors / 2020년 3월 9일

22 고객님이 그런 부정적인 경험을 겪게 해 드려 죄송합니다.

23 이 문제를 바로잡기 위해서, 저희는 빌려주는 사람들에게 그들의 물건 사진을 정기적으로 업데이트해 줄 것을 요구하고 있습니다.

24 이것이 다른 사용자들에게 그 제품의 정확한 상태를 알 수 있도록 해 줄 것입니다.

25 제가 당신의 반려동물을 돌볼 수 있어요!

26 Pet Sitter Finder는 반려동물을 좋아하는 사람들과 반려동물 주인들을 위한 완벽한 앱이다.

27 그것은 반려동물 주인들이 그들의 반려동물을 돌보는 데 신뢰할 만한 사람들을 찾도록 돕는다.

28 반려동물 주인이 반려동물을 돌보는 사람들을 찾을 때, 그 또는 그녀는 게시물을 올린다.

29 그리고 나서 반려동물을 돌보는 사람들이나 개를 산책시키는 사람들이 주인에게 메시지를 보낼 수 있다.

30 주인은 그들의 후기들을 확인하고 최고의 사람을 선택한다.

31 George / 2019년 11월 12일

32 저는 교외로 나갈 때마다 이 앱을 사용해요.

33 하지만 저의 개인 정보에 대한 몇 가지 걱정이 있어요.

34 만약 다른 사람이 제 전화번호를 다른 목적으로 사용하면 어쩌죠?

35 Pet Sitter Finder / 2019년 11월 14일

36 저희는 이 문제를 알고 있습니다.

37 저희는 현재 사용자들이 자신의 개인 정보를 보여주지 않으면서 자유롭게 소통할 수 있는 시스템을 개발하는 중입니다.

38 Samantha / 2020년 2월 22일

39 동물들이 제 아파트에서는 허락되지 않아서, 저는 반려동물을 키울 수 없어요.

40 그런데 Pet Sitter Finder를 이용하면서, 저는 개를 산책시키는 즐거움을 경험할 수 있어요.

41 아들: 정말 좋은 앱들이네요!

42 우리는 텐트를 빌리고 우리 개를 돌볼 누군가를 찾을 수 있어요.

43 아빠: 그렇지.

44 이런 종류의 서비스가 '공유 경제'의 일부란다.

45 사람들은 자신의 물건을 다른 사람들과 공유할 수 있고 적은 비용이나 무료로 그들에게 서비스를 제공할 수 있어.

46 아들: 하지만 사실 이런 서비스들은 몇 가지 약점들을 가지고 있어요.

47 몇몇 사람들이 서비스에 대해 부정적인 후기들을 남겼잖아요.

48 아빠: 글쎄, 나는 사람들이 그 서비스들을 더 많이 사용할수록, 그것들이 더 개선될 것이라고 생각해.

---

## 본문 TEST Step 4 · Step 5　　　　　p.37~42

1 Life in the Sharing Economy

2 Son: What should we do this weekend, Dad?

3 Dad: Why don't we go camping?

4 Son: But we don't have a tent.

6 Should we buy one?

43

6 Also, who will take care of our dog?

7 Dad: Don't worry. I know some apps that can help us.

8 Borrow from your neighbors!

9 Ask Your Neighbors helps people easily find items that they can borrow from others.

10 First, users download the app and search for another user that has the item they need.

11 Then they pick up the item and return it later.

12 Jasmine: December 12, 2019

13 I asked for a board game and got one in less than 30 minutes.

14 I love saving money by borrowing things that I don't often need.

15 Also, I think it's environmentally friendly.

16 The fewer products we buy, the more resources we save.

17 Cassandra: March 7, 2020

18 Seeing a lot of positive reviews, I decided to borrow a bike helmet.

19 When I got it, however, it was broken.

20 I was so upset!

21 Ask Your Neighbors: March 9, 2020

22 We're sorry that you had such a negative experience.

23 To fix this issue, we are asking lenders to update the pictures of their items regularly.

24 This will let other users know the exact condition of the product.

25 I can look after your pet!

26 Pet Sitter Finder is the perfect app for pet lovers and pet owners.

27 It helps pet owners find reliable people to look after their pets.

28 When a pet owner is looking for pet sitters, he or she uploads a post.

29 Pet sitters or dog walkers can then send messages to the owner.

30 The owner checks their reviews and chooses the best person.

31 George: November 12, 2019

32 I use this app whenever I'm going out of town.

33 I have some concerns about my personal information though.

34 What if people use my phone number for other purposes?

35 Pet Sitter Finder: November 14, 2019

36 We're aware of this issue.

37 We're now developing a system that allows users to communicate freely without showing their personal information.

38 Samantha: February 22, 2020

39 Animals aren't allowed in my apartment, so I don't have any pets.

40 However, by using Pet Sitter Finder, I can experience the joy of walking a dog.

41 Son: What great apps!

42 We can borrow a tent and find someone to take care of our dog.

43 Dad: That's right.

44 These kinds of services are part of the "sharing economy."

45 People can share their items with others and provide services to them at a small fee or for free.

46 Son: But these services do have some weaknesses.

47 Some people left negative reviews about the services.

48 Dad: Well, I think the more people use the services, the more they will improve.

## 구석구석지문 TEST Step 1 p.43

**Do It Yourself**

1. Last Sunday, went to see

2. Cheering for, had, nice time together

3. Happily, won the game

4. Feeling happy, decided to celebrate

5. Eating fried chicken together, talked about

**After You Read C Get the BIG Picture**

1. Sharing Economy

2. can share, with, provide, to others

3. helps, find, to borrow from others

4. helps people save, resources

5. regular updates, each item's condition

6. benefit, weakness

**Culture Link**

1. Sharing, Around

2. give, a ride on my way to work

3. get to, for a small fee

4. Ride sharing, reduces the number of, which, environmentally friendly

**Do It Yourself**

1. Last Sunday, my family went to see a baseball game.
2. Cheering for our team, we had a really nice time together.
3. Happily, our team won the game.
4. Feeling happy about the win, we decided to celebrate.
5. Eating fried chicken together, we talked about the game.

**After You Read C Get the BIG Picture**

1. Sharing Economy
2. where people can share their items with or provide services to others
3. helps people find items to borrow from others
4. helps people save money and resources
5. needs regular updates on each item's condition
6. <⊕ benefit, ⊖ weakness>

**Culture Link**

1. Sharing Economies Around the World
2. I sometimes give other people a ride on my way to work.
3. They can get to their destinations for a small fee, and I can make some money.
4. Ride sharing also reduces the number of cars on the road, which is environmentally friendly.

| | | |
|---|---|---|
| 01 일, 과제, 과업 | 02 위협, 협박 | 03 출납원 |
| 04 요리법 | 05 흔한 | 06 길을 찾다, 항해하다 |
| 07 예측, 예보 | 08 인지하다, 감지하다 | |
| 09 자원, 재원 | 10 배달, 전달 | 11 인공적인, 인위적인 |
| 12 굉장한, 아주 멋진 | 13 목적지, 도착지 | 14 인식하다 |
| 15 감지하다 | 16 밝은, 희망적인 | 17 차이, 차이점 |
| 18 자율 주행하는 | 19 공연하다, 실행하다 | |
| 20 영양소, 영양분 | 21 ~에 (필요한 것을) 갖추다 | |
| 22 떼, 군중, 벌 떼 | 23 칭찬 | 24 현실 |
| 25 지능, 정보 | 26 재해, 참사, 재난 | |
| 27 생존자, 살아남은 사람 | | 28 보장하다 |
| 29 탈출하다, 달아나다, 벗어나다 | | 30 해법, 해답, 해결책 |
| 31 현재의, 존재하는 | 32 길, 경로 | 33 안전, 안전한 곳 |
| 34 발명, 발명품 | 35 처리하다, 다루다 | |
| 36 ~에 노력을 들이다, 애쓰다 | | 37 ~의 자국을 뒤밟다 |
| 38 ~와 같은 | 39 다양한 | 40 ~의 도움으로 |
| 41 ~하기 위하여 | 42 결정을 하다 | 43 앞날을 생각하다 |

| | | |
|---|---|---|
| 01 intelligence | 02 cashier | 03 present |
| 04 technology | 05 praise | 06 recipe |
| 07 destination | 08 swarm | 09 artificial |
| 10 perceive | 11 threat | 12 solution |
| 13 difference | 14 perform | 15 safety |
| 16 awesome | 17 survivor | 18 bright |
| 19 disaster | 20 navigate | 21 escape |
| 22 nutrient | 23 self-driving | 24 ensure |
| 25 recognize | 26 delivery | 27 route |
| 28 equip | 29 resource | 30 sense |
| 31 common | 32 forecast | 33 convenient |
| 34 invention | 35 with the help of | |
| 36 deal with | 37 such as | 38 a variety of |
| 39 look toward | 40 make decisions | |
| 41 so that ~ | 42 throughout the day | |
| 43 work on | | |

1 threat, 협박, 위협   2 recognize, 인식하다

3 perform, 공연하다, 실행하다   4 solution, 해법, 해답

5 survivor, 생존자   6 artificial, 인공적인, 인위적인

7 route, 경로　8 sense, 감지하다　9 task, 일, 과제, 과업
10 intelligence, 지능, 정보　11 invention, 발명, 발명품
12 navigate, 길을 찾다, 항해하다
13 perceive, 인지하다, 감지하다
14 nutrient, 영양소, 영양분　15 delivery, 배달, 전달
16 disaster, 참사, 재난, 재해

**Listen & Talk 1 A**

have, heard of / haven't, Could you explain what it is / that, weather forecast, is going to rain, makes, sound / convenient

**Listen & Talk 1 B**

inventions / great, invention / senses, it, suggests recipes / helpful / does, think of, flying / how it works / destination that, set, While it's flying / awesome, What, of / take pictures of flying

**Listen & Talk 1 C**

watching / who, one of, arms, Surprisingly, the drums / How, with / Actually, controlled, brain / awesome, explain in more detail / what, with, are turned into, travel from, to / technology

**Listen & Talk 2 B**

As, harder, may not be, resources, increasing, For this reason, it is likely that, how we get, Instead, will be grown, using, less land, other resources, such as, rich, nutrients

**Listen & Talk 2 C**

had to, in line, for almost twenty minutes / we'll never have to wait in line / do you mean / without cashiers, what, walk out / How, for / sensors, keep track of, send the information / them / It's likely that, kind of, common

**Do It Yourself A**

have, played, exciting / have, popular / it, are equipped with / explain in more detail / what human players do, develop their skills / why, felt like / It is likely that, get stronger and stronger

**Listen & Talk 1 A**

G: Hey, have you heard of a smart umbrella?

B: No, I haven't. Could you explain what it is?

G: Sure. It's an umbrella that gives you the weather forecast for the day. If it is going to rain, the umbrella makes a sound.

B: That's very convenient.

**Listen & Talk 1 B**

G: Look at these. They are the new inventions of the month!

B: They all look great. What is the invention on the first page?

G: It's a new smart refrigerator. It senses the items inside it and suggests recipes.

B: That sounds helpful.

G: It does. What do you think of this flying camera? I want to buy it.

B: A flying camera? Could you explain how it works?

G: Of course. This machine flies to a destination that we have already set. While it's flying, it can take pictures from 500 meters above the location.

B: That sounds awesome. What do you want to take pictures of?

G: I want to take pictures of flying birds!

**Listen & Talk 1 C**

B: What are you watching?

G: It's a show about a man who lost one of his arms in an accident. Surprisingly, he can play the drums very well.

B: How can he play the drums with only one arm?

G: Actually he uses two arms. One is a robot arm controlled by his brain.

B: That's awesome. Could you explain in more detail?

G: Sure. First, he thinks what he wants to do with his arm. Then those thoughts are turned into electronic signals. The signals travel from his brain to his robot arm and move it.

B: That's amazing! I think this technology can help many people.

**Listen & Talk 2 B**

M: As climate change is going to make farming harder, there may not be enough resources for the increasing number of people on Earth. For this reason, it is likely that we will have to change how we get our food. For example, we won't kill animals for food. Instead, meat will be grown in a lab using animal cells. This will require less land, water, and other resources. Also, bugs such as ants will become part of our daily meals. You might not want to eat them, but they are actually very rich in nutrients!

G: I had to wait in line at the store for almost twenty minutes.

B: That's too bad. Maybe in the future we'll never have to wait in line.

G: What do you mean?

B: I read about a store without cashiers. You take what you want to buy and just walk out.

G: That's it? How do you pay for it?

B: There are cameras and sensors in the store. They keep track of the items you choose and send the information to an app on your smartphone.

G: Then the app pays for them when you leave the store?

B: Exactly. It's likely that these kinds of stores will be more common in the future.

B: Hey, have you played this game? It's really exciting.

G: Yes, I have. That game is pretty popular these days.

B: The developers used AI technology in it. The game characters are equipped with AI.

G: Oh, really? Could you explain in more detail?

B: Sure. The AI characters in the game learn from what human players do and develop their skills.

G: Oh! That's why I sometimes felt like they already knew my moves!

B: They're very smart. It is likely that the AI in games will get stronger and stronger.

## 본문 TEST Step 1      p.52~53

01 Life with
02 Where Do, See
03 not only, movies, anymore
04 Around, variety of tasks
05 delivery, flying, public places
06 delivery, in, sky
07 arms in, factory
08 service robot at
09 Are Becoming Smart
10 past, performed, tasks, programmed
11 getting, smarter, able, humans
12 What, possible, artificial intelligence
13 perceive environments, make decisions
14 recognize speech, jokes, humans
15 answer, questions, control machines
16 act just like real
17 walk, owners, recognize praise

18 around Us, Present, Future
19 things faster, easier
20 anywhere, in disaster areas
21 helps, throughout, day
22 cleaning would, easier, had
23 also, with, sense emotions
24 self-driving, doesn't need, driver
25 sensors, navitgate, relax, ride
26 swarm, large, another, like
27 used, variety, including, sites
28 work, tasks, solutions as
29 disaster areas, dangerous, humans
30 survivors, deal, routes, escape
31 Looking toward, Future
32 future, looks bright, perfect
33 expect, become, convenient, help
34 worry, cause, threats, safety
35 find, solutions, ensure, good

## 본문 TEST Step 2      p.54~55

01 with Robots
02 Where Do, See
03 not only, anymore
04 a variety of tasks
05 flying, in public places
06 delivery
07 arms, factory
08 A service robot
09 Becoming Smart
10 performed, programmed them to do
11 getting, smarter, be able to
12 What makes this possible
13 perceive environments, decisions
14 recognize speech
15 control machines
16 act just like
17 owners, recognize praise
18 around Us, Present
19 faster, easier
20 anywhere, in disaster areas
21 helps, throughout the day
22 would be easier, had one
23 sense emotions
24 self-driving car, a driver
25 can navigate, so that, can
26 a group of robots, communicate with one another
27 can be used, including, building sites
28 work on, as a group
29 disaster areas, dangerous for humans
30 so that, can escape to safety
31 Looking toward
32 not perfect
33 to become, with the help of
34 they might cause, such as
35 to find, to ensure, good

1 로봇과 함께하는 삶

2 우리는 어디에서 로봇을 보는가?

3 로봇은 더는 영화와 책 속에만 있는 것은 아니다.

4 전 세계적으로 로봇은 다양한 임무를 수행하고 있다.

5 하늘에는 날아다니는 배달 로봇, 공장에는 로봇 팔, 그리고 공공장소에는 서비스 로봇이 있다.

6 하늘에서 날아다니는 배달 로봇

7 공장의 로봇 팔들

8 평창 올림픽의 서비스 로봇

9 로봇이 똑똑해지고 있다

10 과거에 로봇은 인간이 로봇에게 실행하도록 프로그램을 설정한 단순 업무만을 수행했다.

11 그러나 로봇은 이제 '더 똑똑'해지고 있으며, 곧 인간처럼 생각할 수 있을지도 모른다.

12 이러한 것을 가능하게 만드는 것은 인공 지능(AI)이다.

13 인공 지능을 가진 로봇은 환경을 인식하고 의사 결정을 할 수 있다.

14 그들은 또한 인간의 말을 인지하고, 농담을 건네며, 인간과 게임을 할 수 있다.

15 〈인공 지능 스피커〉 그들은 당신의 질문에 대답할 수 있고, 당신의 집에 있는 기계들을 조종할 수 있으며, 당신을 위해 음악을 재생할 수도 있다.

16 〈인공 지능 반려동물〉 그들은 마치 진짜 개처럼 행동한다.

17 그들은 그들의 주인과 함께 걷고 놀며 칭찬을 알아챈다.

18 우리 주변의 로봇들 – 현재와 미래

19 로봇은 일을 더 빠르고 더 쉽게 해 주고 있다.

20 그들은 어디에서나 우리를 도울 수 있다. 우리의 집에서, 길에서 또는 재난 지역에서 말이다.

21 〈집안일 도우미 로봇〉 이 로봇은 온종일 당신의 가족을 돕는다.

22 만약 당신이 이 로봇 하나를 가지고 있다면 요리와 청소가 더 쉬워질 것이다.

23 이 로봇은 또한 가족 모두와 이야기를 나누며 감정을 파악할 수 있다.

24 〈자율 주행 자동차〉 자율 주행 자동차는 운전자를 필요로 하지 않는다.

25 카메라, 감지기 그리고 소프트웨어를 갖춘 채, 이 자동차는 당신이 쉬면서 주행을 즐길 수 있도록 당신을 위해 길을 찾아갈 수 있다.

26 〈로봇 군집〉 로봇 군집은 개미나 벌처럼, 서로 의사소통할 수 있는 로봇의 대규모 집단을 말한다.

27 이 로봇들은 농장이나 건설 현장을 포함한 다양한 장소에서 사용될 수 있다.

28 그들은 하나의 집단으로서 임무를 완수하고 해결책을 찾는다.

29 〈수색 구조 로봇〉 수색 구조 로봇은 사람에게 위험한 재난 지역에 투입될 수 있다.

30 그들은 생존자를 찾고 위험한 상황을 처리하며, 사람들이 안전한 곳으로 대피할 수 있도록 길을 확보한다.

31 미래에 대한 전망

32 로봇과 함께하는 우리의 미래는 밝지만 완벽하지는 않다.

33 어떤 사람들은 로봇의 도움으로 삶이 더욱 편리해질 것을 기대한다.

34 그러나 다른 사람들은 우리의 일자리와 안전에 대한 위협과 같이, 로봇이 일으킬지 모르는 문제들에 대해 걱정한다.

35 중요한 것은 가능한 해결책을 찾아내는 것과 로봇이 오로지 좋은 일을 위해서만 쓰이게 됨을 확실히 하는 것이다.

1 Life with Robots

2 Where Do We See Robots?

3 Robots are not only in movies and books anymore.

4 Around the world, robots are doing a variety of tasks.

5 There are delivery robots flying in the sky, robot arms in factories, and service robots in public places.

6 A delivery robot in the sky

7 Robot arms in a factory

8 A service robot at the PyeongChang Olympics

9 Robots Are Becoming Smart

10 In the past, robots performed only easy tasks that humans programmed them to do.

11 However, robots are now getting "smarter," and soon they might be able to think like humans.

12 What makes this possible is artificial intelligence (AI).

13 Robots that have AI can perceive environments and make decisions.

14 They can also recognize speech, tell jokes, and play games with humans.

15 AI Speakers: They can answer your questions, control machines in your home, and play music for you.

16 AI Pets: They act just like real dogs.

17 They walk and play with their owners and recognize praise.

18 Robots around Us – Present and Future

19 Robots are making things faster and easier.

20 They can help us anywhere — in our homes, on roads, or in disaster areas.

21 Home Helper Robot: This robot helps your family throughout the day.

22 Cooking and cleaning would be easier if you had one.

23 It also talks with family members and can sense emotions.

24 Self-Driving Car: A self-driving car doesn't need a driver.

25 With cameras, sensors, and software, it can navigate roads for you so that you can relax and enjoy the ride.

26 Robot Swarm: A robot swarm is a large group of robots that can communicate with one another, like ants or bees.

27 They can be used in a variety of places, including farms or building sites.

28 They work on tasks and find solutions as a group.

29 Search-and-Rescue Robot: Search-and-rescue robots can go into disaster areas that are dangerous for humans.

30 They find survivors, deal with dangers, and clear routes so that people can escape to safety.

31 Looking toward the Future

32 Our future with robots looks bright but not perfect.

33 Some people expect life to become more convenient with the help of robots.

34 However, other people worry about problems they might cause, such as threats to our jobs and safety.

35 The important thing is to find possible solutions and to ensure that robots are only used for good.

## 구석구석지문 TEST Step 1     p.62

**Presentation Time Step 3**

1. What do you think
2. helping people clean their houses
3. looks similar to, vacuum cleaners, have some differences
4. unlike today's robot vacuum cleaners, is controlled by

**After You Read B**

1. tried to cheer up, work for
2. because of, bad grades
3. hit, help a boy to escape
4. communicated with one another, by working together

**Think and Write Step 3**

1. in
2. will be, different from
3. It is likely that, a big change in location

---

4. won't have to
5. Instead, using a variety of apps
6. positive effect, would be, because, not have to go, come back
7. could be, negative effects
8. wouldn't be able to, as
9. what school life will be like, as, as it is now

## 구석구석지문 TEST Step 2     p.63

**Presentation Time Step 3**

1. What do you think this painting shows?
2. I think it shows a machine helping people clean their houses.
3. The machine looks similar to today's robot vacuum cleaners, but they have some differences.
4. For example, unlike today's robot vacuum cleaners, the machine in the painting is controlled by a human.

**After You Read B**

1. home helper robot: I tried to cheer up a child of the family I work for.
2. He felt sad because of his bad grades.
3. search-and-rescue robot: Last week, after a storm hit, I cleared a route to help a boy to escape.
4. robot swarm: We communicated with one another and built a tower by working together.

**Think and Write Step 3**

1. School Life in 30 Years
2. In 30 years, school life will be very different from now.
3. It is likely that there will be a big change in location.
4. Students won't have to go to school.
5. Instead, they will study at home using a variety of apps.
6. One positive effect of such a change would be that students could save time because they would not have to go to school and come back.
7. However, there could be some negative effects too.
8. For example, students wouldn't be able to meet their friends as often.
9. We don't know exactly what school life will be like in the future, but I hope it will be as fun and meaningful as it is now.

## Lesson 8

### 단어 TEST Step 1 — p.64

| | | |
|---|---|---|
| 01 도둑 | 02 오르다, 올라가다 | 03 친절 |
| 04 길 | 05 생존 | 06 여행; 여행하다 |
| 07 전체의, 모든 | 08 비교하다 | 09 선구자, 개척자 |
| 10 강경히, 강하게 | 11 공격하다 | 12 밑, 바닥 |
| 13 분리된, 서로 다른 | 14 목적지, 도착지 | 15 옳은 |
| 16 지혜로운, 현명한 | 17 깨닫다, 자각하다 | 18 더 멀리; 더 먼 |
| 19 가버린, 떠난 | 20 창조하다 | |
| 21 서두르다, 서둘러 가다 | | |
| 22 (미래의) 언젠가, 훗날 | | 23 선구자, 개척자 |
| 24 굶주림 | 25 두꺼운, (나무가) 울창한 | |
| 26 지혜, 슬기 | 27 보호하다 | |
| 28 ~에 이르다[닿다], 도착하다 | | |
| 29 동의하지 않다, 의견이 다르다 | | 30 안내인, 가이드 |
| 31 똑바로 | 32 (시간이) 걸리다 | |
| 33 움직이다, 감동시키다 | | |
| 34 (문제, 곤경을) 해결하다, 풀다 | | 35 ~ 덕분에 |
| 36 마침내, 결국 | 37 ~에 따라 행동하다 | |
| 38 ~로 나아가다 | 39 길을 잃다 | 40 나가는 길, 출구 |
| 41 가는 길에 | 42 ~으로 죽다 | 43 ~하지 않고 |

### 단어 TEST Step 2 — p.65

| | | |
|---|---|---|
| 01 hunger | 02 kindness | 03 protect |
| 04 agree | 05 wise | 06 hurry |
| 07 survival | 08 thick | 09 compare |
| 10 thief | 11 wisdom | 12 correct |
| 13 realize | 14 pioneer | 15 separate |
| 16 attack | 17 solve | 18 destination |
| 19 straight | 20 create | 21 path |
| 22 guide | 23 strongly | 24 disagree |
| 25 further | 26 whole | 27 take |
| 28 gone | 29 move | 30 bottom |
| 31 climb | 32 reach | 33 someday |
| 34 travel | 35 the way out | 36 act on |
| 37 in the end | 38 become lost | 39 on the way |
| 40 thanks to | 41 die of | 42 without ~ing |
| 43 make one's way to ~ | | |

### 단어 TEST Step 3 — p.66

1 attack, 공격하다  2 climb, 오르다, 올라가다

3 hunger, 굶주림  4 separate, 분리된

5 move, 감동시키다

6 disagree, 동의하지 않다, 의견이 다르다

7 agree, 동의하다  8 survival, 생존  9 path, 길

10 destination, 목적지, 도착지  11 kindness, 친절

12 pioneer, 선구자, 개척자  13 realize, 깨닫다, 자각하다

14 compare, 비교하다  15 protect, 보호하다

16 wisdom, 지혜, 슬기

### 본문 TEST Step 1 — p.67~69

01 Five Wise Men  02 One, wise, met on

03 agreed to travel together

04 way, became lost, thick  05 any further, way out

06 thinking, while, strongly, left

07 second, right, because, correct

08 third, walk back  09 way, so, leave that

10 walk around, forest

11 disagreed, keep walking straight

12 forest, go on forever  13 new path, open

14 Looking, fifth, shook, solve

15 climb, tallest, could find

16 climbed, decided, separate ways

17 reached, top, whole forest

18 paths, shortest way out  19 hurried down, others

20 got, bottom, was gone

21 thought, himself, found, out

22 thought, wrong, only wise  23 However, wrong

24 Everyone, wise

25 chosen, path, created, future

26 walked deeper into, forest

27 attacked, died of hunger

28 learned how, protect himself

29 end, forest, survival skills

30 right, group of thieves

31 took, from, made, join

32 While, with, great kindness

33 thieves, moved, kindness, wisdom

34 Later, become wise men

35 walked back, safe path

36 without getting lost, longer

37 went straight became, pioneer

38 forest, places, had been

39 Thanks to, enjoy, lands

40 who climbed, became, guide

41 Since, able, ways, destinations

42 how, found, own paths

43 Like, compare, journey, another

**50** 정답 및 해설

44 have, your own path

45 make, decision, act on

46 realize, been living, right

01 Wise Men

02 One day, met

03 agreed to travel

04 became lost, thick forest

05 any further, way out

06 for a while, strongly feel

07 because, correct

08 Let's walk back

09 so, leave that way

10 walk around

11 disagreed, keep walking straight

12 go on forever

13 new path, open

14 shook his head, how to solve

15 to climb, could find

16 separate

17 reached, whole forest

18 Looking at, shortest way out

19 hurried down, the others

20 was gone

21 thought to himself, best way out

22 wrong, the only wise

23 However, wrong

24 Everyone, wise

25 had chosen, created his future

26 walked deeper into

27 was attacked, died of hunger

28 how to protect himself

29 made his way out of, survival skills

30 a group of thieves

31 join them

32 While, great kindness

33 were moved by, kindness

34 Later, become wise men

35 walked back, a safe path

36 without getting lost, even though

37 went straight, pioneer

38 had been

39 Thanks to

40 who climbed

41 different paths, the quickest ways, their destinations

42 This is how, their own paths

43 Like, one journey, another

44 have to, your own path

45 make, decision, act on it

46 have been living, right for

1 5명의 지혜로운 사람들

2 어느 날 5명의 지혜로운 사람들이 길에서 만났다.

3 그들은 여행을 함께 하기로 했다.

4 그러나 도중에 그들은 울창한 숲속에서 길을 잃게 되었다.

5 더 멀리 가기 전에 그들은 멈추고 빠져나갈 최선의 방법을 찾기로 결정했다.

6 잠시 동안 생각한 후, 첫 번째 남자는 "우리가 왼쪽으로 가야 한다는 생각이 강하게 들어요."라고 말했다.

7 두 번째 남자가 "우리는 오른쪽으로 가야 해요. 왜냐하면 '오른쪽'은 또한 '옳은'이라는 의미이기 때문이죠."라고 말했다.

8 그러자 세 번째 남자가 "뒤로 돌아갑시다.

9 우리가 그 길로 왔으니 그 길로 나갈 수 있을 겁니다.

10 그러면 우리는 숲을 한 바퀴 돌 수 있고요."라고 말했다.

11 네 번째 남자가 이의를 제기하며 "나는 우리가 똑바로 계속 걸어 나가야 한다고 생각해요.

12 숲이 영원히 계속될 수는 없으니까요.

13 새로운 길이 열릴 것입니다."라고 말했다.

14 모두를 바라보면서 다섯 번째 남자가 고개를 저으며 "나는 이것을 해결하는 방법을 알아요. 잠깐 기다려 보세요."라고 말했다.

15 그는 그가 찾을 수 있는 가장 높은 나무를 오르기 시작했다.

16 그가 올라가자 다른 모든 사람들은 각자 서로 다른 길을 가기로 결정했다.

17 다섯 번째 남자가 꼭대기에 이르자 그는 전체 숲을 볼 수 있었다.

18 모든 길을 바라보며 그는 빠져나갈 가장 짧은 길을 찾았다.

19 그는 다른 사람들에게 알리기 위해 급히 내려갔다.

20 하지만 그가 밑으로 내려왔을 때, 모든 사람들은 이미 가 버리고 없었다.

21 그는 '다들 어디 간 거야? 내가 빠져나갈 최선의 길을 찾았는데.'라고 마음속으로 생각했다.

22 그는 그들이 모두 틀렸고 자신이 유일하게 현명한 사람이라고 생각했다.

23 그러나 그가 틀렸다.

24 모두가 지혜로웠다.

25 각자 자신의 길을 선택했고 자신의 미래를 만들었다.

26 왼쪽으로 간 남자는 숲속으로 더 깊이 걸어 들어갔다.

27 그는 야생 동물들의 습격을 받았고 거의 굶어 죽을 뻔했다.

28 머지않아 그는 자신을 지키고 먹을 것을 찾는 방법을 터득했다.

29 결국 그는 숲 밖으로 빠져나왔고 다른 사람들에게 생존 기술을 가르쳤다.

30 오른쪽으로 간 남자는 도둑 무리를 만났다.

31 그들은 그에게서 모든 것을 가져갔고 그를 그들과 합류시켰다.

32 그는 그들과 함께 있는 동안 그들에게 많은 친절을 베풀었다.

33 그 도둑들은 그의 친절에 감동을 받았고 그의 지혜에서 배우게 되었다.

34 나중에 그들 또한 지혜로운 사람들이 되었다.

35 뒤돌아 간 남자는 숲 주변에 안전한 길을 만들었다.

36 사람들은 이 길을 이용할 때 길을 잃지 않고 자신이 가고자 하는 길에 다다를 수 있었다. 비록 이동 시간이 약간 더 오래

걸려도 말이다.

37 똑바로 간 남자는 개척자가 되었다.

38 그는 숲을 벗어나 아무도 이전에 가 본 적이 없는 곳을 발견했다.

39 그 남자 덕분에, 사람들은 이 새롭고 아름다운 지역을 즐길 수 있었다.

40 나무 위로 올라간 남자는 가이드가 되었다.

41 그는 여러 다양한 길을 발견했었기 때문에, 사람들에게 자신의 목적지에 이르는 가장 빠른 길을 찾는 법을 가르쳐 줄 수 있었다.

42 이런 식으로 다섯 남자는 자신만의 길을 찾아냈다.

43 그들처럼 우리는 각각 인생에서 자기 자신만의 여행을 하고 있고, 우리는 한 여정을 다른 것과 비교할 수 없다.

44 당신은 당신 자신만의 길을 만들어가야 한다.

45 자신의 목소리를 듣고, 결정하고, 그 결정에 따라 행동하라.

46 그러면 언젠가 당신은 당신에게 맞는 삶을 살아가고 있다는 것을 깨닫게 될 것이다.

## 본문 TEST Step 4·Step 5    p.76~81

1 The Five Wise Men

2 One day, five wise men met on the road.

3 They agreed to travel together.

4 On the way, however, they became lost in a thick forest.

5 Before walking any further, they decided to stop and find the best way out.

6 After thinking for a while, the first man said, "I strongly feel that we should go left."

7 The second man said, "We should go right, because *right* also means 'correct.'"

8 Then the third man said, "Let's walk back.

9 We came that way, so we can leave that way.

10 Then we can walk around the forest."

11 The fourth man disagreed and said, "I think we should keep walking straight.

12 The forest cannot go on forever.

13 A new path will open."

14 Looking at them all, the fifth man shook his head and said, "I know how to solve this. Just wait."

15 He started to climb the tallest tree he could find.

16 As he climbed, everyone else decided to go their separate ways.

17 When the fifth man reached the top, he could see the whole forest.

18 Looking at all the paths, he found the shortest way out.

19 He hurried down to tell the others.

20 However, when he got to the bottom, everyone was gone.

21 He thought to himself, *Where did they go? I found the best way out.*

22 He thought they were all wrong and he was the only wise man.

23 However, he was wrong.

24 Everyone was wise.

25 Each man had chosen his path and created his future.

26 The man who went to the left walked deeper into the forest.

27 He was attacked by wild animals and almost died of hunger.

28 Soon he learned how to protect himself and find food.

29 In the end, he made his way out of the forest and taught others survival skills.

30 The man who went to the right met a group of thieves.

31 They took everything from him and made him join them.

32 While he was with them, he showed them great kindness.

33 The thieves were moved by his kindness and learned from his wisdom.

34 Later, they also became wise men.

35 The man who walked back created a safe path around the forest.

36 Using this path, people could get where they were going without getting lost, even though the trip took a little longer.

37 The man who went straight became a pioneer.

38 He left the forest and discovered places no one else had been before.

39 Thanks to him, people could enjoy these new beautiful lands.

40 The man who climbed the tree became a guide.

41 Since he had found many different paths, he was able to teach people how to find the quickest ways to their destinations.

42 This is how the five men found their own paths.

43 Like them, we are each on our own journey in life, and we cannot compare one journey to another.

44 You have to create your own path.

45 Listen to yourself, make a decision, and act on it.

46 Then, someday, you will realize that you have been living the life that is right for you.

적중 1○○ + 특별부록

# Plan B

# 우리학교 최신기출

능률 · 김성곤 교과서를 배우는

학교 시험문제 분석 · 모음 · 해설집

전국단위 학교 시험문제 수집 및 분석
출제 빈도가 높은 문제 위주로 선별
문제 풀이에 필요한 상세한 해설

중3-2
영어

능률 · 김성곤

적중 100 + 특별부록

# Plan B

# 우리학교 최신기출

중3-2
영어

능률 · 김성곤

◎ 선택형 문항의 답안은 컴퓨터용 수정 싸인펜을 사용하여 OMR 답안지에 바르게 표기하시오.
◎ 서술형 문제는 답을 답안지에 반드시 검정 볼펜으로 쓰시오.
◎ 총 30문항 100점 만점입니다. 문항별 배점은 각 문항에 표시되어 있습니다.

[전북 ○○중]

**01** Which word means "to make smaller in size"?　(3점)

① renew
② reuse
③ reduce
④ recycle
⑤ replace

[전북 ○○중]

**02** 다음 문장의 빈칸에 들어갈 단어가 <u>아닌</u> 것은?　(3점)

- The _____ from trees helps animals avoid direct sunlight.
- A piece of wood was floating on the _____ of the water.
- I have some _____ about my test grade.
- I am the _____ of these four dogs.

① owner
② statue
③ shade
④ surface
⑤ concerns

[서울 강남구 ○○중]

**03** 다음 중 어법상 옳은 문장을 <u>모두</u> 고른 것은?　(3점)

ⓐ This is how Jessi dances.
ⓑ Mary isn't happy about the way her haircut looks.
ⓒ This is the stadium the basketball game will be held.
ⓓ I don't like the way she laughs.
ⓔ Many tourists visited the art gallery in that Picasso's works were being displayed.
ⓕ The annual book sales event is taking place at all avenues where participating bookstores are located.
ⓖ I forgot to visit the doctor's office where I had scheduled to take a medical check up at yesterday.

① ⓐ, ⓑ, ⓒ
② ⓐ, ⓑ, ⓓ, ⓕ
③ ⓐ, ⓒ, ⓓ, ⓕ, ⓖ
④ ⓑ, ⓒ, ⓓ, ⓕ, ⓖ
⑤ ⓑ, ⓓ, ⓔ, ⓕ, ⓖ

[전북 ○○중]

**04** 다음 우리말을 '관계부사'를 이용하여 영어로 쓰시오.　(4점)

나의 엄마는 나의 언니가 운전하는 방식을 좋아하지 않는다. (8 words)

→ _____

**05** 다음 대화의 빈칸에 들어갈 표현으로 바르지 <u>않은</u> 것은? (3점)

> A: Have you heard of charging roads? They're amazing!
> B: No, I haven't. Tell me about them.
> A: They charge the batteries of electric cars. They will save resources.
> B: That sounds awesome. _____ them.

① I'm eager to use

② I'm dying to use

③ I can't wait to use

④ I can't stand using

⑤ I'm looking forward to using

**06** Choose something similar to the underlined expression in the dialogue below. (3점)

> B: Our club is holding a photo contest next week.
> G: What kind of photos will be in it?
> B: The theme is pollution around the world. We are holding this contest to raise students' awareness of environmental problems.
> G: That sounds nice. <u>I can't wait to see it!</u>

① I haven't seen it before!

② It is possible for me to see it!

③ I didn't forget to see it!

④ I'm too busy to go and see it!

⑤ I'm looking forward to seeing it!

**07** 다음 밑줄 친 우리말을 영어로 바르게 옮긴 것은? (4점)

> Every field has different ways of protecting the environment. With more innovation, humans and nature (<u>함께 조화를 이루며 살아갈 수 있을 것이다</u>) far into the future.

① can will leave together in harmony

② can be going to leave for harmony

③ will can live together in harmony with

④ will be live together for harmony with

⑤ will be able to live together in harmony

**[8-9]** 다음 대화를 읽고 물음에 답하시오.

> G: Jiho, hurry up! The elevator is going up soon.
> B: The science room is just on the third floor. Why don't we take the stairs?
> G: I don't want to walk all the way up there.
> B: Come on. Elevators use lots of energy. We need to save energy to ⓐ_____ the environment.
> G: But one elevator ride doesn't use that much energy.
> B: That's true, but the energy from all the elevator rides ⓑ_____ over time. ⓒ_____, ⓓ_____ the environment starts with the little things.
> G: ⓔ_____ Let's take the stairs.

**08** 위의 두 사람의 대화와 관련된 속담으로 가장 적절한 것은?

(3점)

① Nothing ventured, nothing gained.

② A friend in need is a friend indeed.

③ He who makes no mistakes makes nothing.

④ Little drops of water make the mighty ocean.

⑤ Never put off till tomorrow what you can do today.

**09** 위 대화의 ⓐ~ⓔ에 들어갈 표현에 대한 설명으로 적절하지 않은 것은?

(4점)

① ⓐ to keep from being damaged, attacked, stolen, or injured

② ⓑ to work together in doing something

③ ⓒ From my point of view

④ ⓓ being careful about something

⑤ ⓔ Your opinion makes sense and is worth considering.

**10** 다음 중 어법상 올바른 문장은?

(3점)

① My mom doesn't like why my sister drives.

② I can't forget the day where I won the class election.

③ That is the reason how I like documentaries.

④ Do you remember the day when we moved the piano upstairs?

⑤ He explained the way how the system worked.

**11** Which is correct about the passage?

(4점)

> Tim: What are we going to do this weekend, Jill?
>
> Jill: Why don't we go to the sheep park near my house?
>
> Tim: A sheep park? How interesting! Are there really sheep in the park?
>
> Jill: Yes. They are there to protect the environment.
>
> Tim: How can they help the environment?
>
> Jill: You know, people usually use chemicals to kill unwanted plants. The sheep in the park eat those plants, so the chemicals are not needed.
>
> Tim: What a bright idea! I can't wait to visit the park!

① Tim has been to the sheep park.

② Tim can't go to the sheep park with Jill.

③ They are going to the sheep park near Tim's house.

④ People use chemicals because sheep eat many plants.

⑤ Sheep in the park can protect the environment by eating unwanted plants there.

**12** 다음 중 두 문장 ⓐ와 ⓑ를 한 문장으로 연결한 것이 <u>어색한</u> 것을 <u>두 개</u> 고르면? (4점)

① ⓐ: The winter was very cold.

ⓑ: I traveled in Canada then.

ⓐ+ⓑ: The winter in which I traveled in Canada was very cold.

② ⓐ: I recently went back to the town.

ⓑ: I grew up in the town.

ⓐ+ⓑ: I recently went back to the town where I grew up in.

③ ⓐ: This is the famous museum.

ⓑ: I visited the building yesterday.

ⓐ+ⓑ: This is the famous museum that I visited yesterday.

④ ⓐ: I know the reason.

ⓑ: He didn't come to school for the reason.

ⓐ+ⓑ: I know the reason why he didn't come to school for.

⑤ ⓐ: *Chuseok* is the day.

ⓑ: You can see a full moon on the day.

ⓐ+ⓑ: *Chuseok* is the day when you can see a full moon.

**[13–14]** 다음 대화를 읽고 물음에 답하시오.

A: I read a cool article today.

B: What was it about?

A: It was about a new bag. It just looks like a plastic bag, but it's made mostly of corn.

B: That sounds really amazing.

A: Yes, but there's more. The bag breaks down in soil in only three months and disappears in about three minutes in warm water!

B: Wow! That will help us reduce plastic waste by a lot!

A: I know! The company will start selling the bag sometime this year. ⓐ_____

**13** 위 대화의 빈칸 ⓐ에 들어갈 말로 가장 적절한 것은? (3점)

① I keep using it!

② I'm happy to sell it!

③ I can't wait to use it!

④ I've never seen it before!

⑤ I'm looking forward to making it!

**14** 위 대화에 언급된 봉지에 대한 내용과 일치하는 것은? (3점)

① 오늘 TV 광고에 나왔다.

② 주재료는 옥수수와 플라스틱이다.

③ 찬물에서 3분 이내에 녹아 없어진다.

④ 땅속에서 분해되는 데 겨우 3개월 걸린다.

⑤ 올해 말에 개발되어 내년에 판매될 예정이다.

The underwater museum is about 14 meters below the surface and contains ⓐ500 statues. ⓑThey are made from materials that support sea life. ⓒThey provide additional places for plants and animals to live on. Over time, many types of sea life will grow on ⓓthe statues, which will make the artwork unique. The artists want people to see a variety of sea life on the statues. If people realize how rich sea life is, ⓔthey will understand how important it is to save the sea.

[경기 ○○중]

**15** 위 글의 밑줄 친 ⓐ~ⓔ 중에서 가리키는 것이 <u>다른</u> 것은?

(3점)

① ⓐ      ② ⓑ      ③ ⓒ

④ ⓓ      ⑤ ⓔ

[경기 ○○중]

**16** 위 글에 대한 설명으로 옳은 것을 〈보기〉에서 고른 것은?

(3점)

> **보기**
>
> (A) 수중 박물관은 가로세로 14미터로 지어졌다.
> (B) 동상들이 수중 박물관을 독특하게 만들었다.
> (C) 다양한 해양 생물이 동상들에서 살아갈 것이다.
> (D) 동상들을 만든 재료들이 바다를 오염시킬 수도 있다.
> (E) 사람들이 해양 생물이 얼마나 풍요로운지 깨닫는다면 바다를 보호하는 것이 얼마나 중요한지 알 것이다.

① (A), (B)    ② (B), (C)    ③ (B), (D)

④ (C), (E)    ⑤ (D), (E)

Today, I'd like to make a suggestion about the trash problem at our school. I've found that many students just throw things away instead of recycling them. As you know, (A)_____, recycling is very important because it saves resources and helps protect the environment. So, in my opinion, we need to reduce the number of trash cans at school to encourage recycling. Why don't we place four different colored recycling bins on every floor instead? This will remind students to separate the paper, glass, plastic, and cans properly.

[충북 ○○중]

**17** 다음 중 남자의 연설 내용과 일치하지 <u>않는</u> 것은? (4점)

① He recommends a new recycling system in school.

② He thinks students need to recycle things instead of just throwing them away.

③ He believes recycling is a good way to protect the environment.

④ He suggests using four different colored recycling bins and not using trash bins.

⑤ He thinks a new recycling system can encourage students to separate the trash.

## 18 위 글의 흐름으로 보아, 빈칸 (A)에 들어갈 말로 가장 적절한 것은? (3점)

① however

② in addition

③ as a result

④ for example

⑤ at the same time

[19–23] 다음 글을 읽고 물음에 답하시오.

It is important ⓐfor us to find ways to protect the environment. Some people ⓑhave founded creative ways to save the earth. One example is an underwater museum in Cancun, Mexico. Let's meet Dr. Rosa Allison, an art professor, and ⓒlisten her explanation about the special museum.

Cancun is a city ⓓwhere 4.8 million tourists travel every year. ⓔOne of the most popular activity Ⓐto do there is looking at the area's beautiful sea life underwater. However, tourist activities are seriously damaging parts of the sea near Cancun.

ⒷTo prevent this, artists did something interesting. They thought if they attracted tourists to a different part of the sea, the dying areas could have time Ⓒto get better. They made an underwater museum away from the places (B)_____ sea life was dying. It's about 14 meters below the surface and contains 500 statues.

The statues are made from materials that support sea life. They provide additional places for plants and animals Ⓓto live on. Over time, many types of sea life will grow on the statues, which will make the artwork unique. The artists want people Ⓔto see a variety of sea life on the statues. If people realize how rich sea life is, (가) 그들이 바다를 지키는 것이 얼마나 중요한지를 이해하게 될 것입니다.

## 19 Which is true according to the above passage? (4점)

① A popular activity in Cancun is growing the area's beautiful sea life underwater.

② The underwater museum in Cancun provides additional food for plants and animals.

③ The main purpose of making an underwater museum was to show various sea life to people.

④ Some parts of the sea near Cancun are becoming damaged, not by tourist activities, but by the fishing industry.

⑤ Many types of sea life growing on the statues make the artwork unique and show people how rich sea life is.

## 20 위 글의 밑줄 친 Ⓐ~Ⓔ 중 to부정사의 쓰임이 다른 두 개는? (3점)

① Ⓐ　　　　② Ⓑ　　　　③ Ⓒ

④ Ⓓ　　　　⑤ Ⓔ

## 21 위 글의 ⓐ~ⓔ 중 어법상 어색한 것은 모두 몇 개인가? (3점)

① 1개　　　② 2개　　　③ 3개

④ 4개　　　⑤ 5개

## 22 위 글의 밑줄 친 우리말 (가)를 주어진 단어를 재배열하여 완성하시오. (단, 주어진 단어를 모두 사용할 것.) (4점)

they will understand _____.
(to / the sea / how / save / is / it / important)

→ _____

## 23 위 글을 읽고 답할 수 있는 질문은? (3점)

① How can we find creative ways to save the earth?

② When was the underwater museum built?

③ How many people visit Mexico every year?

④ What are the most popular museums in Cancun?

⑤ What is damaging parts of the sea near Cancun?

[24–30] 다음 글을 읽고 물음에 답하시오.

In Singapore, people are using architecture to protect the environment on land. Let's hear what Rajesh Khan, an architect, says about eco-friendly buildings.

Singapore is hot throughout the year. Most buildings need air conditioning, (가)_____ a lot of energy and contributes to ⓐ_____. (A) That's why architects in Singapore have begun to design eco-friendly buildings (나)_____ air conditioning but are still cool inside. (B) For example, many buildings in Singapore are designed to have an open structure. (C) This natural air flow is how these buildings stay cool.

In addition to making open structures, architects add large gardens. (D) This greenery provides shade and protects parts of the building from direct sunlight, which keeps the building cooler.

Eco-friendly buildings like these not only help protect the environment, but also provide people (a)_____ a good quality of life. (E) Those are the goals of this new style of architecture. Hopefully, architects will keep coming up (b)_____ new eco-friendly ideas.

Every field has different ways of protecting the environment. With more innovation, humans and nature will be able to live together in harmony far into the future.

## 24 위 글의 빈칸 (a), (b)에 공통으로 들어갈 단어는? (3점)

① of　　　② to　　　③ for

④ from　　　⑤ with

**25** 위 글의 흐름상 빈칸 (가), (나)에 차례로 들어갈 가장 알맞은 말은? (3점)

| (가) | (나) |
|------|------|
| ① that use | - which uses more |
| ② that uses | - which use less |
| ③ which uses | - that use less |
| ④ which uses | - that use more |
| ⑤ which use | - that uses less |

**26** 위 글의 흐름으로 보아 주어진 문장이 들어가기에 가장 적절한 곳은? (3점)

> This structure makes it possible for outside air to move throughout a building.

① (A)　　　② (B)　　　③ (C)
④ (D)　　　⑤ (E)

**27** 위 글의 내용과 일치하지 <u>않는</u> 것은? (3점)

① 싱가포르에서는 사람들이 환경을 보호하기 위해 건축을 이용하고 있다.
② 싱가포르는 연중 내내 더운 곳이다.
③ 싱가포르의 많은 건물들은 비개방형 구조를 갖도록 설계된다.
④ 친환경 건물들은 환경을 보호하는 것을 도울 뿐만 아니라 양질의 삶을 제공한다.
⑤ 바라건대, 건축가들이 새로운 친환경 아이디어를 계속해서 생각해 낼 것이다.

**28** 위 글의 내용으로 보아 다음 질문에 답할 수 <u>없는</u> 것 <u>두 개는?</u> (4점)

① What are the goals of this new style of architecture?
② How did architects in Singapore make buildings cool inside?
③ How many buildings have been designed to have an open structure?
④ What are the examples of other fields to protect the environment?
⑤ Does every field have different ways of protecting the environment?

**29** 위 글의 제목으로 가장 적절한 것은? (3점)

① Singapore: Must See Attraction
② Building Construction Trends to Watch
③ What Is the Weather Like in Singapore?
④ How to Improve Air Circulation in Buildings
⑤ Eco-Friendly Building Designs in Singapore

**30** 위 글의 내용에서 빈칸 ⓐ에 알맞은 표현을 쓰시오. (4점)

> Most buildings need air conditioning, which uses a lot of energy and contributes to _____.
> (a significant variation of average weather conditions)

→ _____

# 3학년 영어 2학기 중간고사(5과) 2회

문항수 : 선택형(26문항)  서술형(4문항)

20  .  .  .

◎ 선택형 문항의 답안은 컴퓨터용 수정 싸인펜을 사용하여 OMR 답안지에 바르게 표기하시오.
◎ 서술형 문제는 답을 답안지에 반드시 검정 볼펜으로 쓰시오.
◎ 총 30문항 100점 만점입니다. 문항별 배점은 각 문항에 표시되어 있습니다.

[충북 ○○중]

**01** 다음 중 영영 풀이가 바르지 않은 것은?    (3점)

① architect: a person who is designing buildings
② come up with: to provide with a reason to do something
③ take sides: to support one person or group in an argument
④ deal with: to handle or solve something such as a problem
⑤ contribute to: to play a role in the cause or result of something

[서울 강남구 ○○중]

**02** 다음 영영 풀이에 해당하는 단어로 가장 적절한 것은?   (3점)

> information to help people understand something

① expiration
② exploration
③ identification
④ innovation
⑤ explanation

[서울 강남구 ○○중]

**03** 다음 중 짝지어진 단어의 관계가 서로 같지 <u>않은</u> 것은?   (3점)

① eat : edible = add : additional
② act : activity = attract : attraction
③ art : artist = architecture : architect
④ proper : properly = green : greenery
⑤ credible : incredible = appear : disappear

[서울 강남구 ○○중]

**04** Which are NOT grammatically correct?(정답 2개)    (3점)

① I need for you to sign right here.
② It is very thoughtful for them to prepare the gift for him.
③ Our aim is for students to learn it as quickly as possible.
④ It was impossible for them to win the match.
⑤ It was considerate of Jason to let everyone go home early.

[전북 ○○중]

**05** Which question has a <u>different</u> meaning from the others?   (2점)

① What should I do?
② What do you think I should do?
③ What makes you think so?
④ What would you do if you were me?
⑤ What would you do if you were in my shoes?

**06** 다음 대화의 빈칸에 들어갈 알맞은 문장은? (3점)

> A: I think we're using too many plastic bags.
> B: I agree. It's not good for the environment. How can we reduce our use of plastic bags?
> A: In my opinion, _____.

① we had better use plastic bags

② we need to remove trash cans

③ plastic bags are useful in our life

④ we need to save the energy to save the environment

⑤ we should bring reusable bags when we go shopping

**07** 다음 빈칸에 차례로 들어갈 가장 알맞은 말은? (3점)

> Cancun is a city where 4.8 million tourists travel every year. One of the most popular activities to do there is (a)_____ at the area's beautiful sea life underwater. However, tourist activities are seriously (b)_____ parts of the sea near Cancun.

     (a)       (b)

① looking – damaging

② to look – damaged

③ looking – damaged

④ to look – to damage

⑤ looking – to damage

**08** 다음 우리말을 영어로 쓰시오. (단, 'to부정사와 의미상 주어'를 사용할 것.) (4점)

> 그녀는 아침에 일찍 일어나는 것이 쉽지 않았다.

→ _____

**09** 다음 대화의 흐름으로 보아 밑줄 친 (A)~(E) 중 어색한 것은? (3점)

> A: Jiho, hurry up! The elevator is going up soon.
> B: The science room is just on the third floor. (A)Why don't we take the stairs?
> A: (B)I don't want to walk all the way up there.
> B: Come on. Elevators use lots of energy. (C)We need to save energy to protect the environment.
> A: But one elevator ride doesn't use that much energy.
> B: That's true, but the energy from all the elevator rides adds up over time. (D)In my opinion, taking care of the environment starts with the little things.
> A: You have a point. (E)Let's take the elevator.

① (A)    ② (B)    ③ (C)

④ (D)    ⑤ (E)

**10** Which is the <u>inappropriate</u> expression? (3점)

① A: I think we're using too many plastic bags.

B: I agree. It's not good for the environment.

② A: Jiho, hurry up! The elevator is going up.

B: The science room is just on the second floor. Why don't we take the stairs?

③ A: I read a cool article yesterday.

B: What was it about?

④ A: What are we going to do this weekend?

B: Why don't we go to the sheep park near my house?

⑤ A: I want to buy a new bag.

B: You already have too many bags. In my opinion, you're bored with new bags.

**12** 다음 대화의 빈칸에 들어갈 말의 의도가 나머지 넷과 <u>다른 것</u>은? (3점)

A: Have you heard of edible spoons? They're amazing!

B: No, I haven't. Tell me about them.

A: They are made of grain. They will save resources.

B: That sounds awesome. _____

① I'm dying to use it!

② I'm eager to use it!

③ I can't wait to use it!

④ I should have used it!

⑤ I'm looking forward to using it!

**11** 다음 중 어법상 <u>어색한</u> 문장은? (3점)

① Fortunately the table was big enough for all of us to sit around.

② It was careless of you to leave the door of the gym open.

③ It was easy for me to move the table.

④ It is foolish for you to spend 7 hours playing computer games.

⑤ It takes about 3 hours to get from Seoul to Busan by KTX.

**13** 다음 중 어법상 옳은 문장의 개수는? (4점)

ⓐ It was exciting of me to live in this place.

ⓑ It took much effort for me to find out the right place.

ⓒ It is impossible of me to get up at 6 in the morning.

ⓓ It was foolish of him to make the same mistake again.

ⓔ It is inconsiderate of my neighbors to make so much noise at night.

ⓕ It is dangerous for you to take someone else's medicine for the same condition.

① 2개          ② 3개          ③ 4개

④ 5개          ⑤ 6개

**14** 다음 〈보기〉처럼 관계대명사 또는 관계부사를 활용하여 두 문장을 한 문장으로 완성하시오. (6점)

<Example>
This is the house. + I used to live in the house.
→ This is the house which I used to live in.
→ This is the house in which I used to live.
→ This is the house where I used to live.

(1) My family went to the beach.
+ My parents first met on the beach.
→ My family went to the beach _____
_____
_____ .

(2) That is the reason.
+ I like documentaries for the reason.
→ That is the reason _____
_____
_____ .

(3) I can't forget the day.
+ I won the class election on the day.
→ I can't forget the day _____
_____
_____ .

[15–16] 다음 대화를 읽고 물음에 답하시오.

Ann: I read a cool article today.
Sam: What was it about?
Ann: It was about a new bag. It just looks like a plastic bag, but it's made mostly of corn.
Sam: That sounds really amazing.
Ann: Yes, but there's more. The bag breaks down in soil in only three months and disappears in about three minutes in warm water!
Sam: Wow! That will help us reduce plastic waste by a lot!
Ann: I know! The company will start selling the (A)_____ sometime this year. I can't wait to use it!

**15** Which of the following statements about the dialogue is TRUE? (3점)

① Ann made a bag by using corn.
② The bag is made mostly of plastic.
③ The bag made of corn is good for the environment.
④ It disappears in about three minutes in cold water.
⑤ Sam has already read the article about a new bag.

**16** 위 대화의 내용으로 보아, 빈칸 (A)에 들어갈 말로 가장 적절한 것은? (3점)

① bag          ② soil
③ corn         ④ water
⑤ plastic

**17** Which is NOT correct according to the text? (4점)

Today, I'd like to make a suggestion about the trash problem at our school. I've found that many students just throw things away instead of recycling them. As you know, however, recycling is very important because it saves resources and helps protect the environment. So, in my opinion, we need to reduce the number of trash cans at school to encourage recycling. Why don't we place four different colored recycling bins on every floor instead? This will remind students to separate the paper, glass, plastic, and cans properly.

① Recycling can save resources and help protect the environment.

② The writer suggests that there should be a new recycling system at school.

③ It's encouraging that the number of students interested in recycling is steadily increasing.

④ The main purpose of reducing the number of trash cans in school is to encourage students to recycle.

⑤ Different colored recycling bins will remind students to separate items to recycle into different bins properly.

**18** 다음 빈칸 (A)에 들어갈 말로 가장 적절한 것은? (3점)

Via Verde, meaning 'Green Way', is a project started in Mexico City that turns concrete highway pillars into vertical gardens. A vertical garden is a way to grow plants on walls. These gardens are an innovative way to produce oxygen, reduce dust, and absorb $CO_2$, heat, and city noise. And (A)_____.
Also, the process of creating them is environmentally friendly. The materials used to construct these structures are made entirely from recycled plastic.

① they reduce air pollution

② they make the water clean

③ they remove a lot of waste

④ they disappear from the streets

⑤ they change Mexico City into a green house

In Singapore, people are using architecture to protect the environment on land. Let's hear what Rajesh Khan, an architect, says about (A)eco-friendly buildings.

Singapore is hot throughout the year. ⓐMost buildings need air conditioning, which uses a lot of energy and contributes to climate change. That's why architects in Singapore have begun to design eco-friendly buildings that use less air conditioning but are still cool inside. ⓑFor example, many buildings in Singapore are designed to have an open structure. This structure (가)_____ throughout a building. ⓒThis natural air flow is how these buildings stay cool.

In addition to making open structures, architects add large gardens. This greenery provides shade and protects parts of the building from direct sunlight, which keeps the building cooler. ⓓIt also gives ocean animals a nutritious substitute.

ⓔEco-friendly buildings like these not only help protect the environment, but also provide people with a good quality of life. Those are the goals of this new style of architecture. Hopefully, architects will keep coming up with new eco-friendly ideas.

**20** 위 글의 밑줄 친 (A)에 대한 설명으로 옳은 것은? (3점)

① 에어컨을 더 많이 사용해야 한다.

② 빌딩을 짓기 위해 돈이 많이 든다.

③ 직사광선으로부터 빌딩 전체를 보호해 준다.

④ 더위를 피하기 위해 폐쇄형 구조를 가지고 있다.

⑤ 바깥 공기가 빌딩 구석구석까지 통하게 한다.

**21** 위 글의 제목으로 가장 알맞은 것은? (4점)

① Must See Attractions in Singapore

② Eco-Friendly Building Designs in Singapore

③ How to Improve Air Circulation in Buildings

④ The World's Most Unique Eco-Friendly Buildings

⑤ Why Air Conditioning Causes Climate Change

**22** 위 글의 빈칸 (가)에 들어갈 알맞은 말을 아래 조건을 활용하여 영작하시오. (4점)

조건
• 문장의 해석: '이러한 구조는 바깥 공기가 건물 구석구석까지 이동할 수 있게 해 줍니다.'
• 단어 'possible, it, make, outside air, move'를 반드시 사용할 것.
• 필요시 어형 변화 및 단어를 추가할 것.

→ This structure _____

_____ throughout a building.

**19** 위 글에서 전체 흐름과 가장 관련이 없는 문장은? (3점)

① ⓐ　　　② ⓑ　　　③ ⓒ

④ ⓓ　　　⑤ ⓔ

## 23 위 글의 내용과 일치하지 <u>않는</u> 것은? (3점)

① 싱가포르는 일 년 내내 덥다.

② 싱가포르의 많은 건물들은 개방형 구조를 갖도록 설계된다.

③ 싱가포르의 건축가들은 개방형 구조 이외에 커다란 정원을 추가한다.

④ 싱가포르의 대부분 건물들은 에어컨 가동을 필요로 하며 기후 변화의 원인이 되고 있다.

⑤ 싱가포르에서 새로운 건축 양식의 유일한 목표는 건축가들이 친환경 아이디어를 생각해 내는 것이다.

## 24 위 글을 읽고 아래와 같이 요약할 때 빈칸에 들어갈 적절한 표현으로 짝지어진 것은? (4점)

Singapore is always hot, so people are using a lot of energy to cool their buildings with air conditioners. Eco-friendly buildings have open structures that allow (A)_____ to cool the buildings instead. Eco-friendly buildings also have large gardens that provide shade and protect the buildings from (B)_____. This is not only keeps the buildings cool, but also provides people with a better quality of life. These types of (C)_____ will allow humans and nature to live together in harmony.

| | (A) | (B) | (C) |
|---|---|---|---|
| ① | the greenery | a chemical process | circumstances |
| ② | air conditioning | climate change | architectures |
| ③ | natural air flow | direct sunlight | innovations |
| ④ | the greenery | pollution | architectures |
| ⑤ | natural air flow | heating system | innovations |

[25-27] 다음 글을 읽고 물음에 답하시오.

To prevent this, artists did ⓐ<u>something interesting</u>. They thought if they attracted tourists to a different part of the sea, the dying areas could have time to get better. (A)<u>그들은 해양 생물이 죽어가는 지역으로부터 떨어진 곳에 수중 박물관을 만들었습니다.</u> It's about 14 meters below the surface and ⓑ<u>contains</u> 500 statues.

The statues ⓒ<u>are made from</u> materials that support sea life. They provide additional places for plants and animals ⓓ<u>to live on</u>. Over time, many types of sea life will grow on the statues, which will make the artwork unique. The artists want people to see a variety of sea life on the statues. If people realize how rich sea life is, they will understand ⓔ<u>how important is it</u> to save the sea.

## 25 위 글의 밑줄 친 ⓐ~ⓔ 중 어법상 <u>어색한</u> 것은? (3점)

① ⓐ      ② ⓑ      ③ ⓒ

④ ⓓ      ⑤ ⓔ

## 26 위 글의 밑줄 친 우리말 (A)를 바르게 영작한 것은? (3점)

① They made an underwater museum away from the places that sea life was dying.

② They made an underwater museum that sea life was dying away from the places.

③ They made an underwater museum when sea life was dying away from the places.

④ They made an underwater museum away from the places where sea life was dying.

⑤ They made an underwater museum where sea life was dying away from the places.

**27** 위 글의 내용과 가장 일치하지 <u>않는</u> 것은? (4점)

① The artists want to give the dying areas time to get clean.
② The museum was built underwater to protect the sea.
③ The statues can be homes for plants and animals thanks to their materials.
④ The statues will become unique over time with many types of sea life.
⑤ The artists want to see a variety of sea life on the statues.

**28** 위 글의 밑줄 친 ⓐ~ⓔ 중, 어법상 올바른 것은? (4점)

① ⓐ     ② ⓑ     ③ ⓒ
④ ⓓ     ⑤ ⓔ

**29** 위 글의 밑줄 친 to protect와 to부정사의 역할이 <u>다른</u> 것은? (3점)

① I have decided <u>to stay</u> at home tonight.
② I've got some letters <u>to write</u>.
③ I want a machine <u>to answer</u> the phone.
④ Would you like something <u>to read</u>?
⑤ Our decision <u>to wait</u> for them was wise.

[28–30] 다음 글을 읽고 물음에 답하시오.

It is important for us to find ways <u>to protect</u> the environment. Some people ⓐ<u>has found</u> creative ways to save the earth. One example is an underwater museum in Cancun, Mexico. Let's meet Dr. Rosa Allison, an art professor, and ⓑ<u>listens to</u> her explanation about the special museum.

Cancun is a city (A)<u>in which</u> 4.8 million tourists ⓒ<u>travels</u> every year. One of the most popular activities to do there ⓓ<u>are looking</u> at the area's beautiful sea life underwater. However, tourist activities ⓔ<u>are</u> seriously damaging parts of the sea near Cancun.

**30** 위 글의 밑줄 친 (A)in which 대신 쓸 수 있는 표현을 쓰시오. (3점)

→ _____

| 반 | | 점수 | |
|---|---|---|---|
| 이름 | | | |

문항수 : 선택형(27문항)   서술형(3문항)   20 .  .  .

◎ 선택형 문항의 답안은 컴퓨터용 수정 싸인펜을 사용하여 OMR 답안지에 바르게 표기하시오.
◎ 서술형 문제는 답을 답안지에 반드시 검정 볼펜으로 쓰시오.
◎ 총 30문항 100점 만점입니다. 문항별 배점은 각 문항에 표시되어 있습니다.

[전북 ○○중]

**01** 다음 중 단어의 영영 풀이가 <u>어색한</u> 것은? (3점)

① explanation: information to help people understand something
② opinion: one's beliefs, ideas, thoughts, and assumptions about a matter
③ architect: the style and design of buildings
④ awareness: knowledge of a situation or a fact
⑤ app: a piece of software that is designed for a mobile device

[경기 ○○중]

**02** 다음 중 영영 뜻풀이가 바르게 연결되지 <u>않은</u> 것은? (3점)

① come up with: to make a choice
② achieve: to successfully complete something
③ motivate: to make someone want to work hard
④ approach: to move towards or nearer to someone or something
⑤ analyze: to examine or think about something to understand

[전북 ○○중]

**03** 다음 괄호 안의 단어를 활용하여 비교 구문의 문장을 완성하시오. (4점)

_____ I climbed, _____ I felt.
(high / cold)

→ _____ _____

[부산 ○○중]

**04** 다음 빈칸에 들어갈 말로 가장 적절한 것은? (3점)

She found herself in _____ with her parents over her future career.

① sigh          ② handle
③ conflict       ④ support
⑤ exchange

[서울 양천구 ○○중]

**05** 다음 대화 중 밑줄 친 부분이 대화의 흐름이나 어법상 옳지 <u>않</u>은 것은? (3점)

① A: What will you do if it's fine tomorrow?
  B: <u>Being fine tomorrow</u>, we'll go on a picnic. If it's not, we'll stay at home.
② A: What did you do on your first anniversary?
  B: <u>Being so tired</u>, I went to bed early.
③ A: I didn't know it rained last night.
  B: You know what? <u>Walking home in the rain</u>, I got wet.
④ A: Can you tell me how to get to the office?
  B: <u>Turning to the left</u>, you'll see tall buildings. The office will be there.
⑤ A: Did you invite the couple to your birthday party?
  B: I invited the man. But <u>the woman being rude</u>, I didn't invite her to the party.

Amy: What should we sell at the flea market next month?

Sam: Before we choose anything to sell, I think we need to do some market research.

Amy: Market research? Why do we need that?

Sam: Because it helps us find out what items are popular these days.

Amy: I see. Then we can decide _____ _____ at the market.

Sam: That's right. It will also help us set reasonable prices for our items.

Amy: Cool. Is there anything else we should do?

Sam: Oh, don't forget to register our names by this Friday.

Amy: Right. Thanks for reminding me.

[서울 강남구 ○○중]

**07** 위 대화의 빈칸에 들어갈 말을 sell을 포함하여 세 단어로 쓰시오. (4점)

→ _____

[서울 양천구 ○○중]

**06** 다음은 Amy가 Sam과의 대화 후 쓴 메모이다. ⓐ~ⓔ 중 위 대화의 내용과 일치하는 것은? (4점)

Amy's Note
☑ ⓐThe first thing to do : choosing what to sell
☑ The market research helps me
- ⓑFind out what items were popular in the past
- ⓒSet reasonable prices
- ⓓDecide where to sell
☑ ⓔBy Friday, I should make a good brand name for our items

① ⓐ      ② ⓑ      ③ ⓒ
④ ⓓ      ⑤ ⓔ

[경기 ○○중]

**08** 다음 중 어법상 올바른 것은? (3점)

① It is important of me to wear the mask.

② Walked into the room, they locked the door.

③ The hard you study, the good your grades will be.

④ If my mom were at home, I would ask her to pick me up.

⑤ Lunch break at school is the time where I can play soccer with my friends.

**09** 다음 대화 내용을 바르게 이해한 사람을 〈보기〉에서 고른 것은? (3점)

> A: Which do you prefer, the Special Sandwich or the Classic Sandwich?
> B: Well, the Special Sandwich is the healthier choice. It's made with lots of fresh vegetables and other healthy ingredients.
> A: But it's much more expensive than the Classic Sandwich.
> B: I know, but I prefer the Special Sandwich to the Classic Sandwich. Eating healthy is important to me.
> A: I prefer the cheaper one. I'll spend my money on books instead.
> B: I guess our spending habits are different.

**보기**

Tom: 스페셜 샌드위치는 신선한 야채가 들어 있어.
Judy: 클래식 샌드위치가 스페셜보다 비싸.
Chris: B는 스페셜 샌드위치를 더 좋아해.
Linda: A는 비싼 샌드위치를 더 좋아해.

① Tom, Judy
② Judy, Chris
③ Tom, Chris
④ Chris, Linda
⑤ Tom, Linda

**10** 다음 중 문장 전환이 올바른 것을 <u>모두</u> 고른 것은? (4점)

> ⓐ Having nothing to do, I'll stay at home.
> → If I had nothing to do, I'll stay at home.
> ⓑ Since I didn't want to interrupt the conversation, I stood quietly.
> → Having not wanted to interrupt the conversation, I stood quietly.
> ⓒ As it was fine, we went for a walk.
> → It being fine, we went for a walk.
> ⓓ Because he lives in Canada, he is proficient in English and French.
> → Living in Canada, he is proficient in English and French.
> ⓔ As the sun has set, we can't play baseball any more.
> → The sun setting, we can't play baseball any more.

① ⓐ, ⓑ      ② ⓐ, ⓒ
③ ⓑ, ⓓ      ④ ⓒ, ⓓ
⑤ ⓒ, ⓔ

**11** 다음 중 어법상 적절하지 <u>않은</u> 것은? (3점)

① The stronger the wind blows, the colder I feel.
② The more books you read, the wiser you will become.
③ The more he practiced, the faster he could run.
④ The more actively you move, the tireder you will be.
⑤ The hotter the weather gets, the shorter pants I wear.

Sue: I tried Spring Chips recently, and now I want to review them.

Tim: That sounds fun. How will you do your review?

Sue: I'll make a video and post it on my blog. I want to focus on their delicious taste!

Tim: Okay, but (가)_____ (A)[talking / talk] about their bad points too.

Sue: I won't. I also want to give a (B)[balancing / balanced] review.

Tim: Good. Your video will make it easier for people to choose better products.

Sue: That's exactly (C)[which / what] I want. I'd like to give people more useful information about the product.

**13** 위 대화의 내용과 일치하지 <u>않는</u> 것은? (3점)

① Product reviews help people to choose better products.

② The review will be about the good taste of the Spring Chips.

③ Tim talks about the importance of giving a balanced review.

④ Sue will only talk about the good points of the Spring Chips.

⑤ Sue will review the Spring Chips by uploading the review video on her blog.

**12** Which of the following fits in blank (가)? (3점)

① try to

② feel free to

③ remember to

④ make sure to

⑤ don't forget to

**14** 위 대화의 괄호 (A), (B), (C) 안에서 바르게 짝지어진 것은? (3점)

| | (A) | (B) | (C) |
|---|---|---|---|
| ① | talking | balancing | which |
| ② | talking | balanced | which |
| ③ | talk | balancing | which |
| ④ | talk | balanced | what |
| ⑤ | talk | balancing | what |

## 15 다음 글의 흐름상 (A)~(D)의 순서로 가장 알맞은 것은? (4점)

> A: What great apps! We can borrow a tent and find someone to take care of our dog.

> (A) Well, I think the more people use the services, the more they will improve.
>
> (B) People can share their items with others and provide services to them at a small fee or for free.
>
> (C) But these services do have some weaknesses. Some people left negative reviews about the services.
>
> (D) That's right. These kinds of services are part of the "sharing economy."

① (A) - (C) - (B) - (D)

② (A) - (D) - (C) - (B)

③ (C) - (A) - (D) - (B)

④ (D) - (B) - (C) - (A)

⑤ (D) - (C) - (B) - (A)

> A: I think my hair is too curly. I want to straighten my hair. (A)_____
> B: Sure. I know two places, Styles Studio and Hair Castle.
> A: (B)_____
> B: Well, Styles Studio provides free treatment to keep your hair healthy.
> A: That's great. What about Hair Castle?
> B: Hair Castle doesn't provide treatment for free, but they give student discounts.
> A: Okay. (C)_____
> B: I like Styles Studio better than Hair Castle. It's important for me to get hair treatment regularly.

## 16 위 대화의 (A)~(C)에 들어갈 문장을 〈보기〉에서 골라 순서대로 나열한 것은? (3점)

> 보기
>
> ⓐ How about you?
> ⓑ Which do you prefer?
> ⓒ What do you like best about it?
> ⓓ Is there any difference between the two?
> ⓔ Can you recommend a good place?
> ⓕ What is your favorite one?

① ⓔ-ⓑ-ⓓ        ② ⓔ-ⓓ-ⓑ

③ ⓔ-ⓓ-ⓒ        ④ ⓕ-ⓑ-ⓐ

⑤ ⓕ-ⓓ-ⓔ

## 17 위 대화의 (C)에 들어갈 말과 바꾸어 쓸 수 있는 것은? (3점)

① Which place did you go to?

② Which place do you like better?

③ What is your favorite hair style?

④ Do you often visit Styles Studio?

⑤ How often do you get hair treatment?

## 18 다음 밑줄 친 (A)의 우리말과 일치하도록 <보기>의 괄호 안에 주어진 어구들을 모두 사용하여 문장을 완성할 때 네 번째 오는 것은? (4점)

<Jasmine : December 12, 2019>

I asked for a board game and got one in less than 30 minutes. I love saving money by borrowing things that I don't often need. Also, I think it's environmentally friendly. (A)우리가 더 적은 수의 상품을 살수록, 우리는 더 많은 자원을 절약한다.

보기

(we / save / the fewer products / buy / the more resources)

* 필요하다면 단어 두 번 사용

→ _____, _____.

① we

② buy

③ save

④ the fewer products

⑤ the more resources

## [19–23] 다음 글을 읽고, 물음에 답하시오.

I can look after your pet!

*Pet Sitter Finder* is the **(a)**_____ app for pet lovers and pet owners. It helps pet owners find **(A)**[reliable / reasonable] people to look after their pets. When a pet owner is **(b)**_____ pet sitters, he or she **(B)**[downloads / uploads] a post. Pet sitters or dog walkers can then send messages to the owner. The owner checks their reviews and chooses the **(C)**[best / worst] person.

*George*: November 12, 2019

I use this app ⓐwhenever I'm going out of town. I have some concerns about my personal information though. ⓑWhat if people use my phone number for other purposes?

*Pet Sitter Finder*: November 14, 2019

We're aware of this issue. We're now developing a system ⓒthat allow users to communicate freely without showing their personal information.

*Samantha*: February 22, 2020

Animals ⓓaren't allowed in my apartment, so I don't have any pets. However, ⓔby using Pet Sitter Finder, I can experience the joy of walking a dog.

Son: What great apps! We can borrow a tent and find someone to take care of our dog.

Dad: That's right. These kinds of services are part of the "sharing economy." People can share their items with others and provide services to them at a small fee or for free.

Son: But these services do have some **(c)**_____. Some people left negative reviews about the services.

Dad: Well, I think (가)더 많은 사람들이 그 서비스들을 사용할수록, 그것들이 더 개선될 것이라고 생각해.

**19** 위 글의 (a)~(c)에 들어갈 단어를 바르게 짝지은 것은? (3점)

| | (a) | (b) | (c) |
|---|---|---|---|
| ① | perfect | looking for | weaknesses |
| ② | perfect | looking after | strengths |
| ③ | imperfect | looking for | weaknesses |
| ④ | imperfect | looking after | weaknesses |
| ⑤ | imperfect | looking for | strengths |

**21** 위 글의 Pet Sitter Finder에 관한 내용으로 옳은 것은? (3점)

① 애완동물을 돌봐 줄 사람을 자동으로 찾아준다.

② 이용자의 개인 정보 유출 문제가 발생한 적이 있다.

③ 애완동물을 가진 사람만 이 앱을 이용할 수 있다.

④ 대부분의 아파트에서는 애완동물을 키울 수 없다.

⑤ 애완동물을 돌봐 준 사람에 대해 평가를 할 수 있다.

**22** 위 글의 괄호 (A), (B), (C) 안에서 문맥에 맞는 표현이 알맞게 연결된 것은? (4점)

| | (A) | (B) | (C) |
|---|---|---|---|
| ① | reliable | uploads | best |
| ② | reasonable | downloads | best |
| ③ | reliable | downloads | worst |
| ④ | reasonable | uploads | worst |
| ⑤ | reliable | downloads | best |

**20** 위 글의 밑줄 친 (가)를 올바르게 영작한 것은? (3점)

① more people use the services, more they will improve

② the most services people use, the more will they improve

③ the more services people use, the more will they improve

④ the most people use the services, the more they will improve

⑤ the more people use the services, the more they will improve

**23** 위 글의 밑줄 친 ⓐ~ⓔ 중 어법상 올바르지 않은 것은? (3점)

① ⓐ      ② ⓑ      ③ ⓒ

④ ⓓ      ⑤ ⓔ

*Ask Your Neighbors* (A)_____ people easily find items ⓐthat they can borrow from others. First, users download the app and search for another user ⓑthat has the item they need. Then they pick up the item and return it later.

*Jasmine* : December 12, 2019
I asked for a board game and (B)_____ (가)one in less than 30 minutes. I love saving money by (C)_____ things ⓒthat I don't often need. Also, I think ⓓthat it's (D)_____ friendly. 우리가 더 적은 제품들을 구매할수록, 우리는 더 많은 자원들을 절약하게 되는 거예요.

*Cassandra* : March 7, 2020
(나)Seeing a lot of positive reviews, I decided (E)_____ a bike helmet. When I got it, however, it was broken. I was so upset! (다)_____

*Ask Your Neighbors* : March 9, 2020
We're sorry ⓔthat you had such a negative experience. To fix this issue, we are asking lenders to update the pictures of their items regularly. This will let other users know the exact condition of the product.

[전북 ○○중]

**24** 위 글의 밑줄 친 (가)one이 가리키는 것을 본문에서 찾아 세 단어로 쓰시오. (3점)

→ _____ _____ _____

[충북 ○○중]

**25** 위 글의 빈칸 (A)~(E)에 들어갈 말로 알맞은 것은? (3점)

① (A) help
② (B) get
③ (C) borrowing
④ (D) environmental
⑤ (E) borrowing

[서울 강남구 ○○중]

**26** 위 글의 밑줄 친 (나)를 부사절로 알맞게 바꾼 것은? (3점)

① If I see a lot of positive reviews
② After I saw a lot of positive reviews
③ Although I saw a lot of positive reviews
④ Since people saw a lot of positive reviews
⑤ When people saw a lot of positive reviews

**27** 위 글의 빈칸 (다)에 들어갈 말로 적절하지 <u>않은</u> 것은? (4점)

① I will never use this app again.

② I felt guilty that the helmet was broken.

③ This kind of happening shouldn't happen again.

④ I hope next users will avoid such a bad experience like me.

⑤ I want you to warn the lender of the inconvenience I had because of the broken helmet.

**28** 위 글의 밑줄 친 @~@의 that 중, 생략할 수 <u>없는</u> 것은? (3점)

①  @        ②  ⓑ        ③  ⓒ

④  ⓓ        ⑤  ⓔ

**29** 위 글의 밑줄 친 우리말과 일치하도록 아래 문장을 완성하시오. (5점)

→ _____ we buy,

_____ we save.

**30** 위 글의 내용과 일치하지 <u>않는</u> 것은? (3점)

① Ask Your Neighbors는 새로운 물건을 쉽게 구입하기 위한 앱이다.

② Jasmine은 30분 이내에 보드 게임을 구할 수 있었다.

③ Jasmine은 Ask Your Neighbors가 친환경적이라고 생각한다.

④ Cassandra가 구한 물품에는 하자가 있었다.

⑤ Ask Your Neighbors는 Cassandra의 의견에 댓글을 달았다.

◎ 선택형 문항의 답안은 컴퓨터용 수정 싸인펜을 사용하여 OMR 답안지에 바르게 표기하시오.

◎ 서술형 문제는 답을 답안지에 반드시 검정 볼펜으로 쓰시오.

◎ 총 30문항 100점 만점입니다. 문항별 배점은 각 문항에 표시되어 있습니다.

[전북 ○○중]

## 01 다음 단어의 영영 풀이로 알맞지 <u>않은</u> 것은?  (3점)

① improve: to make something worse

② climate: the general weather of a region

③ architect: a person who designs buildings

④ prevent: to stop something from happening

⑤ share: to own or use something with other people

[경기 ○○중]

## 02 다음 빈칸에 들어갈 수 <u>없는</u> 것은?  (3점)

- It is no _____ of mine.
- If the price of something is _____, it is fair.
- A _____ is a sum of money which is returned to you.
- If you _____ something with another person, you both have it.

① share

② cheap

③ refund

④ concern

⑤ reasonable

[전북 ○○중]

## 03 다음 문장을 분사구문을 이용하여 완성하시오.  (4점)

Because she was just fourteen, Kate couldn't watch the movie.

→ _____ _____ _____, Kate couldn't watch the movie.

[경기 ○○중]

## 04 다음 대화의 흐름으로 보아, 빈칸 (A)에 들어갈 말로 가장 적절한 것은?  (3점)

A: Jinho, look! These two speakers look pretty cool.

B: Yeah, they do. Which do you prefer, the red one or the black one?

A: I prefer the red one to the black one. It's only 20 dollars, and it comes with a discount coupon for music downloads.

B: (A)_____ the black one is 40 dollars, I think it's the right one for me. I heard it has better sound quality.

① Because

② Although

③ Furthermore,

④ Therefore,

⑤ In other words,

**05** 다음 문장을 분사구문을 이용하여 두 문장의 의미가 같도록 문장을 완성하시오. (4점)

> While we were eating fried chicken together, we talked about the game.
> → _____, we talked about the game.

→ _____

**06** Choose what the girl is going to do after the dialogue. (3점)

> Maria: I want to buy a new bag.
> Jason: You already have too many bags. In my opinion, you don't need any more.
> Maria: But I'm bored with my old bags.
> Jason: Then how about using old clothes to make a new bag? You can find out how to do it online.
> Maria: Oh, that sounds interesting! I can't wait to make my own bag.

① to ask Jason to make a new bag

② to go shopping to buy a new bag

③ to sell one of Maria's old bags online

④ to look up how to use clothes to make a bag

⑤ to return the bag Maria borrowed from Jason

**07** 다음 빈칸에 들어갈 말로 적절한 것은? (2점)

> _____ my teeth, I listened to the radio.
> (이를 닦는 동안, 나는 라디오를 들었다.)

① Brush

② Brushed

③ Brushing

④ To brush

⑤ To brushing

[8–9] 다음 대화를 읽고 물음에 답하시오.

> A: I think my hair is too curly. I want to straighten my hair. Can you recommend a good place?
> B: _____
> A: (A) _____
> B: _____
> A: _____
> B: (B) _____
> A: _____
> B: I prefer Styles Studio to Hair Castle. It's important for me to get hair treatment regularly.

**08** 위 대화를 통해 알 수 <u>없는</u> 것은? (3점)

① A가 원하는 머리 모양

② 학생 할인을 제공하는 미용실

③ B가 다니는 미용실의 이용 요금

④ B가 Style Studio를 선호하는 이유

⑤ 미용실에서 헤어트리트먼트 서비스를 제공하는 이유

**09** 다음 〈보기〉의 ⓐ~ⓕ를 배열하여 대화를 완성할 때, (A)와 (B) 에 들어갈 내용을 순서대로 짝지은 것은? (4점)

> **보기**
>
> ⓐ Is there any difference between the two?
> ⓑ That's great. What about Hair Castle?
> ⓒ Sure. I know two places. Styles Studio and Hair Castle.
> ⓓ Okay. Which do you prefer?
> ⓔ Hair Castle doesn't provide treatment for free, but they give student discounts.
> ⓕ Well, Styles Studio provides free treatment to keep your hair healthy.

① ⓐ, ⓔ    ② ⓑ, ⓔ
③ ⓒ, ⓕ    ④ ⓐ, ⓕ
⑤ ⓑ, ⓓ

**10** 다음 대화의 괄호 (A)와 (B)에서 알맞은 말을 골라 쓰시오. (3점)

> A: I'm going to get a refund for these clothes this evening. I found I have similar (A)[it / ones].
> B: Okay. Don't forget (B)[bringing / to bring] your receipt. Last time you couldn't get a refund because you didn't bring it.
> A: Okay, Mom. I won't forget it this time.

(A) _____

(B) _____

**11** 다음 주어진 우리말과 일치하도록 〈보기〉를 참고하여 분사구문은 부사절로, 부사절은 분사구문으로 바꾸어 쓰시오. (6점)

> <Example>
> Although I go to bed early, I can't get up early.
> → Going to bed early, I can't get up early.
> Feeling cold, I put on a coat.
> → Because I felt cold, I put on a coat.

(1) Reading the letter, he was really surprised.
그는 편지를 읽은 후, 매우 놀랐다.

→ _____, he was really surprised.

(2) I still feel cold though I am sitting in the sun.
나는 해가 드는 곳에 앉아 있지만 여전히 춥다.

→ I still feel cold, _____.

(3) Not knowing what to do, he asked me for advice.
그는 무엇을 해야 할지 몰랐기 때문에 나에게 조언을 구했다.

→ _____, he asked me for advice.

[12-13] 다음 대화를 읽고 물음에 답하시오.

A: What should we sell at the flea market next month?

B: Before we choose anything to sell, I think we need to do some market research.

A: Market research? Why do we need that?

B: Because it helps us find out what items are popular these days.

A: I see. Then we can decide what to sell at the market.

B: That's right. It will also help us set reasonable prices for our items.

A: Cool. Is there anything else we should do?

B: Oh, we must (A)register our names by this Friday.

A: Right. Thanks for reminding me.

**13** 위 대화의 내용상 (A)의 의미로 가장 적절한 것은? (3점)

① to put your name on a list

② to give someone a special job

③ to take a choice about something

④ to use money to pay for something

⑤ to give a name to someone or something

**12** 위 대화의 내용과 일치하지 <u>않는</u> 것은? (3점)

① 두 사람은 벼룩시장에서 물건을 팔 계획이다.

② 두 사람은 벼룩시장에서 팔 물건을 결정하지 못했다.

③ 두 사람 모두 시장 조사의 필요성에 대해 동의하고 있다.

④ 시장 조사를 통해 요새 어떤 물건이 인기 있는지 알 수 있다.

⑤ 시장 조사를 통해 물건의 도매 가격을 알 수 있다.

[14-15] 다음 대화를 읽고 물음에 답하시오.

Amy: Which do you prefer, the Special Sandwich or the Class Sandwich?

Lori: Well, the Special Sandwich is the healthier choice. It's made with lots of fresh vegetables and other healthy ingredients.

Amy: But it's much more expensive than the Classic Sandwich.

Lori: I know, but (A)_____. Eating healthy is important to me.

Amy: I prefer the cheaper one. I'll spend my money on books instead.

Lori: I guess our spending habits are different.

**14** Which of the following fits in blank (A)? (3점)

① I like the Classic Sandwich to the Special Sandwich.

② I prefer the Special Sandwich than the Classic Sandwich.

③ I prefer the Classic Sandwich than the Special Sandwich.

④ I like the Classic Sandwich better than the Special Sandwich.

⑤ I prefer the Special Sandwich to the Classic Sandwich.

**15** Which of the following is NOT true according to the dialog? (4점)

① 두 사람은 선호하는 샌드위치에 관해 이야기하고 있다.

② 스페셜 샌드위치는 신선한 채소와 건강한 재료로 만들어져 있다.

③ 스페셜 샌드위치가 클래식 샌드위치보다 비싸다.

④ Amy는 스페셜 샌드위치를 선호한다.

⑤ Lori는 구입할 때 가격을 제일 중요한 요소로 생각하지 않는다.

**[16–17]** 다음 글을 읽고 물음에 답하시오.

Dear dog owners,

  Are you planning to go away on vacation with your family and looking for a friendly and reliable dog sitter? Or do you just need someone to walk your dog? I can take care of your pets while you're gone. I am an experienced dog sitter because I owned a dog for many years. My dog died two years ago, and I have provided dog sitting services since then. I can go to your place and look after your dogs or bring them to my home for overnight stays. I live in a large house located close to a dog park where your dogs can run around. Have your dogs looked after for a small fee!

- Dog Walking – $15 per hour
- House Sitting (includes walking and playing) – $20 per hour
- Overnight Dog Sitting – $40 per night (20% off for 3 nights in a row)
- Picking and Drop – Offs – $10

**16** 위 글을 읽고 다음 질문에 바르게 답한 것은? (3점)

> Q: How much should I pay for a two-hour house dog sitting service?

① $15          ② $20          ③ $30

④ $40          ⑤ $60

## 17 위 글의 내용과 일치하는 것은? (3점)

① The dog sitter lives far from a dog park.

② The dog sitter has never raised his own dog.

③ The dog sitter provides only day care services.

④ You can use Picking and Drop-Offs service for free.

⑤ The dog sitter can take care of your dogs in his place.

## 18 다음 대화의 빈칸에 들어갈 말로 가장 적절한 것은? (3점)

Son: What great apps! We can borrow a tent and find someone to take care of our dog.

Dad: That's right. These kinds of services are part of the "_____."
People can share their items with others and provide services to them at a small fee or for free.

Son: But these services do have some weaknesses. Some people left negative reviews about the services.

① Flea Market

② New Policy

③ Social Economy

④ Western Economy

⑤ Sharing Economy

## [19~24] 다음 글을 읽고, 물음에 답하시오.

Borrow from your neighbors!

*Ask Your Neighbors* (가)_____ that they can borrow from others. First, users download the app and search for another user that ⓐ_____ the item they need. Then they pick up the item and return it later.

*Jasmine* : December 12, 2019

I asked for a board game and got one in less than 30 minutes. I love saving money ⓑ_____ borrowing things that I don't often need. Also, I think it's environmentally friendly. 우리가 더 적은 제품을 구매할수록, 우리는 더 많은 자원을 절약하게 된다.

*Cassandra* : March 7, 2020

ⓒ_____ a lot of positive reviews, I decided to borrow a bike helmet. When I got it, however, it was broken. (A)_____

*Ask Your Neighbors* : March 9, 2020

We're sorry that you had ⓓ_____ a negative experience. To fix this issue, we are asking lenders to update the pictures of their items regularly. This will let other users ⓔ_____ the exact condition of the product.

**19** 위 글의 빈칸 (가)에 들어갈 말을 문맥과 어법에 맞게 〈보기〉의 단어들로 바르게 배열한 것은? (3점)

보기

people / helps / find / easily / items

① people helps find easily items
② helps people easily items find
③ helps people easily find items
④ people helps easily find items
⑤ people find easily items helps

**20** 위 글의 빈칸 ⓐ~ⓔ에 들어갈 알맞은 말이 잘못 연결된 것은? (3점)

① ⓐ - has
② ⓑ - by
③ ⓒ - Seeing
④ ⓓ - such
⑤ ⓔ - to know

**21** 위 글의 밑줄 친 우리말을 주어진 단어를 활용하여 영어 문장으로 완성하시오. (단, 'the 비교급, the 비교급' 구문을 사용할 것) (4점)

(products / resources)

→ _____

**22** 위 글의 흐름으로 보아 빈칸 (A)에 들어갈 표현으로 가장 적절한 것은? (3점)

① I was so upset.
② I was so bored.
③ I was very happy.
④ I was so satisfied.
⑤ I was very pleased.

**23** 위 글의 Ask Your Neighbors에 관한 내용으로 옳지 않은 것은? (4점)

① It is easy to find the items we need.
② It doesn't take so long to get items we want.
③ It helps to develop local economy consistently.
④ It can contribute to protecting our environment.
⑤ It is necessary for lenders to update the pictures of their items regularly.

**24** 위 글의 밑줄 친 ⓒ에 들어갈 말과 쓰임이 <u>다른</u> 것은?　(3점)

① <u>Finding</u> my wallet, I felt relieved.

② She went to bed, <u>finishing</u> the task.

③ Katie enjoyed <u>playing</u> with her cats.

④ <u>Focusing</u> on the classes, he got all As.

⑤ I fell, <u>striking</u> my head against the door.

*George* : November 12, 2019

I use this app (C)_____ I'm going out of town. I have some concerns ⓒ<u>about</u> my personal information ⓓ<u>though</u>. What if people use my phone number for other (D)_____?

*Pet Sitter Finder* : November 14, 2019

We're aware ⓔ<u>of</u> this (E)_____. We're now developing a system that allows users to communicate freely without showing their personal information.

*Samantha* : February 22, 2020

Animals aren't allowed in my apartment, so I don't have any pets. (나)_____, by using Pet Sitter Finder, I can experience the joy of walking a dog.

[25~30] 다음 글을 읽고 물음에 답하시오.

Pet Sitter Finder is the perfect app for pet lovers and pet owners. It helps pet owners find (A)_____ people to look ⓐ<u>for</u> their pets. (가)_____ a pet owner is looking for pet sitters, he or she (B)_____ a post. Pet sitters or dog walkers can then send messages ⓑ<u>to</u> the owner. The owner checks their reviews and chooses the best person.

**25** 위 글에 대한 설명으로 적절하지 <u>않은</u> 것은?　(3점)

① Samantha는 Pet Sitter Finder 앱을 이용하여 반려동물을 구입하였다.

② 반려동물 주인은 Pet Sitter Finder 앱을 사용하여 반려동물 돌보미를 찾을 수 있다.

③ Samantha는 Pet Sitter Finder 앱 덕택에 개를 산책시키는 즐거움을 경험할 수 있다.

④ George는 Pet Sitter Finder 앱을 사용할 때 자신의 전화번호가 다른 목적으로 이용될까봐 걱정한다.

⑤ Pet Sitter Finder 측에서는 사용자들이 개인정보를 노출하지 않고 의사소통하는 방안을 개발하고 있다.

**26** 위 글의 빈칸 (A)~(E)에 들어갈 말로 적절하지 <u>않은</u> 것은?

(4점)

① (A) doubtful

② (B) uploads

③ (C) whenever

④ (D) purposes

⑤ (E) problem

**27** 위 글의 빈칸 (가), (나)에 들어갈 표현으로 알맞은 것은? (3점)

|  | (가) | (나) |
|---|---|---|
| ① | Where | Wherever |
| ② | When | However |
| ③ | When | Whenever |
| ④ | What | Whichever |
| ⑤ | Since | But |

**28** 위 글을 읽고 답할 수 <u>없는</u> 것은?

(4점)

① Why does Samantha use the app?

② How many dogs does George have?

③ What kind of app is Pet Sitter Finder?

④ What system is the app developer making?

⑤ What is George worried about when he uses the app?

**29** 위 글의 밑줄 친 ⓐ~ⓔ 중, 표현이 <u>어색한</u> 것은?     (3점)

① ⓐ          ② ⓑ          ③ ⓒ

④ ⓓ          ⑤ ⓔ

**30** 위 글의 Samantha가 겪는 문제로 가장 알맞은 것은?    (3점)

① 그녀는 반려동물을 돌볼 좋은 사람을 찾을 수 없다.

② 그녀는 그녀의 개를 산책시킬 수 없다.

③ 그녀는 그녀의 아파트에서 반려 동물을 키울 수 없다.

④ 그녀는 반려동물과의 소통을 어려워한다.

⑤ 그녀는 앱 사용법을 잘 모른다.

# 3학년 영어 2학기 중간고사(7과) 1회

문항수 : 선택형(29문항)  서술형(1문항)　　　20 ．　．　．

◎ 선택형 문항의 답안은 컴퓨터용 수정 싸인펜을 사용하여 OMR 답안지에 바르게 표기하시오.

◎ 서술형 문제는 답을 답안지에 반드시 검정 볼펜으로 쓰시오.

◎ 총 30문항 100점 만점입니다. 문항별 배점은 각 문항에 표시되어 있습니다.

[서울 양천구 ○○중]

**01** 다음 중 단어의 영영 풀이가 옳은 것은?　　(3점)

① artificial: able to be used easily

② program: to make one's way through an area

③ swarm: a way to go from one place to another

④ perceive: to handle or solve something such as a problem

⑤ sense: to be aware of something without seeing or hearing it

[서울 강남구 ○○중]

**02** 다음 문장의 빈칸에 들어갈 단어의 영영 풀이로 알맞게 짝지어진 것은?　　(4점)

- Her parents give her a small ⓐ_____.
- The judge will ⓑ_____ the winner.
- The school must ⓒ_____ all its computer equipment.
- This hotel is quite good, and the price is ⓓ_____.
- He should ⓔ_____ the birth of his son as soon as possible.

① ⓐ an amount of money that is given back to you when you return goods to a store

② ⓑ to have knowledge about something

③ ⓒ to add the most recent information to something

④ ⓓ having all parts in equal or good amounts

⑤ ⓔ to look carefully for somebody or something

[서울 양천구 ○○중]

**03** 다음 단어의 영영 풀이와 예문이 모두 올바른 것은?　　(4점)

① awareness: knowledge of a situation or fact
   - The study shows a growing awareness of the problems.

② architect: the style and design of buildings
   - One thing that people can enjoy in Prague is its architect.

③ innovation: one's beliefs, ideas, thoughts, and assumptions about a matter
   - We had different innovations about the issue.

④ surface: an object made from stone or metal
   - There are small black dots on the sun's surface.

⑤ in harmony with: with upsetting or harming each other
   - We should live in harmony with other people.

[서울 양천구 ○○중]

**04** 다음 단어 중 문장의 빈칸 어디에도 들어가기 어색한 것은? (주어진 단어 변형 불가)　　(3점)

- His _____ health condition is very bad.
- A microwave is a _____ cooking device.
- These dogs are known for their high _____.
- It was not an easy _____, and I couldn't finish it on time.

① site　　　　② task

③ present　　④ convenient

⑤ intelligence

**05** 다음 ⓐ~ⓔ를 대화의 흐름에 맞게 배열한 것은? (4점)

> Girl: I had to wait in line at the store for almost twenty minutes.
>
> ⓐ I read about a store without cashiers. You take what you want to buy and just walk out.
>
> ⓑ That's too bad. Maybe in the future we'll never have to wait in line.
>
> ⓒ That's it? How do you pay for it?
>
> ⓓ There are cameras and sensors in the store. They keep track of the items you chose and send the information to an app on your smartphone.
>
> ⓔ What do you mean?
>
> Girl: Then the app pays for them when you leave the store?
>
> Boy: Exactly. It's likely that these kinds of stores will be more common in the future.

① ⓑ-ⓒ-ⓓ-ⓔ-ⓐ

② ⓑ-ⓔ-ⓐ-ⓒ-ⓓ

③ ⓑ-ⓔ-ⓒ-ⓐ-ⓓ

④ ⓔ-ⓐ-ⓒ-ⓓ-ⓑ

⑤ ⓔ-ⓓ-ⓑ-ⓒ-ⓐ

**06** 다음 대화의 밑줄 친 우리말을 옮긴 올바른 영어 문장은? (3점)

> Sylvi: Hey Eunbi, are you busy today?
> Eunbi: Unfortunately, yes. What's the matter?
> Sylvi: You remember Manok and Cheonok, right?
> Eunbi: Of course I remember them.
> Sylvi: They just called me to visit their place right now. Can you come with me?
> Eunbi: No, I can't. 만약 나에게 충분한 시간이 있다면, 나는 너와 함께 그들을 방문할 텐데. Maybe next time. Please say hi to Manok and Cheonok for me, Okay?

① If I have enough time, I visit them with you.

② If I had enough time, I visit them with you.

③ If I had enough time, I will visit them with you.

④ If I had enough time, I would visit them with you.

⑤ If I will have enough time, I would visit them with you.

**07** 다음 〈보기〉의 문장을 올바르게 영작한 것은? (3점)

> ┌─ 보기 ─────────────────┐
> 네가 돈을 기부하다니 참 친절하구나.
> └───────────────────────┘

① It is very kind of you donate your money.

② It is very kind of you to donate your money.

③ It is very kind for you to donate your money.

④ It is very kind for you donate your money.

⑤ It is very kind you to donate your money.

**08** 다음 문장의 밑줄 친 부분과 같은 의미가 되도록 올바르게 바꾼 것은? (3점)

> Feeling happy about the win, we decided to celebrate.

① Although we felt happy about the win,

② Before we felt happy about the win,

③ Since we feel happy about the win,

④ Because we felt happy about the win,

⑤ If we feel happy about the win,

**09** 다음 중 어법상 올바른 문장을 모두 고른 것은? (4점)

> ⓐ If I would get up earlier, I hadn't missed the bus.
> ⓑ If you're free tonight, will you have joined us for dinner?
> ⓒ I would go rock climbing with you today if I hadn't hurt my ankle.
> ⓓ Had the shoes cost only twenty dollars, she would have bought them.
> ⓔ If she had told me earlier about the concert, I might have been able to go.
> ⓕ I was late for school because I woke up late. I wish I had set my alarm.
> ⓖ If it were not for failure, we couldn't have fully appreciated success.

① ⓐ, ⓒ, ⓓ, ⓖ

② ⓑ, ⓒ, ⓓ, ⓕ

③ ⓑ, ⓒ, ⓔ, ⓖ

④ ⓒ, ⓓ, ⓔ, ⓕ

⑤ ⓒ, ⓔ, ⓕ, ⓖ

**10** 다음 〈보기〉에서 대화 내용과 일치하는 문장의 개수는? (4점)

> B: What are you watching?
> G: It's a show about a man who lost one of his arms in an accident. Surprisingly, he can play the drums very well.
> B: How can he play the drums with only one arm?
> G: Actually he uses two arms. One is a robot arm controlled by his brain.
> B: That's awesome. Could you explain in more detail?
> G: Sure. First, he thinks what he wants to do with his left arm. Then those thoughts are turned into electronic signals. The signals travel from his brain to his robot arm and move it.
> B: That's amazing! I think this technology can help many people.

보기
- The man plays the drums only with the left robot arm.
- The boy is worried about the side effects of the robot that has AI.
- The man's brain controls his robot arm, which helps it do what he wants.
- The girl is reading a book about a man who lost one arm in an accident.

① 없음　　② 1개　　③ 2개

④ 3개　　⑤ 4개

**11** 다음 ⓐ~ⓔ 중 문맥상 적절하지 <u>않은</u> 것은? (3점)

> A: I had to wait in line at the store for almost twenty minutes.
> B: ⓐ<u>That's too bad.</u> Maybe in the future we'll never have to wait in line.
> A: ⓑ<u>What do you mean?</u>
> B: I read about a store without cashiers. ⓒ <u>You take what you want to buy and just walk out.</u>
> A: That's it? How do you pay for it?
> B: There are cameras and sensors in the store. ⓓ<u>They keep track of the items you choose and send the information to an app on your smartphone.</u>
> A: Then the app pays for them when you leave the store?
> B: Exactly. ⓔ<u>It's unlikely that these kinds of stores will be more common in the future.</u>

① ⓐ  ② ⓑ  ③ ⓒ  ④ ⓓ  ⑤ ⓔ

**12** 다음 문장의 빈칸에 들어갈 말을 어법에 맞게 쓴 것은? (3점)

> Jane really wants to buy a new phone. But she doesn't have enough money. In this situation, how does she feel? "_____"

① If I have enough money, I will buy a new phone.

② If I had enough money, I will buy a new phone.

③ If I had enough money, I would buy a new phone.

④ If I will have enough money, I will buy a new phone.

⑤ If I have enough money, I would buy a new phone.

**13** 다음 중 주어진 문장을 가정법 문장으로 전환할 때, 어법상 올바르지 <u>않은</u> 것은? (4점)

① I don't feel hungry because I had a big lunch.
→ I would feel hungry if I had not had a big lunch.

② Mary is ill, so she is at the hospital.
→ If Mary weren't ill, she won't be at the hospital.

③ I didn't complete my report because my computer broke.
→ If my computer had not broken, I would have completed my report.

④ I'm sorry I didn't have enough time to exercise.
→ I wish I had had enough time to exercise.

⑤ Eric will not attend the wedding because he's on a business trip.
→ If Eric weren't on a business trip, he would attend the wedding.

**14** 다음 밑줄 친 부분의 의미와 같지 <u>않은</u> 것은? (3점)

> Jason eats an orange every morning <u>so that he can get some vitamin C</u>.

① for some vitamin C

② to get some vitamin C

③ so as to get some vitamin C

④ in order to get some vitamin C

⑤ as he can get some vitamin C

M: As climate change is going to make farming harder, there may not be enough resources for the increasing number of people on Earth. (A) For this reason, it is likely that we will have to change how we get our food. (B) For example, we won't kill animals for food. (C) Instead, meat will be grown in a lab using animal cells. (D) This will require less land, water, and other resources. (E) You might not want to eat them, but they are actually very rich in nutrients!

[경기 ○○중]

## 15 위 글에서 다음 문장이 들어가기에 가장 적절한 곳은? (3점)

Also, bugs such as ants will become part of our daily meals.

① (A)  ② (B)  ③ (C)
④ (D)  ⑤ (E)

[서울 강남구 ○○중]

## 16 Which is the main topic of the passage? (3점)

① The cause of recent climate change

② The necessity of animal protection movement

③ The impact of an increasing number of people

④ The importance of nutritious and balanced meal

⑤ The possible solutions for a food shortage problem

Would you like to lie in bed and turn off your bedroom light by speaking the words "turn off the lights"? If so, *Chin-Gu* is perfect for you. *Chin-Gu* is the first smart speaker ⓐmaking by Tangerine Co. It uses AI technology so that it can make your life easier. This device uses artificial intelligence to recognize your voice and follow your instructions. It can be your personal voice assistant!

*Chin-Gu* can help you in many useful ways. First, you can ask *Chin-Gu* any question. This small device will then search the Internet and tell you the answer. Next, *Chin-Gu* can help you ⓑwake up in the morning. Just tell *Chin-Gu* what time to set your alarm for. The device will wake you up at that time by ⓒplaying any music you choose. *Chin-Gu* can even tell you what the weather will be like on that day! Finally, there are bright LEDs on the top of the device, so you can also use *Chin-Gu* as a desk lamp.

The only problem with *Chin-Gu* is its battery, ⓓwhich only lasts for about three hours. So if you are thinking about buying a smart speaker, *Chin-Gu* is the best product ⓔthat you can choose.

[경기 ○○중]

## 17 위 글의 ⓐ~ⓔ 중 어법상 바르지 <u>않은</u> 것은? (3점)

① ⓐ  ② ⓑ  ③ ⓒ
④ ⓓ  ⑤ ⓔ

## 18 위 글의 내용과 일치하는 것은? (3점)

① *Chin-Gu* is the smart lamp with a speaker.

② *Chin-Gu* will tell you what you want to know.

③ *Chin-Gu* is a big sized device using AI technology.

④ You can use *Chin-Gu* over three hours with its battery.

⑤ You can set your alarm by pushing the button of *Chin-Gu*.

## 20 위 글의 내용과 일치하는 것은? (4점)

① 로봇은 영화와 책 속에만 등장하는 존재이다.

② 과거에 로봇은 인간이 로봇에게 실행하도록 프로그램을 설정한 단순 업무도 수행할 수 없었다.

③ 특정 지역에서만 로봇은 단순 업무를 수행하고 있다.

④ 인공지능을 가진 로봇은 환경을 인식할 수 없고 의사 결정을 할 수 없다.

⑤ 로봇은 더 똑똑해지고 있으며 곧 인간처럼 생각할 수 있을지도 모른다.

## 21 위 글의 밑줄 친 (A)what과 용법이 <u>다른</u> 것은? (3점)

① This is <u>what</u> I want.

② <u>What</u> he said is true.

③ Do you know <u>what</u> this is?

④ This ring is <u>what</u> my mom gave me.

⑤ <u>What</u> I can do now is to build a strong house.

## [19-21] 다음 글을 읽고 물음에 답하시오.

**Where Do We See Robots?**

Robots are not only in movies and books anymore. Around the world, robots are doing a variety of tasks. There ⓐ<u>are</u> delivery robots flying in the sky, robot arms in factories, and service robots in public places.

**Robots Are Becoming Smart**

In the past, robots performed only easy tasks ⓑ<u>that</u> humans programmed them to do. However, robots are now getting "smarter," and soon they might be able to think ⓒ<u>like</u> humans. (A)<u>What</u> makes this possible is artificial intelligence (AI). Robots that have AI can perceive environments and ⓓ<u>makes</u> decisions. They can also recognize speech, tell jokes, and ⓔ<u>play</u> games with humans.

## [22-27] 다음 글을 읽고 물음에 답하시오.

Robots are making things faster and easier. They can help us anywhere – in our homes, on roads, or in disaster areas.

· (가)<u>Home Helper Robot</u>: This robot helps your family throughout the day. (A)<u>만약 당신이 하나를 가지고 있다면 요리와 청소가 더 쉬워질 텐데</u>. It also talks with family members and can sense emotions.

· (나)<u>Self-Driving Car</u>: A self-driving car doesn't need a driver. With cameras, sensors, and software, it (B)_____ _____ _____ _____ _____ _____ _____ _____ and enjoy the ride.

## 19 위 글의 밑줄 친 ⓐ~ⓔ 중, 어법상 <u>어색한</u> 것은? (3점)

① ⓐ     ② ⓑ     ③ ⓒ

④ ⓓ     ⑤ ⓔ

- (다)Robot Swarm: A robot swarm is a large group of robots that can communicate with one another, like ants or bees. They can be used in a variety of places, including farms or building sites. They work on tasks and find solutions as a group.
- (라)Search-and-Rescue Robot:
Search-and-rescue robots can go into disaster areas that are dangerous for humans. They find survivors, deal with dangers, and clear routes so that people can escape to safety.

Our future with robots looks bright but not perfect.  Some people expect life to become more convenient with the help of robots. However, other people worry about problems they might cause, such as threats to our jobs and safety. The important thing is to find possible solutions and to ensure that robots are only used for good.

**22** 위 글의 밑줄 친 (A)를 우리말로 옮기시오. (단, if를 첫 번째 단어로 할 것) (4점)

→ _____

**23** 위 글에서 밑줄 친 로봇과 그 로봇이 할 수 있는 말로 바르게 짝지어진 것은? (3점)

① (가): Last week, after a typhoon hit, I cleaned a route to help a boy to escape.

② (나): We can understand each other, so we are useful in a large place.

③ (다): It is impossible for us to build a tower by working together.

④ (라): I'm able to enter dangerous places and help people when they are in danger.

⑤ (나): I taught a child of the family I work for. He worried about this final exam.

**24** 위 글을 읽고 답할 수 없는 것은? (3점)

① Where do robots help us?

② How can you control a robot swarm?

③ What makes a self-driving car navigate roads?

④ Which robot will you choose to build a house?

⑤ What kinds of tasks can a home helper robot do?

**25** 위 글의 내용과 일치하지 않는 것은? (3점)

① 자율 주행차는 운전자가 필요 없다.

② 가사 도우미 로봇은 온종일 당신의 가족을 돕는다.

③ 로봇과 함께하는 미래는 장단점을 모두 갖고 있다.

④ 어떤 사람들은 우리가 로봇의 일자리를 위협하면서 생길지도 모르는 문제점에 대해 걱정한다.

⑤ 로봇이 좋은 일을 위해서만 쓰이는 것은 중요하다.

**26** 위 글을 읽고, 아래 글이 어느 로봇들의 대화인지 고르시오. (3점)

A: Yesterday, I tried to encourage a girl of the family I work for. She felt sad because she lost her dog.
B: A week ago, after a big fire, I went into the place where the fire broke out and saved the survivors.

① robot swarm & self-driving car

② self-driving car & robot swarm

③ home helper robot & robot swarm

④ robot swarm & search-and-rescue robot

⑤ home helper robot & search-and-rescue robot

**27** 위 글의 문맥상 (B)를 〈보기〉의 단어들을 모두 사용해서 완성할 때 여섯 번째 오는 단어는? (보기의 단어는 중복 사용 가능함) (4점)

> **보기**
> you, relax, roads, can, for, so, navigate, that

① so
② can
③ for
④ you
⑤ that

**28** 위 글의 제목으로 가장 적절한 것은? (3점)

① Looking toward the Future
② Where Do We See Robots?
③ Robots Are Becoming Smart
④ Robots Are Threatening to Our Future
⑤ Robots around Us – Present and Future

**29** 위 글의 (A)에 들어갈 말로 적절한 것은? (3점)

① Then
② However
③ In fact
④ In addition
⑤ For example

**[28–30]** 다음 글을 읽고 물음에 답하시오.

In the past, robots performed only easy tasks that humans programmed them to do. (A)_____, robots are now getting "smarter," and soon they might be able to think like humans. What makes this possible is artificial intelligence (AI).

Robots that have AI can perceive environments and make decisions. They can also recognize speech, tell jokes, and play games with humans.
· AI Speakers: They can answer your questions, control machines in your home, and play music for you.
· AI Pets: They act just like real dogs. They walk and play with their owners and recognize praise.

**30** 위 글의 내용과 일치하지 <u>않는</u> 것은? (4점)

① 인공지능 로봇은 사람처럼 생각할 수 있다.
② 인공지능 애완견 로봇은 실제의 개와 매우 유사하다.
③ 인공지능 스피커는 집안의 기기들을 통제할 수 있다.
④ 과거의 로봇은 인간이 프로그래밍한 업무만 수행했다.
⑤ 인공지능 로봇은 언어를 이해할 수 있으나 말은 하지 못한다.

MEMO

# 정답 및 해설

## Lesson 5 (중간)

01 ③  02 ②  03 ②
04 My mother doesn't like how my sister drives.  05 ④
06 ⑤  07 ⑤  08 ④  09 ②  10 ④  11 ⑤  12 ②, ④
13 ③  14 ④  15 ⑤  16 ④  17 ④  18 ①  19 ⑤
20 ②, ⑤  21 ③  22 how important it is to save the sea
23 ⑤  24 ⑤  25 ③  26 ③  27 ③  28 ③, ④  29 ⑤
30 climate change

**01** "크기를 작게 만들다"라는 영영 풀이가 가리키는 단어는 ③ reduce(감소하다, 감소시키다)이다.

**02** 맨 위에서부터 순서대로, shade(그늘), surface(표면), concerns(걱정), owner(주인)가 들어가는 것이 문맥상 가장 자연스럽다.

**03** ⓒ This is the stadium the basketball game will be held. → This is the stadium where the basketball game will be held. / ⓔ in that → in which / ⓖ I forgot to visit the doctor's office where I had scheduled to take a medical check up at yesterday. → I forgot to visit the doctor's office at which I had scheduled to take a medical check up yesterday.로 고쳐야 어법상 적절한 문장이 된다.

**04** 방법을 나타내는 관계부사 how를 쓴다.

**05** 위 대화에서는 전기차의 배터리를 충전하는 charging roads에 대해서 이야기하고 있다. 이에 대한 B의 응답으로는 그것이 멋있다고 말하면서 "빨리 사용해 보고 싶다"고 말하는 것이 적절하다.

**06** "I can't wait to ~"는 "어서 ~하고 싶다"라는 뜻으로 어떤 일에 대한 기대감을 나타내는 표현이다. 따라서 이와 바꿔 쓸 수 있는 표현은 "I'm looking forward to ~"이다.

**07** 조동사 will과 can은 함께 쓰일 수가 없기 때문에 will be able to를 대신 쓴다.

**08** 위 대화에서 B는 엘레베이터를 덜 사용하는 작은 일부터 시작하면 더 많은 에너지를 아낄 수 있고 환경을 보호할 수 있다고 이야기하고 있다. 따라서 위 대화와 관련된 속담으로 가장 적절한 것은 ④ Little drops of water make the mighty ocean.(티끌 모아 태산이다.)이다.

**09** ⓑ에는 adds up(더해지다)이 들어가는 것이 흐름상 가장 적절하다. ⓐ protect ⓒ In my opinion ⓓ taking care of ⓔ You have a point.

**10** ① why → how / ② where → when / ③ the reason how → the reason why / ⑤ the way how → the way로 고쳐야 어법상 적절한 문장이 된다.

**11** 위 대화에서 Jill의 말에 따르면, 공원에 있는 양들이 잡초들을 먹음으로써 사람들이 제초제를 쓰지 않게 만들기 때문에 환경을 보호한다고 언급했다.

**12** ② I recently went back to the town where I grew up in.은 I recently went back to the town where I grew up.으로, ④ I know the reason why he didn't come to school for.는 I know the reason why he didn't come to school.로 고치는 것이 어법상 적절하다.

**13** 위 대화에서 옥수수로 만든 친환경적인 봉지에 대해서 이야기하고 있다. A는 그것이 기대가 된다고 하면서 빨리 사용해 보고 싶다고 말하는 것이 흐름상 가장 적절하다.

**14** 위 대화에 따르면, 땅속에서 분해되는 데 단 3개월 걸린다("The bag breaks down in soil in only three months")고 한다.

**15** ⓔthey는 사람들을 가리킨다. 나머지는 모두 500 statues(500개의 동상)를 가리킨다.

**16** 위 글에 따르면, 동상들은 동식물들이 살아갈 장소를 제공하며 ('They provide additional places for plants and animals to live on'), 사람들이 해양 생물이 얼마나 풍요로운지 깨닫는다면, 바다를 보호하는 것이 얼마나 중요한지 깨달을 수 있을 것('If people realize how rich sea life is, they will understand how important it is to save the sea.')이라고 언급되어 있다.

**17** 위 글에 따르면, 화자는 휴지통의 수를 줄이자고 제안했지만 휴지통을 쓰지 말자고 주장하지는 않았다.

**18** 위 글에 따르면, 많은 학생들이 물건들을 재활용하는 대신에 그냥 버리고 있지만 재활용하는 것은 환경을 보호하는 것을 돕기 때문에 중요하다고 이야기하고 있다. 따라서 빈칸에 들어갈 말로 가장 적절한 것은 ① however(그러나)이다.

**19** 마지막 문단에 따르면, 동상에서 자라는 많은 해양 생물들이 예술 작품을 독특하게 만들며, 사람들에게는 해양 생물이 얼마나 풍부한지를 보여준다고 하였다.

**20** ⓑ는 to부정사의 부사적 용법, ⓔ는 to부정사의 명사적 용법으로 사용되었다. 나머지는 모두 형용사적 용법으로 사용되었다.

**21** ⓑ have founded → have found / ⓒ listen → listen to / ⓔ One of the most popular activity → One of the most popular activities

**22** 의문사를 이용해 문장 내에서 목적어가 될 수 있는 간접의문문을 만들 수 있다. 이때 간접의문문은 '의문사+주어+동사' 순으로 쓴다.

**23** 두 번째 문단에 따르면, 관광객들의 관광 활동이 칸쿤 근처의 바다를 심각하게 훼손하고 있다('tourist activities are seriously damaging parts of the sea near Cancun.')고 언급되어 있다.

**24** (a) provide A with B: A에게 B를 제공하다 / (b) come up with: ~를 제시하다, 제안하다

**25** (가)에는 관계대명사의 계속적 용법이 사용되었으므로 which uses가, (나)에는 한정적 용법이 사용되었으므로 that use less가 들어가는 것이 어법상 가장 적절하다.

**26** '이 구조는 바깥 공기가 건물 안을 순환할 수 있도록 한다.'라는 문장이 들어가기에 가장 적절한 곳은 개방 구조의 자연스러운 공기 흐름이 건물들을 시원하게 유지시켜 준다고 이야기하고 있는 (C)이다.

**27** 위 글에 따르면, 싱가포르의 많은 건물들은 개방형 구조를 갖게 되었다고 언급되어 있다.

**28** ③ How many buildings have been designed to have an open structure?(개방형 구조로 디자인한 건물은 몇 개인가?)와 ④ What are the examples of other fields to protect the environment?(환경 보호를 하는 다른 분야의 예시는 무엇인가?)에 대해서는 위 글에서 언급된 바 없다.

**29** 위 글에서는 싱가포르의 건물들의 구조가 친환경적으로 설계되어 있어서 환경을 보호할 수 있도록 한다는 내용에 대해서 이야기하고 있다. 따라서 위 글의 제목으로 가장 적절한 것은 ⑤ Eco-Friendly Building Designs in Singapore(싱가포르의 친환경적인 건물 디자인)이다.

**30** climate change: 기후 변화

# Lesson 5 (중간)  2회

> **01** ② **02** ⑤ **03** ④ **04** ①, ② **05** ③ **06** ⑤ **07** ①
> **08** It was not easy for her to get up early in the morning.
> **09** ⑤ **10** ⑤ **11** ④ **12** ④ **13** ③
> **14** (1) which[that] my parents first met on = on which my parents first met = where my parents first met
> (2) which[that] I like documentaries for = for which I like documentaries = why I like documentaries
> (3) which[that] I won the class election on = on which I won the class election = when I won the class election
> **15** ③ **16** ① **17** ③ **18** ① **19** ④ **20** ⑤ **21** ②
> **22** makes it possible for outside air to move **23** ⑤ **24** ③
> **25** ⑤ **26** ④ **27** ⑤ **28** ⑤ **29** ① **30** where

**01** ② come up with은 '~를 제시하다, 제안하다'라는 뜻으로 사용된다.

**02** '사람들이 어떤 것을 이해할 수 있도록 도와주는 정보'라는 영영풀이가 가리키는 것은 ⑤ explanation(설명)이다.

**03** ④ proper : properly는 형용사와 부사의 관계이며, green :

greenery는 형용사와 명사의 관계이다.

**04** ① for you to sign → you to sign / ② for them → of them 으로 고쳐야 어법상 적절한 문장이 된다.

**05** ③ What makes you think so?는 "왜 그렇게 생각하니?"라는 뜻을 가진 문장이다. 나머지는 모두 "내가 어떻게 해야 하니?"라는 뜻으로 상대방에게 조언을 구하는 표현이다.

**06** A와 B는 비닐봉지가 많이 쓰인다고 말하면서 그것은 환경에 좋지 않다고 이야기하고 있다. 따라서 B의 질문에 대한 A의 대답으로 가장 적절한 것은 ⑤ we should bring reusable bags when we go shopping.(우리는 쇼핑 갈 때 재사용할 수 있는 봉지를 들고 가야 해.)이다.

**07** (a)에는 동명사인 looking이, (b)에는 현재분사인 damaging이 들어가는 것이 어법상 가장 적절하다.

**08** to부정사(구)가 주어로 쓰일 경우, 주어 자리에 형식상의 주어(가주어) 'it'을 쓰고 원래 주어(진주어)인 to부정사(구)는 문장의 끝으로 보낸다. 이때 의미상 주어는 'for+(대)명사'의 형식으로 쓴다.

**09** (E)는 "Let's take the stairs."로 바꿔 쓰는 것이 흐름상 자연스럽다.

**10** 새로운 가방이 갖고 싶다는 A의 말에 대해 "넌 이미 많은 가방을 갖고 있어. 내 생각엔, 넌 새로운 가방이 지겨워하는 거야."라는 B의 대답은 흐름상 자연스럽지 않다.

**11** ④ for you → of you 로 고쳐야 어법상 적절한 문장이 된다.

**12** 위 대화에서는 먹을 수 있는 숟가락에 대해서 이야기하고 있다. 이에 대한 B의 응답으로는 그것이 멋있다고 말하면서 "빨리 사용해 보고 싶다"고 말하는 것이 적절하다.

**13** ⓐ of me → for me ⓒ of me → for me

**14** 두 문장을 연결할 때 겹치는 부분을 선행사로 만들고 관계대명사를 이용해 연결할 수 있다. 선행사가 사람이면 who나 whom, that을, 사물이나 동물은 which나 that을 쓴다. 한편 '전치사+관계대명사'라는 형식의 관계부사를 이용해 문장을 연결할 수 있다.

**15** 위 대화에 따르면, 옥수수로 만든 봉지는 빠르게 분해되기 때문에 환경 보호에 도움이 된다고 언급되어 있다.

**16** 위 대화에서는 옥수수로 만든 친환경적인 봉지에 대해서 이야기하고 있다. 따라서 빈칸에 들어갈 말로 가장 적절한 것은 ① bag이다.

**17** 위 글에 따르면, 재활용하는 것에 관심 있어 하는 학생들의 숫자가 늘고 있다는 내용은 언급되어 있지 않다.

**18** 위 글에서 멕시코 시티의 콘크리트 기둥을 수직 정원으로 만드는 것에 대해서 이야기하고 있다. 따라서 빈칸에 들어갈 말로 가장 적절한 것은 ① they reduce air pollution(그것들은 대기 오염을 감소시킨다)이 들어가는 것이 적절하다.

**19** 위 글에서는 싱가포르의 친환경적인 개방형 건물 구조에 대해서 이야기하고 있다. 따라서 ⓓ It also gives ocean animals a nutritious substitute.(그것은 또한 해양 동물들에게 영양가 있

는 대체제를 제공한다.)라는 문장은 흐름상 어색하다.

**20** 위 글에 따르면, 싱가포르의 친환경적인 빌딩은 개방형 구조로 바깥 공기가 빌딩 구석구석까지 통하게 된다고 언급되어 있다.

**21** 위 글에서는 싱가포르의 개방형 건물 구조가 친환경적이라고 이야기하고 있다. 따라서 위 글의 제목으로 가장 적절한 것은 ② Eco-Friendly Building Designs in Singapore(싱가포르의 친환경적인 건물 디자인)이다.

**22** 가목적어 it과 의미상 목적어 for를 써서, makes it possible for outside air to move라고 영작할 수 있다.

**23** 마지막 문단에 따르면, 싱가포르에서 새로운 건축 양식의 목표는 환경을 보호할 뿐만 아니라 사람들에게 좋은 삶을 제공하는 것이라고 언급되어 있다.

**24** 문맥상, (A) natural air flow, (B) direct sunlight, (C) innovations가 들어가는 것이 가장 자연스럽다.

**25** ⓔhow important is it은 how important it is로 고쳐야 어법상 적절한 문장이 된다.

**26** 주어진 우리말은 관계부사 where를 사용해 They made an underwater museum away from the places where sea life was dying.이라고 영작할 수 있다.

**27** 동상을 만든 예술가는 자신이 아니라 사람들이 동상 위의 다양한 해양 생물들을 보기를 원했다고 한다.

**28** ⓐ has found → have found / ⓑ listens to → listen to / ⓒ travels → travel / ⓓ are looking → is looking으로 고쳐야 어법상 적절한 문장이 된다.

**29** 동상을 만든 예술가는 자신이 아니라 사람들이 동상 위의 다양한 해양 생물들을 보기를 원했다고 한다.

**30** in which는 관계부사 where로 바꿔 쓸 수 있다.

## Lesson 6 (중간) 〔1회〕

```
01 ③   02 ①   03 The higher / the colder   04 ③   05 ①
06 ③   07 what to sell      08 ④   09 ③   10 ④   11 ④
12 ⑤   13 ④   14 ④   15 ④   16 ②   17 ②   18 ⑤   19 ①
20 ⑤   21 ⑤   22 ①   23 ③   24 a board game        25 ③
26 ②   27 ②   28 ②
29 The fewer products we buy, the more resources we save.
30 ①
```

**01** ③ architect는 '건축가'를 의미한다.

**02** ① come up with는 '~를 제시하다, 제안하다'라는 뜻으로 사용된다.

**03** 주어진 문장을 영작할 때, 'the+비교급, the+비교급' 구문을 사용해 'The higher I climbed, the colder I felt.'라고 영작할 수

**04** in conflict with: ~와 갈등을 빚고 있는

**05** Being fine tomorrow라는 분사구문은 의미를 확실히 하기 위해 It being fine tomorrow로 쓰는 것이 어법상 적절하다.

**06** Sam은 시장조사가 물건의 적절한 가격을 세울 수 있도록 도와준다(It will also help us set reasonable prices for our items.')고 언급했다.

**07** '의문사+to부정사'를 이용한다.

**08** ① of me → for me / ② Walked → Walking / ③ The hard you study, the good your grades will be. → The harder you study, the better your grades will be. / ⑤ the time where → the time when

**09** 위 대화에 따르면, 스페셜 샌드위치에는 신선한 채소가 많이 들어 있어 더 건강한 선택이며(Tom), B는 클래식 샌드위치보다 스페셜 샌드위치를 선호한다(Chris)고 언급되어 있다.

**10** ⓐ Because I have nothing to do, I'll stay at home. / ⓑ Not having wanted to interrupt the conversation, I stood quietly. / ⓔ The sun having set, we can't play baseball any more.로 고쳐야 어법상 적절한 문장이 된다.

**11** ④ The more actively you move, the tireder you will be. 는 The more actively you move, the more tired you will be.로 고쳐야 어법상 적절한 문장이 된다.

**12** 빈칸에 들어갈 말로 가장 적절한 것은 상대방에게 어떤 일에 대해서 상기시켜주는 표현인 ⑤ don't forget to이다.

**13** 위 대화에 따르면, Sue는 상품의 장점 뿐만 아니라 단점에 대해서도 이야기할 것이라고 언급했다.

**14** (A) don't forget to: ~할 것을 잊지 말아라 / (B) balanced 균형 잡힌 / (C) what (=the thing which) ~하는 것

**15** A가 좋은 앱이라고 말하면서, 텐트를 빌리고 개를 돌봐 줄 사람을 구할 수 있다고 말한다. 이에 B는 이런 서비스를 공유 경제라고 말한다고 대답한다(D). A는 사람들이 다른 사람들과 물건을 공유할 수도 있고 무료로 혹은 적은 돈으로 서비스를 제공할 수도 있다고 덧붙여 설명한다(B). B는 이런 서비스에도 약점이 있다고 대답하면서, 어떤 사람들은 부정적인 리뷰를 남길 수도 있다고 말한다(C). 이에 A가 사람들이 서비스를 더 사용하면 사용할수록 그것들이 개선될 것이라고 말하는 순서로 이어지는 것이 대화의 흐름상 가장 자연스럽다.

**16** A가 자신의 머리를 펴고 싶다고 말하면서 B에게 좋은 미용실을 추천해 달라고 말한다(ⓔ). 이에 B는 두 곳을 이야기해 주자, A가 B에게 두 곳의 차이가 있냐고 묻는다(ⓓ). B가 차이를 설명해 주자 A는 B에게 어떤 곳을 선호하냐고 묻는(ⓑ) 순서로 이어지는 것이 흐름상 적절하다.

**17** (C)에는 문맥상 두 미용실 중 어느 곳을 선호하는지에 대한 질문이

들어가는 것이 적절하다. 따라서 이와 바꿔 쓸 수 있는 표현은 ②
Which place do you like better?이다.

**18** 주어진 우리말을 영작하면, 'The fewer products we buy, the
more resources we save.'가 된다.

**19** (a) perfect: 완벽한 / (b) look for: ~을 찾다 / (c) weakness:
단점, 약점

**20** 주어진 우리말을 영작할 때, 'the+비교급, the+비교급' 구문을 사
용해 ⑤ the more people use the services, the more they
will improve.라고 영작할 수 있다.

**21** 첫 문단에 따르면, 애완동물을 돌봐 준 사람에 대해 평가를 할 수
있다고 언급되어 있다.

**22** (A) reliable: 믿을 수 있는 / (B) upload: 업로드하다 / (C)
best: 최고의

**23** ⓒ that allows users to communicate freely without
showing their personal information.으로 바꿔 쓰는 것이 어
법상 적절하다.

**24** (가)one은 부정대명사로 앞에서 언급된 단수 명사인 a board
game을 가리킨다.

**25** (A) helps, (B) got, (D) environmentally, (E) to borrow로
고치는 것이 어법상 적절하다.

**26** (나)의 분사구문은 '많은 긍정적인 리뷰를 보고 난 후'라고 해석할
수 있다.

**27** Cassandra는 Ask Your Neighbors 앱을 통해 이웃에게 자전
거 헬멧을 빌렸지만 망가져 있어서 화가 났다고 한다. 따라서 ② I
felt guilty that the helmet was broken.(헬멧이 망가져서 죄
책감을 느꼈어요.)는 Cassandra의 반응으로 적절하지 않다.

**28** ⓑ that은 주격 관계대명사이기 때문에 생략할 수 없다.

**29** 주어진 우리말을 영작할 때, 'the+비교급, the+비교급' 구문을 사
용해 'The fewer products we buy, the more resources we
save.'라고 영작할 수 있다.

**30** 첫 문단에 따르면, Ask Your Neighbors는 다른 사람들로부터
빌릴 수 있는 물건을 쉽게 찾을 수 있도록 도와주는 앱이라고 언급
되어 있다.

## Lesson 6 (중간) 2회

**01** ① **02** ② **03** Being just fourteen **04** ②
**05** Eating fried chicken **06** ④ **07** ③ **08** ③ **09** ①
**10** (A) ones (B) to bring
**11** (1) After he read the letter (2) sitting in the sun (3)
Because he didn't know what to do = As he didn't know
what to do

**12** ⑤ **13** ① **14** ⑤ **15** ④ **16** ④ **17** ⑤ **18** ⑤ **19** ③
**20** ⑤
**21** The fewer products we buy, the more resources we save.
**22** ① **23** ③ **24** ③ **25** ① **26** ① **27** ② **28** ② **29** ①
**30** ③

**01** ① improve는 '향상시키다'라는 뜻을 갖는 단어이다.

**02** 빈칸 위에서부터 순서대로, concern(관심, 걱정), reasonable
(합리적인), refund(환불), share(공유하다)가 들어가는 것이 문
맥상 가장 자연스럽다.

**03** 'Because she was just fourteen'이라는 부사절을 분사구문으
로 바꾸면, 'Being just fourteen'이라고 쓸 수 있다.

**04** B는 검은색 스피커가 빨간색 스피커에 비해 비싸긴 하지만 품질이
더 좋아서 자신에게 맞다고 생각한다고 말하고 있다. 따라서 빈칸
에 들어갈 말로 가장 적절한 것은 ② Although(~이긴 하지만)이
다.

**05** While we were eating fried chicken together라는 부사절을
분사구문으로 바꾸면, 'Eating fried chicken'이라고 쓸 수 있
다.

**06** 대화 이후에 Maria가 할 일로 적절한 것은 오래된 천을 이용해 자
신이 직접 가방을 만드는 것이다.

**07** '이를 닦는 동안'이라는 표현은 분사구문을 이용해 Brushing my
teeth라고 쓸 수 있다.

**08** ③ 'B가 다니는 미용실의 이용 요금'에 대해서는 언급된 바 없다.

**09** A가 B에게 좋은 미용실을 추천해 달라고 했고, 이에 B는 두 곳을
추천해 준다(ⓒ). A는 두 곳의 차이가 있냐고 물어 보았고(ⓐ), B
는 Styles Studio에 대해서 말한 후, Hair Castle에 대해 이야기
하며 두 미용실의 차이점을 말해준다. 그리고 A가 B에게 어느 곳
을 선호하냐고 묻는 순서로 이어지는 것이 흐름상 가장 자연스럽
다.

**10** (A) clothes를 가리키는 ones (B) forget to: ~할 것을 잊다

**11** 부사절을 분사구문으로 바꿀 경우, 주어와 be동사를 생략하고 일
반동사를 현재분사형으로 만들어 분사구문을 만들 수 있다. 반대
로 분사구문을 부사절로 바꿀 경우, 어떤 의미를 갖느냐에 따라 접
속사 because, as, while, after 등을 써서 주어와 동사가 쓰이는
절로 만들 수 있다.

**12** 위 대화에 따르면, 시장 조사를 통해서 어떤 물건이 요즘 인기가 많
은지에 대해서 알 수 있다고 언급되어 있다.

**13** (A)register는 '등록하다'라는 뜻으로 사용되었다.

**14** 위 대화의 흐름상 Lori는 건강하게 먹는 것이 중요하다고 했으므
로 신선한 채소가 많이 들어간 스페셜 샌드위치를 클래식 샌드위치
보다 선호한다는 문장이 들어가는 것이 자연스럽다.

**15** 위 글에 따르면, Amy는 더 저렴한 샌드위치를 선호한다고 말했으

므로 클래식 샌드위치를 선호한다고 볼 수 있다.

**16** 위 글에 따르면, 집에서 반려동물을 돌봐 주는 것은 시간당 $20이 라고 언급되어 있다. 따라서 두 시간을 돌봐 주는 비용은 ④ $40이 다.

**17** 위 글에 따르면, 반려동물을 돌봐 주는 사람은 자신의 집에서 돌봐 줄 수도 있다고 언급되어 있다.

**18** 위 대화에서는 이웃과 물건을 공유하거나 서비스를 주고 받는 ⑤ Sharing Economy(공유 경제)에 대해서 이야기하고 있다.

**19** 주어가 Ask Your Neighbors이고 준사역동사 help를 써서 ③ helps people easily find items라고 영작할 수 있다.

**20** 사역동사 let은 목적보어로 동사원형을 취한다. 따라서 ⓔ to know는 know로 고치는 것이 어법상 적절하다.

**21** 주어진 우리말을 영작할 때, 'the+비교급, the+비교급' 구문을 사 용해 'The fewer products we buy, the more resources we save.'라고 영작할 수 있다.

**22** Cassandra는 긍정적인 리뷰들을 보고 자전거 헬멧을 빌렸는데 그것이 망가져 있었다고 한다. 따라서 (A)에 들어갈 표현으로 가 장 적절한 것은 ① I was so upset.(정말 화가 났다.)이다.

**23** Ask Your Neighbors가 지역 경제를 지속적으로 발전시키는 데 도움이 된다는 내용은 언급된 바 없다.

**24** ⓒSeeing은 분사구문으로 쓰인 현재분사이다. 따라서 이와 쓰임 이 다른 것은 동명사로 쓰인 ③ playing이다.

**25** 위 글에 따르면, Pet Sitter Finder 앱을 이용하여 반려동물을 구 입한 것이 아니라 반려동물을 산책시켰다고 한다.

**26** (A) doubtful은 문맥상 reliable(믿을 수 있는)로 바꿔 쓰는 것이 자연스럽다.

**27** (가) When: ~할 때 / (나) However: 그러나

**28** ② How many dogs does George have?(George는 몇 마리 의 개를 키우는가?)에 대해서는 위 글에서 언급된 바 없다.

**29** 문맥상 look after(~를 돌보다)가 들어가는 것이 더 적절하다. 따 라서 ⓐfor는 after로 고쳐야 자연스럽다.

**30** 위 글에 따르면, Samantha의 아파트에서는 반려동물이 허가되지 않는다고('Animals aren't allowed in my apartment') 언급 되어 있다.

## Lesson 7 (기말)

| 01 ⑤ | 02 ③ | 03 ① | 04 ① | 05 ② | 06 ④ | 07 ② | 08 ④ |
|------|------|------|------|------|------|------|------|
| 09 ④ | 10 ② | 11 ⑤ | 12 ③ | 13 ② | 14 ⑤ | 15 ⑤ | 16 ⑤ |
| 17 ① | 18 ② | 19 ④ | 20 ⑤ | 21 ③ | | | |

**22** If you had one, cooking and cleaning would be easier.

| 23 ④ | 24 ② | 25 ④ | 26 ⑤ | 27 ① | 28 ② | 29 ② | 30 ⑤ |
|------|------|------|------|------|------|------|------|

**01** sense는 '지각하다', '감지하다'라는 뜻을 가진 단어이다.

**02** ⓐ에는 present(선물), ⓑ에는 announce(발표하다), ⓒ에는 upgrade(개선하다), ⓓ에는 reasonable(합리적인), ⓔ에는 report(등록하다)가 들어가는 것이 문맥상 가장 적절하다.

**03** awareness는 '의식' 또는 '관심'이라는 뜻을 가진 단어이다. / architect: 건축가, innovation: 개혁, surface: 표면, in harmony with: ~와 조화를 이루어

**04** 위에서부터 순서대로 present(현재의), convenient(편리한), intelligence(지능), task(임무)가 들어가는 것이 문맥상 가장 적 절하다.

**05** 여학생이 거의 20분 동안 가게에서 줄을 서 있었어야 했다고 말하 자, 이에 남학생은 안됐다고 대답하면서, 미래에는 줄을 서지 않아 도 될지도 모른다고 말한다. 여학생은 그게 무슨 의미냐고 묻고, 남 학생은 캐셔가 없는 가게에 대해서 읽어 보았다고 말하면서 그저 원하는 것을 사고 난 뒤 나가면 된다고 말한다. 이에 여학생은 돈은 어떻게 지불해야 하냐고 묻고, 남학생은 가게에 카메라와 센서가 있어서 물건을 고르면 그 물건의 정보를 스마트폰으로 보내고 그렇 게 함으로써 스마트 폰의 앱이 돈을 지불한다고 말하는 순서로 이 어지는 것이 대화 흐름상 가장 자연스럽다.

**06** 현재 사실과 반대되는 가정을 나타낼 때, 'If+주어+were/동사의 과거형 ~, 주어+조동사의 과거형(would/should/could/might) +동사원형 ….' 형식의 가정법 과거를 쓰며, '만약 ~라면, …할 텐 데.'로 해석한다.

**07** to부정사가 주어로 쓰일 경우, 대부분 주어 자리에 형식상의 주어 인 가주어 it을 쓰고 원래 주어인 to부정사구는 문장의 끝으로 보낸 다. 이때 의미상 주어는 사람의 성격에 대해서 이야기할 때는 of를 쓴다.

**08** 밑줄 친 부분은 분사구문으로 문장 내에서 '~했기 때문에'라고 해 석된다. 따라서 이와 의미가 같은 문장은 ④ Because we felt happy about the win이다.

**09** 현재 사실과 반대되는 가정을 나타낼 때, 'If+주어+were/동사의 과거형 ~, 주어+조동사의 과거형(would/ should/could/might) +동사원형 ….의 형식의 가정법 과거 형식을 쓰며, '만약 ~라면, …할 텐데.'로 해석한다. ⓐ는 If I had got up earlier, I would not have missed the bus. / ⓑ는 If you're free tonight, will you join us for dinner? / ⓖ는 If it were not for failure, we couldn't fully appreciate success.로 고쳐야 어 법상 적절한 문장이 된다.

**10** 위 대화에 따르면, 사고로 한 손을 잃은 남자는 로봇으로 된 팔을 이용해서 드럼을 연주한다고 언급되어 있다. 이때 남자의 뇌가 로 봇 팔을 제어해서 그가 원하는대로 움직이게 할 수 있다고 한다.

**11** ⓔ는 It's likely that these kinds of stores will be more common in the future.로 고치는 것이 흐름상 자연스럽다.

**12** 위 글에 따르면, Jane은 새 핸드폰을 사고 싶지만 충분한 돈이 없다고 한다. 따라서 Jane이 할 말로 가장 적절한 것은 ③ If I had enough money, I would buy a new phone.(내가 충분한 돈이 있었으면, 새 핸드폰을 살 텐데.)이다.

**13** Mary는 아파서 현재 병원에 있다고 한다. 따라서 가정법 문장으로 바꾸면, 현재 사실과 반대되는 내용을 가정하는 가정법 과거형을 사용해 If Mary weren't ill, she wouldn't be at the hospital.이 된다.

**14** 'so that+주어+동사 ~' 구문은 문장 뒤에 붙어서 '~하기 위해서'라는 뜻으로 사용된다. 따라서 이와 바꿔 쓸 수 없는 것은 ⑤ as he can get some vitamin C이다.

**15** '또한, 개미와 같은 벌레들은 우리의 일상 식사의 일부가 될 것이다'라는 문장이 들어가기에 가장 적절한 곳은 그것을 먹고 싶지는 않겠지만 그것들은 매우 영양분이 풍부하다고 말하고 있는 (E)이다.

**16** 위 글에서는 기후 변화가 농사 짓는 것을 더 힘들게 만들기 때문에 증가하는 지구의 인구를 위한 자원이 충분하지 않을 지도 모른다고 말하고 있다. 따라서 위 글의 주제로 가장 적절한 것은 ⑤ The possible solutions for a food shortage problem(식량 부족 문제를 위한 가능한 해결책)이다.

**17** ⓐmaking은 '관계대명사+be동사'가 생략된 문장으로 어법상 과거분사인 made가 되어야 적절하다.

**18** 위 글에 따르면, '친구'는 질문을 하면 인터넷을 조사해서 당신이 알고 싶어 하는 것을 말해 줄 것이라고 언급되어 있다.

**19** ⓓmakes는 조동사 can과 함께 쓰이는 동사이기 때문에 ⓓmake로 고치는 것이 어법상 적절하다.

**20** 위 글에 따르면, 로봇은 더 똑똑해지고 있으며 곧 인간처럼 생각할 수 있을지도 모른다('However, robots are now getting "smarter," and soon they might be able to think like humans.')고 언급되어 있다.

**21** (A)what은 관계대명사로 '~하는 것'이라고 해석한다. 따라서 이와 쓰임이 다른 것은 의문사로 사용된 ③이다.

**22** 가정법과거를 이용한다.

**23** (라)탐색 및 구조 로봇(Search-and-rescue robots)은 인간에게 위험한 곳에 대신 들어가 위험에 빠진 사람들을 도와줄 수 있다고 언급되어 있다.

**24** ② How can you control a robot swarm?(로봇들의 떼는 어떻게 통제할 수 있는가?)에 대해서는 위 글에서 언급된 바 없다.

**25** 위 글에 따르면, 로봇이 우리의 일자리를 위협할지도 모른다고 언급되어 있다.

**26** 위 글에 따르면, 가족을 돕는 것은 가사 도우미 로봇(home helper robot)이며, 재난 상황에서 인간이 들어갈 수 없는 곳에 대신 들어가 사람들을 구조하는 것은 탐색 및 구조 로봇(search-and-rescue robot)이다.

**27** 주어진 단어를 사용해 영작하면, '(it) can navigate roads for you so that you can relax'가 된다.

**28** 위 글에서는 로봇들이 점점 똑똑해진다고 이야기하면서 아마 인간처럼 생각하게 될 수도 있다고 말하고 있다. 따라서 위 글의 제목으로 가장 적절한 것은 ③ Robots Are Becoming Smart이다.

**29** 과거의 로봇들은 인간이 프로그래밍한 쉬운 임무만 했지만 현재의 로봇들은 똑똑해지고 있다고 말하고 있다. 따라서 빈칸에 들어갈 말로 가장 적절한 것은 ② However(그러나)이다.

**30** 위 글에 따르면, 인공지능 로봇은 언어를 이해하고 농담도 할 수 있다고('They can also recognize speech, tell jokes, and play games with humans.') 언급되어 있다.

MEMO

MEMO